THE PHYSICAL ANTHROPOLOGY OF IRELAND

NO. 1
TEXT

PAPERS

OF THE

PEABODY MUSEUM OF ARCHÆOLOGY
AND ETHNOLOGY, HARVARD UNIVERSITY
VOL. XXX, NOS. 1–2

THE PHYSICAL ANTHROPOLOGY
OF IRELAND

BY

EARNEST A. HOOTON

AND

C. WESLEY DUPERTUIS

WITH A SECTION ON

THE WEST COAST IRISH FEMALES

BY

HELEN DAWSON

No. 1

TEXT

CAMBRIDGE, MASSACHUSETTS, U.S.A.
PUBLISHED BY THE MUSEUM
1955

PRINTED BY THE CRIMSON PRINTING COMPANY
CAMBRIDGE, MASSACHUSETTS, U.S.A.

3974
32-&

PREFACE

THE idea of an anthropological survey of Ireland, to include social anthropology, archæology, and physical anthropology, was conceived in the early nineteen thirties when the Department of Anthropology of Harvard University was so fortunate as to obtain a grant for research from the Rockefeller Foundation for a period of five years. This ambitious project called for a series of archæological excavations designed to cover the whole period of Irish prehistory and proto-history, an intensive social anthropological study of a typical Irish county (Clare), and an adequate sampling by physical anthropologists of the Irish population in every part of the island.

It was agreed that Ireland would make an ideal country for such a survey for many reasons. In the first place its comparative geographical isolation and its modest size made such a study feasible without the expenditure of many years and vast sums of money (neither available). Again, Ireland in ancient times was one of the leading cultural centers of Western Europe and it has retained, down to the present day, a unique position in its blending of the old with the new in customs, in arts, and industries, in linguistic and racial differentiation, and perhaps spiritually. Here in Massachusetts we live among Americans of recent Irish extraction; we work with them; we play with them; sometimes we dispute with them, and most of the time we are governed by them. The Irish Americans are a people of great vigor, ability, and charm; they are a friendly people unless deliberately antagonized; they never lack a most appealing sense of humor. In the Harvard Department of Anthropology, we felt that no more fitting place could be found for a thorough anthropological survey than this small island, the ancestral home and the shrine of the devotion of so many of our fellow citizens, friends, and Harvard associates, both in the faculty and among the alumni.

It was thought that in Harvard University we could muster a staff that would be able to carry through this project. Professor W. Lloyd Warner, now of the University of Chicago, was a social anthropologist already pioneering in studies of modern civilized communities, having preceded his great survey of a New England town ("Yankee City") by field work among the Australian aborigines. Our curator of European Archæology in the Peabody Museum of Harvard University was Dr. Hugh O'Neill Hencken, whose specialty was the later prehistoric periods of Europe—the Bronze and Early Iron Ages— and especially in the British Isles. Dr. Hencken had been trained at Cambridge University and had done distinguished archæological work in Cornwall and elsewhere. The senior author of the present work was already a veteran of physical anthropological surveys. Finally, we had available a number of advanced and capable graduate students who could be trusted to do most of the actual field work necessitated by the project. So, with this equipment in the way of personnel and experience and with the prospect of financial subvention by the Rockefeller Grant to the extent of about $5,000 per year for 5 years, we plunged ahead.

Lloyd Warner went over to Ireland and surveyed the realm in a preliminary way for the most auspicious area in which to do social anthropology. Having fixed upon County Clare and made the necessary friends and connections there and elsewhere in Ireland, he sent over as his principal research workers, Conrad M. Arensberg and Solon Kimball, two of his most brilliant advanced pupils. Two books resulted from this effort: *The Irish Countryman* (New York, 1937) by Conrad M. Arensberg, and *Family and Community in Ireland* (Cambridge, Mass., 1940) by Conrad M. Arensberg and Solon Kimball.

Dr. Hencken led archæological expeditions to Ireland over a number of years and he and his principal associate, Dr. Hallam L. Movius, Jr. (now Curator of Palæolithic Archæology in the Peabody Museum and Associate Pro-

v

fessor of Anthropology in Harvard University) have produced a long series of large and important monographs and books, dealing with the archæology of Ireland. Nearly all of these monographs have been magnificently published by the Royal Irish Academy.

The physical anthropological expedition was the last to take the field and its personnel consisted of one man, C. W. Dupertuis, an advanced student of Physical Anthropology at Harvard, who had already two years of experience in anthropometry at the Century of Progress Expedition in Chicago, where he conducted the Harvard Anthropometric Laboratory, which measured and observed visitors to the fair. After the first year of anthropometric work in Ireland, Dupertuis went back accompanied by his bride, who thereafter functioned as his recorder and collaborator in the Irish survey. Although the Harvard Anthropological Survey of Ireland soon ran out of funds, so that field work had to be curtailed, we were fortunate enough to secure the collaboration of Miss Helen Dawson, a National Research Council Fellow in Anthropology, who utilized her fellowship in studying the Irish women of the West Coast. Miss Dawson collected an anthropometric sample of some 1800 women, the analysis of which is a part of this work.

One of the greatest difficulties in carrying through research under the auspices of a university is the frequent impossibility of holding the research staff together until the fruits of the studies have been reaped in the form of publications. The brilliant graduate students go into the field and accumulate data; often they return and use some of the data in a preliminary form for their doctoral dissertations. Almost invariably they then have to leave the parent institution to take positions of their own before they have had a chance to clean up the research they have done for the former. They go to teach or to investigate somewhere else and their full energies are immediately and thenceforth expended upon new duties. Consequently, there accumulates at the institutions that have to carry on research by using their graduate students a huge backlog of unfinished business. If anyone is to get this stuff out, it has to be the elder who promoted it, started it, and who through

no fault of his juniors, is left holding the sack (full of pretty solid stuff that is often not quite fresh).

The senior author of this monograph envisaged the probable necessity of his writing up the material of the Irish Anthropometric Survey, since Dr. Dupertuis was immediately called away to other duties after his return from Ireland, and Dr. Dawson, likewise.

The material of the anthropometric survey began to go through the Statistical Laboratory of the Department of Anthropology as soon as it was sent from Ireland. By the early part of 1940, everything had been sorted, tabulated, statistically elaborated, and a first draft of the manuscript (which was thought mistakenly to be a final draft) had been prepared. Unfortunately, there developed at this point a suspicion of the complete accuracy of the statistical reductions that had been effected, which ultimately became a bitter conviction that the whole laboratory job had to be done over again from the start. Some errors had been made in the sortings, so that it might be discovered, e.g., that a few individuals born in County Kerry had been put in the County Clare series. Numerous small arithmetical errors were ferreted out—all made by statistical clerks who had presumably departed, leaving their sins behind them. While the senior author's experience with large statistical samples was sufficiently extensive so that he was convinced that these multiple small inaccuracies would hardly affect any of the means or other constants beyond one decimal place, he could not entertain the idea of publishing material thus tainted.

Fortunately, the statistical laboratory was then in charge of a "gem of purest ray serene" in a statistical sense, and to this young woman was entrusted the task of repunching the I.B.M. cards, resorting them, and recalculating all of the constants. This work was done, and done accurately, in the space of about one year by Agnes West Gebhard.

By this time we were in the midst of a World War and for some 8 years all of the senior author's research time had to be devoted to military anthropometry. It was not until 1949 that work upon the Irish Survey was resumed. It must be confessed that, apart from preoccupation with other duties, the senior author may have been guilty of some procrastination in this matter, since the material had, by this time, grown somewhat mouldy. Also, he had entertained the incredibly naive supposition that, with the new tables, the old manuscript could be corrected and revised in a few months. Of course, it turned out that a complete rewriting was necessary—not because of the initial errors in the tables so much as because one does not come back to something written nearly a decade previously and find it satisfactory.

During the past two summers, it has been possible to summon Dr. Dupertuis from his duties at Western Reserve University to collaborate in reading and checking the manuscript and in preparing the illustrations. Since Dr. Dawson, now a Professor of Human Anatomy at the University of Iowa, had, for various good reasons, another uncompleted manuscript on the West Coast Irish women, it was decided that the senior author should also assume responsibility for the final draft of her work, which had been carried to approximately the same point as the male series, but was fortunately devoid of glaring statistical errors, since Dr. Dawson had done the computations herself.

In the course of the second writing of the Irish male material, it was discovered that the changes in the males by age groups were of such importance to anthropologists in general, apart from those who might have a special interest in a racial anthropometric study of the modern Irish, that it was decided to publish them separately. Accordingly, with the help of a grant from the Wenner-Gren Foundation, this material was published as a monograph of the *American Journal of Physical Anthropology*, under the title "Age Changes and Selective Survival in Irish Males."

It should be mentioned here that the present anthropometric survey does not constitute all of the Harvard effort in the physical anthropology of Ireland. In 1935, Professor W. W. Howells, of the University of Wisconsin was sent to Ireland to make a study of the skeletal remains that were being disinterred (presently to be reburied) in the course of the exploration and renovation of the Gallen Priory, County Offaly. Dr. Howells' admirable study (Howells, 1941) has been utilized in the present work as a basis for the comparison of the modern Irish population and the largest skeletal series of the Irish that has ever been available for examination.

EARNEST A. HOOTON

Harvard University
December, 1953

ACKNOWLEDGMENTS

THE years that have elapsed since the beginning of the field work of this survey have resulted, regrettably, in the forgetting by the participants in the survey of the names of certain persons who helped in one way or another. We wish to apologize to such friends and to assure them that their kindness and cooperation is remembered, if not their names and addresses.

The first class of persons and institutions whose assistance is to be gratefully acknowledged consists of those that cooperated in the field work in Ireland. Foremost among these is the Right Honorable Eamon De Valera, at that time (1934–36) President of the Executive Council and Minister for External Affairs of the Irish Free State. Mr. De Valera not only manifested keen interest in the anthropometric survey, but also offered helpful suggestions and generously allocated 40 pounds toward the expenses of collecting data. It may be added here that Mr. De Valera was equally cooperative in all of the other phases of the Harvard Anthropological Survey of Ireland.

The Hon. Joseph O'Neill, Secretary of the Department of Education for the Irish Free State, cooperated actively with the survey. He was instrumental in getting members of his and other government departments to submit themselves to the anthropometric examination and he dispensed the grant allotted to the work by the government.

The Garda Siochana (Civic Guards) were, in all parts of the Irish Free State, active co-workers in the gathering of anthropometric material. General W. R. E. Murphy, Ma.A., Deputy Commissioner, was interviewed by Dr. Dupertuis in Dublin and provided the essential letters of introduction to all of the Superintendents of the Civic Guard, with, of course, the approval of Colonel E. Broy, the Commissioner.

No less helpful were the prelates of the Catholic Church, both bishops and, in the smaller communities, the parish priests, who helped round up subjects.

The newspapers throughout the country, particularly the *Independent*, the *Irish Times*, and the *Irish Press* in Dublin, promoted the survey by writing articles about its methods and objectives. These were of great assistance to Dupertuis.

The Rt. Hon. Sir Richard Dawson Bates, O.B.E., D.L., M.P., the Home Secretary for Northern Ireland, was so gracious as to give his official sanction to the work in that area.

The Royal Irish Constabulary of Northern Ireland extended the same kind of practical assistance as that provided by the Civic Guard of the Free State. In the historical account of the expedition that follows these acknowledgments, Dr. Dupertuis amplifies this mention of the invaluable assistance provided by both of these police organizations. The heads of the Royal Constabulary who made this cooperation possible were: Inspector General, Lieutenant Colonel Sir Charles W. Wickham, S.S.O., Deputy Inspector General, Frederick A. Britten, O.B.E., B.A.

In addition to the foregoing, the following individuals assisted either Dr. Dupertuis or Dr. Dawson, or both, in securing subjects for measurements: Mr. Patrick MacNamara, Ennis, County Clare; Mr. Dermott Foley, County Librarian, and Mrs. Foley, County Clare; his Reverence the Bishop of Ennis; Miss Jane Harvey, Ennis, County Clare; Dr. Christine Begley, Leenane, Galway.

Finally, we must not forget the 18 months which Helen S. Dupertuis put in as recorder for her husband during his journeyings up and down Ireland—a very difficult assignment for a woman, but one she fulfilled with unflagging energy and never-failing accuracy. Much of the success of the whole endeavor was directly due to her assistance to her husband.

Back in the United States our heavy obligations were for support of a monetary nature, or for services rendered in the elaboration and analysis of the data and in the preparation of the manuscript of this work and in its editing. In the category of statistical, clerical and editorial assistance are included: Agnes West Gebhard, who single-handed, undertook and carried through the second and final statistical analysis of the huge body of data on 10,000 Irish males; Natalie Bill Stoddard, who later worked through the whole mass of material, firstly in her capacity as chief statistician of the departmental laboratory, subsequently as Editor of the Peabody Museum Publications; Kathleen G. Canby, who with great skill and judgment initiated and carried through most of the changes in the manuscript of this work necessitated by the revision and correction of the original tables; Maria von Mering who took charge of the final organization and typing of the manuscript and the arduous task of reading the proofs; Phyllis Adler, who also assisted in this phase; Elmer Rising, the ingenious and skillful cartographer who designed and executed the many intricate distribution maps in this work.

Professor John V. Kelleher, the Harvard authority on Irish history, was most kind and helpful in the matter of making suggestions concerning the correlation of physical type distributions with information on the location in Ireland of the various Keltic tribes.

For the various gifts and grants that made possible the Harvard Anthropological Survey of Ireland, we owe a debt of gratitude to the following persons and institutions, whose contributions were utilized in the different aspects of the survey (not necessarily for the anthropometric work): The Government of the Irish Free State for liberal allotments used mostly in hiring labor for the archæological excavations, but also in small part for the payment of persons who were helping to secure subjects for the anthropometric survey; to the Social Science Division of the Rockefeller Foundation for the research grant to the Department of Anthropology that enabled the Irish project to be initiated and was its main support during the period of gathering data; to the Wenner-Gren Foundation for a research grant to the senior author of this work utilized in part for the completion of the statistical and secretarial work presented in this volume; to Judge Daniel O'Connell, and his brother, the late ex-Congressman Joseph O'Connell, who organized a group of friends of the Harvard Anthropological Survey of Ireland which contributed a substantial sum at a time when the coffers were emptying; to our colleague in the Peabody Museum, Dr. Lloyd Cabot Briggs and to his mother, the late Mrs. L. Vernon Briggs, who not only supported generously the field work in Ireland, but also by a recent and really magnificent donation have made themselves entirely responsible for the expenses of publication of this anthropometric survey.

Of course, over and beyond the gifts made by friends mentioned above, there were personal contributions of money, as well as of time, by the participants in the actual survey and indirectly by their colleagues in the Peabody Museum and the Department of Anthropology. Thus, Dr. Hugh Hencken contributed the proceeds of lecture tours and various other moneys to the preparation of manuscripts and the publication of archæological results. Professor Donald Scott, then Director of the Peabody Museum, sent archæological assistants to Ireland under the auspices of the Museum; the senior members of the Department of Anthropology from the beginning of the survey up to the present, have voted occasional grants for the work from the small research funds in possession of the Department. Professor John Otis Brew, who succeeded Donald Scott as director of the Peabody Museum and who spent one season with Dr. Hencken on the archæological division of the project, lent his enthusiastic support to the continuation of the Museum's interest in this study. At the time of the Rockefeller grant to the Department, Professor A. M. Tozzer was Chairman of the Department and was chiefly instrumental in securing this important subvention. He was most generous in earmarking substantial shares of that grant for the Irish Study.

No portion of the Harvard Anthropological Survey of Ireland was able to operate at any period without the exercise of the most rigid economy; funds that could be called ample were never available. However, the generosity of foundations and individuals and the unselfish devotion of the scientific members of the survey have made possible its completion. Beyond mere travelling expenses and subsistence in the field, none of the principals or active participants in any section of the survey—archæological, social anthropological, or physical anthropological—received any compensation whatsoever.

CONTENTS

xi

CONTENTS xiii

xvi THE PHYSICAL ANTHROPOLOGY OF IRELAND

Conclusions on Ulster 212
General conclusions on relation of morphological type distributions to Keltic invasions and
distributions 213

CORRELATION OF HISTORICAL EVENTS
WITH PRESENT DISTRIBUTION OF
MORPHOLOGICAL TYPES 216
The Vikings 216

THE RELATIONSHIP OF THE ANGLO-
NORMAN CONQUEST AND OF SUB-
SEQUENT HISTORICAL EVENTS IN
IRELAND TO THE PRESENT DISTRI-
BUTION OF MORPHOLOGICAL TYPES 223
Inhabitants of Ulster 226
Inhabitants of Cork and Wexford . . . 226
Inhabitants of Kerry 226
Inhabitants of Kilkenny, Westmeath, Long-
ford, Kings Co., Tipperary 226
Inhabitants of Carlow, Waterford, and
Limerick 226
Inhabitants of Meath, Kildare, Queens Co.,
and Dublin 226
Summary 231

COMPARISON OF THE PRESENT DISTRI-
BUTION OF MORPHOLOGICAL TYPES
IN IRELAND WITH SIMILAR TYPES IN
WALES AND IN THE ISLE OF MAN . . 233

CARLETON S. COON'S PREVIEW OF THE
DATA OF THIS SURVEY 239

SUMMARY OF MORPHOLOGICAL TYPE
SEQUENCES AND CORRELATIONS IN
IRELAND 244
The Pre-Keltic Irish, the Keltic Irish, and the
Post-Keltic Irish 244
The Mesolithic inhabitants of Ireland . . 245
The Neolithic and Megalithic inhabitants
of Ireland 245
The Bronze Age people 245
The peoples of the Iron Ages 246
The Vikings 246
The Anglo-Normans 246
The English and the Scots 246
Effect of the Cromwellian and other trans-
plantations and plantations upon the distribu-
tion of morphological (subracial) types . . 247

PART IV: WEST COAST IRISH FEMALES
by Helen Dawson

SOCIOLOGICAL OBSERVATIONS . . . 251
Marital state 251
Number of siblings 251

Number of children 251
Education 251
Language 252
Religion 252
Occupation 252

MEASUREMENTS AND INDICES . . . 254
Age 254
Weight 254
Stature 254
Span 254
Relative span 255
Biacromial diameter 255
Relative shoulder breadth 255
Sitting height 255
Relative sitting height 255
Head length 256
Head breadth 256
Cephalic index 256
Head height 257
Length-height index 257
Breadth-height index 257
Minimum frontal diameter 257
Fronto-parietal index 257
Bizygomatic diameter 257
Cephalo-facial index 257
Zygo-frontal index 258
Bigonial diameter 258
Fronto-gonial index 258
Zygo-gonial index 258
Total face height 258
Facial index 259
Upper face height 259
Upper facial index 259
Nose height 259
Nose breadth 260
Nasal index 260
Conclusions on sex differences 260

MORPHOLOGICAL OBSERVATIONS . . 262
Skin color, inner arm 262
Vascularity 262
Freckles 262
Moles 262
Hair form 263
Hair texture 263
Hair quantity, head 263
Hair quantity, body 263
Grayness, head 264
Hair color, head 264
Eye color 264
Pigment, mixed eyes 265
Iris 266
Eyefolds, external 266
Eyefolds, median 266
Eyefolds, internal 266

LIST OF LINE-CUT FIGURES

LIST OF TABLES

LIST OF HALF-TONE FIGURES

THE PHYSICAL ANTHROPOLOGY OF IRELAND

INTRODUCTION

GEOGRAPHY AND GEOLOGY

THE ethnography of any country depends primarily upon its geography, and secondarily upon its history in terms of invasion and settlement. The more remote and less fertile and desirable areas are normally the last to be occupied, and serve as refuge areas for early and primitive stocks if these cannot withstand the pressure of later comers. If the first settlers are able to maintain themselves against subsequent immigrants, they may hold the more desirable tracts and force the newcomers into the poorer regions. However, in countries whose settlement goes back to the Stone Age, the early populations are likely to select as the most desirable habitation areas regions which are suitable for fishing and hunting and perhaps relatively poor for agriculture. Thus it appears that the cultural status of settlers is sure to affect their choice of homes. Again, on the whole, the parts of a country which are most accessible and nearest to population reservoirs of potential immigrants are almost certain to be colonized first and to serve as ports of entry for successive waves of immigrants.

Ireland is an island separated from Great Britain on the east by narrow, shallow seas, the least width of which, between the Mull of Cantire (Scotland) and Torr Head, is only 13½ miles. St. George's Channel, at the southeastern extremity, has a minimum breadth of 47 miles. Dublin is only 69 miles from Holyhead in Wales. Thus Ireland is easily accessible from Wales and Scotland.

The island is irregularly rhomboidal and has an average breadth of about 110 miles and a maximum length on the northeast-southwest diagonal of 302 miles. In general, Ireland is basin-shaped.

Coastal rims of mountains surround a central plain which seldom exceeds 250 feet in elevation. The coastal mountains are not continuous, but isolated clusters, extending inland to an extreme distance of about 70 miles. On the east side, the principal mountain clusters are the Wicklow Mountains south of Dublin, and the Mournes in the south of Down. Between these two groups the central plain slopes down to the sea. At the northeastern extremity is the Plateau of Antrim, and between it and the Mournes the coast is again low and accessible. The northern coast is steep, but indented with deep inlets, and the entire western coast has this precipitous character with many fjord-like inlets and a fringe of islands. In the extreme northwest are the mountains of Donegal, one of the three land masses which jut into the Atlantic. Donegal is separated from the central peninsula by Donegal Bay. The central peninsula consists of Mayo and its mountains in the north, separated by Clew Bay from mountainous Connemara in the south. The deep indentation of Galway Bay and, further south, the estuary of the Shannon, delimit a western area in which the central plain extends down to the sea. The southwestern area consists of the mountains of Kerry and Cork, separated into four prongs by deep bays. The eastern parts of the southern coast and the southern extremity of the east coast are in some places relatively low and accessible, giving their commercial importance to Waterford and Wexford, both of which have good harbors.

In addition to the coastal mountains there are a number of inland clusters, such as the Sperrins in Londonderry, many short ranges in Sligo, Mayo and Galway, the Galtees of Tipperary, and Slieve Bloom in Offaly, the furthest inland. The mountains of Ireland do not, however, prevent easy access to the central plain.

This central plain consists of strips of low-lying firm ground alternating with bogs. The latter occur also in the mountains. The principal river which drains the central plain is the Shannon, which rises in a mountain spring in County Cavan and follows a bow-shaped course to the west and southwest.

The central plain is limestone, but the mountains around the rim are of various formations. The hills of the northeast are mainly lava plateaus (fig. 1), but the northwest (Londonderry, Donegal) and the western parts of Mayo and Galway consist largely of metamorphic rocks of ancient but dubious date, modified by extensive invasions of granite. The Wicklow Mountains consist of an exposed granite core, flanked by Silurian shales, slates and sandstones. The Silurian rocks were extensively folded in a southwest-northeast direction before the laying down of the Old Red Sandstone which succeeded them in southern Ireland. Thus the foothills and lowlands of the southeast are largely composed of these Silurian rocks intercalated with intrusive igneous rocks. These folded Silurian beds were overlaid with Old Red Sandstone formed in Devonian times. The latter strata are most fully exposed in high rocky ridges which run from the west of Kerry to central Waterford.

The soils of Ireland are largely fertile and easily cultivable, since heavy clays, sands, and gravel are almost entirely absent. The banks of the principal rivers are lined with flat stretches of land capable of producing fine crops. The sandstone districts have enough soil in the mountain hollows to warrant tillage or to serve as rich pasturage. There is abundant moisture and an equable climate. The greater portion of the counties of Tyrone, Londonderry, and Donegal in the north and northwest is moorland or upland hill pasture, and this is true also of western Mayo, West Galway, southern Kerry, and southwestern Cork. Large areas of this moorland also occur in patches through the country, wherever the hills outcrop. Perhaps the most sharply delimited areas geographically are western Donegal, western Mayo, and the southwestern tip of the island, including south Kerry and west Cork. These have the heaviest rainfall and the sparsest population, together with the least cultivable land.

HISTORICAL SKETCH[1]

The collection of anthropometric data for the racial survey of the males of Ireland was carried out in two phases. The first phase began in January, 1934, and ended in May of that same year. The second phase covered the period from December, 1934, to May, 1936.

Before the actual work of measuring was begun, a tour of the country was made by car in order to observe the people and to map out a plan of action. During this preliminary tour an attempt was made to size up the population and to determine whether there were any distinct types of peoples living in the various parts of the country. Certain impressions were gained on this trip, but it soon became apparent that in no part of Ireland were there any great concentrations of physical types which were peculiar to certain localities and which did not occur in other areas. In short, the population appeared to be composed of several different elements which had become thoroughly mixed over many centuries. It is true that many of the West Galway (Connemara) men looked different from Mayo men and that both these groups possessed certain features that distinguished them from Cork or Kerry or Tipperary men. However, good Galway types occurred, for example, in Leitrim, and Mayo types were to be found in Kilkenny. Furthermore, there was one characteristic which all these types shared in common and which appeared to be prevalent throughout the whole country. This characteristic was the somewhat unusual combination of dark hair and blue eyes.

The results of the preliminary tour indicated that in order to obtain a clear picture of the racial composition of the Irish people, all parts of the country would have to be covered, and it would be necessary to measure a representative sample of men from many localities in each county (fig. 2 and tables I, 1–2). This

[1] The following account of Dr. Dupertuis' field work in Ireland is naturally in his own words. The senior author feels that the interest and importance of this historical sketch of a great individual anthropometric achievement, excuse its lengthiness.

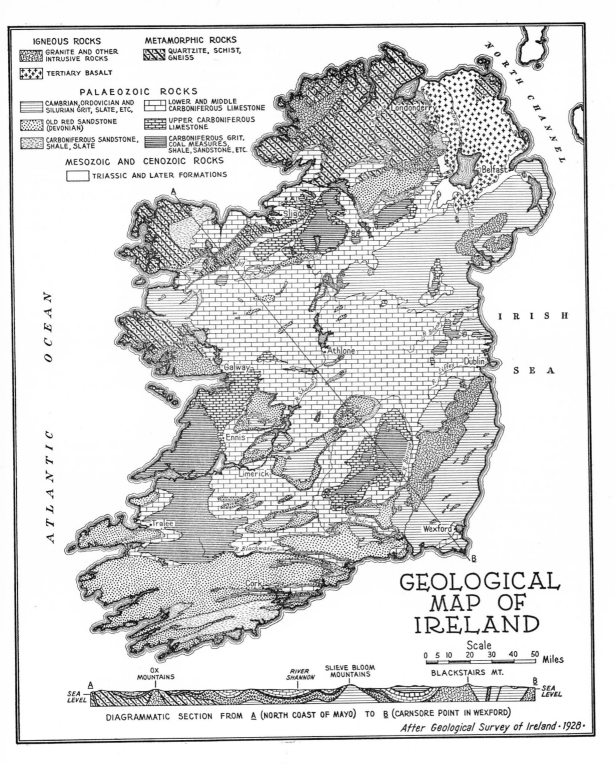

After Geological Survey of Ireland · 1928 ·

FIGURE 1

GEOLOGICAL MAP OF IRELAND, with a diagrammatic section from the north coast of Mayo to Carnsore Point in Wexford.

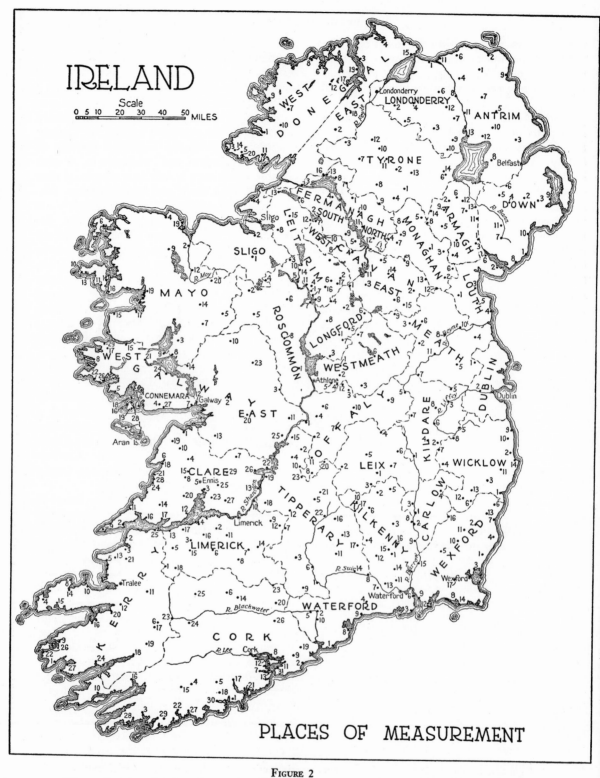

FIGURE 2

MAP OF IRELAND showing places of measurement, which are listed numerically within each county.

plan was set in operation in mid-February, 1934, and the first measurements were made in Moate, County Westmeath, a town located at approximately the geographical center of Ireland.

From Moate it was easy enough to reach most parts of counties Westmeath, Longford, East Galway, and the northern part of County Offaly. Many towns, villages and crossroads in this area were visited during the following six weeks. With the aid of a young man hired as recorder and drummer-up, it was possible to measure a fairly representative sample of the male population in these counties. Many of the first recruits were from among the friends of the recorder, who was well known throughout the countryside, and this fact may account for the rather low average age for the sample from Longford and Westmeath.

At times, help from the parish priests was enlisted. A regular practice was made to call upon the bishops in each diocese where work was begun. In most cases the clergy were sympathetic towards the project and some parish priests were extremely helpful, even to offering themselves as subjects as an example to the men of the village. Often the local parish priest would oblige by announcing the work from the altar on Sunday, telling the people that the measuring team would be in their village on a certain day the following week. This procedure usually brought good results, especially in the case of one priest who urged the men, ". . . for the glory of Ireland to submit to being measured by the good doctor from America."

In some villages a local whipper-in was hired to round up a collection of men from the area. On at least two occasions the village bell ringer was retained to announce the arrival of the measuring team at the school house or village hall. These attempts were not very successful, although a few curiosity-seekers were drawn in.

For no particular justifiable reason other than the desire for a complete change of scenery, it was decided to visit the Aran Islands in Galway Bay as the next stop on the itinerary. Two very enjoyable weeks were spent on Innismore and Innismaan, two of the islands in the Aran group. A certain amount of reticence was at first encountered among these Gaelic speaking islandmen, but with the invaluable aid given by Dr. O'Brien, the dispensary doctor, a fine series of these hardy men was measured.

Back on the mainland again, the next area to be visited was the southern part of County Leitrim and the northern section of County Roscommon. With the help of a number of different recorders and whippers-in, it was possible to measure a sufficient sample of men from both the town and country areas. According to legend, Leitrim is the original home and the present residing place of the descendants of the Firbolgs. These people are described as being swarthy-skinned and dark-eyed, entirely different from other Irishmen. This was an area, then, to be carefully combed for these unusual types. Special efforts were made to visit the more inaccessible localities in the hope of finding at least a few of these brown-eyed people. However, very few brown eyes were to be found. Here, as elsewhere, the men were almost all light-eyed and had the usual dark hair.

The final week or so of this first phase of the Irish survey was spent in measuring a number of Civic Guards in the Dublin barracks and a group of employees of the Guinness brewery, also in Dublin. The directors and brewers of the Guinness company kindly lent their assistance in this venture.

After a few months sojourn in the States in order to fulfill commitments, the junior author returned to Ireland in December, 1934, accompanied by his wife as permanent recorder, to undertake again the anthropometric duties.

Having already covered a large section of central Ireland on the first visit, it was decided next to do the west coast counties starting in Western Galway or Connemara. At this point the procedure for securing subjects for measurement was radically altered. It was decided to enlist the aid of the Civic Guards, the police force of Ireland, to help in securing subjects for measurement. This able and efficient organization is a national institution with headquarters in Dublin. An interview with General Murphy, assistant director, resulted in a letter of introduction to the county superintendents throughout the Free State. Each superintendent then supplied a letter of introduction to the sergeants in charge of the barracks or police stations in each district. Each sergeant in turn detailed a man to go out into the town or village and round up a sample of men for measurement. Whenever possible the measuring was done in the police barracks. At each station the guards themselves were measured in the presence of a few of the villagers, in order to convince the local men that they were not being singled out for conscription or were not to be given the third degree. For the most part the villagers accepted the procedure in the spirit of fun and cooperation. Many, however, must have had some qualms about the whole matter, as the guard went about the town telling Paddy or Mike or Tim to go down to the barracks, "the sergeant wants to see you." Frequently the first men to be sent in were the local town characters, but in the course of time a representative sample of the male population was measured in each area. Often the first few men measured would go out and round up their friends in order to have the pleasure of seeing them go through the "ordeal." A few cigarettes passed out frequently helped to break down the resistance on the part of those who were shy. Most of the subjects were happy to learn their correct stature and weight and many times there was good natured competition in determining who had the greatest absolute or relative span (reach of arms).

On Thursdays it was particularly desirable to do the measuring in the Civic Guards barracks. This was the day when the men from the surrounding country side came to sign for the dole. It was especially important to work in remote country districts on these days since otherwise it would have been impossible to measure many of the men living in the more inaccessible regions. The usual procedure was to measure the men after they had signed for the dole and before they could get out of the barracks. Dole days and County Fair days always produced a good sample of farmers and farm laborers.

Much of the success of the anthropometric survey of Ireland was due to the whole hearted cooperation of the Civic Guards of Eire and the Royal Irish Constabulary in Northern Ireland. These men facilitated the work in many ways. They were always courteous and considerate. Many of them volunteered

to help even when they were off duty. It would be difficult to find a finer group of men than that which makes up the police force in both Eire and Northern Ireland.

The majority of subjects in this survey, then, were secured with the aid of the Irish police forces. For the most part, the work was carried out county by county. Headquarters were set up in the larger towns affording the best hotels. During the course of a week it was possible to work in most of the towns and villages within a radius of 20 to 30 miles. Usually two places were visited each day, one in the morning and one in the afternoon. As each section of the county was covered, a move was made to the next and the same procedure was followed. Occasionally, it was found desirable to measure in a village which did not boast a barracks. In these instances a local man was hired to round up subjects, the place of measurement being a pub or shop owned by a friendly and interested citizen.

Since the occasional hiring of drummers-up put considerable strain on the budget allotted for the work, it was decided to request a small sum of money from the Irish Free State government to cover this expense. Consequently, an interview was arranged with Prime Minister Eamon De Valera, who very graciously agreed to allot 40 pounds to be used in defraying some of the cost of the project. This money was paid through the Department of Education and was personally supervised by the Hon. Mr. O'Neill, Secretary of the Department of Education. Also following the example set by Mr. O'Neill, several members of the secretariat and other government employees offered themselves as subjects for measurement. No special effort, however, was made to secure samples from the larger urban areas, since it was felt that the country people were perhaps more truly representative of Irish racial types and less likely to be mixed with recent foreign blood than would be the city dwellers.

It has already been mentioned that much of the work was carried out in police barracks, in public school houses, and in shops and public houses. It was necessary, however, to branch out occasionally and to set up the equipment wherever and whenever there were good prospects. After mass on Sunday usually was a fruitful time for work, especially in the country districts. There it is the custom for the men to congregate outside the chapel after mass and stand around talking for a half hour or so. Having received permission to work in the social hall connected with the chapel, it was usually possible to persuade a goodly number of men to come in and have their heads measured.

Sometimes, out in the country, work was done in farm houses or laborers' cottages. On these occasions either the best room or the kitchen would be turned over for the occasion. People for miles around came running to see what was going on; or they would start running in the opposite direction for fear the police were after them.

Thus, whenever a group of men was found together, the opportunity was seized to carry on the project. Oftentimes it would be at a bog where the men were cutting turf, or in the fields where they were pitching hay. In fishing villages it was always possible to get a number of men on the quays. In the larger towns, a fair number of subjects could always be found in lumber yards and in houses under construction. On occasion, also, a large number of employees in factories of various sorts were measured. For example, work was carried out in the woolen mills of Foxford, County Mayo, and in the Belleek pottery works where the famous Belleek china is manufactured.

Other places of work included town halls, county courthouses, dispensary doctors' offices, and old people's homes. On a few occasions the attendants in various mental hospitals were also measured. In Galway, for example, a group of soldiers at an army post and also some students in the National University were measured.

Since an attempt to build up a representative sample of types of men from all parts of Ireland was the aim of the survey, every effort was made to measure all classes of society and men of every different age and occupation. Included in the series, then, are measurements on tinkers and landed gentry, on chimney sweeps and even on some peers of Ireland. The government is represented by some members of the Dail and by secretaries and clerks of several of the departments.

In counties like Galway, most of the subjects were measured in the country districts, and as often as possible in the smaller towns and more inaccessible villages. Only a few subjects were actually measured in Galway town itself. On one occasion a few students in the dissecting laboratory at the medical school and a number of monks agreed to act as subjects. A day was spent working in the Claddagh, a fishing village, within the city limits of Galway. The people from the Claddagh had been described as dark Spanish types, perhaps unique specimens in the Irish population. After measuring a number of these fishermen, however, it became evident that they were not different physically from other Irishmen and that their eyes were just as blue.

Clare was the next county to be visited. Our largest series comes from this county principally because the Harvard social anthropologists had selected Clare for their intensive sociological survey. The original plan was to correlate their findings with those from the anthropometric survey. Subsequently, however, it was found impracticable to carry out this proposal. The result was that Clare was more thoroughly covered than any other county in Ireland.

During a period of about five weeks almost one thousand men were measured in County Clare. By good fortune the services of a Mr. Paddy McNamara of Ennis were secured to act as drummer-up for the whole county. Paddy was well known and liked in every part of Clare and it is undoubtedly true that many of the men consented to be measured simply out of friendship to him. Paddy seemed to like the work and he seldom missed a day in the travels to every corner of the county. He knew the county thoroughly, something of its history, where the different types were to be found and where and when groups of men would be assembled on market and Fair days. Paddy McNamara was a great help in County Clare and he became one of the staunchest friends of the anthropometric survey.

From County Clare we continued on up the west coast to County Mayo. From four or five of the larger towns, we were able to reach quite easily most parts of this county. Here we relied mainly on the Civic Guards to secure our subjects. Of particular interest were a few days spent among the people of Achill Island. Many of these people told us they had relatives in Cleveland, Ohio.

County Donegal was the next area to be visited. During this first trip to Donegal most of the time was spent in the mountainous western districts. The eastern and north-eastern sections were reserved for a later visit after the measuring had been finished in the counties of Northern Ireland. Much of West Donegal is very rugged country, many of the localities being almost inaccessible by car. It is almost certain that some of the back-country lanes we traversed seldom felt the crunch of automobile tires.

From Donegal we went south to County Limerick. During the next six weeks the survey of the west coast of Ireland was completed by covering pretty thoroughly counties Limerick and Kerry. By this time it was spring, and during the longer days it was possible to measure 30 to 40 men a day on an average, but occasionally in southern Ireland this figure was surpassed and on one day in Ballyferiter at the southern tip of County Kerry, as many as 64 men were measured, the best record for any one day in Ireland.

From Kerry the survey moved eastward to County Cork, the largest county of Ireland. As usual we followed our policy of keeping away from the larger centers of population, so that our sample from County Cork is largely a rural one and includes only a small number of men who were born in Cork City. It should be stated here, however, that certain parts of the mountainous district in northwest central Cork were not covered. Plans to visit the area fell through, so that this one small region is virtually unrepresented in our sample.

The next county to be covered was Tipperary. Most of southern Tipperary was reached from Cahir, while the center of operations for the north riding was the town of Thurles.

The next move was to County Kilkenny. Most of this county was served from Kilkenny Town which is located roughly in the center of the county. From here a few trips were made to villages in Carlow and southern Leix because they appeared to be more accessible

from Kilkenny Town than from points within the counties themselves.

Having pretty well covered the southern midlands, the survey moved on to County Waterford. There are a number of Irish-speaking villages on the coast of County Waterford which are of particular interest. On several occasions we were told that in one or two of these isolated localities the fishermen were dark and swarthy types. They were referred to as Turks by the people farther inland. Here at last, we thought, is what we have been looking for; a real inbred group of brown-eyed brunets who are perhaps the remnants of an ancient stock different from anything else we had seen in Ireland. The Civic Guards sergeant from a neighboring town felt that he had uncovered a real find and offered to accompany us to one of these small fishing villages. With great anticipation the measuring was begun. The first few men proved to have blue or at least very light eyes as did almost everybody else up to that point. We continued to measure and observe all the men that could be found in the village. Not a brown eye among them. The sergeant was completely dumbfounded. It had long been the belief that this group of people was different; most of the inhabitants of the surrounding area looked upon this group of people as foreigners, dark, swarthy people whose ancestors had come from over the seas. Here, then, was another local myth exploded, just as it had been in the Claddagh in Galway Town and in the fishing villages of County Clare where the people were supposed to have been largely the descendants of survivors of the Spanish Armada, which was reputedly wrecked off the west coast of Ireland.

A tour through County Wexford where we hoped to, and perhaps did, come across some of the descendants of the Viking invaders, finished up the survey of the southeastern corner of the country.

With fall and winter coming on again we made our way slowly, town by town and village by village, up through counties Wicklow and Carlow. Whenever possible we tried to take photographs of a representative group of men we measured in each county. Up to this point we had been fairly successful, but during our stay in these two counties the weather and other local conditions prevented us from taking pictures and, consequently, we have very few pictures showing the fine types of men in this part of Ireland.

A few more weeks were spent by going to counties Leix, Kildare, and Dublin and this gave us a good sample of the inhabitants of these eastern and midland counties. During this period a few localities in southern Offaly, which had been missed previously, were also visited.

The next phase of the work of the survey covered Meath and Louth in the eastern part of the Free State, and Monaghan and Cavan on the border of Northern Ireland. Since this period of work was carried on during the winter months, the work had to be restricted to the Civic Guards' barracks. It was no longer possible to stop occasionally along the country road to measure groups of road workers, turfcutters, or threshers from the fields.

The following four months which were left to finish the survey, were spent in the six counties of Northern Ireland. We found no difference here in the attitude of the people toward our work than in the southern counties. The Home Secretary for Northern Ireland became much interested in the work and offered to assist in any way possible. With the officials of the Royal Ulster Constabulary the same plan of procedure which had been used in the Free State was worked out, and the men of the Constabulary gave the same wholehearted cooperation which we had received from the Civic Guards in Eire. The men were just as willing to act as subjects themselves and just as eager to see their friends get the same "treatment." Of course, not every man who was asked agreed to be measured. This was particularly true in those villages along the border where some of the more suspicious of the local inhabitants got it into their heads that we were measuring men for the Free State Army. We had encountered a similar reluctance on the part of some of the men on the other side of the border where we were accused of recruiting for the "Orange Army."

About two weeks were devoted to measuring a representative sample of the male popu-lation in each of the six Ulster counties. The work was started in County Down and then we moved clockwise around Lough Veagh and covered Counties Armagh, Fermanagh, Tyrone, Londonderry, and Antrim in that order. Proportionately as many towns and villages were visited in these counties as in the south. Although the number of cases in these counties was smaller in some instances, the sample of men measured in Northern Ireland was just as representative of the people of that area as was true for the southern counties.

The collection of data for the racial survey of Ireland was terminated in May, 1936. It had taken approximately two years to cover all parts of the country. During this period, over 10,000 men were measured in some 426 localities in the 32 counties. Some idea of how much traveling was done in order to achieve these results may be gained by stating that over 45,000 miles were travelled by car in a country which is approximately 300 miles long by 150 miles wide.

The experiences we had in carrying out this racial survey of Ireland would fill many volumes. We are constantly calling to mind the beauty of the scenery, the quaint and charming customs of the country folk, and the feeling of friendship and hospitality which one encounters everywhere in Ireland. What could be more beautiful than the September heather in the hills of Tipperary, or the hedgerows of fuschia in Cork and Kerry? Or the browns and grays of the bog and granite country of Connemara? Or the green of the fields as seen in February from atop the ruins of Cashel? For sheer majesty what can compare with the Cliffs of Moher or Slieve League or the mountain of Erigal in Donegal? The rivers, the lakes, the mountains, the farmlands, all express the charm that is Ireland.

From the busy metropolises of Dublin and Belfast to the quiet villages of Wexford and Mayo, one is constantly impressed with the hospitality of the people. They are friendly and gay, keen-minded and possessing that sense of humor for which they are known the world over. Here is a people which is the living embodiment of a priceless heritage and the hope for great days to come.

TECHNIQUES OF THE SURVEY

INSTRUMENTS

Standard anthropometers, sliding, and spreading calipers, of the type prescribed by Martin in his *Lehrbuch*, were utilized in the Harvard Anthropometric Survey of Ireland. No hair color, skin color, or eye color scales were used, because in our opinion all such scales available are either inadequate or entirely useless. The Harvard Anthropometric Laboratory possesses and has tried out the standard types of these devices and many others. No head-spanner was used.

MEASUREMENTS

The measurements taken conform in general to the techniques described by Martin. They are described in more detail and the modifications of the Harvard practices are stated in the work, *Up From The Ape*.

It seems necessary here to refer to our method of taking head height. The upper section of the anthropometer is used, with the upper sliding arm extended horizontally and resting upon the head vertically above tragion and the lower arm retracted to the tragion point. This measurement is described more fully in the work just cited (p. 758). This vertical head height yields lower values than a similar measurement done with a head-spanner in which points of the spanner are introduced into each auditory meatus of the subject. The same value *can* be obtained with a head-spanner if the latter is pulled upward after the points have been introduced into the auditory meatus. This process is painful for the subject, and although it is prescribed for accurate measurements of head height by use of the head-spanner, it is our experience that field anthropometrists generally neglect to pull up the spanner, because it makes the subject feel as if he were being suspended from ice-tongs introduced into his ears. A few trials of this procedure render the securing of further subjects for measurement almost impossible. In any event, the other method is more accurate. We have no use for the so-called "projective measurements." They are hopelessly inaccurate.

A precise determination of the nasion point is essential for correct measurement of nasal height, upper facial height, and total facial height. The method used by Harvard anthropometrists is specified on page 760 of *Up From The Ape*. The naso-frontal suture is palpated with the edge of the thumb-nail and marked with a pencil. When the suture cannot be found by palpation, it is located approximately by the horizontal tangent to the superior palpebral sulci and by the level of the lowest eyebrow hairs (if present).

In measuring sitting height, great care has to be taken to insure that the subject keeps the lumbar curve flexed (i.e., in the position it assumes when the individual is standing erect) and that the height of the seat is such that the thighs are horizontal and the feet resting flat upon the ground.

In the measurement of females, the thoracic diameters were omitted for obvious reasons. In any event, chest breadth and chest depth are very difficult and inaccurate measurements, even in males.

OBSERVATIONS

An elaborate list of graded observations was carried through on each subject. These observations are listed on the anthropometric blank. Measurements and observations are subsequently punched into I.B.M. cards. The anthropometric blank is in itself a code sheet so that no steps are necessary between the actual taking of the field record and the punching of the I.B.M. card.

These graded observations have been developed and elaborated over the years in the Harvard Laboratory and are taught to, and practised by, students of physical anthropology. In many instances they are necessarily subjective and great pains are taken by the instructor and much labor is expended by the student in order to fix in the mind of the latter the ideal standards for the various morphological observations. The originator of this system was the great and late physical anthropologist, Aleš Hrdlička, but the modifications made in the procedure during the course of years at Harvard have been considerable.

In the first place, it must be emphasized

that the standards are the same for both sexes. The referent is modal development in the "ordinary" Northwestern European male. Thus a medium development or size of brow ridges is that which the observer feels to be the commonest, modal, or "average" size of the brow ridges seen in males of our own ethnic and racial stock, on the basis of his own anthropological experience and the instruction imparted to him. The female is judged by this same scale; a "pronounced" size of brow ridges in the female would be those of such development as would be so designated in the male. Obviously if we adopt dual standards of morphological or size judgments for the sexes, we shall be lost, because intersexual data will be incomparable. What is sauce for the gander simply has to be sauce for the goose.

While we constantly strive to keep our anthropometric observers adhering to precisely the same standards of morphological rating, by simultaneous training and by subsequent consultations and comparisons, nevertheless, two observers invariably and inevitably do develop divergences in methods and standards. Long experience with attempting to analyze the data of surveys participated in by more than one observer has made the senior author horribly familiar with these difficulties. It is best to admit them frankly, and when they arise, they must be dealt with in all honesty and candor. Some "anthroposcopic" gradations seem to present little or no difficulty in obtaining agreement between observers; some others are very troublesome. Some observers are able to maintain fixed ideal standards of observation; others fluctuate.

The supposed advantage of using some device such as a skin color or hair color scale, on the supposition that objectivity of rating is thereby achieved, is completely fallacious. There is just as much of a personal equation involved in matching colors from a chart as in grading them verbally according to a stated list of well-defined categories.

PART I

CATHOLICS BY COUNTY SUBGROUPS

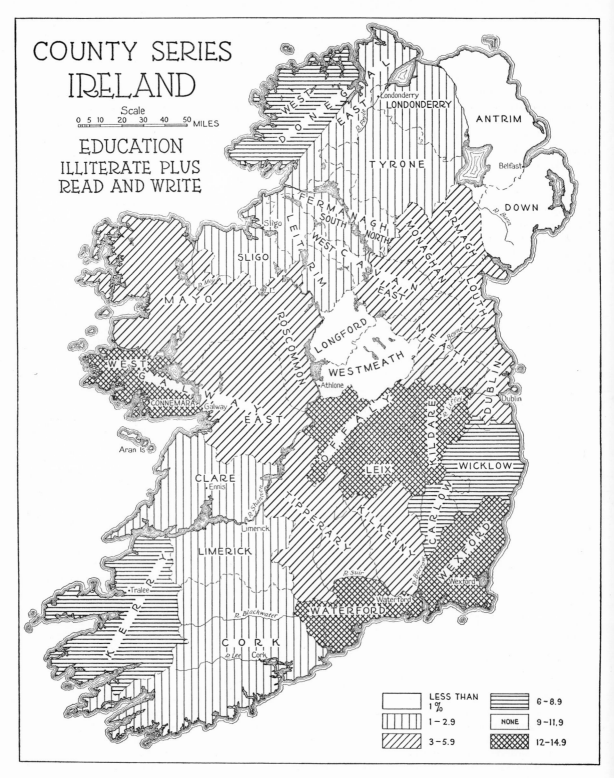

COUNTY SERIES
IRELAND

Scale
0 5 10 20 30 40 50 MILES

EDUCATION
ILLITERATE PLUS
READ AND WRITE

	LESS THAN 1%		6 – 8.9
	1 – 2.9	NONE	9 – 11.9
	3 – 5.9		12 – 14.9

FIGURE 3

SOCIOLOGICAL OBSERVATIONS

Education (Tables II-1, II-2). Education in our county series is subdivided into five categories: *illiterate, read and write* (implies literacy but no formal education); *national school* (equivalent to primary and grammar school); *secondary school* (equivalent to high school); and *university*.

Figure 3 plots the distribution according to percentages of *illiterate* plus *read and write*. Complete illiterates include 3.3 per cent of the county series and are considerably the most numerous in West Galway. This area also has the highest percentage of persons who are literate but have had no formal education (*read and write*). The map, then, suggests that the area of most meager education and highest illiteracy is West Galway. Two other areas show up poorly. They are West Donegal and a block of counties comprising Waterford-Wexford, Wicklow-Carlow, and Offaly-Leix-Kildare. Kerry is also high in illiterates and semi-literates, with 6.5 per cent.

Five county subgroups fall within the 3 to 5.9 percentage group. These are E. Galway-Roscommon, Tipperary-Kilkenny, Meath-Louth-Dublin, Mayo, and E. Cavan-Monaghan-Armagh. Five county subgroups are represented in the next grade—between one and 2.9 per cent of the absolutely or almost totally uneducated. Finally, the Aran Islands, Longford-Westmeath, and Antrim-Down are subgroups that include virtually no illiterates and uneducated persons—less than one per cent. Aran Islands have none at all, but only one person of 139 who has had any education beyond the national school.

It seemed desirable to make some other estimate of general educational rating, in addition to a simple plotting of percentages of illiterates plus those who can read and write but have received no formal education. We have utilized for this purpose the educational ratio, which is the ratio of B (*secondary school* plus *university*) to A (*illiterate* plus *read and write*).

On this basis the Aran Islands rank first, because the small series of men from this isolated group includes no illiterates and no persons who have not attended school. However, while the Arans are least illiterate, they also have considerably the lowest proportion of well-educated men. Their ranking is illusory. They approximate most closely in general educational status Sligo-Leitrim-S. Fermanagh-W. Cavan, which also has nearly all of its sample in the national school category. This county subgroup ties for eleventh rank in the nineteen county samples in the B/A ratio.

In general, however, the educational ratio gives about the same result as does figure 3, which plots percentages of illiterates plus those who can read and write but have had no formal education. Longford-Westmeath may owe its high position in part to the very low mean age of the sample of men measured. On the other hand, Wicklow-Carlow and Waterford-Wexford, which are very low in educational ranking, are the two oldest county subgroups and probably include more poorly educated persons for this reason. However, West Donegal is below mean age and yet ranks very low in education.

Language (Table II-3). More than half of the individuals in our Irish county series (54.8 per cent) have no knowledge of the Irish

FIGURE 3

DISTRIBUTION OF ILLITERACY IN IRELAND. The map showing percentages of illiterates plus those who can read and write but have no formal education shows minimal illiteracy in the Arans, Longford-Westmeath, and Antrim-Down—all areas in which samples are well below mean age. Of the three areas in which illiteracy is highest, Waterford-Wexford and West Galway are above mean age—the former considerably the oldest Irish sample—but Offaly-Leix-Kildare is below mean age. Apart from tenuous age correlations, there is no obvious significance in the distribution.

(Gaelic or Erse) language. Another 30.4 per cent have merely studied Irish in school. However, our information is that "school" Irish amounts to far more than an equivalent of what American school children learn when they study French or German. Many, and perhaps a majority, of these school-taught Irish students can actually speak the language, and are likely to make extensive use of what they have learned. There are, then, 14.8 per cent of our series who are native Irish speakers (fig. 4). Of these, 85, or 1.0 per cent of the total series, speak only Irish.

If we draw a line running south from Londonderry through the course of the Shannon to the city of Limerick, and thence southeast to the town of Waterford, we shall have included to the west and southwest of this boundary all but the merest handful of the 1,315 persons in our series who speak Irish. Actually, however, the area of survival of Keltic speech is not so easily defined. West Donegal is cut off from the next region of Keltic speech to the south (Mayo) by the Sligo-Leitrim-S. Fermanagh-W. Cavan area which, in its large sample of 715 men, includes only 3 Gaelic speakers. Mayo and West Galway are strong centers of the Irish language, but E. Galway-Roscommon to the east and Clare to the south have only 12.7 and 15.6 per cent respectively of Irish speakers. Kerry, which is a strongly Keltic county, is bounded to the northeast by Limerick, which has only 3.2 per cent of native Irish speakers, and to the east by Cork, which has 12.7 per cent.

It is therefore apparent (as may be seen from fig. 4) that the Irish language is confined, for all practical purposes, to the westernmost parts of the western peninsular areas of the island.

The Aran Islands lead in Irish speakers, with 95.0 per cent, and these islands also have the lowest percentage in their series of those who have no knowledge of Irish (3.6 per cent). However, our Aran series of 139 individuals includes but one person who can speak only Irish. The neighboring area of West Galway may possibly lay claim to the distinction of being the greatest seat of the Irish language, since it includes among its 78.3 per cent of Irish speakers no fewer than 69, or 16.0 per cent, who speak only Irish. Only 10.2 per cent of our West Galway series of 432 individuals have no acquaintance with Irish. Kerry and West Donegal are about tied for third place in Irish speech. The former has 46.6 per cent of Irish speakers and the latter 46.2 per cent. Then comes Mayo with 24.1 per cent, Clare with 15.6 per cent, and Cork with 13.0 per cent. E. Galway-Roscommon is recorded as having 12.7 per cent. Waterford-Wexford is the only eastern group that has a respectable number of Irish speakers (5.8 per cent).

Irish has been studied at school by 30.4 per cent of our county series. The smallest proportion of Irish students (0.7 per cent) occurs in the Arans where Irish is spoken by all except 6 persons of 139. This is on the assumption that the one person who studied Irish at school cannot speak it. In two other strongly Irish-speaking areas, West Galway and West Donegal, Irish has been studied at school by only 11.6 per cent and 12.3 per cent, respectively, of the samples. The reasons for the comparative paucity of Irish schooling in these areas, as in the Arans, may be that school facilities are few, or, on the other hand, that the academic pursuit of this dying language in areas where it is still alive is considered a work of supererogation. The only other counties in which so few study Irish are Antrim and Down. However, N. Fermanagh-E. Donegal-Tyrone-Londonderry have only 21.4 per cent of persons who have school Irish, as against 30.4 per cent in the total

FIGURE 4

DISTRIBUTION IN IRELAND OF NATIVE SPEAKERS PLUS IRISH ONLY. The Irish language is confined, for all practical purposes, to the western peninsular areas of Ireland. However, the map does not take into account the 30.4 per cent of our males in the county series who have studied Irish in school and may be able to read and speak it to some extent. Paradoxically, the so-called "Keltic" morphological type is concentrated in precisely the region where almost no knowledge of the Irish language has survived.

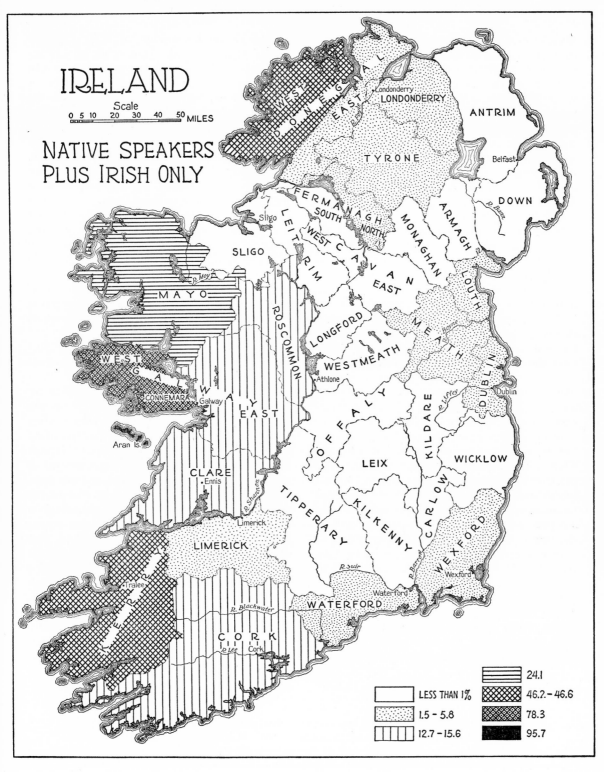

IRELAND

Scale
0 5 10 20 30 40 50 MILES

NATIVE SPEAKERS
PLUS IRISH ONLY

24.1	
LESS THAN 1%	46.2 – 46.6
1.5 – 5.8	78.3
12.7 – 15.6	95.7

FIGURE 4

county series and Sligo-Leitrim-S. Fermanagh-W. Cavan are still lower with only 20.6 per cent.

The county subgroup that leads in percentage of persons who have studied Irish at school is Cork, with 40.2 per cent. Other county subgroups that surpass the mean of the series in their assiduity for the revival of the Irish language are Wicklow-Carlow, Meath-Louth-Dublin, Mayo, Clare, Limerick, E. Galway-Roscommon, Longford-Westmeath, Offaly-Leix-Kildare, Tipperary-Kilkenny, Waterford-Wexford and E. Cavan-Monaghan-Armagh. Of the county subgroups that possess any large percentage of native speakers, Mayo and Kerry are the only ones that show fairly large percentages of individuals who have studied Irish in school.

Occupation (Tables II-4, II-5). Occupational data on the individuals measured and observed were collected by Dr. Dupertuis according to a schedule devised by Dr. Conrad Arensberg, the social anthropologist who, with Dr. Solon Kimball, carried out an intensive social survey of County Clare as a part of the Harvard Anthropological Survey of Ireland. The occupational schedule was very elaborate and involved securing information not only about the individual's occupation, but also that of his father and of his mother's father. It was subdivided into rural and urban occupations. The agricultural categories were subdivided according to size of holding, etc. For anthropometric purposes, these data were far too elaborate to be used in association with measurements. Therefore, we have recombined them according to a simplified scheme. Table II-4 presents these data.

The first class—hired laborers and tinkers—presumably represents individuals of no settled occupation, unskilled, and working intermittently. According to Arensberg, these are the lowest occupational class and are virtually outcasts. They comprise 7.8 per cent of the total county series, or 666 men. In percentages of county groups, they range from none at all in the Aran Islands to 22.8 per cent of the Wicklow-Carlow sample. They are in excess also in E. Cavan-Monaghan-Armagh, Offaly-Leix-Kildare, Meath-Louth-Dublin, and Limerick. Areas in which this class is underrepresented are the Aran Islands, E. Galway-

Roscommon, Longford-Westmeath, Clare, Cork, Sligo-Leitrim-S. Fermanagh-W. Cavan, and Tipperary-Kilkenny.

The second category includes herdsmen, all sorts of farmers, farm stewards, and gardeners. It makes up 14.6 per cent of the total series. It should, perhaps, be considered with the class called "Farm Dependent," which comprises another 7.7 per cent of the county series. Thus 22.3 per cent of the series consists of persons attached to the land in agricultural or stock-raising duties.

By far the highest proportion of any subgroup in these combined categories is found in the Aran Islands with 67.6 per cent in the independent and 20.9 per cent in the dependent status. However, most Aran Islanders also fish. West Galway has 24.9 per cent in the former and 28.0 per cent in the latter class. Sligo-Leitrim-S. Fermanagh-W. Cavan are second highest in the independent farmer and cattle-raiser class, with 40.2 per cent, but only 6.4 per cent of farm dependents are included in this subseries. Other counties in which representation in these two occupational classes is excessively large are E. Galway-Roscommon, Mayo, and West Donegal. It is evident, then, that cattle-raisers and herdsmen, farmers, and farm dependents are excessively numerous in the central area to the west of the Shannon River extending out to the relatively barren peninsular areas of West Donegal and Mayo. In such counties as Meath-Louth-Dublin, Antrim-Down, Waterford-Wexford, and Cork, these classes are very poorly represented. The first two of these areas are, of course, industrial regions. No county group approximates the total series representation in these two classes, each taken separately, but Longford-Westmeath has just about the right proportions of the combined categories.

Fishermen comprise only 2.6 per cent of the series. More than half of these come from two counties—Kerry (13.4 per cent) and Waterford-Wexford (12.7 per cent). Next comes Antrim-Down (9.0 per cent), Aran Islands (5.8 per cent), West Donegal (5.4 per cent), Cork (4.0 per cent), West Galway (2.6 per cent), Meath-Louth-Dublin (2.1 per cent), and the other counties less than one per cent or none at all. Obviously this occupational class is found in excess percentages only in those counties that border on the sea.

The term "Navvy" includes unskilled manual laborers, regularly employed or, at any rate, not habitually unemployed, and not definitely attached to the land. They are more or less town or urban people. This class includes 23.2 per cent, or about one per cent more than the agricultural and herdsmen class. There is none at all of this class in the Arans, but it reaches 35.3 per cent in Longford-Westmeath, 34.7 per cent in Clare, and 31.5 per cent in Limerick. Other subgroups high in this classification are Meath-Louth-Dublin (29.5 per cent), Tipperary-Kilkenny (29.4 per cent), and Offaly-Leix-Kildare (27.7 per cent). The areas high in farmers, herders, and farm dependents are, in general, low in navvies, with the exception of Longford-Westmeath, which is average in agriculturists and cattlemen, but very high in navvies.

Semi-skilled trades include a variety of village, town, and city occupations that cannot be included under the recognized skilled trades. Semi-skilled workers comprise 8.0 per cent of the county series. They are commonest in the north; Antrim-Down (15.3 per cent), and N. Fermanagh-E. Donegal-Tyrone-Londonderry (13.8 per cent). Other areas with more than 10 per cent are Tipperary-Kilkenny, Cork and Clare. All of these areas have large cities or big towns, except Tipperary-Kilkenny. Tipperary includes the most fertile district in Ireland and is a very rich trading region. Kilkenny is a good agricultural county with some industrial development. The Arans and West Galway include practically no persons belonging to this occupational category (so far as represented in our series). Other areas very low in semi-skilled workers are E. Galway-Roscommon and West Donegal.

Transport workers comprise 4.4 per cent of the county series. They are commonest in the subgroups that include industrial centers (except Meath-Louth-Dublin). [We omitted the large cities from the anthropometric survey.] In the Arans there are no transport workers and in West Galway, where there may be little or no transportation, only 1.6 per cent of this category occurs in our sample.

Factory operatives comprise only 1.4 per cent of our county series. They are most numerous in Antrim-Down (4.2 per cent), N. Fermanagh-E. Donegal-Tyrone-Londonderry (4.0 per cent), Tipperary-Kilkenny (3.0 per cent), E. Cavan-Monaghan-Armagh (2.7 per cent), and Waterford-Wexford (2.7 per cent). Three subgroups have no factory workers. These are Aran Islands, Longford-Westmeath, and Wicklow-Carlow.

There are only 2.6 per cent of skilled tradesmen in this series. Percentages range from none in the Aran Islands to 3.4 per cent in N. Fermanagh-E. Donegal-Tyrone-Londonderry and E. Galway-Roscommon.

Tradesmen and shop assistants rate 10.2 per cent of the county series. They range from 0.7 per cent in the Arans to 18.2 per cent in N. Fermanagh-E. Donegal-Tyrone-Londonderry. West Galway, West Donegal, and Antrim-Down are notably deficient in this category.

Clerks (1.8 per cent) are totally absent from the Aran subgroup only. Clare, with 4.4 per cent, has the highest proportion. Antrim-Down and Limerick rank next with 2.8 per cent.

The professions are represented in our series by 207 persons (2.4 per cent). Cork ranks first with 5.4 per cent, Antrim-Down second with 4.9 per cent, and West Donegal third with 4.4 per cent.

The proportion of soldiers in our county series is surprisingly large (11.6 per cent), partly because Dupertuis measured at one or two army posts. The subgroup from E. Galway-Roscommon is definitely overweighted with 26.0 per cent of the military. The Cork series has 17.3 per cent, and Mayo 16.2 per cent. The Arans and Clare have an unduly low representation of this occupational category.

The final occupational category is that of students, comprising 138 persons or 1.6 per cent of the county series. E. Galway-Roscommon has a large representation with 33 men or 6.5 per cent. Kerry and Mayo with 2.9 and 2.8 per cent respectively are also somewhat overloaded.

Table II-5 shows the percentages by county subgroups of those engaged in combined rural and combined urban occupations. "Rural" is composed of the following categories: hired laborer, tinker; herdsman, farmer, farm steward, gardener; farm dependent; fisherman. All other categories are considered as "Urban."

The Aran Islands lead enormously in the rural category with 131 individuals or 94.2 per cent of the sample. Only 8 individuals from the Arans are engaged in work considered urban. West Donegal, Mayo, Sligo-Leitrim-S. Fermanagh-W. Cavan and West Galway also show high percentages of those engaged in rural pursuits (from 42 to 62 per cent as against the total county series mean of 32.7 per cent). Cork is lowest in rural workers with only 15.8 per cent and, curiously, Tip-

perary-Kilkenny, although it includes the most fertile district in Ireland, is also deficient in this category with 19.8 per cent. Clare and Limerick in the southwest and N. Fermanagh-E. Donegal-Tyrone-Londonderry in the north are also low in rural workers with 21.6, 21.4 and 21.2 per cent respectively.

In our Irish sample, the most highly industrialized sections of the country do not necessarily show up with the highest percentage of urban workers. This is probably due to the fact that the survey for the most part avoided the big cities.

MEASUREMENTS AND INDICES

Age (Tables III-1, III-2). For statistical purposes, ages are grouped in this series by five-year intervals. Such a procedure assumes the mean at the midpoint of the class interval and usually does not introduce any important error in large samples. However, the youngest age group, 15-19 years, consists almost exclusively of boys between the ages of 17 and 19, so that the midpoint of 17 years is inaccurate. Neglecting this error at the lower end of the series makes the mean age of the series and of the subgroups somewhat lower than it actually should be. Add to this the fact that ages were recorded as of the last birthday and we may hazard the guess that our series is possibly upwards of a year older than the means given in table III-1. That mean of 8,909 men of the Irish counties, all of the Catholic religion, is 35.70 years.

The 19 county subgroups range in mean age from 30.25 years (Longford-Westmeath) to 40.90 years (Waterford-Wexford). The former group is more than five years below mean age of the series and more than three years younger than any other subgroup. The tender age of this large county subgroup (676 members) may be due in part to the fact that the local assistant who acted as a "whipper-in" was a youth who corralled as subjects an undue proportion of his age mates. In addition to the elderly Waterford-Wexford group (463 members), we have another comparatively elderly sample in the Wicklow-Carlow counties (278 members) with a mean age of 38.30 years. These extreme deviations in mean age will have to be taken into consideration in the distribution of characters

subject to age change. Otherwise they are unimportant and are probably attributable to the accidents of sampling.

The standard deviation of age in the total series is 15.40 years. Most of the standard deviations of the county subgroups cluster closely around the standard deviation of the total series. The lowest (11.20 years) is found in the young Longford-Westmeath subgroup and the highest (17.60 years), in the oldest subgroup, Waterford-Wexford.

The distribution of each five-year age group by counties is given in table III-2. It requires no discussion here, because age changes in the total series of Irish males have already been dealt with in a separate monograph (Hooton and Dupertuis, 1951, pp. 9-42). This table was not included in the age change monograph, because the latter deals with the grand total of Irish males, including Church of Ireland and Presbyterian males, whereas table III-2 is confined to distributions by age groups in the Catholic County series.

Weight (Table III-3). Weight is grouped by class intervals of ten pounds. Weights were taken upon a portable scale, the subject removing hat, coat and vest, and shoes, but retaining his other garments. An average of seven pounds should be subtracted to obtain nude weights.[1] The mean weight of the county series is 157.30 pounds, and the standard deviation, 22.50 pounds. The heaviest subgroup is that of E. Galway-Roscommon with a mean weight of 161.00 pounds. Three other of the west Irish subgroups exceed 160 pounds in mean weight. The lightest group is Longford-Westmeath with an average

---

[1] The obtaining of nude weights under field conditions in such a country as Ireland is altogether impracticable. Ordinarily, it is possible to make a satisfactory correction by subtracting average weights of clothing. In Ireland, such a correction is rendered dubious by the seasonal and local variations in amount and weight of clothing worn. Dr. Dupertuis feels that seven pounds is by no means an excessive amount to subtract, even when individuals were measured without coat, waistcoat, or shoes. Often the woolens worn are very heavy, especially the homespun trousers and

the knitted sweaters, jerseys, etc. Frequently the clothing is moisture laden. Again, on cold damp days heavier clothing is often worn. Dupertuis thinks that the weight of garments in western Ireland probably is greater than in other parts of the island. However, taking into consideration other anthropometric data, it seems improbable that the distribution map is skewed toward heavy weight in the west merely through the operation of this extrinsic factor. The big, heavy men undoubtedly predominate in the west central and southwestern counties.

weight of 151.00 pounds. Since this group is also the youngest of the series and is more than five years below the total series mean age, it seems certain that its weight deficiency is due in part to the inclusion of a high proportion of very young men and subadults.

The standard deviation of weight is lowest in the Aran Islands (17.70 pounds), followed by the young Longford-Westmeath subgroup (19.60 pounds). At the other end of the distribution, the Waterford-Wexford subgroup, which is the oldest in mean age, has the highest standard deviation of weight (25.20 pounds).

The distribution map of weight, figure 5 (graduated in three-pound intervals), shows interesting regional differences. A band of county subgroups of relatively light mean weight extends from the extreme northwest peninsular area of West Donegal along the north coast and down the east coast to the Wexford county line. In the middle of the country this band extends westward to the Shannon, culminating in Longford-Westmeath, a subgroup which has the lowest mean weight.

There are three isolated blocks of intermediate weight: Sligo-Leitrim-S. Fermanagh-W. Cavan in the inner coastal central northwest; the Aran Islands off the coast of Galway; and in the south a band extending across the country from Waterford-Wexford to the Shannon.

A solid zone of heaviest mean weight begins in the western peninsula of Mayo and Galway and runs down the west coast and peninsulas to include Kerry, and, as a southeastern extension, Cork. Actually, although the map does not show it, the areas in which are found the greatest concentration of heavy men are the western peninsulas, which in the north include Mayo and Galway, extending inland through Roscommon, and in the southwest, Kerry.

Stature (Table III-4). The Irish must be

accounted a tall people, since the average of the county series is 171.90 cm. Every subgroup exceeds 170 cm. in mean stature. The tallest average, by a little more than one cm., is attained in the small, inbred group of Aran Islanders. In the next grade of stature (173–173.9 cm.) are E. Galway-Roscommon, Kerry, West Galway. Then come Mayo, Clare and Cork. All of the counties mentioned above comprise a solid block of tall-statured men extending along the west coast to the southwestern tip of Ireland and including also County Cork on the south coast (fig. 6). The central part of the broad band of tall stature is delimited on the east by the course of the Shannon.

The northern counties (including West Donegal) all fall in mean stature between 171 and 172 cm. This stature class includes also the central counties from S. Fermanagh south to Limerick, Tipperary-Kilkenny, and the southeastern counties of Waterford and Wexford. Along the east coast is a band of shorter statures consisting from north to south of E. Cavan-Monaghan-Armagh, Meath-Louth-Dublin, and Wicklow-Carlow.

The zoning of stature from east to west is most instructive. It corresponds very closely with the distribution of weight. The simplest (but not necessarily correct) interpretation of this zoning of stature and weight would be to assume that tall, heavy men, descendants of the earliest inhabitants of Ireland, were gradually shoved into the west and southwest coastal and peninsular areas by a second wave of shorter and lighter men who eventually occupied the eastern half of Ireland and all of the north and northwest. These in turn suffered the incursions along the middle of the east coast of a still lighter and shorter group of migrants. Before such a migrational theory can be accepted, it will be necessary to consider the evidence of the whole array of anthropometric measurements and observations. Environment is a factor that may in-

FIGURE 5

WEIGHT DISTRIBUTION IN IRELAND. The heavy weights in Ireland stretch in a western band from Donegal Bay southward and including Cork. Limerick is excluded from this band. The heavy weight area may be affected by additional clothing worn in the chilly climate here (but hardly in West Donegal). Season of measurement may be a factor. The light weight of Longford-Westmeath is probably due to low mean age. Heavy weight areas are those of concentration of Dinarics, Nordics, and, in part, Nordic Alpines.

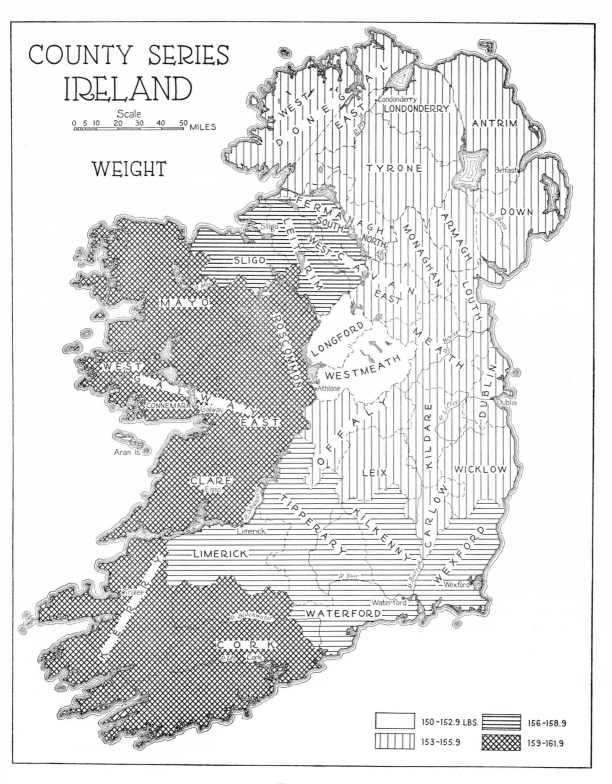

COUNTY SERIES
IRELAND

Scale
0 5 10 20 30 40 50 MILES

WEIGHT

DONEGAL
WEST
EAST
LONDONDERRY
Londonderry
ANTRIM
TYRONE
Belfast
DOWN
R. Bann
FERMANAGH
SOUTH
Sligo
LEITRIM
WEST
CAVAN
NORTH
EAST
MONAGHAN
ARMAGH
LOUTH
SLIGO
MAYO
ROSCOMMON
LONGFORD
WESTMEATH
Athlone
MEATH
R. Boyne
WEST
GALWAY
CONNEMARA
Galway
EAST
DUBLIN
Dublin
R. Liffey
Aran Is.
OFFALY
LEIX
KILDARE
WICKLOW
CLARE
Ennis
R. Shannon
TIPPERARY
KILKENNY
CARLOW
Limerick
LIMERICK
R. Suir
R. Barrow
WEXFORD
Tralee
R. Blackwater
Waterford
Wexford
WATERFORD
CORK
R. Lee
Cork

150–152.9 LBS.   156–158.9
153–155.9   159–161.9

Figure 5

fluence stature and weight, and regional differences might conceivably be explained by the invocation of nutritional and other physical causes. We must defer the discussion of the etiology of distributions until all of the anthropological evidence has been presented.

Span and Relative Span (Tables III-5, III-6). Span is a measurement taken from middle-finger tip to middle-finger tip when both arms are extended horizontally and laterally from the body. It thus includes the length of both upper extremities plus the breadth of the shoulders. It is, to say the least, a very composite measurement, and, in our opinion, of little importance. Nevertheless, we have included it as a part of stock anthropometric technique. Absolute span of the total county series and the county subgroups is presented in table III-5. It requires no commentary beyond the statement that the mean values are high and that it is slightly more variable than stature.

Relative span averages 105.32 for the total series. The county subgroups deviate very little from the total series. Only two subgroups, the young Aran Islanders (104.06) and the young Longford-Westmeath subgroup (104.94) fall below 105, and no subgroup attains 106. The low mean values of the two subgroups named are probably referable to the inclusion in them of many immature individuals.

The Irish, according to these data, have a remarkably high span-stature index, either because their arms are long or because their shoulders are wide, or for both reasons. Most of the members of this series were countrymen or small townsfolk, physically well developed and habituated to out-of-doors work. These conditions tend to increase absolute and relative span, according to some observers. Davenport records the absolute and relative span of some thousands of soldiers of eight European nationalities demobilized from the United States army at the end of the First World War. None of these approaches our Irish in absolute span values.[2] The standard deviations of absolute span in Davenport's European series range from 7.42 cm. to 7.98 cm. Our Irish, with a total series standard deviation of 7.92 cm., approach the upper limits of this range. Relative span in Davenport's European series ranges from 101.6 in Irish to 103.1 in Polish. Our Irish value is 105.32. This latter figure actually exceeds the mean found by Davenport for 6,441 American Negroid troops measured at demobilization (105.2).

Since arm length was not included in the measurement of the Irish series, the significance of the excessive span in the men of this nationality must be deduced by an examination of shoulder breadth. If the latter is greater than would be expected from

FIGURE 6

STATURE DISTRIBUTION IN IRELAND. There is a very definite coincidence of low stature with the concentration of Keltics, and, to a lesser extent, of Nordic Mediterraneans. The tall areas of the Aran Islands, Kerry, West Galway, E. Galway-Roscommon are diverse from the standpoint of morphological type. The tall stature distribution fits that of heavy weight fairly well. The exception is Sligo-Leitrim-S. Fermanagh-W. Cavan, in which stature is shortish but weight is not light. In the Aran Islands stature is very tall and weight not very heavy. Concentration of low statures along the east coast is matched by an especially low mean weight.

[2] Span is measured with the anthropometer according to the technique described by Martin (Martin, 1928, p. 115). This method, whereby the individual places one middle finger against the fixed bar of the anthropometer, held at shoulder level, horizontally, and with the other middle finger pushes the sliding bar as far as possible along the graduated rod, yields maximum arm reach when properly executed. Arm span measured along a wall surface, where the subject merely extends his arms and does not push out a movable bar, is much more likely to give a value below maximum reach. My own experience with army anthropometry and the conditions, instrumental and personal, under which it was carried out, incline me to the opinion that the spans recorded in this material published by Davenport and Love are probably too low.

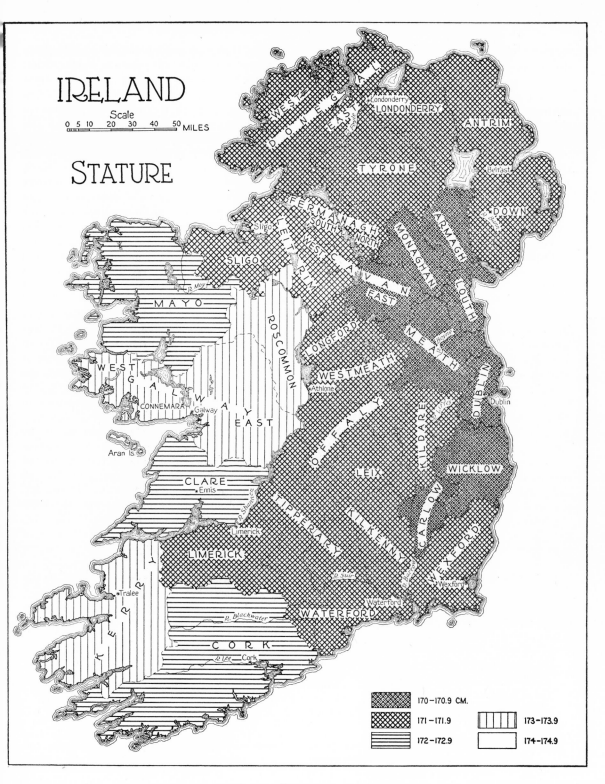

IRELAND

Scale
0 5 10 20 30 40 50 MILES

STATURE

170–170.9 CM.		
171–171.9		173–173.9
172–172.9		174–174.9

FIGURE 6

mean stature, the high span is presumably due to that fact.

Biacromial Diameter and Relative Shoulder Breadth (Tables III-7, III-8). The mean of biacromial diameter for the total county series is 38.57 cm. The subgroups show an extremely small range of variation in their means. The highest value is 38.99 cm. in Clare and the lowest 38.09 cm. in Longford-Westmeath.

Bach, quoted by Martin, tabulated the individual means of absolute and relative shoulder breadth for individuals of varying statures, presumably Germans (Martin, 1928, vol. 1, p. 349). Thus he finds that 576 males between the ages of 20 and 34 years and having statures of 171 cm. had a mean biacromial diameter of 39.1 cm. and a relative shoulder breadth of 22.9. Our Irish series has a mean stature of 171.90 cm., a mean biacromial of 38.57 cm., and a mean relative shoulder breadth of 22.44. Compared with these Germans, our Irish are neither relatively nor absolutely broad-shouldered. Actually, relative shoulder breadth is singularly constant in the county subgroups. It falls below 22 only in the Aran Islands (21.92) and in no subgroup rises to 23. The maximum is in Wicklow-Carlow with 22.68. Since the relative and absolute shoulder breadth of the Irish is only medium, it follows that the excessive relative span is due to their long arms, or perhaps in some degree to the fact that our span data actually record maximum arm stretches, whereas those of some other observers may fall short of this anthropometric ideal.

Chest Breadth, Chest Depth (Tables III-9, III-10). Chest depth and chest breadth were measured after the subject had divested himself of coat and waistcoat (if any). However, many of the individuals wore sweaters and most of them heavy woolen undershirts. Consequently, some subtraction from the re-corded means should be made for clothing. Dr. Dupertuis feels that the excess over nude measurements due to clothing may amount to almost one cm. in the case of chest diameters. The average uncorrected chest breadth for the total county series is 28.86 cm. The subgroup means range from 28.26 (Wicklow-Carlow and Meath-Louth-Dublin) to 29.46 (Mayo).

Chest depth averages 23.20 cm. and the range of the subgroups is roughly one cm. The lowest means are found in the Aran Islanders (22.20 cm.) and in the Longford-Westmeath group, the latter—the youngest subgroup in mean age, and the former—the subgroup with the highest percentage of immature subjects. Waterford-Wexford attains the maximum depth among the subgroups (23.66 cm.). It is the oldest subgroup. Chest depths increase with age, most markedly between the 15–19 and 20–24 year age groups.

Bach found the nude chest diameters of 85 German turners (gymnasts) to average for men of 170 cm. in stature, 28.3 for lateral and 19.5 for sagittal. If we substract one cm. from our means (and this may be too generous an allowance), we obtain 27.86 and 22.20 cm. for our Irish county group. These figures suggest a deeper chest than is found among the Germans. Hrdlička, for Old American males, records values of 29.76 and 21.70 cm. for lateral and antero-posterior diameters, respectively. Allowance for clothing is not stated, but it must be less than in the case of the Irish. The same observer records chest diameters of 28.0 cm. and 21.35 cm. for a small series of immigrant Irish. This is almost the same lateral mean as we found in our large series, but our means of depth are somewhat higher.

Thoracic Index (Table III-11). The thoracic index of our total county series averages

FIGURE 7

DISTRIBUTION OF THORACIC INDEX IN IRELAND. The high values in Waterford-Wexford and Wicklow-Carlow are associated with highest mean age. Flatter chests in the Aran Islands and Longford-Westmeath go with low mean age, but other flat-chested areas are up to mean age. The flat-chested area around Galway Bay with extensions east of the Shannon in Longford-Westmeath and Limerick may be due to (1) some regional survival type, or (2) in some regions youth of the sample. These flat chests go with high stature and heavy weight, especially in West Galway, and E. Galway-Roscommon. Limerick and Waterford-Wexford are low in stature and weight.

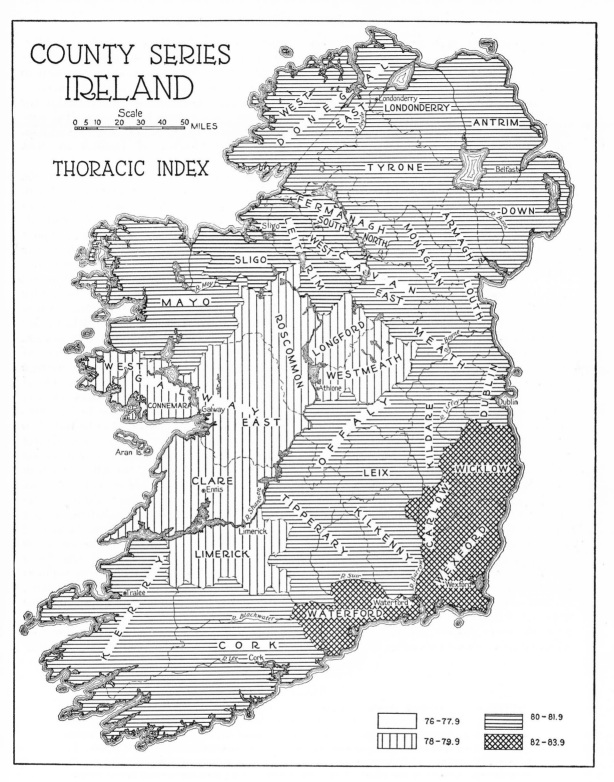

COUNTY SERIES
IRELAND

Scale
0 5 10 20 30 40 50 MILES

THORACIC INDEX

| | 76 – 77.9 | | 80 – 81.9 |
| | 78 – 79.9 | | 82 – 83.9 |

FIGURE 7

80.54 which describes a relatively deep and narrow chest. We must take into consideration, however, that the increment of measurement caused by thickness of clothing would increase the thoracic index, since two thicknesses of clothing would add relatively more to the smaller chest depth than to the larger chest breadth. If we take the index of the means of chest depth and chest breadth (correcting each by the subtraction of one cm.), we arrive at the figure 79.68 for the thoracic index. This may represent a closer approximation to the actual mean thoracic index. It is still far above Hrdlička's figures for Old American (72.93) and even for Irish immigrants (76.2). However, Hrdlička's figures for a number of European immigrant groups range from the Irish minimum to 81.5 for Croatians. He attributes the difference between the flat-chested Old Americans and the Europeans to "difference in occupation."

Davenport's 6,135 soldiers of Irish birth, measured nude at demobilization, yield average transverse chest diameters of 28.77 cm., and an antero-posterior diameter of 21.60 cm. The index of the means is 75.08, which suggests a wider, flatter chest than is found in our Irish series. It is possible that differences in technique tend to exaggerate the chest depth in our series. It is very probable, however, that our Irish are legitimately characterized by very deep chests relative to their breadth.

The distribution map of the thoracic index (fig. 7) reveals the maximum of deep and narrow chests in the coastal southeastern and middle eastern counties of Waterford-Wexford and Wicklow-Carlow. Slightly lower chest indices continue up the east coast to include Meath-Louth-Dublin and E. Cavan-Monaghan-Armagh, and extend into the central inland part of the country through Tipperary-Kilkenny and Offaly-Leix-Kildare. (This nuance is not shown in the map.) Elsewhere, a broad zone of still more moderate chest indices sweeps northeastward from Kerry and Cork to the extreme tip of Ireland, including all of the northern counties. In the same range of moderate chest index is Mayo in the west. However, a zone of minimum chest indices stretches from E. Galway-Roscommon and includes West Galway, Clare, and Limerick. Limerick and Longford-Westmeath are extensions of this zone east of the Shannon. The culmination of this flat-chested arc is reached in the Aran Islands.

Sitting Height and Relative Sitting Height (Tables III-12, III-13). The total county series mean for sitting height is 91.48 cm.— a large figure. The minimum of 90.88 cm. is found in Longford-Westmeath and E. Cavan-Monaghan-Armagh; the maximum, 92.41 cm. in Kerry. The standard deviation of the total series is 3.60 cm. and ranges from 3.33 cm. to 3.84 cm. in the county subgroups.

Our mean for the sitting height of Irish exceeds all of those recorded by Davenport for American and European soldiers measured in this country at demobilization after the First World War. Davenport records for Irish 90.46 cm. Hrdlička's mean for 727 Old Americans with an average stature of 174.3 is 91.8 cm. However, our Irish county series has a mean stature of only 171.90 cm.

Relative sitting height of the county series averages 53.22 cm. The range of county subgroups is from 52.28 in the Aran Islands to 53.54 in Wicklow-Carlow. These two groups are the extremes of the county means. The rest cluster closely around the mean of the total series.

These relative sitting heights are high for tall people. Except for the Aran Islands, all of our county subgroups exceed the means recorded by Davenport for soldiers. His Irish soldiers average 52.79. It appears that the great stature of the Aran Islanders must be due to exceptionally long legs.

Thus our Irish series, with the exception

FIGURE 8

DISTRIBUTION OF HEAD LENGTH IN IRELAND. The area of greatest head length is the crescent from Sligo Bay to Galway Bay including the Aran Islands. It is more restricted than the area of highest head circumference, and much more restricted than the Nordic areas, although the latter include it. Shortest heads are spotty in distribution (West Donegal, Antrim-Down, Offaly-Leix-Kildare, Waterford-Wexford), and go with small head circumferences, not with brachycephaly.

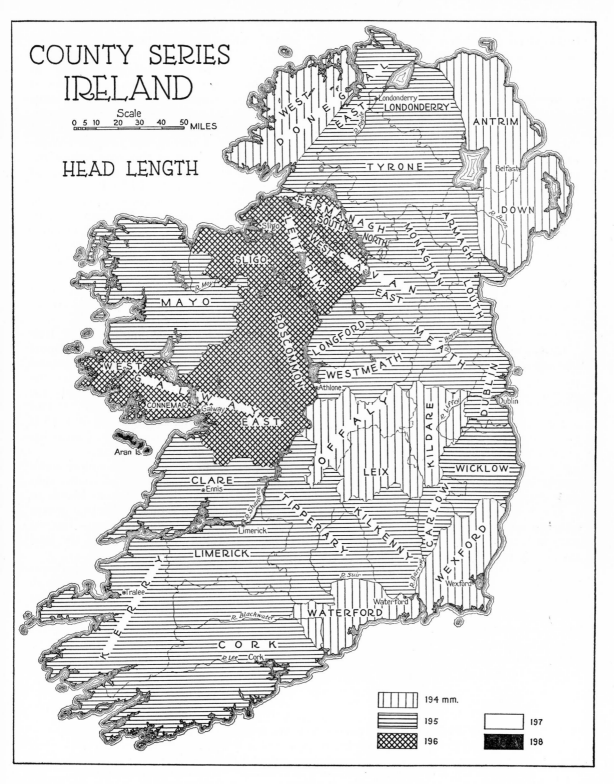

COUNTY SERIES
IRELAND

Scale
0 5 10   20   30   40   50 MILES

HEAD LENGTH

⊞	194 mm.	
⊟	195	□ 197
⊠	196	■ 198

FIGURE 8

of the Aran Islanders, is very long-bodied.

Head Length (Table III-14). The mean head length of the county series is 195.63 mm. and the range in the subgroups is from 194.76 in Waterford-Wexford to 198.36 in the Aran Islands. On the whole, these Irish are homogeneously long-headed. The outstanding fact of head length distribution is the high average of the crescent which begins on the south shore of Sligo Bay and swings south to the Bay of Galway and westward to include West Galway and the Aran Islands (fig. 8). The shortest headed areas include West Donegal and Antrim-Down to the north, together with the southeastern coastal counties of Waterford-Wexford, and a block of southeast central counties extending westward from Kildare to the Shannon.

Head Breadth (Table III-15). Irish heads are also moderately and consistently broad. The average of the series is 154.12 mm. However, there is evidence of a distinct regional variation in this dimension, inasmuch as the highest means of breadth are found in Kerry, Clare, Cork, Limerick and Mayo in the west, whereas the east coast is narrower-headed. Figure 9 shows clearly the wedge of comparatively narrow heads with its base in the middle of the east coast and its truncated apex at the Shannon. The extreme southeastern, north (except West Donegal), and northeastern counties are transitional to the great zones of wider heads which extend from Sligo-Leitrim-S. Fermanagh-W. Cavan in the north down west of the Shannon to Clare, bending eastward to include Tipperary-Kilkenny, and also including to the west West Galway and the Aran Islands.

Cephalic Index (Tables III-16, III-17). The average cephalic index of the county series is 78.84 per cent and the range of subgroup means is only from 77.79 (Aran Islands and Meath-Louth-Dublin) to 80.01 (Kerry). Meath-Louth-Dublin presents the lowest subgroup standard deviation (2.91), but several coun-

ties are fairly close to the maximum (3.42). Because of the limited total range of the county subseries in the cephalic index, it was necessary to plot the distribution map (fig. 10) by ½ unit variations instead of total units. This more delicate scale shows up regional differences which would be lost in the coarser grouping. However, this plot is very revealing. It shows two areas of low mean mesocephaly; a small western block comprising West Galway and the Aran Islands; a large eastern and central block centering about Meath-Louth-Dublin and radiating north to the borders of Down and Tyrone, and west to the Shannon and the borders of Leitrim, W. Cavan, and Fermanagh. This eastern block of comparatively dolichocephalic head form is encircled to the northwest and south by a zone of higher mesocephaly. This mesocephaly becomes more elevated in the peninsular areas of West Donegal and Mayo, and in the south central counties of Limerick and Tipperary-Kilkenny.

Clare and Cork are areas of still higher mesocephaly transitional to the sub-brachycephalic County Kerry. Thus round-headedness is most common in the southwestern corner of Ireland, but is also somewhat high in the two northwestern peninsular areas, with the exception of the southern part of the mid-western peninsula—West Galway.

Inspections of the maps and tables of head length and head breadth clarify the distribution of the cephalic index. The only area in which the average of the cephalic index is plainly dominated by extreme head length is the crescent which extends from Sligo Bay to the Bay of Galway, cutting off Mayo to the west and bounded on the east by the Shannon, on the south by County Clare. Here are the areas of longest mean head averages, culminating in the Aran Islands and West Galway.

To the east of this crescent is the other area of long-headedness extending from Longford-Westmeath and Offaly on the west to

FIGURE 9

DISTRIBUTION OF HEAD BREADTH IN IRELAND. The narrowest heads are in the east, especially the Keltic, but also the Nordic Mediterranean areas. They are widest in the brachycephalic areas: Mayo, Clare, Kerry, and Cork, but not West Donegal. The areas of longest heads are in the next to the top class in head breadth.

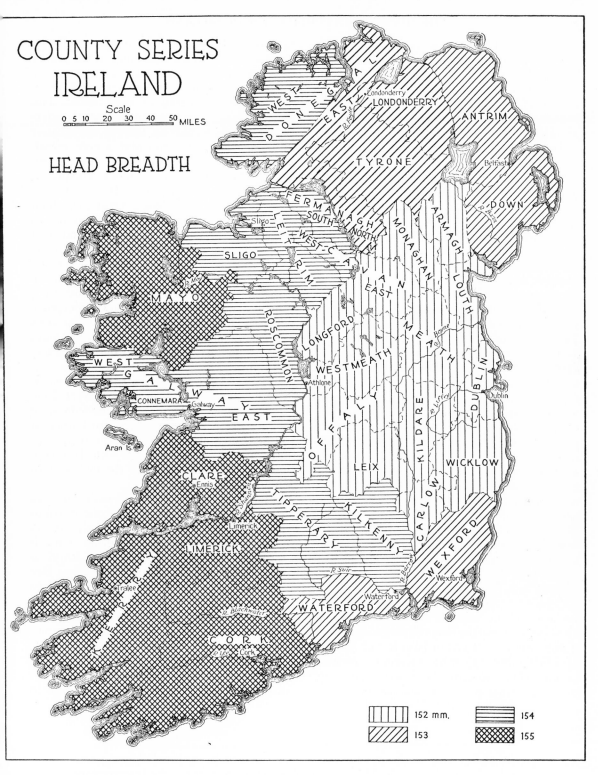

COUNTY SERIES
IRELAND

Scale
0 5 10 20 30 40 50 MILES

HEAD BREADTH

| | 152 mm. | | 154 |
| | 153 | | 155 |

FIGURE 9

the east coast and culminating in the dolicho-cephaly of Meath-Louth-Dublin. But this area owes its comparative long-headedness to di-minished head breadth rather than to increased head length. It is thus suggested that at least two types of dolichocephals are involved.

The areas of high mean head breadth are Mayo and all of the southwestern counties. These fall all within the same category of mean head length and head breadth, but the averages of Kerry are slightly lower in the former and slightly higher in the latter, thus producing the highest mean cephalic index. The high mesocephaly of West Donegal is due to slightly diminished head breadth and some-what more diminished head length. Mayo has very broad heads, but they are also very long. This latter situation also holds for Limerick. In Waterford-Wexford and Antrim-Down the comparatively low mesocephaly is due also to diminished head width.

Table III-17 gives the percentages of doli-chocephals, mesocephals, and brachycephals by county groups. It adds little to the distribu-tion map, except to emphasize what has al-ready been said. The Arans are the most dolichocephalic county, closely pressed by Longford-Westmeath, Meath-Louth-Dublin, and E. Cavan-Monaghan-Armagh. These coun-ties are at the bottom in ranking of brachy-cephalics. Conversely, Kerry, Clare, Mayo and Cork, which are at the bottom of the doli-chocephalic listing, top the brachycephals. Limerick is interesting in that it has the highest percentage of mesocephals but is also second lowest in dolichocephals.

In each of the three listings there are county groups which closely approximate their aver-ages. In the dolichocephals, these groups are Sligo-Leitrim-S. Fermanagh-W. Cavan, and Tipperary-Kilkenny. In the mesocephals, the Waterford-Wexford group, and in the brachy-cephals, Antrim-Down, and N. Fermanagh-E. Donegal-Tyrone-Londonderry. The distribu-tion map shows all of these counties to be part of the inner crescent of transitional meso-cephalics. This crescent extends from Antrim-Down on the northeast coast, west and south to E. Galway-Roscommon, on the west of the Shannon; then south and east from Tipperary to Waterford-Wexford on the southeast cen-tral coast.

The average means of the three ranking tables show that Ireland is predominantly mesocephalic (64.1), but more dolichocephalic (23.3) than brachycephalic (12.5).

The further significance of these distribu-tions will be discussed in the synthesis of county metric and morphological characters.

Head Circumference (Table III-18). Head circumference varies with length and breadth of the head, but is usually affected more by the extreme variations of the former diameter. The Irish county mean of 572.15 mm. is high. The range of variation is from 569.45 in An-trim-Down to 577.10 mm. in the Aran Islands. The concentration of highest mean circumfer-ences occurs in the crescent running from Sligo Bay to the Bay of Galway and cutting off Mayo in the west, with E. Galway-Roscommon showing the highest average (fig. 11). An isolated area of next to the highest mean cir-cumference is Cork in the southwest. The position of Cork seems to be due to its high mean head breadth in association with the re-tention of above average head length.

The zone of least cranial circumference stretches down the east coast from Antrim to the border of Wexford, extending inland to include Offaly-Leix-Kildare. On the whole, these diminished circumferences seem to be associated more with meager head breadth than with diminished head length, although both fall below the Irish mean. Meath-Louth-Dublin is a slight exception in that its head length of 195.66 is .03 mm. above the mean (195.63 mm.).

Head Height (Table III-19). Mean head

FIGURE 10

DISTRIBUTION OF CEPHALIC INDEX IN IRELAND. The lowest cephalic indices are in the area of Keltic concentration: Longford-Westmeath, Meath-Louth-Dublin and neighboring county areas. They fit less well with areas of Nordic Mediterranean concentration. The exceptions are the Arans and West Galway. The highest cephalic indices are in Kerry especially, Clare, and also in Cork. The eastern coast and midlands types are narrow-headed and small-headed, having a fair correspondence with the focus of Keltics.

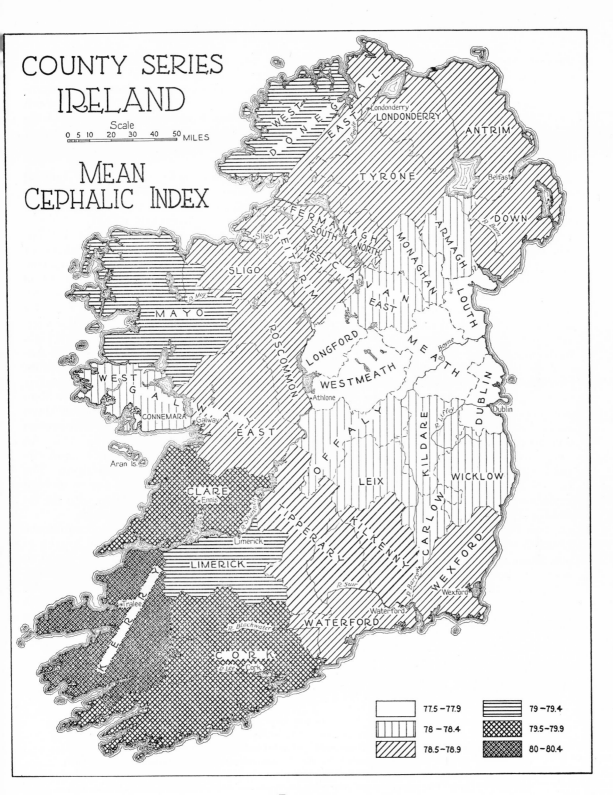

COUNTY SERIES
IRELAND

Scale
0 5 10 20 30 40 50 MILES

MEAN
CEPHALIC INDEX

77.5 – 77.9	79 – 79.4
78 – 78.4	79.5 – 79.9
78.5 – 78.9	80 – 80.4

FIGURE 10

height varies in the subgroups from 120.18 mm. in the Aran Islands to 126.74 mm. in N. Fermanagh-E. Donegal-Tyrone-Londonderry. The county average is 124.98 mm. The zone of least head height is again the Sligo-Galway crescent, but including to the east Longford-Westmeath. Two of the isolated western peninsular areas—West Galway, Mayo, and Kerry —also show diminished mean head heights.

Length-Height Index (Table III-20). The average length-height index is 63.89 and the range in subgroups from 60.50 in the Aran Islands to 64.85 in N. Fermanagh-E. Donegal-Tyrone-Londonderry. The zone of low length-height index is the same Sligo-Galway crescent, again with the addition of Longford-Westmeath, E. Cavan-Monaghan-Armagh to the northeast, and the Aran Islands to the west.

Breadth-Height Index (Table III-21). Breadth-height index means in the county subgroups vary over a restricted range (from 77.99 in Aran to 82.46 in N. Fermanagh-E. Donegal-Tyrone-Londonderry). Four groups exceed 82.00 in their mean. Wicklow-Carlow, Offaly-Leix-Kildare, and Meath-Louth-Dublin form a block of central east coast counties in which high index is conditioned by diminished breadth. N. Fermanagh-E. Donegal-Tyrone-Londonderry owes its high mean to increased head height. The southwestern counties—Cork, Limerick, Clare, and Kerry—run low in breadth-height index because of great breadths. The Sligo-Galway crescent is another area of rather low breadth-height index, but West Donegal dissociates itself from this zone in the average of the index.

Bizygomatic Diameter (Table III-22). The mean value of bizygomatic diameter for the county series is 140.80 mm.—a generous figure. The maxima, 142.00 mm. or slightly in excess, occur in Kerry, Clare, and Cork, but all of the western groups except West Donegal show relatively high averages. The eastern counties and Longford-Westmeath show narrower faces, as indicated by subgroup means.

A mid-county group, Offaly-Leix-Kildare, achieves the minimum of face breadth, but actually the average of this group is only slightly below that of the generally narrow-faced zone which stretches from Antrim in the north along the east coast and is delimited in the south by the northern boundaries of Wexford, Kilkenny, and Tipperary, and on the west by the Shannon River, and the counties of Leitrim, W. Cavan, N. Fermanagh, Tyrone and Londonderry (fig. 12).

The extreme north and northwest (West Donegal, N. Fermanagh-E. Donegal-Tyrone-Londonderry) extending through Sligo-Leitrim-S. Fermanagh-W. Cavan, form a block with diameters that approximate the county total mean, 140.80 mm. Another block is found in the extreme southeast and includes Tipperary-Kilkenny and Waterford-Wexford. Mayo, West Galway, and E. Galway-Roscommon is a zone of still higher bizygomatic diameters, as is Limerick. The area of greatest mean zygomatic breadths is concentrated in the southwest (Cork, Kerry and Clare).

Thus the areas of greatest breadths are all situated in the western part of Ireland from Mayo down to Cork.

Cephalo-Facial Index (Table III-23). The cephalo-facial index relates the breadth of the face (bizygomatic) to maximum head breadth. The range in means of this index is very small —from 91.04 in West Donegal to 91.79 in E. Galway-Roscommon. Ireland is, then, quite extraordinarily homogeneous in this index.

Total Face Height (Table III-24). The Irish have, on the whole, long faces. Outstanding in this respect are the Aran Islanders with the high mean of 129.85 mm. Others that exceed the county series average markedly are W. Galway (128.60 mm.) and, to a lesser extent, E. Cavan-Monaghan-Armagh (127.90 mm.).

The face height situation is much complicated by age differences. Older groups include more individuals who have lost teeth and have

FIGURE 11

DISTRIBUTION OF HEAD CIRCUMFERENCE IN IRELAND. The interval is only one mm.; hence the map exaggerates the differences. East coast low values go with Keltic and Nordic Mediterranean types. The belt of high circumference is again associated loosely with high stature, high weight, and, in most cases, with flat chests.

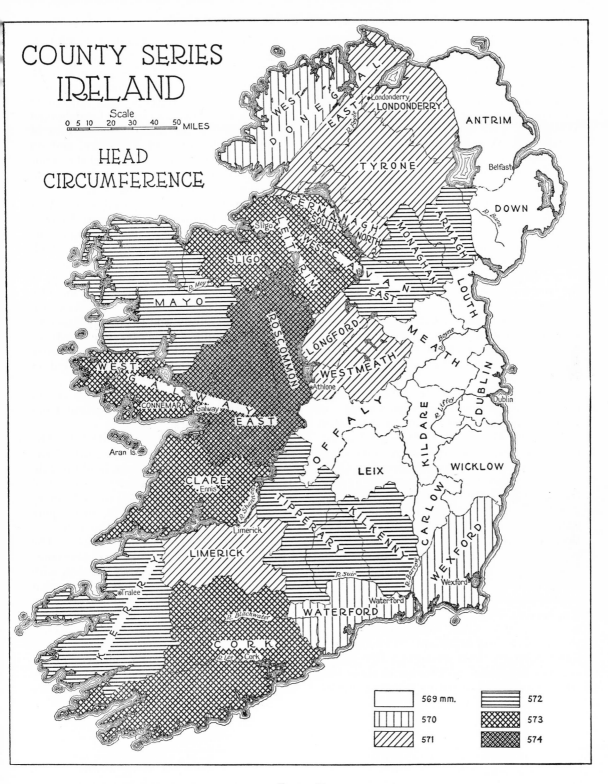

COUNTY SERIES
IRELAND

Scale
0 5 10   20   30   40   50 MILES

HEAD
CIRCUMFERENCE

	569 mm.		572
	570		573
	571		574

FIGURE 11

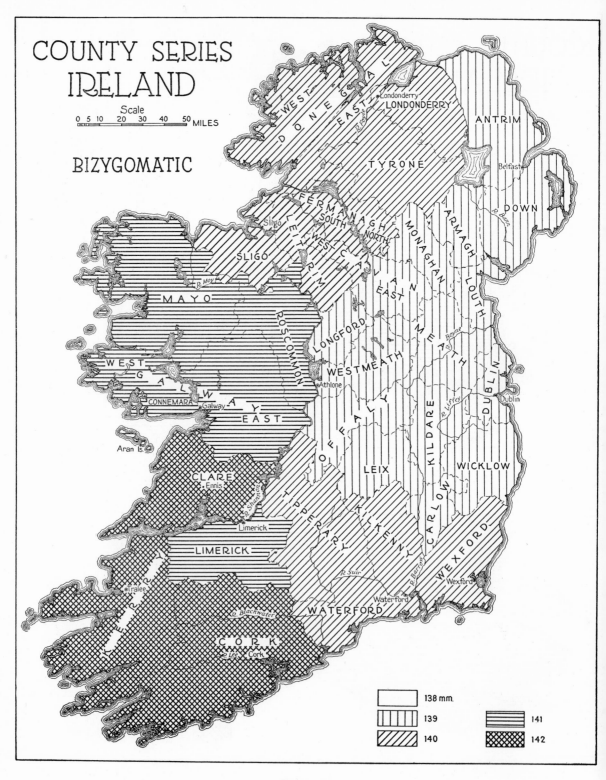

COUNTY SERIES
IRELAND

Scale
0 5 10   20   30   40   50 MILES

BIZYGOMATIC

	138 mm.
	139
	140
	141
	142

FIGURE 12

DISTRIBUTION OF BIZYGOMATIC DIAMETER IN IRELAND. The west is regular in distribution. All areas west of the Shannon and west of Antrim are high. The highest are Clare, Kerry, and Cork. The lowest distribution is in the east coast and midlands—areas of Keltic and Nordic Mediterranean type. The low face length and high bizygomatic diameter are found especially in Clare. The Arans and West Galway have very high face lengths and moderately high bizygomatic diameters.

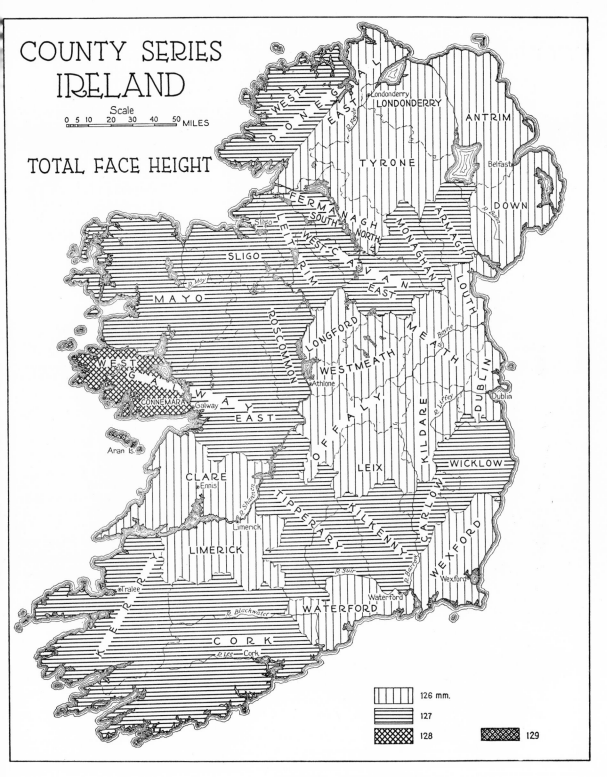

COUNTY SERIES
IRELAND

Scale
0 5 10 20 30 40 50 MILES

TOTAL FACE HEIGHT

	126 mm.
	127
	128
	129

FIGURE 13

DISTRIBUTION OF TOTAL FACE HEIGHT IN IRELAND. The longest-faced area is in the Arans and
West Galway.

undergone shortening of the face due to dental loss and alveolar absorption. Yet variation in group means cannot be interpreted solely by the invocation of this factor. The longest-faced group is the Aran Islands, which is the sixth youngest group. The youngest group, Longford-Westmeath, has the lowest total face height, and West Galway, which is the second highest in face height, is about half a year above mean series age.

The distribution map (fig. 13) of total face height is "messy." The maximum is in the Aran Islands. Next door is the long-faced West Galway group. All of the western peninsular areas have moderate faces, but Clare and Limerick form an island of short faces to the west.

Distributions of face height do not fit well those of bizygomatic diameter.

Upper Face Height (Table III-25). Upper face height yields the generous series mean of 72.80 mm. The maximum subgroup value is 73.85 mm. in Kerry, and the minimum, 70.60 mm., occurs in Longford-Westmeath. The shortest upper faces are found, then, in Longford-Westmeath, and in the Sligo-Galway crescent (fig. 14). A zone of slightly longer faces runs from West Galway down through Clare and Limerick, includes the Aran Islands, and then jumps to Meath-Louth-Dublin on the east coast. All of the other county subgroups exceed 73 mm. in average height of the upper face.

There is really little variation in the means of the county subgroups. Ireland is fairly homogeneous in this measurement.

Facial Index (Table III-26). The total mean of the county series in the facial index (90.20) indicates prevalent leptoprosopy. This is true of every county subgroup with the exceptions of Clare, Cork and Limerick, whose means are in the upper reaches of the mesoprosopic range. The range of means is from a minimum of 89.25 in Clare to 91.70 in the Aran Islands. The map of the facial index (divided by half-index units), figure 15, shows a triangular block of relatively high leptoprosopy beginning in the northeast with Armagh, extending down the east coast as far as the northern border of Wexford, with its western apex formed by Longford-Westmeath and Offaly. This wedge is thrust between a northern and a southeastern block of less pronounced leptoprosopy.

A western and isolated area of leptoprosopic dominance occurs in West Galway and the Aran Islands. The somewhat shorter and broader faces occupy the central western and southwestern half of Ireland, beginning in the north with Mayo, and culminating in the south in Clare, Limerick and Cork.

The maps of total face height and bizygomatic diameter explain somewhat the distribution of the facial index. Thus it is apparent that West Galway, the Aran Islands, and E. Cavan-Monaghan-Armagh owe their high average leptoprosopy to great total face height, while Cork has very broad faces and moderate facial height. Narrow faces, rather than very long faces, characterize the eastern wedge of leptoprosopy. Clare has more than average face breadth and strongly diminished facial height, and, for this reason, ranks in the highest grade of relative euryprosopy. Thus the regional situation is rather complicated. In a general way, it may be stated that the broadest faces are distributed in the west and accentuated in the southwest and, similarly, the lowest mean facial indices. However, there are two regions in the west in which the sweep of the broadest faces is interrupted by areas of com-

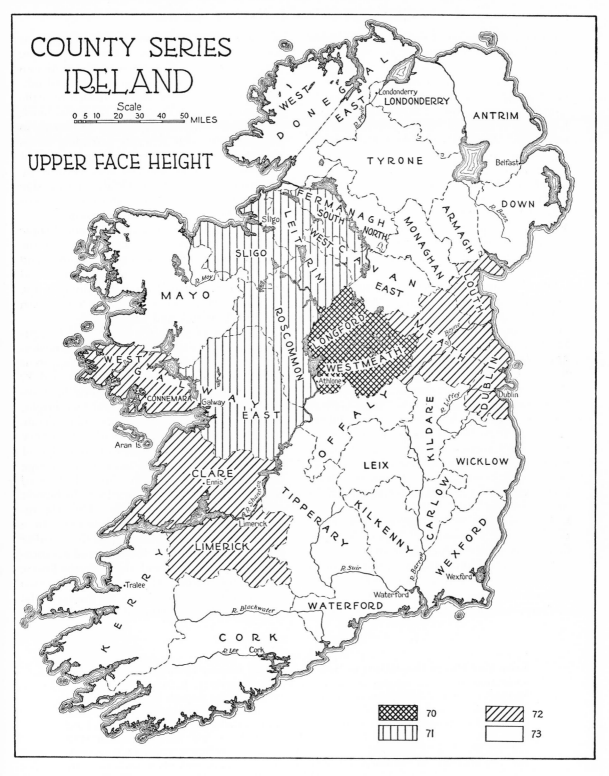

COUNTY SERIES
IRELAND

Scale
0 5 10 20 30 40 50 MILES

UPPER FACE HEIGHT

WEST DONEGAL
EAST DONEGAL
Londonderry
LONDONDERRY
ANTRIM
TYRONE
Belfast
DOWN
R. Bann
SLIGO
Sligo
LEITRIM
FERMANAGH SOUTH
FERMANAGH NORTH
WEST CAVAN
MONAGHAN
ARMAGH
EAST CAVAN
LOUTH
MAYO
R. Moy
ROSCOMMON
LONGFORD
WESTMEATH
Athlone
R. Boyne
MEATH
DUBLIN
Dublin
WEST GALWAY
CONNEMARA
Galway
GALWAY EAST
Aran Is
OFFALY
KILDARE
R. Liffey
WICKLOW
LEIX
CLARE
Ennis
R. Shannon
TIPPERARY
KILKENNY
CARLOW
R. Barrow
WEXFORD
Limerick
LIMERICK
Wexford
KERRY
R. Suir
Waterford
Tralee
R. Blackwater
WATERFORD
CORK
R. Lee
Cork

▨ 70		▨ 72
▥ 71		☐ 73

FIGURE 14

parative leptoprosopy: West Donegal and Sligo-Leitrim, etc., in the north; the Arans and West Galway in the center.

Upper Facial Index (Table III-27). The range of the upper facial index in county subgroup means is from 50.60 in Longford-Westmeath to 52.76 in E. Cavan-Monaghan-Armagh. The lowest values of this index occur in the Sligo-Galway crescent, but include Longford-Westmeath to the east. However, all of the western counties south of the Erne River have reduced upper facial indices (shorter upper faces relative to their width) than do the northern and eastern counties. It is evident that diminished upper facial indices in the Sligo-Galway crescent are referable in part to actual shortening of the upper face, whereas in Kerry, Cork, Limerick, Mayo, and West Galway, but particularly in the first two named, the reduced upper facial index is rather an effect of enlarged bizygomatic diameter than of maxillary shortening. The upper facial indices are somewhat higher in all of Ireland north of the Erne and east of a line delimited by the course of the Shannon, and a rough prolongation of that line southward to coincide with the eastern borders of Limerick and Cork. Slight bizygomatic reduction is mainly responsible for the more leptene conditions prevailing here.

Nose Height (Table III-28). Ireland is a land of long faces, and consequently, of long noses. The mean of the total county series (56.30 mm.) is a really prodigious figure for nasal height. The actual subgroup variation is very small. Thus the minimum is Longford-Westmeath with an average of 55.30 and the maximum of 57.10 occurs in the Aran Islands. Five of nineteen subgroups fall between 55 and 56 mm., thirteen between 56 and 57 mm., and only one attains the latter figure.

Nose Breadth (Table III-29). The range of nose breadth is from 35.24 mm. in Longford-Westmeath to 36.59 mm. in West Galway.

These are generous breadths, but subgroup variation is quite small.

Nasal Index (Table III-30). The distribution of the nasal index is somewhat peculiar. The most leptorrhine (relatively narrowest and longest noses) are found in two areas: (1) a triangular zone in the south with its apex in the southeast at Waterford-Wexford, its base from Clare to Kerry, including the Arans, but with Cork scooped out of the southern leg; and (2) the isolated peninsula of West Donegal (fig. 16). These are all of the county groups in which the nasal index falls below 64. In the southern leptorrhine zone all of the counties except Limerick owe their position to their great nose heights (lengths) rather than to diminished breadths. But Limerick in the south and West Donegal in the north are markedly leptorrhine because of very narrow noses rather than very long (high) noses. Cork dissociates itself from the southen leptorrhine triangle because its noses are slightly broader than those in the neighboring counties, although just about as high (long).

The modes of high nasal index occur in N. Fermanagh-E. Donegal-Tyrone-Londonderry in the north and West Galway in the west. The total range of nasal index means is so small that the distributional differences are probably of little importance.

Minimum Frontal Diameter (Table III-31). Minimum frontal diameter shows its maximum subgroup means in Mayo, Clare, and Cork, whereas the minimum (107.18) occurs in Longford-Westmeath. On the whole, values increase from east to west.

Fronto-Parietal Index (Table III-32). A band of low fronto-parietal indices occupies the Galway-Sligo crescent, bulging into the Longford-Westmeath subgroup. It is interrupted in the south by Clare and then continues down to Kerry. Antrim-Down in the northeast is also a zone of low fronto-parietals.

Zygo-Frontal Index (Table III-33). This

FIGURE 15

DISTRIBUTION OF TOTAL FACIAL INDEX IN IRELAND. The distribution is low in the west, except for West Galway and the Arans. The lowest is in Clare, Limerick, and Cork. The highest distribution is found in the midlands east of the Shannon, but especially in the E. Cavan-Monaghan-Armagh block to the north and the Offaly-Leix-Kildare, Wicklow-Carlow block to the south. The area of highest facial index certainly coincides with Keltic and Nordic Mediterranean concentration. The Arans and West Galway agree.

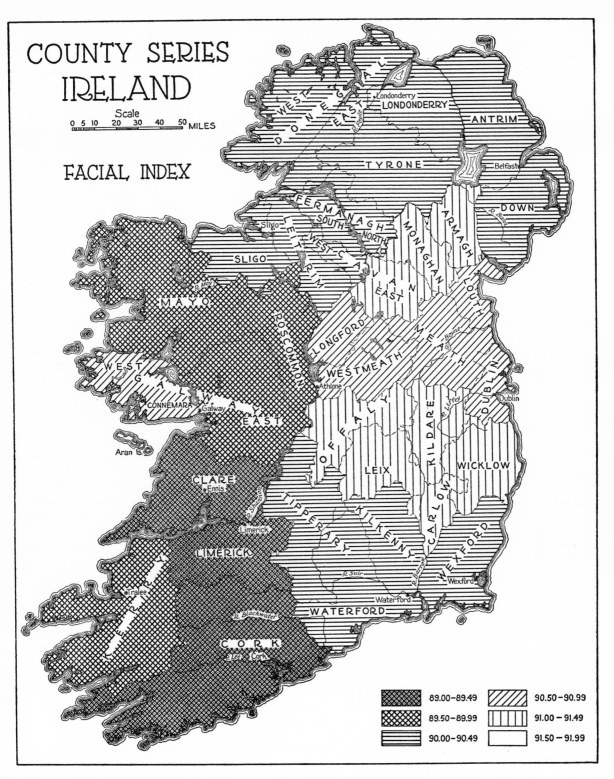

COUNTY SERIES
IRELAND

Scale
0 5 10 20 30 40 50 MILES

FACIAL INDEX

▨ 89.00–89.49	▨ 90.50–90.99
▨ 89.50–89.99	▥ 91.00–91.49
▤ 90.00–90.49	☐ 91.50–91.99

FIGURE 15

index is lowest in the Aran Islands (76.94) and highest in Tipperary-Kilkenny (78.46). The regional differences seem to suggest no pattern.

Bigonial Diameter (Table III-34). The counties which have wide faces also show, generally speaking, increased values of the bigonial diameter (breadth of the jaws). These are, of course, Mayo, West Galway, Aran Islands, Clare, Kerry, and Cork. The minimum subgroup value (107.62 mm.) falls in the comparatively juvenile group measured in Longford-Westmeath.

Zygo-Gonial Index (Table III-35). The zygo-gonial index shows little of interest. The Sligo-Galway crescent shows a slight diminution of the index, but the highest values, found in West Galway, Aran Islands, Offaly-Leix-Kildare, and Waterford-Wexford represent three discrete areas.

Fronto-Gonial Index (Table III-36). In this index, there are no important subgroup deviations with the exception of the high mean value of the Arans (101.90) which exceeds by 1.35 units that of any other subgroup.

FIGURE 16

DISTRIBUTION OF NASAL INDEX IN IRELAND. The nasal index map has been split by half index units in order to show gradation of a generally leptorrhine distribution in Ireland. The highest mean indices are in West Galway and Tyrone-Londonderry. In general, the lowest indices are in the south and West Donegal. The low nasal indices correspond to areas of Dinaric strength except in the Arans, but Mayo is high in Dinaric types and not low in mean nasal index. The two highest nasal index areas are both low in Dinarics, slightly high in East Baltics and Nordic Alpines, but West Galway is very high in Nordic Mediterraneans, and Tyrone-Londonderry in Keltics. Both are high in Pure and Predominantly Nordic types. The nasal index map does not grade well with the sample distribution of morphological types.

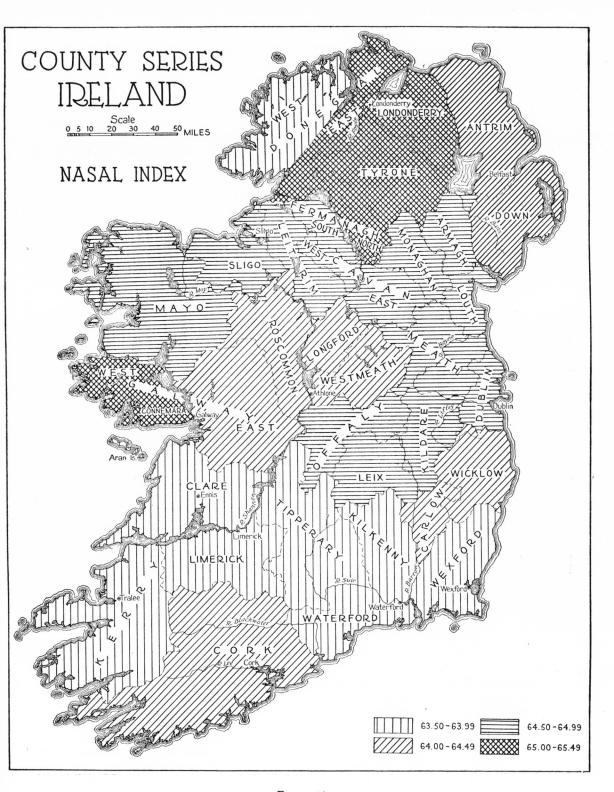

COUNTY SERIES
IRELAND

Scale
0 5 10 20 30 40 50 MILES

NASAL INDEX

| | | | | | | 63.50 – 63.99   ▤ 64.50 – 64.99
| ⟋⟋⟋ | 64.00 – 64.49   ▨ 65.00 – 65.49

FIGURE 16

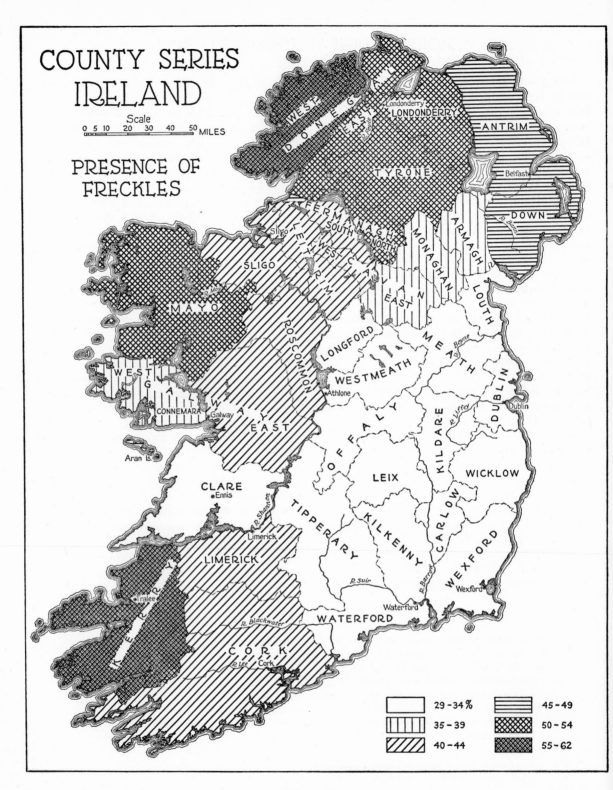

FIGURE 17

MORPHOLOGICAL OBSERVATIONS[1]

Skin Color, Inner Arm (Table IV-1). Pink skin is recorded for 91.6 per cent of all of the Irish county series. Brunet skins are rare except in Longford-Westmeath and in the Aran Islands. An area of relatively high frequency of dark skins (8.2 to 18.6 per cent) extends across the middle of the island from Dublin Bay to West Galway. This dark zone includes Meath-Louth-Dublin, Offaly-Leix-Kildare, Longford-Westmeath, E. Galway-Roscommon, and the Arans. Since this band of relatively high frequency of dark skins cuts across the north to south zoning of eye color and hair color and other anthropometric features, I am inclined to attribute little or no significance to it. The Aran Islands and Longford-Westmeath are, in any case, aberrant subgroups. Longford-Westmeath and Offaly-Leix-Kildare are counties in which there is a high prevalence of the more strongly curved grades of hair, but this is not true of the Aran Islands. Again, County Cork is another area in which deep waved and curly hair abounds, but it includes no excess of dark skins.

Skin color is an observation very difficult to make, in the absence of any satisfactory scale. It is possible that the deviations of these few counties may be due to variability in the standards of the observer as he moved from one county group to another, or to the percentages of outdoor laborers included in the various county series, or to other factors which are racially irrelevant.

Vascularity (Table IV-2). Vascularity implies an abundant blood supply in the deeper layers of the skin. It renders the complexion pink, ruddy, or florid, as contrasted with pale. In Ireland, Dupertuis has reported only 0.7 per cent of males in whom vascularity is absent or submedium. Nearly one-quarter (24.2 per cent) have pronounced vascularity. An area of comparatively slight vascularity includes Longford-Westmeath and Offaly-Leix-Kildare (which happen to be also areas of pronouncedly wavy and curly hair). Across the waist of Ireland (Sligo Bay to Dundalk Bay) is another zone in which pronounced vascularity is somewhat deficient. The ruddiest areas are around Galway Bay and the mouth and lower reaches of the Shannon, including Clare, West Galway, and Limerick. However, in the northeast, Antrim-Down and, to a lesser extent, N. Fermanagh-E. Donegal-Tyrone-Londonderry show excesses of vascularity.

Freckles (Table IV-3). About 40 per cent of all Irish in our county series are more or less freckled. Freckles are due, presumably, to mixed pigmentation and occur especially in individuals who have some of the reddish-gold pigment component in their skin. In Ireland the areas of heaviest freckling (50 per cent and upwards) are West Donegal, Kerry, and Mayo (fig. 17). N. Fermanagh, E. Donegal-Tyrone-Londonderry is also heavily freckled with 50.6 per cent. The Aran Islands lead enormously in the percentage of pronounced and massed freckles with 13.7 per cent as against a mean of 2.9 per cent for the total county series. However, the Arans are deficient in submedium freckling and thus their over-all

FIGURE 17

DISTRIBUTION OF FRECKLING IN IRELAND. The freckling map looks like the western half of the dark-haired map in the peninsular areas, but the eastern half of the country is very poor, especially south of E. Cavan-Monaghan-Armagh, and east of Cork and Limerick, although this is a dark-haired country. A comparison of the light-eyed map and the freckling map suggests that Tyrone-Londonderry is the only area which has a high concentrate of both freckling and light eyes. In West Donegal, Mayo and Kerry, freckling goes with surplus mixed eyes. High freckling does not go with curved hair. It goes with a high concentration of straight hair only in N. Fermanagh-E. Donegal-Tyrone-Londonderry.

[1] For age changes in all morphological features discussed herein, cf. Hooton and Dupertuis, 1951, pp. 43-105.

47

percentage of freckles places them in the intermediate group (40–49 per cent). The areas of intermediate freckling are, then, Antrim-Down (48.1 per cent), Aran Islands (46.8 per cent), Cork (43.4 per cent), Limerick (42.3 per cent), Sligo-Leitrim-S. Fermanagh-W. Cavan (41.8 per cent), and E. Galway-Roscommon (40.7 per cent). All the other county subgroups fall below 40 per cent in freckling. Thus freckling is at a maximum in the western peninsulas, except West Galway, while the whole middle and southern coastal area (i.e., except Cork), falls below 35 per cent of this character.

Freckling is, then, a phenomenon which is at a maximum in the western refuge areas of Ireland which contain the lowest percentages of pure light eyes and the highest proportions of high mesocephals and brachycephals.

Moles (Table IV-4). Pigmented moles, when observable on head, face, neck, and hands, were recorded in the categories of absent, few, and many. The Irish county series includes only 6.1 per cent of males with moles. Two groups of counties—Longford-Westmeath and Offaly-Leix-Kildare—show notable excesses of these skin blemishes. The former has 10.2 per cent and the latter 9.0 per cent. Meath-Louth-Dublin has 8.5 per cent of men who show moles. At the other extreme is Kerry with only 2.8 per cent and the Aran Islands with 2.9 per cent of moles. Other regions low in this feature are West Donegal with 3.8 per cent and N. Fermanagh-E. Donegal-Tyrone-Londonderry with 3.1 per cent. Moles, of course, are found most commonly on the darker complected individuals of the white races.

Hair Form (Table IV-5). Straight hair occurs in 28.7 per cent of the county series, while the more heavily curved varieties of hair (deep waves, curly, frizzly, and woolly) occur in 21.5 per cent. Straight hair is thus more common than the heavily curved varieties. The areas of high frequency of straight hair (35 to over 40 per cent) include the Aran Islands and a northern block consisting of N. Fermanagh-E. Donegal-Tyrone-Londonderry, together with E. Cavan-Monaghan-Armagh, and a southeastern block comprising Wicklow-Carlow, Waterford-Wexford and Tipperary-Kilkenny (fig. 18). These areas with a high percentage of straight hair are separated from each other by a central area of high prevalence of the more heavily curved varieties of hair made up of Longford-Westmeath and Offaly-Leix-Kildare. The southeastern straight-haired block similarly interposes itself between the central curved hair block and a southwestern group in which curved hair has a rather high frequency—County Cork alone (fig. 19). Cork is relatively high in straight hair (33.2 per cent) and in heavily curved hair (25.3 per cent) and is thus deficient in the low-waved type of hair.

Almost exactly one-half of the Irish county series has low-waved hair (49.8 per cent). The distributions above outlined describe a central and western area in which there is a high predominance of low-waved hair. This includes Sligo-Leitrim-S. Fermanagh-W. Cavan (58.0 per cent), Longford-Westmeath (58.1 per cent), E. Galway-Roscommon (55.5 per cent), Mayo (54.5 per cent), West Galway (54.4 per cent), Clare (53.0 per cent), and Limerick (51.9 per cent). The strange feature of this low-waved area is that it includes Longford-Westmeath which is the most curly haired subgroup in the island, or rather that which contains by far the lowest proportion of straight hair (14.2 per cent as against 28.7 per cent for the total series).

It seems probable that low-waved hair represents a more primitive and undifferentiated variety of hair form than do the more extreme categories. But it is also probable that a good deal of low-waved hair is produced by heterozygous intermediates between the strongly-curved and straight varieties. This low-waved

FIGURE 18

HAIR FORM, STRAIGHT: ITS DISTRIBUTION IN IRELAND. The notable features are two discrete areas; the southeastern corner, with the heaviest concentration in Wicklow-Carlow, and a northern island from E. Cavan-Monaghan-Armagh, Waterford and Wexford through Tyrone-Londonderry. These blocks are connected by lesser concentrations in Meath-Louth-Dublin and are extended to West Donegal and through Cork and Kerry. The most curly hair is in the midlands and westward.

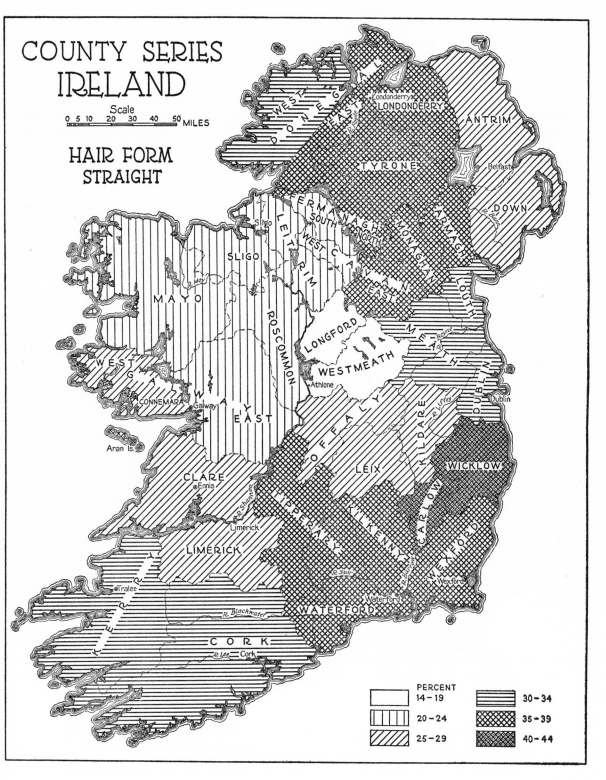

COUNTY SERIES
IRELAND

Scale
0 5 10 20 30 40 50 MILES

HAIR FORM
STRAIGHT

PERCENT
14-19
20-24
25-29
30-34
35-39
40-44

FIGURE 18

block in Ireland corresponds with what has been called the Sligo-Galway crescent, except in including Mayo, Clare, and Limerick. It is roughly coterminous with that part of Ireland which has the least preponderance of dark hair (again excepting Mayo). It is an area in which the taller long-heads of comparatively light pigmentation are most frequent.

The distribution of hair form in Ireland suggests that the earliest population strata, which are generally found in the western and especially the peninsular areas of West Ireland, were low waved. Next came a wave of straight-haired peoples which may originally have occupied the entire eastern and central zone of the island. Finally, there may have been a penetration of curly-haired peoples at two points—the southwestern area at Cork and the central area at Dublin. However, unless confirmatory data in other anthropological characters are available, it would be rash to draw far-reaching inferences from the distribution of hair form alone. The movements of populations in historical times may well have affected such changes as completely to obscure original ethnic dispositions. Again, differences of a regional nature in Irish hair form are by no means great and some of them may be referable to age differences in the subgroups, since pronouncedly curved types of hair diminish rapidly and disappear in the oldest age groups.

Hair Texture (Table IV-6). The proportion of hair of medium texture recorded for the county series is 92.5 per cent. Of the remainder, nearly twice as many instances of coarse hair as of fine hair are noted. Subgroup deviations seem to have little significance. On the whole, coarse hair is more common in the west central and southwest parts of Ireland than in the east central region. But Antrim-Down dissociates itself from the rest of the north and east in this respect. There is no obvious association of hair texture with hair form and hair color.

Hair Quantity, Head and Beard (Tables IV-7, IV-8). Hair quantity, as regards the head, is recorded as medium in such an overwhelming proportion of cases (95.1 per cent) as to render the occurrence of extreme categories too few to be dependable. There is some conformity with expectation in regard to age conditioning, since the youngest subgroup in mean age (Longford-Westmeath) has the second highest percentage of abundant head hair, and the third youngest subgroup (Antrim-Down) has the highest percentage of abundant head hair. However, Wicklow-Carlow (the second oldest subgroup) has one of the highest percentages of head hair quantity.

Aran Islands and Longford-Westmeath are lowest by far in beard quantities (very small, submedium). This is in conformity with their inclusion of the highest percentages of individuals in the 15–19 year age group. Antrim-Down, followed by Waterford-Wexford, the oldest county subgroup, top the list in proportions of pronounced beards, but there is no exact correlation of this observation with mean age of subseries.

Hair Quantity, Body (Table IV-9). The amount of body hair recorded in our Irish county series was medium in 91.1 per cent of cases. Pronounced development of body hair was noted in only 2.6 per cent of the series. Outstanding in this respect are, again, Antrim-Down and Waterford-Wexford. Two subgroups stand out for excesses of individuals having no body hair or a submedium development. These are Longford-Westmeath and the Aran Islands. Both of these subgroups fall below mean age and consequently their relative glabrousness may be attributed to their youth. Yet the subgroups which are above mean age seem to show no proportional increments of body hair.

Antrim-Down, the third youngest subgroup, leads in abundant head, beard and body hair.

Baldness (Table IV-10). Some baldness is evident in 40.8 per cent of Irish males in this series, but it is pronounced in only 7.2 per

FIGURE 19

DISTRIBUTION IN IRELAND OF HAIR FORM; DEEP WAVES, CURLY, FRIZZLY, WOOLLY. This distribution represents in many respects the converse of the straight-haired map. Concentrations are in the midlands between straight-haired areas, with Antrim-Down flanking the straight-haired northern island to the east and Cork the southeastern straight-haired island to the west. But in general there is a central belt of curved hair, running from Dublin to Mayo.

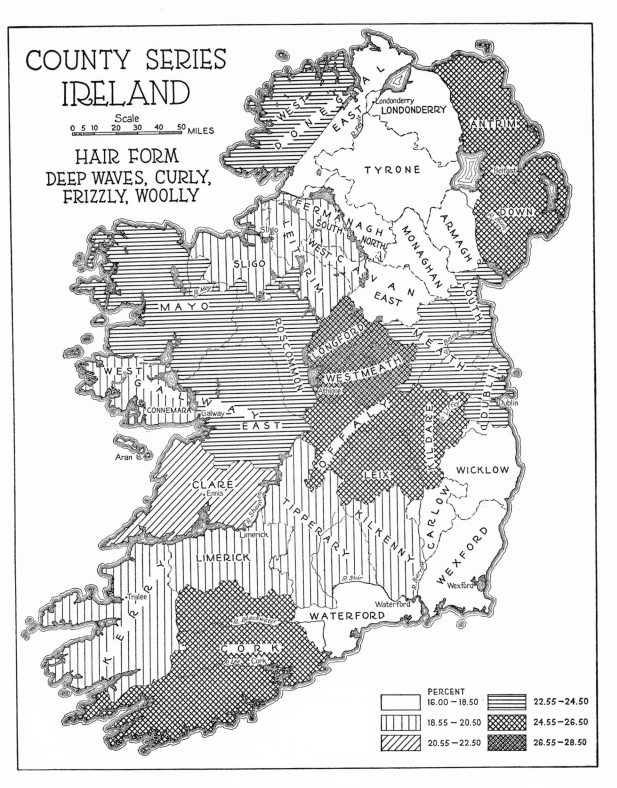

COUNTY SERIES
IRELAND

Scale
0 5 10 20 30 40 50 MILES

HAIR FORM
DEEP WAVES, CURLY,
FRIZZLY, WOOLLY

PERCENT
16.00 – 18.50
18.55 – 20.50
20.55 – 22.50
22.55 – 24.50
24.55 – 26.50
26.55 – 28.50

FIGURE 19

cent. The highest percentage of absence of baldness is in Longford-Westmeath (68.6 per cent) and the lowest in Waterford-Wexford (50.8 per cent). These are, respectively, the youngest and the oldest county subgroups. There is, however, no unit correlation of baldness with mean age of county subgroups.

PERCENTAGE OF MEDIUM PLUS PRONOUNCED
BALDNESS RELATIVE TO MEAN AGE

	BALDNESS	AGE
1. Wicklow-Carlow	27.3	38.30
2. Waterford-Wexford	24.8	40.90
3. Kerry	23.6	37.35
4. Aran Islands	22.3	34.50
5. Tipperary-Kilkenny	20.6	36.95
6. Cork	20.4	37.25
7. Meath-Louth-Dublin	19.7	35.75
8. Mayo	18.8	35.25
9. Clare	18.1	37.30
10. Limerick	18.0	35.80
11. E. Cavan-Monaghan-Armagh	17.9	36.50
12. Antrim-Down	17.8	33.60
13. N. Fermanagh-E. Donegal-Tyrone-Londonderry	17.6	33.90
14. West Donegal	17.5	33.60
15. West Galway	15.5	36.35
16. Sligo-Leitrim-S. Fermanagh-W. Cavan	14.9	34.90
17. Offaly-Leix-Kildare	13.2	35.00
18. E. Galway-Roscommon	12.3	34.40
19. Longford-Westmeath	11.9	30.25

The Aran Islands are conspicuous for high baldness associated with low mean age.

Grayness, Head and Beard (Tables IV-11, IV-12). The data on grayness of head hair agree fairly well with the variation of age in the subgroups. Thus the least gray hair is found in the subgroup of lowest mean age and the most gray hair in the oldest group. Regional differences seem unimportant.

Graying of the beard is absent in 11.3 per cent more of individuals than is recorded in the case of head hair, showing precocity of head hair graying, or possibly less precision in recording beard graying on account of the fact that the face is usually shaven. There is again a rough agreement between amount of graying and mean age of the subgroups.

Hair Color, Head (Table IV-13). Really black hair is quite rare in European whites. Hair that looks black in reflected light generally proves to be dark brown when viewed in transmitted light. The Irish county series shows but 2.8 per cent of black hair. Considerably the highest frequency is recorded in West Donegal with 7.5 per cent, whereas Longford-Westmeath has only 0.3 per cent and the Aran Islands and West Galway also show less than one per cent.

Dark brown hair is the commonest Irish shade (39.8 per cent). The maximum occurrence of dark brown is in E. Cavan-Monaghan-Armagh with 46.8 per cent. However, 11 of 19 county subgroups show more than 40 per cent of this shade. The Aran Islands with 23.0 per cent of dark brown hair and Longford-Westmeath with 27.5 per cent are notably deficient in dark brown as in black.

A flat brown shade occurs in 34.7 per cent of the total series. The Aran Islands with 48.9 per cent and Longford-Westmeath with 43.8 per cent lead in this category, thus compensating for their deficiencies in the darker shades. Most county subgroups approximate the mean of the total series.

Red-brown hair is found in 5.3 per cent of the total series, but in 11.1 per cent of Aran Islanders and in only 1.5 per cent of the men of Meath-Louth-Dublin. Golden brown is a commoner hair shade in Ireland (8.9 per cent). Longford-Westmeath leads in this shade with 13.2 per cent, closely followed by Waterford-Wexford with 12.7 per cent and Cork with 12.0 per cent. Ash brown is a very rare color, found in only 0.5 per cent of the series. Again Longford-Westmeath leads with 1.2 per cent of this shade. In four groups of counties this hair color does not occur at all. Pure golden hair is also rare (0.9 per cent of the series). It is commonest in Kerry (2.0 per cent) and was not recorded in any man of the Aran Islands or of Wicklow-Carlow. There are only 13 ash blonds in the whole series and five of them are in Longford-Westmeath, the youngest age group.

Ireland is famed for red hair, but our county series includes only 4.2 per cent with this shade. By far the most red-headed area is Sligo-Leitrim-S. Fermanagh-W. Cavan with 7.4 per cent, followed by the Aran Islands with 6.7 per cent and West Donegal with 6.6 per cent. Waterford-Wexford is lowest in red hair with only 1.5 per cent. Other county subgroups deviate only slightly from the mean of the series.

Figure 20 shows the distribution of really dark hair in the Irish county series. The percentages of combined black and dark brown hair average for the entire island 42.6 per cent. In the map the shading becomes heavier as the percentage of dark hair increases. All of eastern Ireland is occupied by a band in which dark hair is in excess, with the exception of the central county group of Longford-Westmeath, which is the second lightest-haired of all the series. Since mixed hair darkens with age up to middle years, and since Longford-Westmeath is considerably the youngest subgroup, its position is probably conditioned in part by this age factor. The eastern dark-haired zone culminates in counties Waterford and Wexford at the southeastern extremity of Ireland. This subgroup happens to be the oldest of the series in mean age, exceeding the mean age of Longford-Westmeath by more than 10 years. However, it seems improbable that its ranking in dark hair is affected by its advanced mean age, since dark hair tends to be diminished in middle and advanced years by graying. However, Sligo-Leitrim-S. Fermanagh-W. Cavan, which is the seventh youngest age subgroup, has the highest percentage of pure white hair (5.3 per cent), but ranks close to the bottom in percentage of combined black and dark brown hair. There is then no particular reason for supposing that rankings and distribution in dark hair are affected by the mean age of the county samples apart from the one group of very young men in Longford-Westmeath. Isolated regions of excess dark hair are the western peninsular counties of West Donegal in the north, Mayo in the center, Kerry in the south. These are separated from the eastern dark-haired zone by a band of lighter-haired counties extending down the west central area of Ireland from Londonderry and E. Donegal in the north to Cork in the south.

However, the greatest deficiencies of dark hair are found in the Sligo Bay-Galway Bay crescent with an apex extending east of the Shannon into Longford-Westmeath. It would be incorrect to describe this crescent as "blond," since pure golden and ash shades are

as rare here as elsewhere in Ireland. Its excesses of the lighter pigmentation of hair are found in the flat brown, red-brown, golden brown, and red shades. In this crescent are found the two subgroups with the highest percentage of red hair—Sligo-Leitrim-S. Fermanagh-W. Cavan with 7.4 per cent (nearly twice the average of the entire county series) and the Aran Islands with 6.7 per cent. This crescent is then an area of high rufosity and here also is the most red-brown hair.

Eye Color and Pigment, Mixed Eyes (Tables IV-14, IV-15). The distribution of eye color in Ireland is the most remarkable anthropological phenomenon that the island presents. Only 41 of 8909 men in the county series have pure dark eyes (0.5 per cent). Only four county groups—Sligo-Leitrim-S. Fermanagh-W. Cavan, Longford-Westmeath, Offaly-Leix-Kildare, and Meath-Louth-Dublin—have as much as one per cent of dark eyes.

Gray-brown and green-brown eyes are poorly represented with totals of 5.0 and 3.4 respectively. Gray-brown eyes attain 7.6 per cent in Waterford-Wexford, 6.6 per cent in Antrim-Down, and drop off to 0.7 per cent in the Aran Islands. Green-brown eyes reach a maximum in Antrim-Down with 7.9 per cent and a minimum in the Aran Islands with none at all. Blue-brown eyes constitute no less than 43.9 per cent of the Irish series, ranging in subgroup frequencies from 32.4 per cent (N. Fermanagh-E. Donegal-Tyrone-Londonderry) to 55.4 per cent in the Aran Islands.

Gray and gray-blue eyes are found in but 4.4 per cent. A notable leader in this category is N. Fermanagh-E. Donegal-Tyrone-Londonderry with 7.9 per cent, whereas Kerry has but 1.5 per cent of this shade. Pure blue eyes attain the unusual frequency of 42.4 per cent. E. Cavan-Monaghan-Armagh tops the list with 51.4 per cent, while Cork (33.4 per cent) and Kerry (34.5 per cent) are at the bottom.

Figure 21, showing the distribution of combined light eyes (gray, gray-blue, and blue) by county subgroups, reveals interesting regional variations. The highest percentages of combined light eyes comprise a north central block including N. Fermanagh-E. Donegal-Tyrone-Londonderry, E. Cavan-Monaghan-Armagh, and a southern including Wicklow-Carlow and Waterford-Wexford. The whole central part of the country from Sligo Bay to Waterford has slightly lower percentages of combined light eyes, while the smallest percentages are found in the western peninsulas of West Donegal and Kerry, with a southern extension in Cork.

From these distributions it appears that West Galway dissociates itself from the other western peninsular areas in this category in that it ranks tenth of the county subgroups and is thus considered as belonging to the group of intermediate percentages of combined light eyes. This intermediate group includes the whole central part of the country reaching to the coast at Meath-Louth-Dublin and Antrim-Down, and the Sligo-Galway Bay crescent with Clare.

Pigmented mixed eyes constitute a little more than half of the Irish series. A mixed eye is one in which the periphery or background of the iris is light, whereas more or less superficial red-brown, orange, or yellow pigment occurs in the ciliary zone. We grade these mixed eyes in five categories according to the rough proportions of light background and superficially pigmented area. This distribution in mixed eyes is shown in table IV-15. Only 3.2 per cent of mixed eyes are very pronouncedly dark and 7.2 per cent pronouncedly dark. These very dark mixed eyes occur combined at a maximum of 19.9 in Waterford-Wexford and in 20.5 per cent in Antrim-Down.

Mixed eyes in which the pigmented superficial part is about equal in area with the light background occur in 12.4 per cent. They are most frequent in Longford-Westmeath (18.9 per cent) and Meath-Louth-Dublin (18.8 per cent). Pronouncedly light mixed eyes occur in 17.9 per cent while 59.3 per cent are classified as very pronouncedly light. Thus 77.2 per cent of mixed eyes are light mixed. Waterford-Wexford is notably low in percentage of light mixed eyes as are also Longford-Westmeath and Antrim-Down.

Iris (Table IV-16). Iris pattern is not altogether satisfactorily described in our scheme. A clear eye (without) pattern may be brown, blue, or gray, but there are virtually no brown eyes in this series. Most of the clear eyes are blue or blue-gray. There are 22.3 per cent of clear eyes with the highest frequency (40.7 per cent) in Longford-Westmeath and the lowest (8.8 per cent) in Kerry. The Aran Islands are very high also in clear eyes (38.1 per cent). The medium to dark mixed eyes (and some of the light) are most frequently rayed in pattern. Rayed eyes attain a maximum in Waterford-Wexford (34.9 per cent) and fall to 16.1 per cent in E. Galway-Roscommon. The description "zoned" is applied to a mixed eye which has a regular concentric pigmented zone around the pupil and a lighter zone at the periphery. This pattern of eye is relatively uncommon (1.7 per cent). It occurs most frequently in Longford-Westmeath (4.1 per cent). Spotted eyes are found quite sporadically in 2.8 per cent of the series. Curiously, the minimum is in Longford-Westmeath with only 0.5 per cent. Waterford-Wexford has 5.0 per cent. A diffuse eye is one in which portions of the iris are irregularly stained with pigment as if it had run and blotted but without definite pattern. In this category Dr. Dupertuis also included all otherwise unclassified eyes. This type of eye is reported in no less than 32.6 per cent of the series and the observer may then have included in the category some of the few dark eyes (but hardly any of the pure lights). At any rate, Mayo, Kerry, West Donegal and Cork all exceed 40 per cent in this category, and these all rank in the leaders of the lighter mixed-eyed counties. In

FIGURE 20

DISTRIBUTION OF DARK HAIR IN IRELAND. The heavy distribution of dark hair covers the whole eastern half of Ireland except Longford-Westmeath. The greatest concentrations are in E. Cavan-Monaghan-Armagh and Waterford-Wexford; also in West Donegal, Mayo and Kerry. Waterford-Wexford and E. Cavan-Monaghan-Armagh agree in concentration of dark hair and straight hair (paucity of curved hair). Antrim-Down is high in both curved hair and dark hair; so are Offaly-Leix-Kildare. Ireland is generally modally dark-haired except for a band running from Tyrone west of the Shannon down through Cork, with an eastward bulge at Longford-Westmeath and a westward fork including West Galway and the Aran Islands. Notable coincidences of dark hair and light eyes are in E. Cavan-Monaghan-Armagh and Wicklow-Carlow (but these caught in the Keltic type).

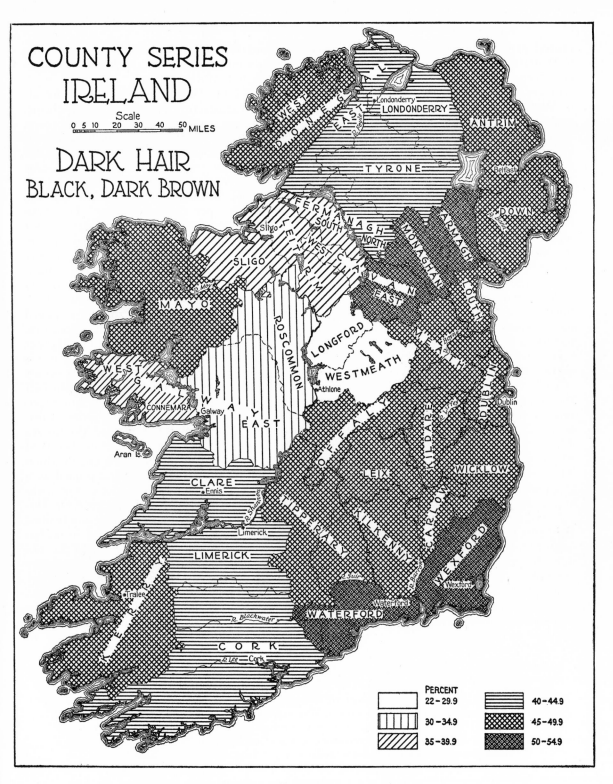

COUNTY SERIES
IRELAND

Scale
0 5 10 20 30 40 50 MILES

DARK HAIR
BLACK, DARK BROWN

PERCENT
22 – 29.9
30 – 34.9
35 – 39.9
40 – 44.9
45 – 49.9
50 – 54.9

FIGURE 20

the Aran Islands, Dr. Dupertuis found only 16.5 per cent of diffuse eyes. Scalloped eyes are usually pure light eyes—most commonly blue but sometimes light mixed. These are found in 18.7 per cent of the series. The highest frequencies are in N. Fermanagh-E. Donegal-Tyrone-Londonderry with 32.8 per cent and in Wicklow-Carlow with 29.7 per cent which are the county groups that lead in combined light eyes and are close to the top in pure blue eyes. These scalloped patterns are found in only 4.9 per cent of the Longford-Westmeath subgroup.

Eyefolds, External (Table IV-17). Males with deep set eyes and moderately well developed brow ridges are likely to develop an external epicanthic fold of the upper lid in maturity and old age. Some grade of this feature occurs in 13.3 per cent of males of the Irish county series. The external eyefold is slight (submedium) in 6.5 per cent, medium in 5.6 per cent, and pronounced in 1.2 per cent. In our series, the Tipperary-Kilkenny subgroup shows the highest general occurrence of this feature with 19.9 per cent. At the other extreme is West Donegal with only 8.5 per cent. In general, the subgroup variations seem neither large nor important. These external folds increase with age.

Eyefolds, Median (Table IV-18). The median epicanthic fold commonly occurs in young adult males with a low palpebral opening. It usually merges with an external fold in maturity and old age. Three per cent of the Irish county series show this median fold. It is commonest in Tipperary-Kilkenny where some grade of development occurs in 5.7 per cent.

Eyefolds, Internal (Table IV-19). The internal epicanthic fold is nearly incompatible with the high narrow nasal roots which are prevalent in Ireland. It is found in only one per cent. The highest incidence is in the young

Longford-Westmeath subgroup with 2.5 per cent.

Eye Obliquity (Table IV-20). In 64.4 per cent of this series the palpebral slits have their long axes approximately horizontal. In 29.7 per cent there is some degree of elevation of the external canthi, so that the eyes appear to slant upward from the inside. In 5.8 per cent the external corners are depressed so that the eyes slant down.

By far the highest incidence of horizontal eyes is that recorded in the Aran Islands (90.6 per cent). In Longford-Westmeath eye obliquity is absent in 84.0 per cent of cases. The lowest frequency of horizontal eyes is in N. Fermanagh-E. Donegal-Tyrone-Londonderry with 44.6 per cent. Other groups with low frequencies of non-oblique eye slits are Antrim-Down, E. Cavan-Monaghan-Armagh, and Wicklow-Carlow. These same four subgroups exhibit the largest proportions of eye slits which have a submedium upward obliquity (39 to 43 per cent).

Obliquity in the other direction—downward —is comparatively rare, but reaches a frequency of 8.1 per cent in West Galway. Other counties in which this feature is markedly above average are Clare (7.9 per cent), E. Cavan-Monaghan-Armagh (7.7 per cent) and West Donegal (7.5 per cent). The minimum occurrence is in the Aran Islands (1.4 per cent).

Eye Opening Height (Table IV-21). The height of the palpebral opening was recorded as medium in 91.0 per cent of the county series. Variation toward low openings occurred in 6.0 per cent of cases. These are most frequent in Waterford-Wexford (11.4 per cent) and rarest in West Donegal (2.8 per cent).

Pronounced height of the palpebral opening occurs in 3.0 per cent of the county series. It is least frequent in the Aran Islands (0.7 per cent) and commonest in Tipperary-Kilkenny

FIGURE 21

DISTRIBUTION OF LIGHT EYES IN IRELAND. The smallest concentrations (35–39.9 per cent) are in Kerry, Cork, West Donegal, Mayo, and Aran Islands. Blue eyes are concentrated most highly in the north central area and in Wicklow-Carlow (55–59.9 per cent). Secondary concentrations are in Waterford-Wexford. One might assume that two areas of entrance for blue eyes are Londonderry and north and southeast coasts.

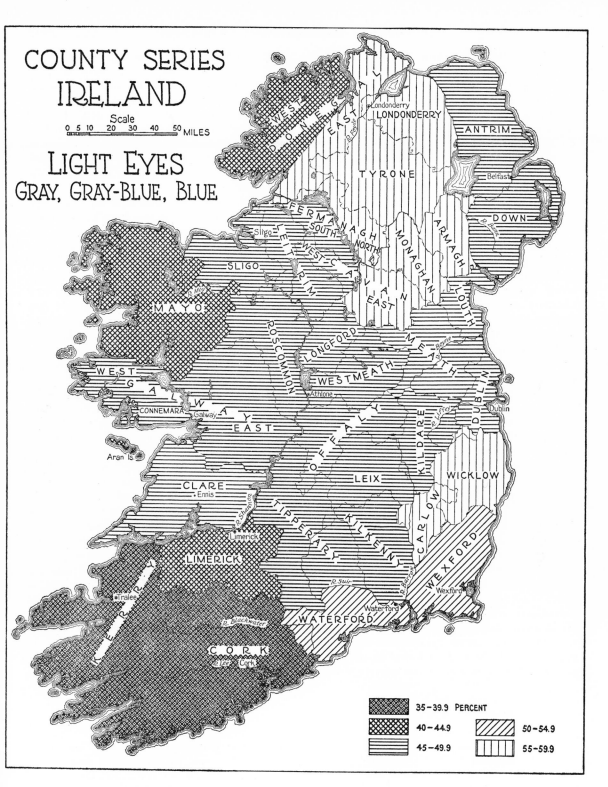

COUNTY SERIES
IRELAND

Scale
0 5 10 20 30 40 50 MILES

LIGHT EYES
GRAY, GRAY-BLUE, BLUE

35-39.9 PERCENT
40-44.9
45-49.9
50-54.9
55-59.9

FIGURE 21

and Longford-Westmeath (4.3 per cent). The trends toward the extremes of palpebral opening are nowhere marked.

Eyebrow Thickness and Concurrency (Tables IV-22, IV-23). A medium eyebrow thickness occurs in 93.1 per cent of the Irish series. The variations toward both extremes are small and insignificant.

On the whole, eyebrow concurrency is prevailingly medium (64.7 per cent), but oftener submedium (23.2 per cent) than pronounced (10.3 per cent). The highest frequency of strongly concurrent eyebrows is in Meath-Louth-Dublin with 15.3 per cent; the highest percentage of non-concurrent eyebrows is 3.1 per cent in E. Galway-Roscommon. However, regional variations in this trait seem generally unimportant. Persons with light eyebrows are most likely to have their eyebrows graded as "non-concurrent." Meath-Louth-Dublin is near the top in darkness of head hair, E. Galway-Roscommon near the bottom.

Meath-Louth-Dublin has both the highest percentage of thick eyebrows and of pronounced eyebrow concurrency, but a casual inspection shows no striking evidence of association on the basis of modal occurrences. To test these details of morphological association of graded attributes, it would be necessary to run multiple sortings, which are impracticable in a survey of this magnitude.

Brow Ridges (Table IV-24). Five grades of brow ridge size in the Irish series, beginning with *absent* and culminating in *very pronounced* are distributed in an almost symmetrical manner with a slight skewing toward smallness. If we map the excess of large brow

ridges over submedium and absent brow ridges (table IV-24), it becomes apparent that Kerry, the Aran Islands, and Cork are most robustly endowed with these features, which are also in excess in E. Galway-Roscommon, Longford-Westmeath, Tipperary-Kilkenny, Waterford-Wexford, Antrim-Down, and Clare. West Galway and E. Cavan-Monaghan-Armagh have the lowest percentages of large brow ridges.

Forehead Height (Table IV-25). Only 3.7 per cent of our Irish county series are recorded as having foreheads of submedium height, but 53.7 per cent have pronouncedly high foreheads. The excess of pronounced foreheads over submedium and medium high foreheads is greatest in the northeast and north central parts of Ireland (fig. 22), excluding West Donegal. The Sligo-Galway crescent and adjacent counties of Clare and Longford-Westmeath are deficient in high foreheads and the Aran Islands most of all.

Forehead Slope (Table IV-26). The numerous categories of this observation require combination and simplification. Forward slopes imply a bulging forehead; absent, comparatively vertical; and submedium, only very slightly sloping backward. The first two categories are comparatively rare; the last is the modal Irish forehead slope.

If these three categories of slope are combined, we obtain, in the first column of table IV-26, the rankings in aggregate percentages of foreheads that are not receding. They range from 66.2 per cent in N. Fermanagh-E. Donegal-Tyrone-Londonderry to 26.6 per cent in the Arans.

It is clear enough that the greatest predom-

FIGURE 22

DISTRIBUTION OF FOREHEAD HEIGHT IN IRELAND. The area of the greatest excess of pronounced forehead height over medium plus submedium is in all of northeastern Ireland (Antrim-Down, N. Fermanagh-E. Donegal-Tyrone-Londonderry, E. Cavan-Monaghan-Armagh). But moderate excesses also occur in West Donegal and in the whole of the eastern half of southern Ireland, except Longford-Westmeath. The greatest deficiency of high foreheads is in the Arans, and in a broad band extending southeast from Sligo Bay to Galway Bay and including both West Galway and Clare.

There is no close distributional similarity between excess of high foreheads and excess of foreheads with little slope, except in a concentration of both features in the north. The southern coast from Wexford through Cork is not particularly notable for excess of non-sloping foreheads, although it is marked by high foreheads. A large part of the low forehead area west of the Erne and the Shannon has an excess of steep foreheads, especially Sligo-Leitrim-S. Fermanagh-W. Cavan and Mayo. Steep foreheads are in general in far greater excess than high foreheads.

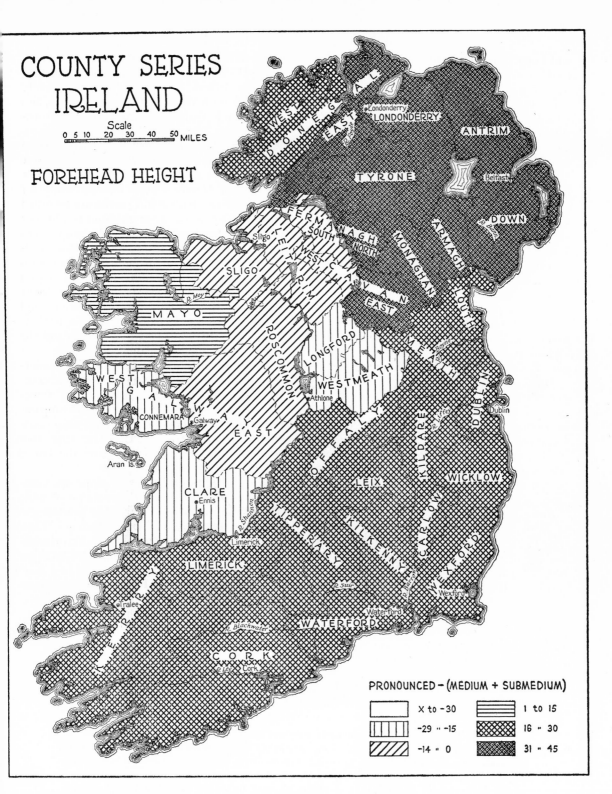

FIGURE 22

inance of vertical or erect foreheads is in the north of Ireland and that far fewer of these categories are found in the area around Galway Bay and in some of the southeastern counties. However, a merging of the pronounced categories of forehead slope shows that these have no marked geographical associations. The highest occurrences are in Waterford-Wexford, Wicklow-Carlow, Antrim-Down and Cork.

The greatest county fluctuations fall between the submedium and medium categories. The Arans and Longford-Westmeath owe their low position in forehead verticality to excesses of medium over submedium slopes rather than to any high frequencies of low foreheads.

On the whole, whatever way the data are analyzed (and several combinations have been tried), it does not appear that the regional variations are clearly patterned.

The map of forehead slope (fig. 23) records the excesses of non-sloping (absent + forward + submedium) foreheads over those of medium and greater slope. The whole of the north forms a block of relatively great predominance of non-sloping foreheads, but there are two outlying areas (Mayo and Tipperary-Kilkenny) of comparable frontal verticality. These are parts of two bands of moderate excesses of steep foreheads running away from the main concentration.

Nasion Depression (Table IV-27). Variations toward slight or absent nasion depressions occur in 14.9 per cent of the county series. The Longford-Westmeath subgroup with 23.8 per cent of submedium, small, or absent depressions is outstanding in this variational trend—quite possibly because of its very low mean age. Kerry, Wicklow-Carlow, E. Cavan-Monaghan-Armagh, and Antrim-Down tend to show few of these undeveloped nasion depressions.

Antrim-Down leads easily in proportion of pronounced and very pronounced nasion depressions (38.8 per cent), while the other northern counties (N. Fermanagh-E. Donegal-Tyrone-Londonderry) are not far behind (36.1 per cent). Dr. Dupertuis' perspicacity in separating West Donegal from the other northern counties is evidenced here by the fact that West Donegal has only 23.6 per cent of men with pronounced nasion depressions. In the south, Kerry shows a high frequency of strong nasion depressions (32.8 per cent). Longford-Westmeath has the lowest frequency of marked nasion depressions (14.1 per cent). Another weak area is West Galway (16.0 per cent).

The distribution suggests that the area of submedium to weak or absent nasion depressions is the block of counties composed of Sligo-Leitrim-S. Fermanagh-W. Cavan, E. Galway-Roscommon, and culminating in Longford-Westmeath.

Nasal Root, Height and Breadth (Tables IV-28, IV-29). The Irish have nasal roots of medium height in 77.2 per cent of cases and of medium breadth in 72.3 per cent. Variations toward pronounced and very pronounced height (19.7 per cent) are more than six times as common as those in the opposite direction. The notably high-rooted areas are the Aran Islands, Wicklow-Carlow, Tipperary-Kilkenny, Waterford-Wexford, Meath-Louth-Dublin, and West Donegal. Waterford-Wexford and Tipperary-Kilkenny also lead in broad-rooted noses. In general, Irish noses that are not of medium root breadth are broad in this part of the nose. The Longford-Westmeath subgroup is outstanding because of its vast predominance of nasal roots of medium

FIGURE 23

DISTRIBUTION OF DEGREE OF FOREHEAD SLOPE IN IRELAND. Excesses of steep foreheads (with no slope or little slope) are concentrated in West Donegal and in Central Ulster with outlying bands extending west in Northern Connaught, and from Antrim-Down southwest terminating in Limerick. The most intense concentration of steep foreheads is within the area of greatest frequency of high foreheads. Areas of deficiency of high foreheads do not exactly coincide with areas of little forehead slope, except in a zone from Longford-Westmeath southwest. The south shore of Sligo Bay is high in steep foreheads but also falls within the area of deficiency of high foreheads. The same holds for a coastal strip extending from Wicklow clear around the south through Kerry.

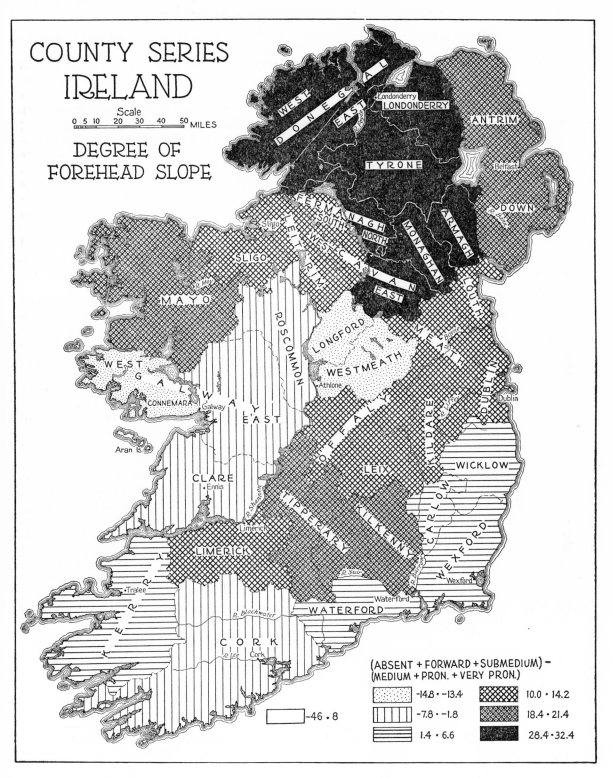

COUNTY SERIES
IRELAND

Scale
0 5 10 20 30 40 50 MILES

DEGREE OF
FOREHEAD SLOPE

(ABSENT + FORWARD + SUBMEDIUM) −
(MEDIUM + PRON. + VERY PRON.)

⠄⠄⠄	−14.8 · −13.4	▨	10.0 · 14.2
▥	−7.8 · −1.8	▩	18.4 · 21.4
▤	1.4 · 6.6	■	28.4 · 32.4

□ −46 · 8

FIGURE 23

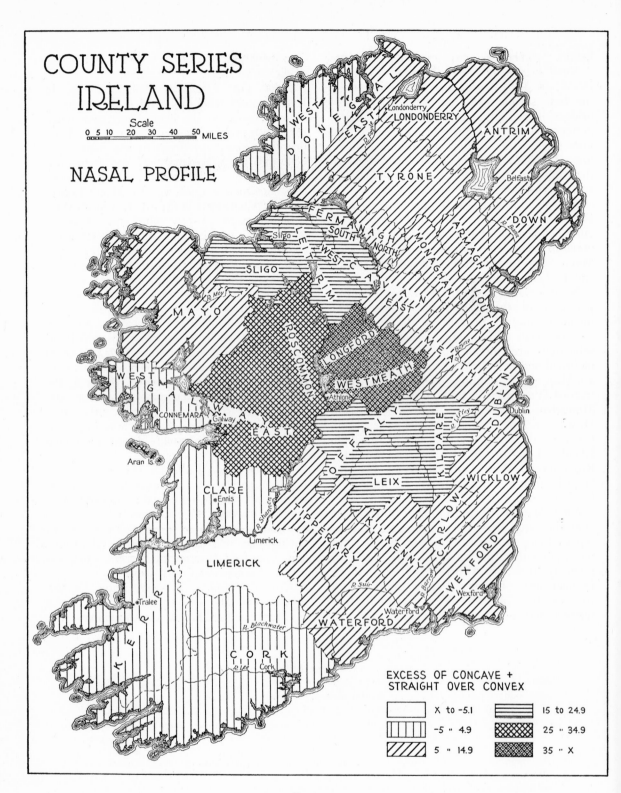

COUNTY SERIES
IRELAND

Scale
0 5 10   20   30   40   50 MILES

NASAL PROFILE

EXCESS OF CONCAVE +
STRAIGHT OVER CONVEX

	X to -5.1		15 to 24.9
	-5 " 4.9		25 " 34.9
	5 " 14.9		35 " X

FIGURE 24

height, combined with medium breadth. *Nasal Bridge, Height and Breadth* (Tables IV-30, IV-31). More than three-quarters of the Irish sample (76.2 per cent) have nasal bridges of medium height, while those of pronounced height are more than six times as numerous as those which are adjudged to be low. The latter include only 3.1 per cent and their county distribution is probably haphazard. High-bridged noses are excessively present in Wicklow-Carlow, Tipperary-Kilkenny, Waterford-Wexford, Cork, and Kerry. Notable deficiencies of this nasal form are to be noted in Longford-Westmeath, West Galway, Mayo, Sligo-Leitrim-S. Fermanagh-W. Cavan, and E. Galway-Roscommon.

Narrow nasal bridges occur in less than one per cent of the Irish county series. The medium category prevails on the average in 78.2 per cent of individuals. Certain county subgroups are notable for high proportions of broad and very broad nasal bridges. These are Meath-Louth-Dublin (31.8 per cent), Waterford-Wexford (31.6 per cent), E. Cavan-Monaghan-Armagh (29.3 per cent), Antrim-Down (28.9 per cent). On the other hand, broad nasal bridges are deficient in the Aran Islands, Longford-Westmeath, E. Galway-Roscommon, West Donegal, West Galway, Sligo-Leitrim-S. Fermanagh-W. Cavan, Mayo, Limerick, and Clare.

Nasal Septum (Table IV-32). There is an overwhelming predominance of convex nasal septa among the Irish of our series. The mean percentage of convexity is 61.7, and the range from 47.5 in Wicklow-Carlow and N. Fermanagh-E. Donegal-Tyrone-Londonderry to 73.6 per cent in West Donegal. The western and southwestern areas have, in general, the largest excesses of convex septa. These decline with age.

Nasal Tip, Thickness (Table IV-33). In Ireland noses tend to be thick in the tip as well as broad in the bridge and root when they diverge from the medium category. Thin, or submedium, tips occur in less than 2 per cent and thick (pronounced and very pronounced) tips in 25.1 per cent. The counties most notable for thick tips are Meath-Louth-Dublin, Waterford-Wexford, E. Cavan-Monaghan-Armagh. A few subgroups (Aran Islands, 12.9 per cent; Longford-Westmeath, 14.0 per cent; E. Galway-Roscommon, 16.5 per cent) vary strongly toward proportional deficiency of thick tips, which increase with age.

Nasal Tip, Inclination (Table IV-34). It is very remarkable that Dr. Dupertuis should have recorded in Ireland such a vast predominance (94.0 per cent) of nasal tips which are inclined upward and so few (1.7 per cent) with downward inclination. The most strongly up-tilted noses occur in West Donegal, the second youngest subgroup. However, depressed tips seem only insignificantly commoner in the older county subgroups, although the nasal tip usually droops somewhat with age.

Nasal Wings (Table IV-35). Alae are of medium spread in 88.5 per cent of cases. Little is worthy of note in the subgroup variations. However, Sligo-Leitrim-S. Fermanagh-W. Cavan stands out for its 9.9 per cent of flaring alae, whereas the Aran Islands, Clare, and Longford-Westmeath present small excesses of compressed nasal wings.

Nostril Visibility, Frontal (Table IV-36). Frontal visibility of the nares is absent in 4.8 per cent—presumably in the individuals who

FIGURE 24

NASAL PROFILE DISTRIBUTION IN IRELAND. The map suggests a regional concentration of straight plus concave nasal profiles in the central plain, on both sides of the Shannon, and incidentally, in the area of light hair, low foreheads, large head circumferences, and excesses of the Nordic morphological types. Possibly the negative side of the map is even more instructive. It. shows that the area of nasal convexity tends to approximate that of brachycephalic concentration.

Although the areas of strongest concentration of straight plus concave nasal profiles are all those of county groups well below the mean age, it should be noted that the oldest county subseries are not the leaders in nasal convexity, or rather in the predominance of convexity. Limerick, which has the largest excess of convex profiles, is scarcely above mean county age, and West Donegal, another region of high convexity, is a very young county group.

have the longest nasal tips. Waterford-Wexford and Clare lead in absence of frontal visibility, but it is exceptional everywhere. The Aran Islands and Longford-Westmeath show marked excesses of pronounced frontal visibility.

Nasal Profile (Table IV-37). Noses in Ireland are most commonly straight in profile (47.6 per cent), but nearly as often convex (44.9 per cent). Concave noses are found in only 7.4 per cent. Since a saddle-shaped nose is a primitive and infantile feature—generally represented in old-fashioned caricatures of the type Irishman—it is interesting to note the areas in which this nasal profile is commonest (fig. 24). These are, in order, Mayo (9.9 per cent), Kerry (9.4 per cent), West Donegal (9.0 per cent), Tipperary-Kilkenny (8.9 per cent), West Galway (8.5 per cent), Clare (8.2 per cent), and Offaly-Leix-Kildare (8.1 per cent). On the whole, then, concave noses are found most commonly in the western coastal area, with the notable exception of the Aran Islands, which has the lowest proportion (2.2 per cent). They are also common in the Sligo Bay area, together with the central block which includes Offaly-Leix-Kildare and Tipperary-Kilkenny. Probably these noses are commonest in the ethnically oldest samples of our Irish population.

The eccentric Longford-Westmeath subgroup shows the highest percentage of straight noses (straight plus straight snub tip) with 65.5 per cent, but it exceeds only slightly the inbred Aran Islanders with 64.0 per cent. Other areas of possibly significant excesses of straight noses are Offaly-Leix-Kildare (52.8 per cent), N. Fermanagh-E. Donegal-Tyrone-Londonderry (51.3 per cent), Waterford-Wexford (50.8 per cent), Sligo-Leitrim-S. Fermanagh-W. Cavan (50.7 per cent), and E. Galway-Roscommon (50.6 per cent). Thus a band of straight-nosed predominance extends down the center of the country from the extreme north to Waterford-Wexford in the southeast corner (with the exception of the Tipperary-Kilkenny area).

However, convex profiles in the total series are only 2.7 per cent fewer than straight noses. The areas of convex predominance are Limerick (54.1 per cent), West Donegal (52.4 per cent), Cork (51.7 per cent), Clare (50.6 per cent), and West Galway (50.2 per cent). About all that can be said of this distribution is that it is westerly. By far the fewest convex noses occur in the two standout subgroups: Longford-Westmeath (29.2 per cent) and the Aran Islands (33.8 per cent). These are the groups with excessive predominance of straight nasal profiles. West Donegal is very high in nasal convexity and slightly above average in nasal concavity; Kerry is high in the latter and somewhat high in the former. The same applies to Mayo and, in smaller degree, to West Galway.

Lips, Integumental Thickness (Table IV-38). Integumental lips vary from medium thickness only in a little more than 5 per cent of cases. The rather small subseries from Antrim-Down (152 men) shows a pronounced integumental lip thickness in 8.6 per cent of cases, while in the large Clare series (946 men) the frequency drops to 2.7 per cent. These variations seem unimportant. The observation is difficult and unreliable because apparent thickness of the upper integumental lip is conditioned by alveolar prognathism, tooth loss, etc.

Upper Lip, Membranous Thickness (Table IV-39). The lower membranous lip is usually thicker than the upper, but the upper lip is the more variable and better for observational purposes. Membranous upper lips are usually of medium thickness (72.9 per cent) and far oftener thin than thick. The Aran Islands lead in very small and submedium membranous upper lips with 41.0 per cent as against a mean of 24.4 per cent for the total county series. Other county groups with excesses of thin lips are Clare (31.2 per cent),

FIGURE 25

DISTRIBUTION IN IRELAND OF MID-FACIAL PROGNATHISM. This is an eastern phenomenon, with the greatest concentration in Wicklow-Carlow. It seems to coincide to some extent with the heavy Keltic concentrates. Wicklow-Carlow is also heaviest in straight hair concentration. There is a notable lack of mid-facial prognathism in Kerry, Limerick, Clare, Mayo, and in general where we have strong Dinaric concentrates.

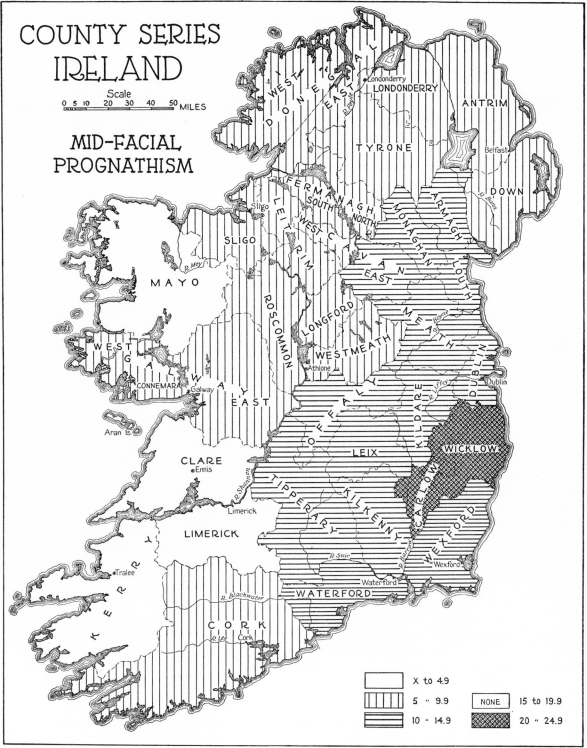

COUNTY SERIES
IRELAND

Scale
0 5 10 20 30 40 50 MILES

MID-FACIAL
PROGNATHISM

WEST DONEGAL EAST
Londonderry
LONDONDERRY
ANTRIM
TYRONE
Belfast
R. Foyle
DOWN
R. Bann
SLIGO
Sligo
FERMANAGH
SOUTH NORTH
LEITRIM
WEST CAVAN
EAST
MONAGHAN
ARMAGH
LOUTH
MAYO
ROSCOMMON
LONGFORD
MEATH
R. Moy
R. Boyne
WESTMEATH
DUBLIN
Athlone
R. Liffey
Dublin
WEST GALWAY
CONNEMARA
Galway
EAST
OFFALY
KILDARE
LEIX
WICKLOW
Aran Is.
CARLOW
CLARE
Ennis
WEXFORD
TIPPERARY
KILKENNY
R. Shannon
Limerick
R. Barrow
R. Suir
Wexford
LIMERICK
KERRY
Tralee
R. Blackwater
Waterford
WATERFORD
CORK
R. Lee
Cork

☐	X to 4.9	
⊞ (vertical)	5 " 9.9	NONE 15 to 19.9
≡ (horizontal)	10 " 14.9	▨ 20 " 24.9

FIGURE 25

Wicklow-Carlow (29.8 per cent), Waterford-Wexford (29.1 per cent), Tipperary-Kilkenny (26.8 per cent), Cork and Offaly-Leix-Kildare (26.3 per cent). Other county subgroups cluster closely around the mean with Mayo most deficient in thin lips with a percentage of 17.2. On the whole, thicker lips are found in the north and thinner lips in the south.

Lips, Eversion (Table IV-40). Approximately three-quarters of the county series show medium lip eversion. This feature is pronounced in only 3.9 per cent and submedium in 22.1 per cent. Clare shows the highest percentage of submedium lip eversion (30.0 per cent). The northern counties (Antrim-Down, N. Fermanagh-E. Donegal-Tyrone-Londonderry) show the highest percentage of pronounced lip eversion, just as they excel in thick membranous upper lips.

Lip Seam (Table IV-41). Lip seams are recorded as absent in 97.9 per cent of the county series, as might be expected in a population which has thin lips and little eversion. Longford-Westmeath leads in the combined categories of submedium and medium lip seam with 4.4 per cent, closely followed by Sligo-Leitrim-S. Fermanagh-W. Cavan with 4.3 per cent. The mean of the total county series is only 2.1 per cent.

Alveolar Prognathism (Table IV-42). Alveolar prognathism seems extraordinarily rare in Ireland, as only 2.4 per cent is reported for the total county series. The Longford-Westmeath subgroup, however, shows 8.0 per cent of various grades of alveolar prognathism, Wicklow-Carlow has 6.1 per cent, and Antrim-Down has 5.9 per cent. West Donegal with a series of 212 men has only one case recorded in which alveolar prognathism is present. A comparison of the tables for tooth loss suggests no clear relationship between the latter and amount of alveolar prognathism (e.g., West Donegal shows nearly the least tooth

loss and no alveolar prognathism whatsoever).

Mid-facial Prognathism (Table IV-43). Mid-facial prognathism has a very interesting geographical distribution in Ireland in that it attains an extreme of 23.7 in Wicklow-Carlow as against 8.1 per cent for the total county series (fig. 25). It is moderately developed from Armagh southward along the east coast to Waterford-Wexford and bending inland to include Offaly-Leix-Kildare and Tipperary-Kilkenny. Antrim-Down dissociates itself from the above zone and joins the area of less evident facial projection farther to the west. This region of little mid-facial prognathism extends from Donegal and Londonderry south to the border of Clare, but includes also the isolated Cork subgroup on the south coast. The minimum incidence (amounting to virtual absence) occurs in the Aran Islands, Mayo, Clare, Kerry, and Limerick. The distribution suggests, in general, that the earlier population zones in Ireland have the least mid-facial projection.

Chin Prominence (Table IV-44). Nearly 80 per cent of Irish have chins of medium projection, while of the remainder slightly more than half are of submedium prominence. Cork, Limerick, and Kerry are areas in which strongly projecting chins are most in evidence, closely followed by Tipperary-Kilkenny, Longford-Westmeath, the Aran Islands, Waterford-Wexford, and Wicklow-Carlow. Thus there is a band of chin prominence all across the southern third of Ireland from Kerry to Wexford with isolated blocks in the Aran Islands and Longford-Westmeath. The other county groups of Ireland to the north and in the center show diminishing proportions of projecting chins. West Galway shows the lowest percentage of pronounced chin prominence (5.1 per cent).

Chin Type (Table IV-45). Pointed or median chins are recorded in only 3.4 per cent of the county series. The remarkable predom-

FIGURE 26

TOOTH LOSS DISTRIBUTION IN IRELAND. Tooth loss depends upon age as well as upon prevalence of dental disease. The whole south coast exhibits maximum tooth loss, and the southern half of the island and the east coast up to Down are bad. Waterford-Wexford, Cork, Kerry, Clare, and Wicklow-Carlow are all over mean age. Most of the areas in which tooth loss is less are under mean age, but there is no exact correlation. Limerick, the best southern county with respect to tooth loss, but the worst of all Ireland in caries, is below the mean ages of the surrounding counties.

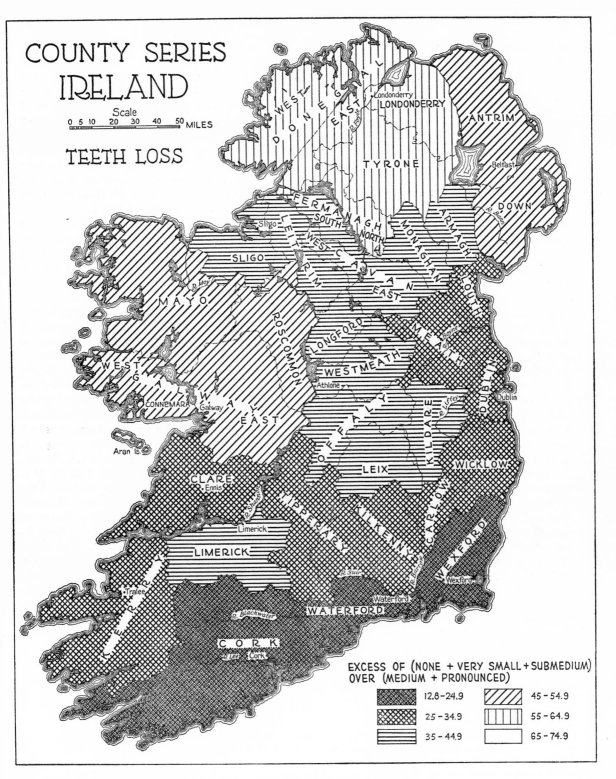

COUNTY SERIES
IRELAND

Scale
0 5 10   20   30   40   50 MILES

TEETH LOSS

EXCESS OF (NONE + VERY SMALL + SUBMEDIUM)
OVER (MEDIUM + PRONOUNCED)

▨	12.8 – 24.9	▨	45 – 54.9
▨	25 – 34.9	▥	55 – 64.9
▤	35 – 44.9	☐	65 – 74.9

FIGURE 26

inance of square or bilateral chins in Ireland is unusual (96.6 per cent). In Old American criminals (4,183), only 43.60 per cent of individuals have bilateral chins (Hooton, 1939, table VI-133).

The discrepancy is probably due to the fact that Dr. Dupertuis consistently palpated the chin prominence, whereas the observers in the criminal survey probably recorded a chin as bilateral ordinarily only when it was "cleft." Most male chins which appear to be "median" have an underlying bilaterality of the mental ossicles.

Teeth, Eruption (Table IV-46). Eruption of the teeth is reported as complete in only 73.3 per cent of the county series. Presumably partial eruption applies, almost exclusively, to delay or suppression of the third molars. Clare shows the highest percentage of completely erupted dentition (84.4 per cent) and Longford-Westmeath the lowest (60.5 per cent). Clare has an average age of 37.30 years which is 1.6 years above mean age, but Longford-Westmeath is the youngest subgroup (30.25 years). The oldest subgroup, Waterford-Wexford, ranks second in proportion of complete eruption with 79.6 per cent.

Age is certainly a conditioning factor, but tendencies toward suppression of the third molar probably complicate the situation.

Bite (Table IV-47). For some reason, probably dental loss, the type of bite is recorded for only 6,872 men of our county series of 8,909. Submedium overbites are so heavily predominant (96.0 per cent) that we must conclude that the Irish have in general a preponderance of normal occlusions, unless the bias of the observer was toward leniency in recording degree of overbite. Pronounced overbites are found in only 3.0 per cent. They reach 6.5 per cent in Wicklow-Carlow and drop to 0.8 per cent in the rather small Antrim-Down subgroup. It is strange to find edge-to-edge bites in only 0.4 per cent of the Irish county series, in view of the fact that marked wear and shortening of the teeth are common.

Teeth, Wear (Table IV-48). The Irish county series shows 75.8 per cent of teeth which are unworn or very slightly worn. The highest figure is attained in N. Fermanagh-E. Donegal-Tyrone-Londonderry with 86.8 per cent. This group is less than two years below mean age. The most heavily worn teeth are found in Kerry with 11.6 per cent. Great dental attrition is also above average in Wicklow-Carlow, Limerick, Clare, Waterford-Wexford, and Mayo. N. Fermanagh-E. Donegal-Tyrone-Londonderry displays the minimum of pronounced tooth wear with 1.2 per cent, followed closely by the eccentric Aran Islands with 1.5 per cent.

Teeth, Loss (Table IV-49). The series of 8,903 men examined for tooth loss reveals 710 individuals or only 8.0 per cent who have lost no teeth. More than half of the dentition is missing in 24.2 per cent. The greatest loss is found in the oldest group—Waterford-Wexford—but all of the southern and southwestern counties are bad in respect to retention of teeth. On the other hand, the Aran Islands, off the coast of Clare (a bad county for teeth), have considerably the best rating, followed by N. Fermanagh-E. Donegal-Tyrone-Londonderry, and West Donegal while West Galway, Mayo, and Antrim-Down also rank creditably in this scale.

Figure 26 and table IV-49 show the excess of the combined categories *none*, plus *very small* plus *submedium* over *medium* plus *pronounced*. From the map it is apparent that the areas characterized by least tooth loss are the three most northern county subgroups, Mayo, and, around Galway Bay, the Arans, West Galway and E. Galway-Roscommon.

Teeth, Caries (Table IV-50). In a series of 6,857 males whose teeth were observed, only 58, or 0.8 per cent, are recorded as having no dental caries. This small number would certainly be reduced if the data consisted of careful examinations by a trained dentist. Five

FIGURE 27

DISTRIBUTION OF CARIES IN IRELAND. The striking feature of this map is the contrast between the Ulster north, with its high excess of individuals with relatively few caries, and the opposite condition in the southwest. Limerick is worst, but is flanked by bad situations in Clare, Kerry, and Cork. The contrast may to some extent be referable to dental care and the lack of it, but the factors are probably more potent.

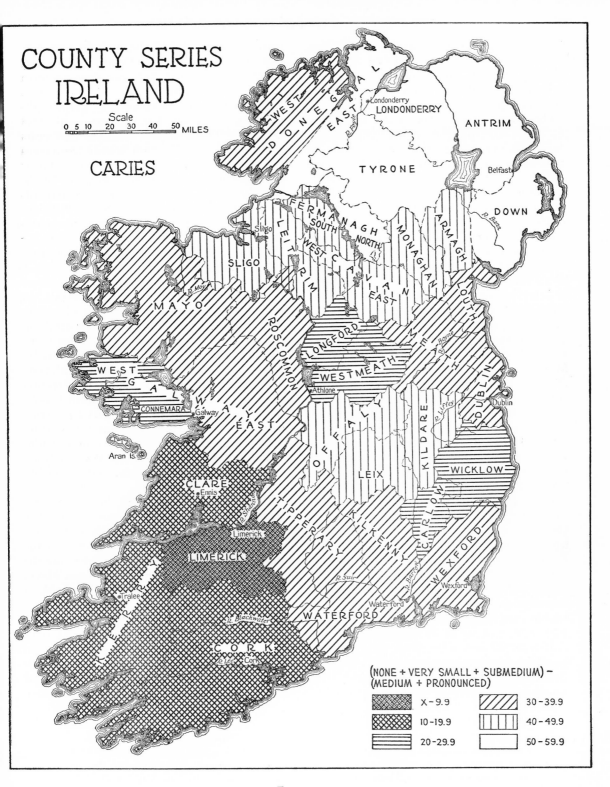

COUNTY SERIES
IRELAND

Scale
0 5 10 20 30 40 50 MILES

CARIES

(NONE + VERY SMALL + SUBMEDIUM) –
(MEDIUM + PRONOUNCED)

▓	X – 9.9	▨	30 – 39.9
▨	10 – 19.9	⦀	40 – 49.9
▤	20 – 29.9	☐	50 – 59.9

FIGURE 27

categories of caries are recognized, according to the number of teeth affected (shown mainly by fillings) in the individual. If we take the sum of the first three categories (*none* plus *very small* plus *submedium*) and subtract from it the sum of the other two categories (*medium* plus *pronounced*), we have a basis for mapping our rough estimate of the relative frequency of dental decay (fig. 27). The worst county is Limerick, followed by Kerry, Clare, and Cork. This seems to establish the greatest frequency of caries in the southwestern counties. Teeth are considerably better in West Galway, Mayo, West Donegal, E. Galway-Roscommon; still better in the Aran Islands and the pinched area between Sligo and Dundalk bays, but best of all in the north central and northeastern counties, N. Fermanagh-E. Donegal-Tyrone-Londonderry, and Antrim-Down. In the center, Longford-Westmeath, and in the southeast, Wicklow-Carlow, are bad spots for caries, but, on the other hand, Offaly-Leix-Kildare is very good, and Tipperary-Kilkenny and Waterford-Wexford better than average.

Face Shortening (Table IV-51). Slightly more than 25 per cent of the county series are reported to have incurred some diminution of the facial length due to wear of teeth or dental loss involving shrinkage of the alveolar processes. These results of age and dental pathology naturally affect most seriously the subgroups of oldest mean age. Thus 40.6 per cent of Waterford-Wexford, the oldest subgroup of the series, has been affected to some extent. Yet the means of the group show no deficiency of upper facial height nor of upper facial index. It seems improbable then that this factor needs to be taken into consideration in the anthropometry of the series. Least affected by this alleged face shortening are the Aran Islands which display only 16.8 per cent. It is almost as rare in Longford-Westmeath, Antrim-Down, West Donegal, and Mayo. These are all groups below mean age.

Teeth, Crowding (Table IV-52). Dr. Dupertuis reported medium crowding of the teeth in 51.6 per cent of cases and pronounced crowding in 5.8 per cent. This condition is least prevalent in the Aran Islands (absent in 58.5 per cent) and in West Galway (absent in 51.5 per cent). Pronounced crowding is

especially in excess in Waterford-Wexford and Wicklow-Carlow.

Malars, Frontal and Lateral Projection (Tables IV-53, IV-54). On the basis of Dupertuis' observations, the Irish must be designated as a stock with a tendency toward marked frontal projection of the malars and even more pronounced lateral projection. Frontal projection of the malars is indicated to be absent or submedium in only 0.5 per cent of cases, but pronounced anterior projection is present in 16.5 per cent. Over 20 per cent pronounced frontal projection of the malars is recorded for the counties of West Galway, Limerick, Kerry, and Sligo-Leitrim-S. Fermanagh-W. Cavan. At the other end of the scale are N. Fermanagh-E. Donegal-Tyrone-Londonderry (11.3 per cent), Cork (11.6 per cent), Waterford-Wexford (12.5 per cent), Longford-Westmeath (12.6 per cent).

Nearly 35 per cent of the county series have pronounced or very pronounced lateral malar projection and virtually none have submedium projection (0.4 per cent). This lateral projection is most extreme in Mayo (48.1 per cent), West Galway (46.1 per cent), Limerick (46.1 per cent), Kerry (45.8 per cent). Thus Mayo leads in lateral projection, but is not among the leaders in pronounced malar frontal projection. Lateral projection is least in the Aran Islands (15.1 per cent), Longford-Westmeath (19.2 per cent), and Offaly-Leix-Kildare (22.7 per cent).

Malar projections (frontal or lateral) show little relation to age.

Gonial Angles (Table IV-55). The ruggedness of the Irish face is further indicated by projection of gonial angles which is submedium in but 2.8 per cent of cases and pronounced or very pronounced in 32.7 per cent. Aran Islands, Meath-Louth-Dublin, E. Cavan-Monaghan-Armagh, and Longford-Westmeath show the highest percentages of submedium lateral protrusion of mandibular angles. At the other end of the scale are Limerick, Kerry, and Mayo—each with more than 40 per cent of gonial angles which have pronounced or very pronounced lateral projection. The entire north is also very high in this feature (West Donegal, 39.6 per cent; Antrim-Down, 38.8 per cent; N. Fermanagh-E. Donegal-Tyrone-Londonderry, 38.7 per cent).

Ear Helix (Table IV-56). Irish ears show, on the whole, a high percentage of very small or slightly (submedium) rolled helices (22.9 per cent). This variation is most frequent in Wicklow-Carlow (33.4 per cent) and N. Fermanagh-E. Donegal-Tyrone-Londonderry (31.2 per cent). It is also frequent in the western peninsular areas of West Donegal and Mayo and in Cork, Tipperary-Kilkenny, and Waterford-Wexford in the south. It is least common in the Sligo-Galway crescent. Again the Aran Islands are peculiar (7.9 per cent of submedium helices).

The other extreme of variation—pronounced roll of helix—seems to be curiously concentrated in northern and eastern Ireland (Antrim-Down, E. Cavan-Monaghan-Armagh, N. Fermanagh-E. Donegal-Tyrone-Londonderry, Meath-Louth-Dublin, and Sligo-Leitrim-S. Fermanagh-W. Cavan). In these counties deeply rolled helices range from 6.0 per cent to 9.2 per cent. On the other hand, West Donegal with 0.5 per cent achieves the minimum.

Ear Antihelix (Table IV-57). The antihelix is poorly developed in only 4.7 per cent of the Irish county series and absent in but a few individuals. The areas of high frequency of submedium antihelices are Longford-Westmeath, Clare, and the Aran Islands.

The Aran Islands are again tiresomely out of line in turning out 25.2 per cent of individuals stated to have prominent antihelices. This is almost twice the average frequency of the county series and far above any other group. Tipperary-Kilkenny (19.1 per cent) and Kerry (18.6 per cent) rank next. West Galway and Clare are lowest in proportions of prominent antihelices. The distribution seems irrational. There is no age regression.

Darwin's Point (Table IV-58). Darwin's Point is present in some degree in 25.7 per cent of the series. It is usually small or submedium (22.7 per cent). This cartilaginous node is most frequently absent in the Aran Islands (87.8 per cent) and in Kerry (81.4 per cent). Its greatest frequency is in Longford-Westmeath (41.7 per cent). Other subgroups with high frequencies are E. Cavan-Monaghan-Armagh, Sligo-Leitrim-S. Fermanagh-W. Cavan, E. Galway-Roscommon, Wicklow-Carlow, Meath-Louth-Dublin, N. Fermanagh-E. Donegal-Tyrone-Londonderry, Antrim-Down.

Ear Lobes, Attachment and Size (Tables IV-59, IV-60). Soldered lobes are rare in this Irish series, but a well developed or small lobe with its anterior edge attached to the cheek is found in 40.4 per cent. The completely free lobe is then in the majority. Attached lobes are commonest in Tipperary-Kilkenny (51.1 per cent), Kerry (50.6 per cent), and in N. Fermanagh-E. Donegal-Tyrone-Londonderry (50.6 per cent). Free lobes attain their maximum in Longford-Westmeath (78.4 per cent) and in the Aran Islands (77.0 per cent). They are unduly frequent also in E. Galway-Roscommon, in Sligo-Leitrim-S. Fermanagh-W. Cavan and, to a lesser extent, in Clare and West Galway. Apparently the Sligo-Galway crescent is notably rich in this evolved type of appendage to the auricle.

Size of ear lobes is rarely recorded as submedium and is pronounced or large in no less than 45.2 per cent of the county series. Waterford-Wexford, the oldest age subgroup, in accordance with expectation shows the highest percentage of large ear lobes (59.2 per cent). The minimum (36.2 per cent) occurs in West Galway, which is not significantly below mean age. Other areas low in proportions of large ear lobes are E. Galway-Roscommon, Clare, and Mayo.

Ear Protrusion (Table IV-61). Submedium protuberance of the ears is very rare in this series, whereas outstanding ears occur in 21.9 per cent of cases. The northern counties lead in this aural protrusion (N. Fermanagh-E. Donegal-Tyrone-Londonderry, 36.2 per cent; Antrim-Down, 31.6 per cent). West Donegal is, however, associated with Mayo, Sligo-Leitrim-S. Fermanagh-W. Cavan and E. Galway-Roscommon in deficient proportions of outstanding ears. Longford-Westmeath and Waterford-Wexford, the youngest and oldest subgroups, are also somewhat deficient in pronounced ear protrusion.

Temporal Fullness (Table IV-62). Our experience is that this observation is often unreliable and unsatisfactory. Submedium temporal fullness is shown in 15.8 per cent of cases—a proportion not very high for a population which is, on the whole, long-headed. The two sore-thumb groups—Longford-Westmeath and the Aran Islands—again stand out in falling far below the series means in proportions of submedium temporal fullness. County Clare is conspicuous with 25.3 per cent of submedium temporals. Mayo, Cork, Kerry, and Limerick are also high in this variation.

Slight excess percentages of pronounced fullness of the temporal region occur in the Sligo-Galway crescent and include Mayo and Longford-Westmeath. Kerry, Cork, and Limerick form another western peninsular block with small excesses of pronounced temporal fullness.

Occipital Protrusion (Table IV-63). Degree of projection of the occiput seems to be another morphological observation that is subject to considerable personal equation and variability in standards of judgment. Three-quarters of the county series have occipital protrusion graded as medium. More than twice as many have pronounced protrusion as submedium or none at all. It is clear enough from the tabulation of excesses of *pronounced* over *absent* plus *submedium* that marked occipital projections are commonest along the east coast and, especially, in the middle of that strip. E. Cavan-Monaghan-Armagh and Meath-Louth-Dublin are the leaders in this occipital jutting. Antrim-Down, however, does not manifest the same high proportions of occipital protrusion which characterize the neighboring counties.

In the northwest, west, and southwest—notably West Donegal, West Galway, Clare and Kerry—non-projecting or flattened occiputs show their highest incidence.

Lambdoid Flattening (Table IV-64). This phenomenon is of unknown cause. It seems to occur most frequently in mesocephals and may be the effect of a growth disharmony between the parietals and the occiput. Its distribution in Ireland is very strange. In the first place, its absence is recorded in only 19.1 per cent of the total county series. The northern counties (except West Donegal) are most erratic in showing absence of lambdoid flattening in 63 to 70 per cent. In Waterford-Wexford, flattening is absent in 44.5 per cent and in most other east coast and east central subgroups it is absent in between 25 and 40 per cent. On the other hand, it is absent in very small percentages in the western and southwestern counties and also in Longford-Westmeath.

The heaviest proportions of pronounced lambdoidal flattening occur in the Aran Islands (46.4 per cent) and in Limerick (44.7 per cent). Clare, Cork, and West Galway are also high in pronounced lambdoidal flattening. Both medium and pronounced lambdoidal flattening are rarest in the northern counties (excepting West Donegal).

Occipital Flattening (Table IV-65). It is strange to find more than 18 per cent of occipital flattening (presumably natural rather than artificial) in a predominantly long-headed country. This phenomenon is by far most pronounced in the northern counties (except West Donegal) where it is noted in 44 to 56 per cent of cases. In the Aran Islands, on the other hand, it occurs in only 5.8 per cent of cases and it is nearly as rare in West Galway, E. Galway-Roscommon, and Mayo. These are areas of marked and fairly marked lambdoidal flattening.

Facial Asymmetry (Table IV-66). Facial asymmetry is recorded in 25.9 per cent of cases—a very high figure. The larger side of the face is the right in 18.1 per cent of cases and the left in 7.8 per cent of cases. The Aran Islands are, as ever, peculiar in showing by far the least facial asymmetry (2.9 per cent). Longford-Westmeath is also far below average. Highest in facial asymmetry are Clare (36.0 per cent), Limerick (34.5 per cent), Cork (32.7 per cent), Tipperary-Kilkenny (31.2 per cent), and Antrim-Down (30.2 per cent).

ANALYSIS AND SUMMARY

IN THE analysis of the county series, certain counties or parts of counties have been thrown together in order to avoid the necessity of dealing with too large a number of subgroups comprising inadequate samples. These combinations were made by Dr. Dupertuis on the basis of his judgment as to geographical and anthropological similarity. To synthesize the results of the county study, it seems desirable, firstly, to summarize the findings of each county subgroup, and then to attempt to combine them into larger geographical and ethnographical regions, which may seem to present within themselves similarities of component samples or relative homogeneity and, with each other, important anthropological differences.

Remarks about the metric and morphological features of the county subgroups will be confined largely to those characters in which the sample seems to diverge distinctively from the total Irish county series (tables V-1 through V-43).

WEST DONEGAL

West Donegal is that portion of the extreme northwestern county of Ireland lying to the west of a line drawn from Donegal Bay northeastward to Lough Swilly. It includes the more mountainous and less fertile area of this large county. Most of it consists of mountain, bogland, and moor. Geologically, the region shows a dominance of the old Dalradian metamorphic rocks with intrusions of granite. The soil is mostly thin, cold, and very rocky. In many regions agriculture has been impeded by the boggy nature of the ground. In the whole county about 15 to 18 per cent of the land is under cultivation, 64 per cent in pasture, and the rest waste. The southwestern part of this region is one of the wettest areas of Ireland, with a mean annual rainfall of 60 inches. West Donegal is a poor county with a sparse population and only a few small towns. Agriculture is backward, stock raising more advanced. Deep sea fishing is important.

From this remote and infertile area, Dr. Dupertuis secured an anthropometric sample of some 212 individuals. The series ranks 16 in educational status among the 19 subgroups. Native Irish speakers number 46.2 per cent; 12.3 per cent have learned some Irish in school, and 41.5 per cent have no Irish. Thus 58.5 per cent of the men of our sample read or speak Keltic or do both. It is, then, a refuge area for the ancient language.

The occupations of our West Donegal series present some interesting divergences from those of the total series. The sample is slightly high in the lowest class, hired laborers and tinkers, but close to average in farmers and herdsmen. It is definitely high in farm dependents (rank 4) and in fishermen (rank 5). It is very low in navvies and semi-skilled workers and shop assistants; close to average in factory operatives, skilled trades. It is high (probably accidentally) in the professions and in soldiers. The sample contains no students. The largest occupational classes in the sample are those of navvies and soldiers, each with 30 individuals, or 14.6 per cent.

The mean age of the West Donegal series is 33.60 years, about two years below the average age of the total county series. The average weight, 155.30 pounds, is 2.0 pounds below the series mean. Stature in this group, 171.48 cm., is insignificantly below the series average, but, on the world scale, tall. Absolute span is below the series mean but relative span is slightly high. Absolute and relative shoulder breadth are both insignificantly below the Irish average. Head length is definitely shorter than the series average and falls in with the diminished means found in Antrim-Down, Offaly-Leix-Kildare, Waterford-Wexford, and Wicklow-Carlow. Head breadth, on the contrary, is insignificantly above that of the total series. Consequently, the mean cephalic index, 79.11, aligns the men of West Donegal with the more brachycephalic, or less mesocephalic, section of Ireland. Head circumference is more than 2 cm. below average and head height a little above that of the total series. This increased head height (with diminished length) elevates the length-height index (which here approaches the series maximum). Facial breadth is also a trifle low and the cephalo-facial index (ratio of face breadth to head breadth) is lower than in any other county subgroup (91.04), but hardly significantly so. Faces in West Donegal are slightly high, especially the upper face height. The leptoprosopic total facial index is not outstanding, but the upper facial index is definitely high. The West Donegal nose is a trifle shorter, but significantly narrower, than the mean of the total county series. In fact, the second lowest mean nasal breadth (35.39 mm.) is found in this group. The nasal index is, accordingly, somewhat low (rank 17 in the series). The relation of jaw breadth to forehead breadth (98.90) is lowest in the county subgroups. Forehead breadth is somewhat high, as is also its relation to head breadth. Very definitely elevated is the zygo-frontal index (minimum frontal diameter expressed as a percentage of face breadth).

West Donegal has the highest proportion of men with swarthy skin (1.9 per cent), but this proportion consists of only 4 individuals and may be insignificant, since the subseries is rather small. Otherwise, skin color does not deviate from the means found in the county totals in any important respect. Pronounced vascularity is slightly below average. However, there are more freckled persons in this West Donegal series than in any other county series. According to expectation, moles are slightly deficient. Straight hair is in moderate excess and deep waves are a little commoner than usual. There seems to be a small deficiency of coarse hair. Hair quantity of head, beard, and body is medium to a much greater extent than in most Irish regions. Baldness is about average but graying of hair is below average, which might be expected from two years deficiency in mean age as compared with the total county series.

In hair color, West Donegal is notable for its highest subgroup proportion of black hair (7.5 per cent). It is about average in dark brown, brown, and red-brown; shows a definite excess of red, and notable deficiencies of all of the other lighter shades. West Donegal is then an especially dark-haired county with considerable rufosity—the latter correlating with high frequency of freckles. In West Donegal there is a small excess of blue-brown mixed eyes and a slight deficiency of blue. No pure dark eyes are found. On the whole, eye color belongs with the more heavily pigmented counties. The West Donegal eyes include an unusual proportion (40.5 per cent) of irides classified as diffuse in pattern. Scalloped irides are relatively deficient. External and median eyefolds are very rare, but internal folds, though also very few, are commoner than in any subseries except Longford-Westmeath. Palpebral slits are somewhat high and usually not slanted. Eyebrow thickness and concurrency is classified to an overwhelming extent as medium. Brow ridges are, on the average, smaller than in most other Irish county subgroups. Foreheads are higher than average and in general the least sloping of all county series averages. Nasal tips are overwhelmingly medium in thickness. West Donegal is second highest in proportion of convex noses and markedly deficient in straight nasal profiles. There is also a slight excess of concave noses here. Nasal tips are directed upward a little oftener than the average and septa reach the series maximum of convexity. Alae are excessively of medium flare.

The following are the most notable features of the men of West Donegal: (1) in metric characters, slight inferiorities in stature and weight, shorter and broader heads (high relative to length), narrow faces and narrow, relatively long noses; (2) in morphological features, freckles, excesses of the comparatively rare black and red hair shades, blue-brown eyes, small brow ridges, high, steep foreheads, and convex noses.

MAYO

County Mayo is the northern part of the central projection of Ireland into the Atlantic. The western part of the county is rugged, mountainous, and comparatively barren. The eastern part drops down into the limestone plain and is fertile. Only about 14 per cent of the land in Mayo is under cultivation. The population is mostly rural and the county contains only a few small towns. Fishing, agriculture, and stock-raising are the principal occupations.

The Mayo series consists of 580 men. In education it ranks 13 of the 19 subgroups. Mayo has 24.1 per cent of Irish speakers and is thus one of the strongholds of the Keltic language. Occupationally, this group is somewhat overloaded with farmers and farm dependents, and low in navvies and in some of the more urban callings. It also has a slight excess of soldiers and includes a relatively high proportion of students (2.8 per cent).

The men of Mayo average 160.8 pounds in weight, which is 3.50 pounds above the series mean and gives them second ranking in county weights. While stature is about at the series mean, the Mayo men have relatively long arms and the highest relative span (105.88) in the subgroup series. They are definitely broadchested and the mean thoracic index is on the low side. The Mayo men have broad heads (155.14 mm., which is about one mm. above the county average). Consequently, their average cephalic index (79.41) is also high. They must be accounted one of the groups of Irish most strongly inclined toward roundheadedness. The mean breadth-height index is somewhat low. The bizygomatic diameter of Mayo men is also high (mean, 141.75 mm.). The facial index is below the mean of the series, but the upper facial index is not really low because the Mayo upper face is rather long. Noses are relatively broad. Definitely, the jaw breadth (bigonial diameter) is above average in Mayo, as is also the minimum breadth of the forehead.

Mayo is below the series mode in darkly pigmented skins and slightly high in pronounced vascularity. It is one of the county subgroups in which freckles are excessively prevalent, and yields only to West Donegal and Kerry in this feature. Correspondingly, it is low in moles. The county shows a deficiency of straight hair, and an excess of low-waved hair and curly hair. It ranks first in curly hair with 6.40 per cent. Mayo is somewhat high in proportions of black and dark brown hair (rank 4) and also has an excess of red hair. As in hair color, so in eye color, it resembles West Donegal in an excess of blue-brown mixed eyes and a deficiency of blue eyes. Diffuse irides are unduly common. On the whole, Mayo belongs with the darker-eyed Irish groups. Obliquity of the eye slits is absent in an unusually large proportion of cases. Mayo men have an excess of forehead slope that is absent or submedium. In this county we find the largest percentage of concave noses (9.0). Prognathism, both mid-facial and alveolar, is notable for its rareness. Loss of teeth in Mayo is well below average. Mayo is high in pronounced caries, but somewhat better than average in total caries. The county ranks first in pronounced lateral projection of the malars (cheek bones). It yields only to Kerry and E. Galway-Roscommon in pronounced jaw angles. The only ear feature which is of note is the prevalence of submedium roll of the helix. Mayo is one of the counties in which lambdoid (crown) flattening of the head is unduly common and posterior or occipital flattening rare.

In summary, the Mayo series is metrically outstanding for great body weight, high relative span, broad heads, broad faces, broad foreheads, broad jaws, and relatively broad noses.

In morphological features, Mayo is notable for freckles and light skins, curved hair, mixed eyes, steep foreheads, concave noses (although these are absolutely rare as in all Irish counties), prominent cheek bones, everted jaw angles, and lambdoid flattening of the head.

Comparative Data. (Tables V-44, V-45). Excellent comparative data for certain parts of County Mayo are available in the ethnographic report of Dr. Charles R. Browne, published in the last decade of the previous century (1895, pp. 587–647; 1896, pp. 74–111; 1898, pp. 40–72). His subjects were measured on several of the small islands off the west coast of Mayo and Ballycroy, on the coast south of the Mullet. These form a part of the barony of Erris. Dupertuis' Mayo sample consists of 580 men, measured in 20 localities, mostly on the coasts and along the eastern border. It included none of the islanders from the small islands included in Browne's survey, but several subseries from Achill and Belmullet. Nor does it seem that Dupertuis measured in the district defined by Browne as Ballycroy.

Table V-44 compares the means of the three Browne subsamples with those of the total Mayo sample gathered by Dupertuis. The men of Clare Island and Inishturk are somewhat shorter than those of the mainland, whether the latter were measured 50 years ago by Browne or 17 years ago by Dupertuis. All of the mainland statures are the same, and this is a point of considerable interest, in view of the increase of stature noted in recent generations in many countries. It is unfortunate that the Dupertuis sample includes no subjects from the smaller islands, since it would be most interesting to know whether stature there has increased.

Relative spans are closely similar in all of the samples; except the Browne subsample from Mullet, Inishkea, and Portacloy, which seems to have consisted of slightly taller men with relatively shorter spans.

Mean cephalic index does not vary much between the samples except in the group from Ballycroy which shows a considerably higher value. The mean nasal index is considerably the highest in the series from Clare Island and Inishkea.

In the comparison of the eye color data (table V-45), there is to be observed substantially the same disagreement between the earlier data of Browne and that of the Harvard survey as occur in West Galway. Browne's series show nearly twice as many light eyes as does the larger subgroup of Dupertuis and only about one-fourth as many mixed eyes, with also a small excess of dark eyes. In the case of Mayo it seemed possible that the discrepancy might have been due to a lesser mixture between primary eye color types a half century ago than is to be observed recently. Mixed or medium eyes are usually the result of crossings between lights and darks. We should expect more mixed eyes and fewer pure lights and pure darks than were to be found in the same area a half century ago, if communication facilities have increased and there has been more interbreeding over larger areas.

However, it seems to us that the discrepancies in the data are far too great to be accounted for by any such hypothesis. It seems more probable that Browne included in "light" eyes a very high proportion of individuals whose eyes would be classified by us as "light mixed."

In hair color, we again encounter the disagreement observed in the Galway series. Browne's samples have much more fair hair than we have in ours, and also a great deal more black hair. The Dupertuis sample exceeds the earlier groups in red hair, in brown hair and in dark brown hair. We have the same dilemma as in the case of eye color. It would be easy enough to dismiss the disagreements as purely matters of difference in technique of observation, if it were not for the very clear and definite descriptions of pigmental criteria included in Browne's reports. If he adhered rigidly to these criteria and definitions, it is hard to see how his data could differ so widely from ours, unless the population actually has changed in the intervening time. But the present writers know that it is easy to diverge from learned techniques because of hasty and defective observations. Dupertuis used a flashlight to observe the eye color in virtually every case and he undoubtedly detected a pigment in light mixed eyes that the earlier observer (without any flashlight) missed.

In conclusion, it may be stated that the three Browne subsamples from County Mayo are closely similar in metric features to the much larger Mayo series observed nearly a half century later. There are marked differences, however, in hair color and eye color. Browne's series shows nearly twice as many light eyes as that of Dupertuis. Hair color in the two series also differs, but not so markedly as eye color. Browne's series includes slightly less red hair, and considerably more fair hair and black hair than does that of Dupertuis. It seems unlikely that all of these pigmental differences are referable to the techniques of observation employed. It seems probable that mixed eyes may have increased in Mayo during the last half century and that the extremes of light and black hair may also have yielded to the intermediate shade.

SLIGO-LEITRIM-S. FERMANAGH-W. CAVAN

This geographical area, delimited by Dr. Dupertuis for ethnographic purposes, includes parts of four counties: the whole of Sligo and Leitrim, the portion of Fermanagh south and west of the Erne, and the part of Cavan west of this same region. Sligo is a well-wooded county, mostly on the Carboniferous limestone, but with outcropping masses and ranges of the older rocks. The soil is varied, and cattle-feeding is more profitable than farming. Sligo town is a principal port of the west coast and fisheries are important. Leitrim to the east is also wooded and a part of the limestone country, but the climate is moist and unsuitable for grain crops. The soil in the uplands is stiff, cold, and stony. The portion of Fermanagh south of the Erne is limestone. It is a relatively poor cattle-raising and agricultural county with no large towns. The western part of Cavan is also in the limestone region, but has outcrops of other rock formations. It is a damp, windy lake region with a stiff clay soil. Agriculture makes little progress and the principal crops are oats and potatoes. The higher lands are good for cattle-raising. Woods were formerly plentiful.

All of these areas comprised in the subgroup, hereafter called the Sligo group, are among the Irish counties which have suffered the most severely from emigration. They are, on the whole, regions that are relatively undesirable from the point of view of climate and natural resources, although they are picturesque and excellent for vacation resorts and for fishing.

The Sligo series is ample for statistical purposes since it consists of 716 individuals. It is very low in illiterates and persons who have received no education, but it is also low in higher forms of education. On the basis of the educational ratio, it ranks 12. This group includes only 3 Irish speakers, or 0.4 per cent, although 20.6 per cent have studied some Irish at school. It is then, a non-Keltic group, so far as use of the language is concerned. The group has a great excess of farmers and herdsmen (40.2 per cent as against 14.6 per cent in the total series). There are no fishermen in the group. Navvies show more than 8 per cent deficiency. Other classes are proportionately represented, or nearly so.

The mean weight of the Sligo group is 158.50 pounds, which is 1.20 pounds above average. Relative span is slightly high; chest diameters a little reduced. Sitting height, and sitting height relative to stature are rather low. The Sligo men have very long heads (196.11 mm.), and they have a somewhat lower mean cephalic index than the county average. Their head circumferences are also somewhat high. Head height (124.10) is third lowest of all Ireland, as is also the length-height index. Breadth-height indices are also lower than average. Bizygomatic diameter is a trifle above the mean, and the breadth of the face relative to head breadth is slightly elevated. Upper face height and the upper facial index are definitely low, although this condition does not hold in the case of total face height and the total facial index. Sligo men must have deep lower jaws (long chins). Noses are shorter and relatively a little broader than in most of the Irish counties. Sligo ranks 18 in nose height, but 4 in nasal index. The foreheads in the Sligo group are narrower than average and the fronto-parietal index is low. So also is the zygo-frontal index. Breadth across the jaw angles is somewhat meager and the zygo-gonial index reaches the lowest value of the series. It may be noted, however, that the Sligo group is 0.6 years below county mean age.

Sligo ranks second only to Longford-Westmeath in high percentage of low-waved hair (58.0), although this hair form is the commonest everywhere. The Sligo group is distinctive in hair color. It is low in black and dark brown hair, high in red-brown and golden brown, and leads all of the counties in red hair (7.4 per cent). It also has the highest percentage of white hair (5.3) although below mean age. The reason for this is probably the tendency of red hair to lose its pigment in early middle age. Sligo also has a perceptible excess of blue eyes (Ireland must be rated one of the bluest-eyed countries in the world). Clear or homogeneous irides are also above average. Obliquity, or slant of the eye openings, is rarer than in most counties. Although eyebrows are not more than ordinarily thick, the Sligo group is above average in percentage of strongly concurrent eyebrows (11.7 per cent). Foreheads run rather low here and pronounced nasion depressions are distinctly rare. Height and breadth of the nasal root avoid extremes of variation. The same is true of the nasal bridge. The Sligo group leads in percentage of men with flaring nasal wings (9.9 per cent). A small excess of straight noses and a corresponding deficiency of convex noses is to be noted. A medium obliquity of the axes of the nostrils is correspondingly high. The group contains a slight excess of men with thick membranous lips and pronounced lip eversion, but these features are by no means characteristic of the subseries as a whole. The Sligo group is very low in mid-facial prognathism. The area is further notable for submedium chin prominence (although again a minority feature). More than a third (34.2 per cent) of the Sligo men show incomplete tooth eruption. Normal bites (submedium over) are more than usually prevalent. Tooth wear and tooth loss are distinctly below the Irish average. Caries are less common than ordinary. Crowding of the teeth is less frequent than in most groups. Sligo men have unusual frontal prominence of the malars but in lateral projection they do not stand out from the total Irish county series. Free ear lobes are unusually frequent in the Sligo subseries. Temporal fullness is more often pronounced than in most subgroups.

Metrically the men of the Sligo group are notable for excess weight, long heads, tending toward dolichocephaly, low heads and constricted jaws and foreheads. The most notable distinction of the Sligo group is in its primacy in red pigment of the hair. It is also superior in quality of teeth, perhaps in part because the subseries is below mean age.

WEST GALWAY

West Galway is that part of the county lying to the west of Loughs Mask and Corrib. It is a mountainous, granite country, which is very barren. Fishing is an important industry. The country is very sparsely inhabited.

The West Galway series includes 432 men. Here illiteracy is highest (10.9 per cent), and also the literates who have had no formal education (4.4 per cent). Balancing the educated against the highly educated, West Galway stands out as considerably the lowest in educational ranking of all Ireland. The county includes 78.3 per cent of Irish speakers, a proportion unsurpassed anywhere in Ireland with the exception of the neighboring Aran Islands. There are no less than 16.0 per cent of our West Galway (Connemara) men who speak only Irish. More than half of the West Galway series are farmers and farm dependents. It leads all Irish counties in the latter

class (28.0 per cent), and tends to be deficient in most of the town or urban occupations.

The West Galway men average 160.60 pounds and are thus 3.3 pounds above mean Irish weight. They are third heaviest of the Irish subgroups. They are also among the tallest men of Ireland (172.98 cm.), averaging more than one cm. above mean Irish county height. They have very broad and relatively shallow chests. Absolute sitting height is average, but relative sitting height is second lowest in the Irish county series. Head length (196.62 mm.) is second largest in the series, and the cephalic index (78.45) is slightly below the Irish mean. Head circumference is also large. Face breadth runs more than average and face height distinctly so. The West Galway men rank second only to the Aran Islanders in total face height, but upper face height is mediocre. The total face is longer relative to its breadth than in most Irish series. The upper facial index is, on the contrary, slightly below average, so that here, as in some other areas in Ireland, facial length seems particularly concentrated in the lower jaw. Noses in Connemara are slightly high and a little more than usually wide, so that the nasal index is slightly elevated and, in fact, is second highest in Ireland. Jaws attain more than average breadth and the zygo-gonial index is high. There is some excess of breadth also in the forehead.

The men of West Galway rate among the most ruddy complected of Ireland (i.e., vascularity is pronounced in an excessive percentage). Baldness runs below average for Ireland (West Galway ranks 16). Hair color is marked by a slight deficiency of the darkest shades; a small excess of red-brown and golden brown. Eye obliquity is absent in an excessive number of cases. There is a small excess of pronouncedly sloping foreheads, but the frontal region tends to be, to an unusual extent, of medium height and slope. Nasion depressions adhere to a medium category in an excessive proportion of West Galway men. In fact most nasal features are classified as overwhelmingly medium, with the exception of a moderate excess of convex septa and a surplus of convex profiles with snub tips. Chin projection is submedium to a slight extent in West Galway, and there are a few more pointed (median) chins here than are ordinarily found in Irish county series. Tooth loss is markedly below average, and wear slightly above the modal amount. Crowding of the teeth is less common than in most Irish groups.

This county leads in marked frontal jut of the cheek bones and is extremely high in lateral projection of these facial cornerstones. Occipital protrusion in West Galway is apparently less than in almost any other Irish area. Lambdoid flattening is considerably in excess. Occipital flattening is deficient.

The men of West Galway are metrically notable for high stature, heavy weight, broad flat chests, relatively short trunks, long heads, long and relatively narrow faces, and broad jaws. Morphologically, they are noted for high vascularity and a tendency of most facial features to be medium in category, but malars are notable for frontal jutting and also for lateral projection.

Comparative Data (Tables V-46, V-47). Comparative data for West Galway collected and published by Dr. Charles R. Browne (1894, pp. 317–70; 1899, pp. 223–68; 1901, pp. 503–34) include samples from Garumna and Lettermullen, from Inishbofin and Inishark, and from Carna and Mweenish, totalling 451 adult males. The Dupertuis sample includes subjects from many of the places in which Browne measured nearly half a century earlier. On the whole, the sample of the Harvard Irish survey is much more widely distributed than that of the Anthropological Laboratory of Trinity College.

In table V-46 the means of the three small West Galway samples, as calculated by Browne, are compared with the means of the much larger subseries measured by Dupertuis. Many of the measurements taken by Browne were not statistically elaborated by him or were used merely in indices relating them to total stature.

As far as can be judged from the data, the ages of the individuals in the Browne samples are not dissimilar to those of our subseries. Browne's little group of men from Inishbofin and Inishark seems to have been much shorter than any of our subsamples throughout Ireland, but his other two Galway groups closely straddle our total stature mean. Relative sitting heights are very similar. The relative spans of two of Browne's subseries are a little lower, but hardly significantly so. The short-statured men from Inishbofin and Inishark have a somewhat higher mean cephalic index than any of the other Galway subgroups. These places are islands off the northwest coast of Galway and the Dupertuis series includes no subjects from either of them. The nasal indices of the Browne samples are a little lower than ours.

The data on hair color and eye color gathered by Browne can be correlated with our material only roughly. The eye color comparisons show in every case an enormously larger proportion of light eyes and a similar deficiency of "medium" eyes in the Browne material. It would be comforting to brush aside these differences as due to variations in the techniques of observation or of color classification. However, the very clear definitions of the categories of eye color, following methods and instructions laid down by Beddoe (cf. Haddon and Browne, 1893, p. 772) render this explanation improbable.

The groupings of eye color used in the earlier survey lend themselves perfectly to a regrouping of our categories into comparable classes. It is, of course, possible that Browne was a little less particular than Dupertuis in excluding from the pure light eyes those which showed small flecks of yellow, but were predominantly blue or gray. It is also possible that he was somewhat less rigorous than Dupertuis in the classification of the pure darks. At any rate Browne's samples contain a total of 3.99 per cent of dark eyes as against 0.23 per cent in the Dupertuis data. We are inclined to believe that the West Galway sample of nearly a half century earlier than ours actually did contain many more pure light eyes, many fewer medium or mixed eyes, and a few more darks.

The hair color specifications laid down by Haddon and Browne also enable us to regroup our own observations so that the classes should be closely comparable. Red hair is much less common in two of Browne's series than in ours, but the men of Inishbofin and Inishark have about the same amount of red hair as occurs in our total West Galway sample. But fair hair is certainly much com-

moner in the earlier series. In the shades
lumped under brown, two of the earlier subseries and the total of Browne's subseries are
very close to our figure. However the men
from Inishbofin and Inishark have significantly
less brown hair than is found in any of the
other samples. The slack is taken up in the
dark brown hair in which the men from these
two islands slightly surpass our Harvard
sample and greatly surpass Browne's other
two samples. Browne's "black" hair color included individuals with "that very intense
brown which occurs in people who in childhood have had dark brown (or in some cases
deep red) hair, but which in the adult cannot
be distinguished from coal-black, except in
a very good light" (Haddon and Browne,
1893, p. 773). Dupertuis' observations do not
include these very dark brown hair shades
under "black" and it is probable that the inclusion of them by Browne is sufficient to
account for the excess of blacks in that student's material.

It is probably safe to conclude that there
are real differences between the samples of the
earlier student and those gathered by Dupertuis, as follows: the Browne material includes
a larger proportion of short, rather round-
headed men with darker hair shades than is
represented by the modes and means of the
Harvard West Galway sample. Possibly a subsample could be extracted from the Dupertuis
sample that would correspond with the Inishbofin and Inishark men of a half century ago.
The data suggest that the West Galway Irish
of the late 19th century were lighter in eye
color and hair color than the men of 1935-37.
There is no indication of any particular metric
change in the men from Garumna, Lettermullen, Carna and Mweenish, between the generation studied by Browne and that studied by
Dupertuis.

THE ARAN ISLANDS

The Aran Islands, or south Aran, are three
limestone islands lying in Galway Bay and
belonging to Galway. Because of their isolation, they constitute a separate ethnographic
area, and are so treated in this survey. Fishing
is naturally an important industry here, but
agriculture and stock-raising also occupy the
attention of many of the male inhabitants.

Our Aran series consists of 139 men and
is thus the smallest sample in the county subgroups. There are no illiterates and uneducated men in this series, but only one who
has had any other education than that of the
national school. Thus the Arans are also most
homogeneous from the point of view of education. This group has 95.0 per cent of native
Irish speakers—by far the largest proportion.
The series includes only 5 men who do not
know the Irish language and only one who
has acquired a knowledge of it at school. It
is, then, the greatest stronghold of the Keltic
tongue. This series has the highest proportion
found in any group engaged in farming or
cattle-raising (88.5 per cent). Fishermen
number only 8, or 5.8 per cent, but all Aran
men do some fishing. Many occupational
classes are totally unrepresented: hired laborers and tinkers, navvies, semi-skilled trades,
transport and factory workers, skilled trades
and clerks, and students. Markedly deficient
occupational representation occurs in all
classes except the three first named. Hence
this series is most homogeneous from the
point of view of occupation.

The Aran series averages 34.50 years, which
is 1.2 years below mean age. Mean weight
(156.30) is 1.0 pound below average and mean
stature is 174.48 cm., more than one cm.
above that of any other Irish subseries. Absolute span, however, is below that of some of
the other tall groups and relative span is consequently the lowest of the series (104.06).
Shoulder breadth is below the Irish average
and relative shoulder breadth (21.92) is the
minimum of the Irish county subseries. Chests
are not particularly wide and are shallower
than in any other group (mean chest depth,
22.20 cm.). For this reason the thoracic index
(76.78) is far and away the lowest of the Irish
county subgroups and falls 3.76 units below
the total series average. Absolute sitting height
is low for the Irish, and relative sitting height
(52.28) is again the series minimum, and
almost one unit below the total mean.

The mean length of the Aran head (198.36
mm.) considerably exceeds that of any other
Irish group and would be enormous in any
ethnic series. Head breadth is only insignificantly above average. In the mean cephalic

index (77.79) the Aran Islanders are in a tie with Meath-Louth-Dublin as the most dolichocephalic groups in Ireland. This mean is a little more than an index unit below the total series average. Actually the Arans slightly exceed all other county groups in percentage of dolichocephals but they are not the lowest in brachycephals. The average of head circumference (577.10 mm.) is the largest recorded in Ireland. Head height (120.18) is far lower than elsewhere, and consequently the length-height and breadth-height indices reach minimum values here also.

Bizygomatic diameter in the Arans is not unusual, but total face height (129.85 mm.) is 2.75 mm. above average and 1.25 mm. above the next ranking group, West Galway. Accordingly, the Aran Islanders are the most leptoprosopic group in Ireland (91.70). However, they exceed several other Irish county groups in this index by insignificant margins only. Upper face height in the Arans is insignificantly lower than in Ireland as a whole, and the upper facial index is not extraordinary but slightly below the total county mean. Therefore the great length of the Aran face seems to lie in the depth of the lower jaw. Yet the noses of Aran are the longest recorded (57.10 mm.). The nasal index is low, but not uniquely so. Minimum frontal diameter is relatively and absolutely low. The relation of the forehead breadth to head breadth (fronto-parietal index) is lowest for the total series (70.36). Another minimum is attained in the zygo-frontal index. Bigonial diameter, or jaw breadth at the hinder angles, reaches a maximum here (110.78 mm.) and the zygogonial index is correspondingly the highest, as is also the fronto-gonial index (101.90).

In the Aran Islands, 14.4 per cent of men have brunet skins. Thus skin color (on supposedly unexposed parts) runs darker than in any other Irish group except Longford-Westmeath. However, vascularity is slightly above average. Pronounced freckling reaches a maximum here, although the gross amount of freckling falls below that of many other county subgroups. Moles are excessively rare. There is a considerable excess of straight hair and deficiency of all curved varieties. In sparsity of beard and body hair, this area easily surpasses all others. Considering mean age, the amount of medium plus pronounced baldness in the Arans is high (22.3 per cent). Graying of head and beard hair is deficient, as should be expected from low mean age.

The Aran Islanders have considerably the lowest proportion of really dark (dark brown plus black) hair (23.7 per cent) to be found in the Irish county series. At the same time, they lead by a vast margin in flat brown hair (48.9 per cent), red-brown hair (11.1 per cent), and rank second only to the Sligo group in percentage of red hair (6.7 per cent). No single case of dark eyes (completely brown) is recorded in the Arans. Blue-brown eyes occur in 55.4 per cent, and blue in approximately the normal amount for the Irish with 41.7 per cent. Aran mixed eyes are on the light side. The proportion of clear irides (38.1 per cent) is very high. Eyefolds of any kind are rare. Slanting eye slits (eye obliquity) are observed less frequently than in any other Irish county subgroup. Eyebrow concurrency runs a little high. The Arans have the largest proportion of big brow ridges and fall below all other groups in the small proportion of men with high foreheads. Moderate forehead slopes are excessively prevalent. The nasal root of the Aran Islander is higher than in any other Irish district. It is never low. Nasal tips directed downward or horizontal are rare in Ireland, but these two categories combined occur more commonly in the Arans than elsewhere. Yet pronounced frontal visibility is also unusually common here (although this feature is rare in every district). Nasal profiles tend to be straight more frequently than convex. The most notable feature about the lips is the recorded occurrence in no less than 41.0 per cent of Aran Islanders (as contrasted with 23.2 per cent in the total series) of the lip thickness combination in which the upper lip is submedium and the lower medium. The lower lip is ordinarily thicker than the upper. In table IV-39 the observations refer to the more variable thickness of the upper lip with reference to the lower lip—ordinarily medium in thickness and taken as such unless otherwise noted. The percentage of cases in which the lower lip requires a different grading with respect to thickness is negligible and can be disregarded, providing that it be remembered that normally the lower lip is slightly thicker than the upper. There is about 8 per cent of various grades of mid-facial prognathism in the total county series, but of all the counties this condition is least prevalent in the Arans (1.4 per cent). An excessive proportion of Aran men in our series (37.0 per cent) have only partial eruption of the teeth (presumably suppression or incomplete eruption of third molars). On the whole, tooth loss here is less than in any other Irish group. Caries are fewer than in most Irish counties. The average amount of face shortening by tooth wear is reduced. There is much less crowding of the teeth in the Arans than elsewhere in the country.

In ears, the Aran Islanders are peculiar in showing pronounced development of the antihelix in 25.2 per cent, which is almost twice the frequency of the total series. Darwin's Point is much rarer here than anywhere else in Ireland. Free ear lobes also approach their maximum (77.0 per cent). The Aran Islands exhibit the maximum of pronounced lambdoid flattening of the head, but many western county groups have as much or more lambdoid flattening of all grades. Occipital flattening and facial asymmetry are less common here than anywhere else in Ireland.

It is thus apparent that the Arans are characterized by a population which is even more distinctive anthropometrically than geographically. The men of these islands diverge significantly from the run-of-the-mine Irish in nearly every metric and indicial feature. Tallness, long-headedness, chamaecephaly, leptoprosopy, and linearity of body build are the outstanding characters of the men of Aran.

Dark skins, straight hair, sparsity of beard and body hair, large brow ridges, low foreheads, high straight noses, and good teeth characterize the Aran Islanders morphologically.

It is obvious that the Aran Islanders are also morphologically distinctive. Presumably this group is the most inbred and homogeneous of all of our county series. The Arans are certainly a refuge area, but we must defer to a later stage of our investigation the question as to the significance of the Aran physical type—whether it is the more or less unmixed remnant of a very early stock, or merely a

group which has attained homogeneity and has varied from general Irish county types because of long continued inbreeding.

Comparative Data (Tables V-48, V-49). The first of several small ethnographic surveys in Western Ireland was published by Professor A. C. Haddon and Dr. C. R. Browne in 1893 (see References). These investigators made observations on the hair color and eye color of some 134 adult males, but measured only 27. Their data, as far as they are comparable with ours, are given in tables V-48, V-49. The 27 males measured by Haddon and Browne averaged nearly 8 years older than the mean of our sample. However, shrinkage of stature in a few old men can hardly explain the inferiority of nearly 10 cm. of the earlier sample. Not even the tiny size of the Haddon-Browne sample can account for the great difference. Since the means of stature of the men from the small islands of Clare and Inishturk, County Mayo, and of Inishbofin and Inishark, County Galway, also show marked inferiority to those of the mainlanders of the adjacent areas measured by Browne, it seems probable that isolation, perhaps inbreeding, and possibly nutritional factors may have kept stature means down. The statures of Browne's mainlanders are not, generally speaking, inferior to those from approximately the same regions measured 5 decades later by Dupertuis. However, Dupertuis' Aran Islanders are the tallest men of all our Irish subgroups. Perhaps today the younger men of the Aran Islands spend a good deal of time on the mainland and get away from the limitations of island diet, if such limitations there be. Some of the discrepancy between the statures of the earlier and later sample may perhaps be explicable on the basis of differences in local composition of the two series. Browne's small series consisted of 7 men from Inishmaan who averaged 170.8 cm. and, if one who was 74 years of age and much bent over were excluded, the Inishmaan mean would be raised to 171.8 cm. However, the average height of Browne's 20 Aranmore men was only 162.1. Dupertuis measured 42 men from Inishmaan and 95 from Aranmore. Evidently nearly two-thirds of his series was derived from the largest island, as was also nearly seven-eighths of Browne's series. If the Aranmore men were actually today much shorter than those from Inishmaan, as Browne found in his earlier study, the Dupertuis sample, also over-weighted with the former islanders, ought to be closer to the total stature mean found by Browne than it is. We must conclude that there has probably been a very considerable increase in the stature of Aran Islanders over the fifty years that elapsed between the two sets of measurements. The modern phenomenon of increasing stature is well known in many parts of the world, and best known in the United States. It seems strange that such a change should have been operative so markedly in the Arans and perhaps in the other small islands off the west coast but not apparent on the mainland. Of course, in the absence of subjects in the Dupertuis sample from the small islands off the Mayo coast, we are unable to check specifically the stature variations over a period of half a century which are patent in the two Aran series. Although inbreeding does not necessarily lower stature, it has been observed frequently that outbreeding causes a marked elevation of stature. It seems probable the Dupertuis' sample of Aran Islanders may have more outside strains in their recent ancestry than had the men of Aranmore in the late 19th century.

The eye color observations of the two samples show the same differences as are evident in the comparison of Browne's Mayo and Galway subseries with those of Dupertuis. The Browne series shows more than twice the proportion of light eyes found by Dupertuis and only about one-seventh of the number of medium eyes. Browne observed 4 Aran Islanders with dark eyes, from a total of 134 adult males, whereas Dupertuis found none in 139. It is, of course, possible that the differences are primarily those of technique in observing eye color. On the other hand, it is quite conceivable that the modern Aran men have more mixed eyes, being presumably more mixed in their ancestry.

Browne's hair color observations on the Aran Islanders accord much better with those taken later by Dupertuis than do the data of the former pertaining to Mayo and Galway samples. Dupertuis finds nearly twice as many Aran Islanders with red hair as were observed by Browne. The latter has 8 men

with "fair" hair, or 5.97 per cent, whereas Dupertuis found none. The figures in the two samples for brown hair, dark hair, and black hair are closely similar.

Since the Browne sample from the Aran Islands is presumably closer by far in genetic composition to the Dupertuis sample than are any of Browne's small series elsewhere in Galway and in Mayo to the corresponding samples of Dupertuis, we are in a position to deal with the comparison of the Aran samples more confidently. The fact that the hair color distributions are so closely similar in these Aran samples raises the probability that the differences observed between the other comparisons in respect of hair color, at any rate, are not referable to the personal equations of the observers but are, to a large extent, real. The same cannot be said of eye color, since the vast discrepancy in medium and also in light eyes observed is not diminished in the Aran comparison.

CLARE

County Clare in its eastern part is mountainous, interspersed with areas of rich pasture land; the west is boggy, the north rocky and suitable for sheep-grazing. The southern part, along the banks of the Fergus and the Shannon, is rich lowland, much of it adapted for tillage. The western part of the county consists of sandstones and shales, the north of barren limestone terraces; on the east are bold masses of the Old Red Sandstone. The county is, in general, better suited to grazing than to tillage, and not one-fifth of the area is under cultivation. Fishing is important. About one-seventh of the county is quite barren. All of the towns are small and most of the population is rural.

Our Clare series consists of 944 men, and is by far the largest subseries of the Irish county Catholic series. The size of this sample is due to the fact that the Harvard Survey of Ireland concentrated its social anthropological work in Clare, so that it was desirable to secure from this area a series of sufficient size to make it possible to subdivide it into local groups, in the event that the social anthropologists desired it. In this report the Clare series is treated as a unit.

The educational status of the sample is comparatively high. There are only 9 illiterates, and no literates who have never attended school. Clare ranks 4 according to our educational rating among the 19 county subgroups. Our sample is more urban than is entirely representative of the total series. Irish speakers include 15.6 per cent, while 33.0 per cent have studied Irish in school. This county is, then, one of the Keltic refuge areas. Occupationally, our Clare series is distinctly low in hired laborers and tinkers, in farmers, herdsmen and farm dependents, in fishermen and in soldiers. Its great occupational excesses are in navvies (34.70 per cent), skilled tradesmen (3.2 per cent as against 2.6 per cent in the total series), in clerks (4.4 per cent), and in the professions (3.1 per cent).

In age the Clare series averages 37.30 years, which is 1.60 years above the mean of the total county series. Weight exceeds the total mean by 1.8 pounds. Although stature and span are not remarkable, the men of Clare are notable for having the broadest shoulders (38.99 cm.) found in any Irish subgroup. Relative shoulder breadth is also nearly maximum, being exceeded only in Wicklow-Carlow. Chest dimensions are elevated, and the chest is slightly more flattened than in many Irish counties.

Clare nearly coincides with the total series mean in head length, but average head breadth is elevated 1.53 mm. Consequently, the cephalic index (79.62) is relatively high, being exceeded only by that in Kerry. Facial breadth is also high in Clare (142.00 mm.), but face heights are insignificantly below average. Hence, the total facial index (mean 89.2) is the lowest of the Irish subgroups. Even this mean does not describe a short broad face, but rather one which is "longish." The upper face height and the upper facial index are slightly below the Irish mean, so that it is apparent that here, as in many other counties, the leptoprosopic total facial index is ascribable principally to great depth of the lower jaw. The average Clare nose is rather long and of slightly more than mean width, so that the nasal index is a little above the series mean. Jaw breadth is somewhat elevated, and the minimum breadth of the forehead is greater than the average of any other county subgroup.

Skin color in Clare shows a slight deficiency of brunet shades, while pronounced vascularity (ruddiness and quick vasomotor reactions) is noted in 34.4 per cent, which is the maximum of the Irish series. Freckling is decidedly below average. Clare is somewhat high in low-waved hair. Since this county is above mean age, a slight elevation of percentages of men showing baldness and graying of head and beard is recorded.

Clare shows a moderate excess of convex nasal septa over straight and concave forms, but convex septa occur in 61.7 per cent of all the Irish series, so that the figure for Clare (69.5 per cent) is not astonishing. Convex noses (a prevalent southwestern Irish feature) are also in excess as contrasted with the total series. Submedium lip eversion is an excess which is barely worthy of mention. Clare is third lowest among the counties in mid-facial prognathism.

It is an interesting fact that Clare shows the smallest percentage (15.6) of individuals whose teeth are only partially erupted. It should be noted in this connection that Clare jaws are unusually broad for Ireland. This is the only county group which includes any considerable proportion (2.1) of men with an underbite, and the subseries also shows a slight excess of pronounced overbites. Persons who have lost many teeth are commoner in Clare than in any other county. The county is second only to Waterford-Wexford in multiplicity of tooth loss. No individual of 648 Clare men whose teeth were examined was free of caries, and the percentage with multiple and pronounced caries (20.2 per cent) is considerably above any other group, and almost twice the average of the series. Face shortening through tooth wear is unduly frequent. On the whole, the teeth of County Clare are a good deal worse than average Irish teeth.

Submedium temporal fullness is much commoner in Clare than elsewhere (25.3 per cent as contrasted with 15.8 per cent in the total series). Pronounced lambdoid flattening is strongly in excess of average. Clare leads in percentage of men with perceptible right facial asymmetry.

Broad heads, broad faces, broad jaws and broad shoulders are, then, the outstanding anthropometric characters of the men of

County Clare. On the whole, the morphological observations in Clare tend to pile up in medium categories. Marked vascularity, excess of convex noses, and poor teeth are outstanding characteristics. The Clare subseries, being the largest, naturally tends to approximate fairly closely the total series distribution of morphological attributes.

KERRY

Kerry, the extreme southwestern county of Ireland, is excessively picturesque, mountainous, barren, and wet. The bulk of the geological formations is the Old Red Sandstone, although some of the valleys are on the Carboniferous limestone. Grazing is prosecuted more than agriculture, and the Kerry cattle are famous. Fishing is an important industry. The climate, though moist, is mild.

We have an ample series of 538 men from County Kerry. Illiteracy is somewhat high, and in general educational ranking the county is tied with Sligo for eleventh place in the 19 county subseries. Kerry has 44.2 per cent of native Irish speakers, in addition to 29.2 per cent who have studied Irish. It is one of the four most strongly Keltic areas; the Aran Islands, West Galway, and West Donegal being the other three. The series is markedly deficient in agriculturalists and herdsmen, like the Clare series, but it is highest of all the Irish series in fishermen (13.4 per cent).

The men of Kerry average 37.35 years— 1.65 years above mean series age. They are among the heaviest Irish samples (mean weight 160.5 pounds), and they are also more than one cm. above Irish height, ranking third in mean stature in the county series. In span, the Kerry men tie with E. Galway-Roscommon for first place. In sitting height they achieve the series maximum. Head length is a little shorter than average, and head breadth (155.92 mm.) is the maximum in Irish county groups. Kerry alone of the Irish counties attains a mean cephalic index above 80 (80.01). This county has the fewest dolichocephals and the most brachycephals. The breadth-height index is lowest of the series (80.03). The average breadth of the Kerry face (142.30 mm.) is surpassed nowhere in Ireland and is approximated closely only in the neighboring counties, Clare and Cork. The total facial index

is rather low in Kerry; i.e., the length, or height, of the face relative to breadth is somewhat diminished. Nevertheless the upper face height (from root of nose to alveolar point on the gums between the upper middle incisors) is 1.05 mm. above the Irish average. Thus the lower jaw tends to be shallower than in most Irish. Noses rank second in length but are relatively narrow. Forehead breadth relative to head breadth (fronto-parietal index) is next to the lowest in the series; and forehead breadth relative to facial breadth occupies the same position. The breadth of the jaws is great and ties with West Galway for second rank in the total series.

Kerry yields only to West Donegal in proportions of freckled individuals. Naturally, then, it is low in moles. There is a small excess of straight-haired men, and a moderate surplus of graying heads and beards in accordance with some elevation in mean age. In hair color, Kerry is slightly up in the darkest shades and low in the flat brown, redbrown, and golden brown, as well as in red shades. This county happens to have the highest percentage of men with golden hair (2.0 per cent), but this figure means only 11 individuals. Golden hair is extremely rare in Ireland. There are almost no pure dark eyes in Kerry (one man of 539), but there is a high excess of mixed blue-brown eyes (occurrence 54.5 per cent, a figure exceeded in the Aran Islands and Cork, but approached elsewhere only in Mayo and West Donegal, each with 49.5 per cent). Kerry and Cork have the smallest percentages of blue eyes (Kerry 34.5, Cork 33.4), and again West Donegal and Mayo fall into the same grouping with these southwestern counties. In combined light eyes (gray, gray-blue, and blue), Kerry ranks lowest of all counties, with Cork only slightly higher. Diffuse and scalloped irides are both in excess in this county. Big brow ridges are somewhat commoner than average in Kerry, and small brow ridges correspondingly rarer. High foreheads are more prevalent than in the total Irish series. The Kerry men are notable for an excess of pronounced nasion depressions (connected with big brow ridges). Nasal bridges tend toward increased height and breadth, with high frequency of convex septa and tendency toward thick tips. There are slight excesses of convex nasal profiles, but the rare concave profile, found in only 7.4 per cent of the total series, reaches 9.4 per cent and is surpassed in Mayo alone, and there by an insignificant amount only (Mayo occurrence 9.9 per cent). Kerry is very low in mid-facial prognathism. Chins are more than ordinarily prominent.

The teeth of 421 Kerry men show, as a whole, more wear and abrasion than are recorded for any other subseries. There is more tooth decay here than in most Irish counties. In fact, the dental caries of this county is exceeded by Limerick alone.

Pronounced frontal projection of the malars is found in Kerry men in 21.9 per cent (as against 16.5 per cent in the total series). Kerry is one of 4 western counties or areas in which this condition is notably present. Lateral malar projection is also in marked excess. Jaw angles are more prominent than in any other county.

An excess of about 6 per cent of prominent antihelices of the ear is noted in Kerry, but this feature occurs in a total of only 18.6 per cent. Hence it cannot be judged typical of the county. Darwin's Point is less than ordinarily common. Soldered and attached ear lobes are found in moderate excess. Pronounced ear protrusion is marked in a slightly higher percentage of cases than in the total series. Submedium occipital protrusion is recorded in 11.3 per cent of the Kerry series, whereas the total Irish mean is 8.0 per cent. Kerry ranks second to West Donegal in this minor feature. There is also a strong and important excess of medium and pronounced lambdoid flattenings.

Large, heavy, sub-brachycephalic men with broad faces, square jaws, and long narrow noses are, then, the hypothetical average type for Kerry. The most notable morphological feature of Kerry is the enormous excess of blue-brown eyes. Other memorable excesses are in freckling, malar projection, protrusion of gonial angles, lambdoid flattening, and wear of the teeth.

CORK

Cork, in the southwestern part of Ireland, is the largest county in the island. The western and northwestern parts of the county are mountainous and barren. North of the Black-water River the country is more level and is an extension of the central plain. The central and eastern portions are low and often well-wooded. The "Hercynian Folds" run from east to west, consisting of anticlinal sandstone ridges and synclinal limestone valleys. The Devonian Old Red Sandstone forms these anticlines in the north, while in the south the Lower Carboniferous Yellow Sandstone and Carboniferous slate predominate.

About one-sixth of the area is barren and agriculture varies according to region and soil. It is favorably developed in the parts near the sea, whereas some of the less fertile areas are more suitable for cattle-raising. Dairy products are notable. Fishing is a most important occupation. In addition to the large city of Cork, the county includes a number of fair-sized towns. The harbor of Cork and Queenstown is by far the best on the south coast of Ireland.

The Cork series consists of 575 men. It is low in illiteracy and has the highest percentage of men who have reached the secondary schools (22.0). It is high also in university men. The gross percentage of fairly well educated persons attains its maximum here, but the educational rating (which is the ratio of illiterate and uneducated to highly educated) puts Cork in fifth place among the county series. There are in the Cork series 12.7 per cent of native Irish speakers, but 40.2 per cent have studied Irish in school. This is the largest proportion of school Irish found in any county, and is probably the result of the superior educational facilities offered by a county which includes one of the largest Irish cities. Occupationally, Cork is exceptionally low in hired laborers and tinkers, agriculturalists and farm dependents. It is high in semi-skilled occupations, in transport workers, skilled tradesmen, shopkeepers and their help. It leads in the professions with 5.4 per cent, and has excesses of soldiers and students. The Cork sample is the most urban in origin of any of our county subseries.

The mean age of the Cork sample is 37.25 years, 1.5 years above the total series average. Mean weight is 2.30 pounds higher than the entire Irish county average and stature is up 0.57 cm. The men of Cork are among the tallest and heaviest of Irishmen. Head length in Cork is only a little above the series average, but breadth (155.56 mm.) is decidedly large. The cephalic index is elevated 0.66 index units above the total Irish mean. Head circumferences and head height are both up, and the breadth-height index of the head is below the mean Irish value. Cork and Clare rank second to Kerry in high value of the bizygomatic diameter (142.00 mm.). Cork yields only to Clare in lowness of mean of total facial index (89.35), which implies relatively the shortest and broadest faces. However, it must be reiterated that this position is merely with reference to total Irish, all of whom have, on the average, long and relatively narrow faces. Upper face height in Cork, as in Kerry, is very high (73.70 mm.). Nose height (56.90 mm.) ranks third highest in the series. Nose breadth is a little above average. Minimum frontal diameter in Cork is third highest in mean value of any county series and jaw breadth (bigonial diameter) is also high.

The Cork series has significant excesses both of straight hair and of deep-waved hair. It is also rather high in curly hair. Hair of fine texture also seems a little commoner than usual. Heavy beards are also in excess, together with heavy body hair. It should be noted, however, that these excesses occur in variations which are in total occurrence very infrequent, so that the excesses noted by no means indicate that the typical inhabitant of the county would show such a feature. Small surplus of graying in head and beard is probably attributable to elevation of mean age of the sample. In hair color, Cork is distinguishable by an unusually high frequency (12.0 per cent) of golden brown hair, more of the rare golden shade than usual, and by a slight reduction in the average amount of red hair. A really notable feature in Cork, however, is the heavy dominance of blue-brown eyes (55.0 per cent as against 43.9 per cent in the total series), and a sharp reduction in percentage of blue eyes (33.4 per cent as against 42.4 per cent in the total series). Blue eyes are least frequent here of all Irish county subgroups. Mixed eyes in Cork are usually very light, and in all of the pure light eyes Cork is lowest of all counties except Kerry. This is one of the counties in which a diffuse or unpatterned iris is greatly in excess (40.6 per cent as against 32.6 per cent in the total series).

Cork is also one of the counties in which large brow ridges are more than ordinarily common. They occur in 25.0 per cent, as against 20.8 per cent in the total series. High foreheads are in excess to the amount of about 6 per cent, and strongly sloping foreheads are about 3 per cent commoner than usual. Nasion depressions are a little stronger here than in most counties. The nasal bridge tends to be high and broad in an excess proportion of cases; 67.0 per cent of Cork men have convex nasal septa, but this figure is less than 6 per cent over the total series mean. There is a similarly small but significant excess of thick nasal tips; 51.7 per cent have convex nasal profiles, and this again represents an excess of about 6 per cent. Lip eversion is slightly reduced in this series. As contrasted with these somewhat trivial differences, it may be noted that prominent chins are found in 14.4 per cent of Cork men. This represents the highest frequency in any of the Irish series. Tooth loss in Cork is somewhat high, and a medium wear of the teeth decidedly in excess. Caries are commoner than usual and also crowding of the teeth.

Cork has some excess of submedium roll of the helix of the ear, and of pronounced antihelices, but Darwin's Point is below average in frequency. Ear lobes tend to be large and there is an excess of the attached type. Pronounced lambdoid flattening exceeds mean proportions in the total series, while occipital flattening is rare. Cork is very high in facial asymmetry.

Larger than average size and weight, broad heads, broad faces, and absolutely long noses are the outstanding anthropometric features of our series from County Cork. On the whole, while Cork shows many significant differences from the total series average, few of them tend to distinguish the county in any typological way. In most features Cork resembles Kerry, but its county type is less clearly defined and presumably more composite.

LIMERICK

Limerick is a western county bounded on the north by the Shannon estuary, on the west by Kerry, on the south by Cork, and on the east by Tipperary. It is mostly fairly level limestone country, but there are outcropping ridges of the Old Red Sandstone. It includes the greater part of the Golden Vale—the most fertile area in Ireland. Along the banks of the Shannon the meadow land is low and rich, but in the mountains the soil is barren. The city of Limerick, partially occupied by Danes from the 8th to the 11th century, is the most important port of western Ireland. In Limerick the central plain extends down through the Shannon valley and this rich region is partially encircled by an amphitheatre of hills to the west, south, and east.

The Limerick anthropometric series consists of 339 males. Education of the sample is somewhat above the Irish mean. The men of Limerick rank sixth among the counties in educational rating. The county contains only 3.2 per cent of Keltic speakers, but 35.1 per cent have studied Keltic in school. Limerick is very high in the lowest occupational class: hired laborers and tinkers (10.7 per cent, as against 7.8 per cent in the total series). Agricultural, herdsmen, and farm dependent classes are deficient to an aggregate of about 12 per cent, and there are only three fishermen in the series, although salmon fishing is important in the county. Navvies are heavily represented with 31.5 per cent of the series (8.3 per cent excess). Most of the classes of more or less urban occupations are slightly in excess in the Limerick series, whereas the rural pursuits are underrepresented.

The men of Limerick are 0.10 years above total series mean age and 0.6 pounds above mean weight. They are insignificantly above the total series mean of stature. Most of their measurements and indices are close to general Irish levels. Not until we come to head breadth do we find a Limerick criterion of anthropometric distinction from total Irish. The mean of this measurement (155.50 mm.) exceeds Irish totals by 1.38 mm. and ranks fourth in the Irish counties (exceeded only by the neighboring counties of Kerry, Clare, and Cork). Correspondingly, the mean cephalic index is elevated (79.47) by 0.63 index units. Head height is a little above average, as is also face breadth. The total facial index (89.45) is low for Ireland, and associates Limerick with the neighboring southwestern counties. Nasal breadth is definitely reduced and the nasal index is second lowest of the county

series. The fronto-parietal index is rather low.

Limerick is above average in pink skins and definitely high in pronounced vascularity (32.0 per cent, against 24.2 per cent in the total series). Heavy and medium freckling occur in slight excesses. Coarse hair (perhaps fortuitously) is commoner than in any other Irish county but still rare (6.4 per cent). This county also leads in submedium quantity of head hair, with 5.3 per cent. Graying of head hair and of beard exceed the county norm. The county has a modest excess (5.2 per cent) of blue-brown eyes, and of diffuse irides (4.4 per cent surplus). The mixed eyes tend to be pronouncedly light, but in pure light eyes Limerick ranks 16 of the 19 county groups. Limerick is the only county in which is recorded no single instance of an internal eyefold, although this fold is rare everywhere (0.9 per cent in the total series). Eyebrow concurrency is slightly deficient. The Limerick nose is marked by some excess of the convex type of septum (which predominates all over Ireland), but is really remarkable for its primacy in convex nasal profiles (54.1 per cent as against 44.9 per cent in the total series). This county, with 13.5 per cent of pronouncedly projecting chins, ranks second in the Irish series in this variation. Medium and pronounced tooth wear is excessive to an aggregate of 9.0 per cent, and this is the worst Irish county in dental caries in the ratio of persons with good teeth to those with bad teeth. It is high in pronounced overbites (5.2 per cent) and somewhat high in pronounced tooth loss (26.5 per cent—2.3 per cent excess).

Limerick ranks second in percentage of men with pronounced frontal projection of the malars (25.3 per cent as against 16.5 per cent in the total series). It occupies the same position in lateral projection, which is significantly high (an excess of 15.4 per cent of pronounced and very pronounced). There is a 10 per cent excess of pronounced and very pronounced gonial angles.

The Limerick ear shows some distinctiveness in submedium roll of the helix, pronounced development of the antihelix, high frequency of attached ear lobes and large ear lobes, more than ordinary amount of ear protrusion. It ranks second in pronounced lambdoidal flattening with 44.7 per cent (as against 26.0 per cent in the total series). It is also marked by very high frequency of both left and right facial asymmetries.

Broad heads and faces, unusually narrow noses, and a brachycephalic tendency are thus about the only differentiating anthropometric features in Limerick which seem of any importance. The Limerick sample is more notable morphologically than anthropometrically. It is sociologically a rather low class sample, although showing good representation of most urban occupations. Slightly undersized, broad headed and broad faced, it is remarkable in observed characters for high vascularity, excess of blue-brown eyes, primacy in convex noses and high rank in projecting chins and cheekbones and jaws. It seems to have the worst teeth of all county series and is among the leaders in facial lopsidedness.

E. GALWAY-ROSCOMMON

Galway east of Lough Corrib is a level champaign country resting upon a limestone base, but with a good deal of bog. The southern part is partly a continuation of the Golden Vale of Limerick, but is in part mountainous. In general, eastern Galway is fertile, and excellent for tillage and pasture. Even the intermediate areas form good pasturage. For this reason E. Galway has been grouped with Roscommon and separated from the barren and rugged West Galway. Most of Roscommon is flat and undulating, but in various places there are sandstone ranges. Nearly all of the eastern boundary of the county is formed by the Shannon. Some of the richest grazing land in Ireland is included in the region known as the Plains of Boyle. Along the Shannon, however, there is a great deal of bog.

The E. Galway-Roscommon series includes 513 men. This group has the highest percentage of university men (7.2) but is deficient in secondary school attendants to the extent of 4 per cent. It ranks 8 in the 19 county subseries in the educational ratio. In E. Galway-Roscommon 12.7 per cent are Keltic speakers, and another 31.0 per cent have studied Irish in school. It is lowest in hired laborers and tinkers (1.8 per cent) of any county series except the Arans, but very high in farmers and herdsmen (22.9 per cent, as against 14.6 per cent in the total series). Farm dependents,

however, are very few (4.5 per cent). There are but three fishermen in this subgroup. It is deficient in navvies, semi-skilled workers, and transportation, and has only two factory workers. This subgroup has another very large excess in the military (26.0 per cent as against 11.6 per cent in the entire series). In fact, soldiers constitute far more of this group than of any other. Hence there may be some selection of superior physical types.

The age of this series (34.40 years) is 1.3 years below the county average. The age ranking is 15 in the 19 subseries. Weight (161.0 pounds) is 3.7 pounds above the county average and heaviest of all Ireland. Stature (173.16 cm.) is next to the Irish maximum (1.26 cm. above the Irish mean). Gross span ties with that of Kerry for first place, but relative span is ordinary. Biacromial diameter (38.78) is significantly elevated and chests are broad, but the thoracic index (78.54) is depressed one whole unit below average. Sitting height is second highest in the series. Head length is almost one mm. above the series mean, and is third in county rankings; the cephalic index (78.51) is slightly depressed, but not significantly so. Head circumference (574.40 mm.) is second only to the Aran series. The head height in E. Galway-Roscommon is slightly low, but the diminution from the value of the total series is not significant. Length-height and breadth-height indices are definitely below mean Irish values. Bizygomatic diameter in E. Galway-Roscommon is 0.85 mm. above the total series average, and the cephalo-facial index (91.79) is higher than that of any other county subgroup. The zygo-frontal index is third lowest in the series, exceeding only the means of the Kerry and Aran groups. This position results from slightly narrow foreheads associated with somewhat broad faces. The upper face of the E. Galway-Roscommon series is next to the lowest (71.80 mm.) and the upper facial index (50.72, as against 51.62 in the total series) also ranks 18. Nose height and nose breadth are both slightly diminished; the nasal index is virtually at the mean. The zygogonial index ties with that of Sligo-Leitrim-S. Fermanagh-W. Cavan for the lowest mean of the county series—a result of large facial breadth and moderate jaw breadth.

In E. Galway and Roscommon low-waved

hair is exceptionally common (55.5 per cent),
and deep-waved is also in excess (20.6 per
cent, as against 18.0 per cent in the total series). By way of compensation there is a
deficiency of straight hair. Baldness and graying are less than average, probably because the
series is below mean age. This group is rather
low in dark hair, ranking 17 in combined
black and dark brown hair. Its excesses in
hair shades are in flat brown, red-brown, gold-
en brown and red. It is then a part of one
of the more rufous areas. The percentage of
blue eyes (46.0 as against 42.4 in the total
series) is slightly elevated, but total light eyes
are only 2.1 per cent above the series mean.
The pigment in mixed eyes is to an excessive
extent "pronouncedly light," whereas "very
pronouncedly light," although predominant
here as in every Irish subgroup, is a little below average (57.9 per cent, as against 59.3
per cent for the total series). Clear irides are
in excess to about 7 per cent, and rayed eyes
notably deficient. Eye obliquity is less than
ordinarily common. Pronounced eyebrow concurrency is found in 13.0 per cent of cases—
an excess of 3.3 per cent over the total series.
Other data indicate that this county subseries
tends to a stronger than average "meeting"
of the eyebrows. Brow ridges are rarely small.
Foreheads of medium height are excessively
prevalent and slope is also prevailingly medium. In most nasal features this county subgroup shows a marked tendency to pile up
most observations in the medium category.
Straight noses occur in an excess of about 3
per cent (largely at the expense of convex
form). Tooth loss is below the county average; caries is a little below ordinary Irish
frequency, but it must be recalled that this
subseries is considerably below mean age.
Crowded teeth are somewhat more numerous
than average. Pronounced gonial angles are
somewhat deficient. E. Galway-Roscommon
has 11.2 per cent excess of free ear lobes over
the series proportion. Ear lobes are overwhelmingly of medium size. Pronounced
temporal fullness (28.0 per cent) ties with
Kerry for second place. Occipital flattening is
less than ordinarily prevalent.

On the whole, then, the men of E. Galway-
Roscommon are the second tallest and the
very heaviest in Ireland, as represented by

county groups; they are further marked by
relatively flat and broad chests and by long
heads tending toward dolichocephaly. The upper face tends to be rather short and broad,
the forehead and jaws narrow relative to
bizygomatic breadth. Low-waved hair with
a good deal of red pigment and some excess
of pure blue eyes are notable morphological
features. Most facial features are excessively
"medium" in development.

LONGFORD-WESTMEATH

Longford and Westmeath are two agricultural counties in central Ireland, bounded on
the west by the Shannon. They are included
in the great Carboniferous limestone central
plain. In many places the soil overlying this
limestone is a deep, rich loam, excellent for
pasturage and tillage. There are numerous
loughs and a great deal of bog land. In the
north, Longford is hilly, with Silurian beds of
sands and slate in the anticlinal folds, and exposures of the Old Red Sandstone, the soil
being thin and poor. There are no large towns
in these counties.

The Longford-Westmeath series includes
675 men. There is only one illiterate here, although this series is low in highly educated
men. The county ranks second in educational
status, and perhaps really should be rated first
instead of the Arans, because it has 14.8 per
cent of secondary school and university men
whereas the Aran figure is only 0.7 per cent.
Only 4 men of the series (0.6 per cent) speak
Irish, but 35.2 per cent have studied the language in schools. It is very low in hired laborers and tinkers, and notably deficient (to
the extent of about 5 per cent) in herdsmen
and farmers, but this deficiency is more than
compensated by an excess of 6 per cent in farm
dependents. The largest excess in the Longford-Westmeath series is the navvy class,
which constitutes 35.3 per cent, a figure approximated only in County Clare, and 12.1 per
cent above the total series mean. Soldiers are
deficient in Longford-Westmeath, to the extent of 1.3 per cent.

The Longford-Westmeath series averages
only 30.25 years and is thus more than 5 years
below mean age, and nearly three and one-
half years younger than the next youngest
group. A good many of the striking metric

and morphological differentiae of this group are probably referable, in part or wholly, to its tender mean age. (Cf. Hooton and Dupertuis, 1951.) Weight, for example, (mean, 151.0 pounds), is 6.3 pounds below the series average, and is probably so low because of the high proportion of young men in this sample. Stature (171.36 cm.) is significantly below the total series mean, but is not the minimum of the Irish county series. Relative span (104.94) is lower than that of any other group save the Aran subseries, but, at that, is not far below the general county average (105.32). Shoulder breadth is low, both absolutely and relatively; chest diameters are also markedly deficient, and the thoracic index is depressed, indicating relatively shallow chests (matched in West Galway and exceeded only in the Arans). Sitting height and relative sitting height are moderately depressed. Heads are of medium length, but below average breadth, so that the cephalic index (77.91) is 0.93 index units below the total county mean. Head height is exceptionally low (123.14 mm.) and both length-height and breadth-height indices are depressed. Bizygomatic diameter is somewhat small and total facial height (126.35 mm.) is lowest of the series. Upper face height also reaches the series minimum, as do both nose height and nose breadth. The same minimum value is attained in forehead breadth and jaw breadth. These men of Longford-Westmeath are rather smaller all around than most of the Irish countrymen, whether or not because of their inferior average age.

This series includes the largest percentage of pale-skinned men (1.0), but also considerably the highest proportion of brunets (18.6). The latter is an excess of some 10 per cent. Pronounced vascularity is markedly deficient in occurrence. Freckles are less than usually common, although the deficiency is not as large as might be expected from the excess of brunet skin color. Moles (7 per cent) are commoner than in any other county series. This county has by far the lowest percentage of men with straight hair (deficiency from the mean of 14.2 per cent) and excesses of all forms of curved hair except frizzly. Longford-Westmeath ranks first among the counties in combined categories of curved hair. It leads in pronounced quantity of head hair

with 5.2 per cent; has next to the highest proportion of submedium beard hair and body hair; and the least baldness and graying of head and beard. These phenomena of hair quantity, and also, of course, the matter of baldness and graying, are directly referable to age. It is possible that the abundance of curly hair may be due to this factor also. In our series, deep-waved and curly hair decline in successive age groups—deep-waved from 25–29 years onward, curly from 20–24 years onward. There is the possibility, however, that persons with more heavily curved hair are contra-selected for survival.

Black hair is rarest in Longford-Westmeath of all Irish groups, with only 0.3 per cent. Dark brown hair is far less common than in any other group except the Arans. The excesses are in golden brown, ash brown, golden, ash, and red, but most of all in flat brown (43.8 per cent as against 34.7 per cent in the total series). Here, again, it seems certain that the generally lighter hair shades of the series are in part conditioned by low mean age, since hair in persons of mixed pigment usually darkens up to maturity. Next to the Arans, dark hair is least common in Longford-Westmeath of all Irish counties. This county group has 1.2 per cent of dark eyes, which ranks it third in the county subseries.

There is a moderate excess of gray-blue eyes, and of green-brown eyes—both rare in Ireland. The corresponding deficiencies are in blue-brown and blue. The mixed eyes run a little darker than ordinary. Clear, rayed, and zoned irides are in excess, but the diffuse form and the scalloped pattern are notably deficient. Median eyefolds and internal eyefolds, though rare, are commoner than in most of the other county series. Obliquity of the eye slits is close to the Irish minimum, exceeding only that of the Arans. Foreheads here average lower than in any other sample (with the exception of the Arans), and are dominatingly of medium slope. This group also leads in submedium nasion depressions and in deficiency of pronounced nasion depressions. Nasal root heights and breadths are not as commonly pronounced as on most other county groups. The same stricture applies to the height and breadth of the nasal bridge. Thin nasal tips (2.8 per cent) are commoner here than elsewhere, and thick tips rarer (with the exception again of the Aran Islands), the medium form being unduly represented. Here is also the greatest excess of nasal tips with medium upward tilt (excess of 8.8 per cent). A small surplus of flaring alae is worthy of note. Parallelism of the axes of the nostrils (5.71 per cent) here attains the Irish maximum. Longford-Westmeath contests with Aran for the honor of having the highest preponderance of straight nasal profiles (55.5 per cent). The deficiency falls in the convex form. There is a total occurrence of 8.0 per cent of alveolar prognathism, as against 2.40 per cent in the combined Irish county series. The highest percentage of individuals with incomplete eruption of teeth (39.5 per cent) is also found in Longford-Westmeath. Teeth are, in general, ordinary in respect to nature of bite and degree of wear. The excess of persons with small dental loss to be expected in such a young group is not fulfilled. Caries are little rarer than in the average group. The group is extremely deficient in pronounced lateral projection of the malars, and somewhat below average in frontal projection. Gonial angles also are less than ordinarily prominent. By far the largest incidence of Darwin's Point on the ear (41.7 per cent) occurs in this county series. Free ear lobes are found, surprisingly, in 78.4 per cent (a figure approached nowhere else except in the Arans). This feature increases with age.

The characters in which Longford-Westmeath is outstanding are mostly of the sort which are likely to be influenced by age changes. (Cf. Hooton and Dupertuis, 1951.) There are a few exceptions, but these are not important. The group shows a curious tendency to fit in with the Aran series although the men of the latter sample are much larger and 3.40 years older in mean age. Some strong community of ethnic strains is probably indicated.

OFFALY-LEIX-KILDARE

Offaly (formerly Kings County), Leix (formerly Queens County), and Kildare form a block of counties lying in the great Carboniferous limestone plain to the east of the Shannon. The Bog of Allen is a name given to a collection of morasses which occupy large areas in these three counties and in Westmeath. The bog is not continuous but is interspersed with strips of dry, cultivable land. It has a general elevation above sea level of 250 feet, and has an average thickness of 25 feet of peat resting on clay and marl subsoils.

Offaly, the most westerly of the three, is separated on the south from Leix by the Slieve Bloom Mountains, which consist of Old Red Sandstone with Silurian inliers. The Shannon skirts the western side of the county. The county has a large area of bogs, and the part bordering upon Tipperary is still richly wooded. The soil is mostly bog or sandy loam, but there are excellent pastures both on the border of Westmeath and on the slopes of the Slieve Bloom Mountains. A good deal of rich meadow land lies along the Shannon. With the exception of the tract belonging to the Bog of Allen, most of the county is under cultivation.

To the south, Leix is of similar geological formation, but the southeastern portion is the Leinster coalfield and a great part of the center is bog. When the bog is drained it makes tillable land. Agriculture, particularly dairy farming, is the principal occupation.

Kildare belongs, for the most part, to the great central plain, but on the east are the mountains of Dublin and Wicklow, and in the center is an elevated plateau. The northern part is boggy and very moist, but the soil, whether lying on limestone or clay slate, is a rich deep loam, which is excellent when drained. The best and most scientifically utilized farming land is found in the valley of the Liffey and in a southern tract watered by the Greese.

The series from these three counties is comprised of 530 adult males. It ranks second only to West Galway in percentages of illiterates and uneducated men and has the fourth lowest proportion of university men (0.9). It ranks 18, or next to the last, in general educational status. There is but one native Irish speaker in this county series, although 35.2 per cent have studied Irish at school. The low class hired laborers and tinkers constitute 16.5 per cent, which is more than twice their ordinary total series representation. The agricultural and herdsmen classes, as well as that of farm dependents, are deficient to an aggregate of 7.4 per cent. Of course, there are no fishermen at all. Navvies (27.7) are 4.5 per cent above total series representation, and there is about a 2 per cent deficiency of tradesmen. On the whole, the series seems to be rather depressed both economically and socially.

This subgroup (hereinafter referred to as the Offaly group) is 0.70 years below mean age; 3.1 pounds below mean weight, and 0.52 cm. below mean stature. The last deficiency is not statistically significant, although probably valid. Span is low, but shoulder breadth is about average. Chests are narrow and shallow. Sitting height is below average. Head length (194.94 mm.) is submedium, and head breadth is also low. The mean cephalic index (78.24) is 0.60 below total Irish county values. Head circumference is small, but head height is somewhat above average. Hence the length-height and, even more, the breadth-height indices of the head are among the higher values found in Ireland. The narrowest mean bizygomatic diameter (139.10 mm.) occurs in this series and the facial index (91.10) is above par by 0.80 per cent. This is one of the four most leptoprosopic county series in Ireland. Upper face height is somewhat above the mean, but total face height is below average. The upper facial index is also high, indicating a relatively long and narrow maxilla. The nasal index (64.86) is 0.48 index units higher than the mean for Irish counties. Foreheads and jaws are narrow.

Brunet skins are found in 9.6 per cent (almost a 2 per cent excess). This county series is lowest in vascularity. Freckles are found in a diminished proportion of cases. Moles occur in 9.0 per cent—next to the highest frequency in Ireland. The Offaly group has a moderate excess of deep-waved and curly hair, with corresponding deficiencies in straight and low-waved varieties. Baldness is less than average. Graying of head hair is slightly deficient, but graying of the beard is average. Dark brown hair (44.5 per cent) is 4.7 per cent in excess. Red-brown is a little above average, and flat brown, golden brown, and red are correspondingly reduced. There are in this county subseries 6 individuals (1.1 per cent) with dark brown eyes, a number and proportion equalled only in Meath-

Louth-Dublin. However, eye color is not generally distinctive here. Blue-brown, the commonest combination of Irish mixed eyes, is low by 3.8 per cent and the rare gray-blue and green-brown varieties are above par. An upward slant of the eye slits occurs in an excess of 12.3 per cent. Absent and submedium brow ridges are slightly more common than ordinary. High foreheads are predominant. The bridge of the nose tends to be broad in 25.2 per cent of cases, which is an excess of 4.6 per cent. Nasal septa show a 12 per cent excess of straight and concave forms, as contrasted with convex septa which ordinarily are found in nearly 62 per cent of Irish and which for the Offaly group are 12 per cent below par. Nasal tips in this county group run thicker than average. Straight noses are found in 52.8 per cent of the Offaly group, which is fourth in the whole assemblage of county series in this form of nasal profile. Correspondingly, convex nasal profiles are somewhat deficient. Lip eversion is less than average for Irish counties. Tooth wear in this group seems to be less than average. Medium and pronounced caries are less than usually prevalent. Medium projection of cheekbones and jaw angles is recorded in an overwhelming majority of this subseries. Pronounced ear lobes are slightly in excess of the total series.

In summary, the men of Offaly-Leix-Kildare are somewhat undersized for Irishmen, and have slightly smaller heads, narrower faces, and noses a little broader than average, with excesses of straight nasal profiles. Skin color is less ruddy than ordinary; hair oftener wavy or curly, eyes frequently slanting upward.

TIPPERARY-KILKENNY

The greater part of Tipperary is an undulating plain. This area is Carboniferous limestone country. In the south are the Knockmeal and Galtee Mountains, which are formed of the Old Red Sandstone. In the east are Upper Carboniferous shales and sandstones lying along an anticlinal axis. Anthracite is mined on this plateau. Another range of the Old Red Sandstone hills extends across the county from northwest to northeast. The center is occupied by the Golden Vale—the most fertile area in Ireland. Detached portions of the Bog of Allen encroach upon the northeastern portion of the county. The limestone in the low areas is overlaid with a rich calcareous loam. On the higher lands the soil is light and thin. The principal occupation of the county is agriculture, since this is one of the best farming areas in Ireland.

To the east, Kilkenny represents also in large part an extension of the central limestone plain, but in the southeastern part of the county is an extension of the mountains of Wicklow and Carlow, while in the north the plain is interrupted by a hilly area in which anthracite is mined. In the south the ridges of Slivenaman are Old Red Sandstone with a Silurian core. The ground of Kilkenny is mostly high-lying and the soil is dry. Along the banks of the rivers Suir, Nore, and Barrow, are rich alluvial soils. On the limestone the deep soil is admirably adapted for the growing of wheat. To the north of the coal measures are moorland tracts devoted to pasturage. Kilkenny is then a fine agricultural country.

The series from Tipperary-Kilkenny numbers 650 men. It is marked by neither an excess of illiterates nor a surplus of well educated men. It ranks 9 in educational status. In this county group only 5 men speak Irish, but 35.4 per cent have some scholastic acquaintance with this Keltic language. It is markedly low in hired laborers and tinkers, agriculturalists, herdsmen, and farm dependents. It includes only 5 fishermen; 29.4 per cent of the series is composed of navvies, an excess of 6.2 per cent. Semi-skilled workers and factory operatives are also slightly high, as are tradesmen, clerks, and professional men.

The men of Tipperary-Kilkenny average 36.95 years, which is 0.75 years above mean age for the total county series. They are about a pound above average weight. They are low to some slight extent in chest breadth and also slightly high in chest depth, so that the thoracic index (81.90) is 1.36 units above mean Irish values. Head length is slightly below average and head breadth is at the series par. Thus the average cephalic index of this group is slightly above the total county mean, but the difference is unreliable. Head height is significant in elevation and both length-height and breadth-height indices are not greatly, but significantly, above those of the total series. A notable feature of facial dimensions is the great height of the upper face (73.70 mm.). The Tipperary-Kilkenny group ties for second place in this measurement. The upper face, in the Irish scale, is relatively long and narrow, whereas the total facial index does not differ significantly from the Irish mean. Noses here average 56.82 mm. in height, a figure equalled or surpassed only in Clare, Cork, Kerry, and the Aran Islands. Since nasal breadth is insignificantly low, we find the Tipperary-Kilkenny series to have the lowest nasal index of any Irish county (63.66). Foreheads are somewhat above mean county breadth; so are bigonial diameters. The relation of forehead breadth to face breadth (zygo-frontal index) is 78.46, the highest Irish average.

The series is somewhat low in vascularity (deficiency of 2.5 per cent in pronounced category). It has fewer than average freckled persons. It has 7.6 per cent more of straight hair than the series average. A small deficiency in head hair quantity may be referable to the fact that mean age here is nearly a year above average. Baldness is not particularly elevated and graying of head and beard is only slightly high. There is a small excess of dark brown hair, mostly at the expense of medium or flat brown hair. This group has the highest proportion of external eyefolds (19.9 per cent). It also has a slight excess of median eyefolds—the juvenile predecessors of external folds. Submedium upward slant of the eyes is notably high. Brow ridges run slightly larger than ordinary. High foreheads are in excess to nearly 10 per cent. Steep foreheads are also more than ordinarily common. Nasion depressions tend more frequently to be pronounced than in the generality of Irish counties. Nasal roots incline to be high and broad, as are also nasal bridges. Convex septa are in excess. Both concave and convex nasal profiles are slightly more common than in the series as a whole. Lips appear to be of about average thickness and less everted than usually. Teeth, on the whole, seem slightly better than average. The roll of the helix of the Tipperary-Kilkenny ear tends to be submedium and the antihelix more than ordinarily prominent. Darwin's Point is somewhat reduced in frequency. Ear lobes show a strong excess of attached form and incline toward large size. Pronounced occipital protrusion is in moderate excess. Lambdoid flattening is deficient to the extent of 15.4 per cent. There are slight excesses of occipital flattening and of facial asymmetry.

Metrically, the men of these counties are remarkable for rather deep and narrow chests, relatively high heads, relatively broad foreheads, long upper faces, and long and relatively narrow noses.

Morphologically, the outstanding features of Tipperary-Kilkenny men are excesses of straight hair, external eyefolds, high, steep foreheads, deep nasion depressions, large noses and good teeth.

WATERFORD-WEXFORD

Waterford, a southeastern coastal county, is mostly mountainous and rugged, except in the southeastern part, which is generally level. The mountainous areas are largely of Old Red Sandstone. In the synclines are Carboniferous limestone and in the river valleys this formation is overlaid by rich soil. The southeastern districts are by far the most fertile. The city of Waterford is second to Cork in importance as a south coast port.

County Wexford, east of Waterford, and occupying the southeastern corner of Ireland, is mostly low-lying. The western part of the county, however, is bounded by the Leinster mountain chain composed of a granite core and borders of mica-schist. From this range, hummocky Silurian deposits stretch toward the sea, the surfaces much modified by glacial drift. The soil is mostly a cold stiff clay, resting on clay-slate. The interior is much inferior to the coastal districts and contains large tracts of peat-moss and turf. The southeastern region is partly limestone and more fertile. The town of Wexford is headquarters for the salmon-fishing industry. The county produces more barley than any other Irish county. Agriculture is fairly well developed.

The Waterford-Wexford series consists of 462 men. Illiteracy (8.0 per cent) is very high, and the subseries ranks only 17 among 19 Irish subgroups in its educational status. Keltic speakers include 5.8 per cent—far more than are found in any other eastern county subseries. The subseries is slightly high in hired laborers and tinkers (excess 1.12 per cent), and extraordinarily low in the agricultural and herdsmen classes (deficiency 13.1 per cent). It is heavily overloaded with fishermen (12.7 per cent). It is also high in transport workers (7.8 per cent), in tradesmen and shop assistants (14.3 per cent), but low in soldiers (7.8 per cent).

The average age of the Waterford-Wexford series is 40.90 years, which is 5.20 years above mean age of the total series and the oldest group in the series. This age superiority is likely to carry with it troublesome and confusing age changes. Indeed, poor educational status and retention of the Keltic language may be in part a result of the inclusion of larger numbers of elderly men. (Cf. Hooton and Dupertuis, 1951, pp. 6, 7.) Weight is 0.8 pounds below the Irish average; stature is depressed 0.90 cm., a significant amount. Absolute span is down, and shoulder breadth is reduced a small amount. Chest breadth is inferior, but chest depth is the largest in any Irish county (23.66 cm.). The thoracic index (82.94) is higher than that of any other county group save Wicklow-Carlow. (Cf. Hooton and Dupertuis, 1951, pp. 15–17.)

Head length in Waterford-Wexford is comparatively low for Ireland (194.76 cm.), as is also head breadth (153.16 mm.). Head circumference is depressed, but head height is insignificantly above the Irish mean. Hence length-height and breadth-height indices are higher than in most of Ireland. Facial dimensions are also somewhat reduced, with the exception of upper face height (73.25 mm.) which is 0.45 mm. above average. Hence the upper face is relatively longer and narrower than in the combined Irish county series. Nose height is somewhat increased (probably as a result of high mean age) and the nasal index (63.98) is rather low. The fronto-parietal and zygo-frontal indices are rather high, because of comparatively broad foreheads. The relation of jaw breadth to facial breadth (78.14) ties this county group for fourth place with Offaly-Leix-Kildare.

Waterford-Wexford, together with neighboring Wicklow-Carlow, are the Irish groups in which freckled individuals are rarest. Each of these counties has slightly less than 30 per cent of freckling. Waterford-Wexford has an 8.4 per cent excess of straight hair and is second only to Wicklow-Carlow in this attribute. Excesses of heavy beards and body hair in Waterford-Wexford are hardly referable to advanced mean age of the sample. Excesses of baldness, with graying of head and beard, are undoubtedly referable to this age factor. (Cf. Hooton and Dupertuis, 1951, pp. 49–54.) Waterford-Wexford is high in dark hair (excess 7.4 per cent) and low in flat brown, red-brown and red shades, but it is high in golden brown (12.7 per cent). The group has small excesses of gray-brown and green-brown eyes; is low in blue-brown and high in gray-blue and blue shades. Pigment in mixed eyes runs unusually dark. Rayed and spotted irides are considerably commoner than in the general Irish series. There is a moderate excess of external eyefolds (probably connected with advanced age) and marked excess of eye slant. Submedium eye opening height occurs in 11.4 per cent, the largest proportion in Ireland. Brow ridges tend to larger size than usual; foreheads to increased height; 12.3 per cent of Waterford-Wexford men have pronouncedly sloping or extremely sloping foreheads. This is the maximum of the Irish series. Nasion depressions tend to be deep. Nasal roots are remarkably high and broad, as are also nasal bridges. Straight nasal profiles have a slight superiority over convex forms. Lips are thinner and less everted (probably an age effect). This series has 14.9 per cent of mid-facial prognathism—a proportion exceeded only in Wicklow-Carlow. Chin projection tends toward the pronounced grade.

Tooth eruption is more often than usual complete. Pronounced tooth loss reaches 39.1 per cent, the highest figure in the series. Caries are no more than usually prevalent. A considerable shortening of the face through tooth wear and loss is observable. Lateral projection of the malars tends toward reduction.

Waterford-Wexford ears are rather high in submedium roll of the helix and pronounced development of the antihelix. Ear lobes run large (an age effect). There is a considerable excess of pronounced occipital protrusion, together with a marked deficiency of lambdoid

flattening. However, occipital flattening is unusually common.

Thus the men of Waterford-Wexford tend to have square jaws and oblong faces. Metrically they are most remarkable for their deep narrow chests and a slight general size inferiority. Dark straight hair, absence of freckling, blue eyes and gray-blue eyes, large brow ridges and sloping foreheads, prominent, straight noses are the outstanding morphological characteristics of this county sample.

WICKLOW-CARLOW

Wicklow, an eastern coastal county, is more famous for its scenic beauty than for its fertility. The center of the county is occupied by a mountain range which is granite with a marginal zone of mica-schist. The slopes running down to the sea are Silurian shales. These form heather-clad moors, deeply intersected by glens where the streams have cut into the Silurian deposits. The coast is precipitous. The soil of the lower regions is fertile and the greater part of the higher land is covered with turf and heather so that it makes good pasturage. Agriculture is the principal occupation, but in some regions mining is important.

Carlow is a small inland county bounded on the northeast by Wicklow and on the southeast by Wexford. The surface is mostly level or gently undulating, with the exception of the southeast region bordering on Wexford where a granitic range rises. At the west of the county is an elevated tract of land which forms the beginnings of the coal measures of Leinster. While Carlow is mostly a granite county, the valley of the Barrow lies on the Carboniferous limestone. The soil is said to be the most generally fertile in the island, but agriculture is not developed to an extent which utilizes the full capabilities of the land. Dairy farms are most important, together with raising of sheep and poultry.

Our series from Wicklow-Carlow is only 278 men. Illiteracy is high (6.8 per cent). The county ranks 15 of the 19 groups in educational achievement. There are only 0.4 per cent of Keltic speakers, but 38.5 per cent have studied Irish at school. This county group contains by far the largest percentage of the lowest occupational class, hired laborers and tinkers (22.8 per cent). This is three times the ordinary representation of that class. It has a 6 per cent deficiency in the agricultural and farm dependent classes and includes no fishermen at all, although the town of Wicklow is a fishing port.

The Wicklow-Carlow series is second oldest of our county subgroups. Its mean age is 38.30 years, 2.60 years above the total series average. Mean weight—154.80 pounds—is 2.50 pounds below that of the total series. Stature (170.79 cm.) ties for eighteenth place in the county ranking. Shoulder breadth is slightly above average (38.63 cm.). Chests tie with Meath-Louth-Dublin for being narrowest, but are deeper than average. The thoracic index (83.18) is highest in Ireland, indicating relatively very narrow, deep chests. Relative sitting height is also at a maximum.

Head length is somewhat on the short side, as is also head breadth. The mean cephalic index is a trifle low. Head height is distinctly above average. Both length-height and breadth-height indices are significantly elevated. The facial breadth is reduced but total face height is slightly above the mean value. Hence the face is long and narrow and the mean of the total facial index (91.00) is exceeded only in the Aran Islands, E. Cavan-Monaghan-Armagh, and Offaly-Leix-Kildare. Upper face height is markedly elevated, as is also the upper facial index. Noses are slightly longer and broader than average, causing the nasal index to be depressed. The minimum breadth of the forehead in Wicklow-Carlow is small.

Wicklow-Carlow, with Waterford-Wexford, is the least freckled area in Ireland, according to our data. With 40.6 per cent of straight hair, it ranks first among the Irish counties in occurrence of this variety. Here is recorded the highest proportion of fine textured hair (5.8 per cent), but this fact seems of little importance in consideration of the general rarity of fine hair. Baldness and graying are excessive, doubtless because of the high mean age of the subseries. More black-haired persons were found here (proportionately) than in any other group save that of West Donegal, and, in general, darker hair shades are more common than average. Red pigment in the hair is somewhat deficient.

The most notable fact pertaining to pigmentation is that Wicklow ranks second in blue eyes with 49.6 per cent. The mixed eyes that occur in this series tend toward extreme lightness, as do most Irish mixed eyes. Rayed and scalloped irides are in excess, the former associated with mixed eyes, the latter with blue eyes. External eyefolds are less common here than in any other subgroup, except West Donegal, in spite of the high mean age of the sample. Upward slant of the eyes is close to maximum occurrence. Concurrency of eyebrows tends toward submedium. Brow ridges are somewhat weighted toward small size. Foreheads are pronounced in height and, on the whole, are of marked slope. Nasion depressions run deep; nasal roots are high with slight emphasis upon pronounced breadth. The same accent upon height and breadth is recorded in the case of the nasal bridge. Straight or concave nasal septa and thick nasal tips are in excess. Straight and convex nasal profiles occur in almost equal proportions, with a small residue of the concave profiles. Convexity is, however, a little above average Irish occurrence. Lip thickness is definitely low; lip eversion emphasizes the submedium (in contrast to total series proportions). This series has, by a good deal, the highest percentage of mid-facial prognathism recorded among the Irish (23.7 per cent). Teeth seem not to be below the general Irish level of quality, although the series is above mean age. Crowding is, however, somewhat more than usually frequent. The helix of the Wicklow-Carlow ear shows a trend toward submedium roll, which is much stronger than the excess shown in the occurrence of Darwin's Point. Ear lobes exhibit some surplus of the attached variety and are likely to be large, because this part of the ear increases with middle and advanced age. The county is strong in occipital protrusion, relatively low in lambdoid flattening, and has a moderate excess of occipital flattening.

On the whole, the Wicklow-Carlow series closely resembles that of Waterford-Wexford. Reduced size and weight; narrow deep chests; relatively short legs; small, high heads; and long, narrow faces seem to be the most remarkable anthropometric features of the men from these two counties. Dark hair with blue eyes; high, sloping foreheads; high, fleshy noses; and mid-facial prognathism are the characters of the Wicklow-Carlow men not obviously connected with their mean age.

MEATH-LOUTH-DUBLIN

Meath is the central of these three eastern coastal counties and by far the largest. It is flanked on the northeast by Louth and on the southeast by Dublin.

Meath is, in general, a level champaign country, with a low, shelving, and sandy coast. It is divided into two almost equal parts by the river Boyne. To the north is a somewhat broken country of Silurian rocks with intrusive igneous material. To the south is the limestone plain. The soil is mostly rich, deep loam, favorable for agriculture.

Louth is more undulating and includes to the northeast the Carlingford range, which, apparently, consists of granite and other igneous rocks which have broken through the limestone. Most of Louth is a rolling lowland of Silurian shales and fine-grained sandstone. The soil overlying these lowland areas is a rich, deep mould, and agriculture is advanced. The higher regions are moorland.

The northern part of County Dublin is flat with good soil, but to the south the land rises into mountains which are extensions of the Wicklow range. The northern coast is flat, and the southern part rugged.

The geology is rather complicated. In the north is the Silurian upland. North and south of the valley of the Liffey are Carboniferous limestones and to the south the granite of Leinster rises through the Silurian rocks. Glacial boulder clays and drifts cover the lowland. The country is suitable for agriculture, but the encroachment of the metropolis has somewhat discouraged this industry.

The series from these three counties consists of 457 men. It is exactly the median county group in educational status (ratio of illiterates and uneducated to well educated). Only 7 men (1.5 per cent) speak Irish, but 36.5 per cent have studied it. The series includes 14.6 per cent of hired laborers and tinkers, which is nearly twice the proportion found in the series at large. It has only 9.9 per cent of the agricultural, herdsmen, and farm dependent classes, as against 22.3 per

cent in the whole series. The series also has a 6.3 per cent excess of navvies. It has slight excesses in most of the other occupational classes, although it is 1.4 per cent low in soldiers. Probably the occupational status of the series is somewhat lower than it should be to be completely representative of the rural population of these counties.

The mean age of the Meath-Louth-Dublin sample is 33.75 years—1.95 years below the average of the county series. Average weight, 153.00 pounds, is next to the Irish county minimum and is 4.3 pounds below the total series. Stature averages 170.52 cm., which is lowest for Ireland. Absolute span is also lowest; chest breadth ties for the minimum, but chest depth is close to average, although low. Hence the thoracic index is up 1.24 units. Relative sitting height is significantly above the Irish average. While head length is approximately average, head breadth (152.14 mm.) is the Irish minimum. Hence the cephalic index drops to a mean of 77.79, which makes this group the most dolichocephalic of the Irish county series.

Head circumference is deficient, but head height is insignificantly above average. The small head breadth and moderate height combine in the breadth-height index to produce a mean of 82.34, which is second highest in Ireland, and exceeded only in N. Fermanagh-E. Donegal-Tyrone-Londonderry. Face breadth (139.25 mm.) is the third lowest in Ireland, while face height (126.50 mm.) is 0.60 below the total series mean, a deficiency which is almost significant. The total facial index (90.70) rates the men of Meath-Louth-Dublin among the more leptoprosopic Irish. Upper face height is slightly below average, but the upper facial index is significantly elevated because of extremely low facial widths. Noses are short, but of nearly medium width, so that the nasal index (64.98) is high for Ireland. (Meath-Louth-Dublin ranks third in this index.) Forehead and jaw breadths are low, but the zygo-gonial index is slightly elevated.

This series has 10.2 per cent of brunet or swarthy skins and ranks third in intensity of skin pigmentation among the Irish counties. It is moderately deficient in freckling, and somewhat high in moles. Deep waved hair is slightly more common than usual. The darker shades of hair are in excess 6.1 per cent, at the expense of all the light shades. The Meath-Louth-Dublin series nearly ties with Longford-Westmeath in having the highest percentage of dark brown eyes, but these proportions (1.3 and 1.2) mean only very few individuals. There are small excesses of green-brown, gray-blue, and blue eyes, with a deficiency of blue-brown, the most prevalent color combination in Irish mixed eyes. Mixed eyes in these counties are not so pronouncedly light as in most subseries. There are moderate surpluses of rayed, zoned, and scalloped iridical patterns. A slight obliquity of the eye openings is more frequent than is usual in Ireland. Brow ridges tend to submedium size. Forehead height is definitely high. High, broad nasal roots are in excess and also high, broad nasal bridges. Straight or concave septa are more than ordinarily common. Nasal tips incline to be thick. Tooth loss is a little above average. Crowding is moderately in excess. Lateral projection of malars and gonial angles is slightly deficient. An excess of 9.9 per cent in pronounced occipital projection is worth noting. There is a deficiency of 8.8 per cent in lambdoid flattening.

This Meath-Louth-Dublin group is, then, the shortest and the second lightest found among our Irish counties. The men have relatively deep and narrow chests; relatively long trunks and short legs; narrow high heads, narrow and relatively long faces, with noses which are proportionately wider than would be expected from their facial dimensions. Morphologically the series is not very distinctive. A tendency toward darker pigmentation of hair and skin, lack of rufosity and freckling are its main points of interest.

E. CAVAN-MONAGHAN-ARMAGH

E. Cavan, Monaghan, and Armagh constitute a southeastern block of the province of Ulster. All are inland counties. For our purposes, the portion of County Cavan east of the Erne is included with the other two counties in their entirety.

E. Cavan is hilly country with numerous lakes and wooded areas. The town of Cavan and the Erne valley are in the limestone area.

A Silurian axis runs from southwest to northeast, to the south of which is the limestone of the central plain. The climate is damp and windy, the clay soil stiff and watery. The county is known rather for stock raising than for agriculture, which is retarded.

The northwestern part of Monaghan is in the central plain, but the south and east are hilly, and represent a tumbled Silurian area. In the limestone region the soil is fertile, and there is in some other areas a mixed soil of deep clay capable of intensive cultivation. In the hilly regions the stiff clay soil is not very productive and spade husbandry prevails.

Armagh is better country. The northern part is the flat lowland bordering upon Lough Neagh, some of it boggy and resting upon a limestone substratum. In general, the soil in the northern portion is a rich, brown loam, overlying clay and gravel. The southern hilly and barren area is a part of the Silurian axis, with slates and fine-grained sandstone. At some places the granite is exposed and there are also intrusive masses of younger igneous rocks. Agriculture is somewhat neglected, and in the past linen was woven in the country areas to a great extent. There are in this county a number of fair-sized towns.

The Ulster counties have yielded relatively small series of Catholics. The majority of the men measured fall into the Protestant series, which has been kept separate on the assumption that it consists mostly of persons of recent Scottish and English descent. Thus our E. Cavan-Monaghan-Armagh subgroup is composed of only 388 individuals. Educational status is below average, since the county group ranks fourteenth in the educational ratio. Only 0.5 per cent speak Irish, but more than one third have some school acquaintance with it. Of this subseries 17.3 per cent are hired laborers and tinkers—more than twice the normal proportion. The agricultural and farm dependent classes are correspondingly deficient and there is only one fisherman. This county subgroup has a 3 per cent excess in the shopkeeper class and is slightly up in transportation and factory workers.

Mean age of E. Cavan-Monaghan-Armagh is 36.50 years—0.80 years above the county average. Weight (154.30 pounds) is 3 pounds less than the mean of the series. Mean stature

(170.79 cm.) is significantly depressed—the second lowest county average. Absolute span is low and relative span is elevated. Chest breadth (28.44 cm.) is only 0.42 cm. below the total series figure, but chest depth is moderate. The thoracic index is correspondingly high. Absolute sitting height ties with the mean of Longford-Westmeath for the lowest Irish value (90.88 cm.). Head length is insignificantly high and head breadth definitely low (152.44 mm.). Hence the cephalic index (78.00) is 0.84 units below the total mean. The breadth-height index is elevated 0.87 units —a significant difference. Bizygomatic diameter (139.60 mm.) is 1.20 mm. below average. Next comes a curious divergence: total face height in E. Cavan-Monaghan-Armagh is 127.90 mm., an excess of 0.80 mm. over the series mean and the third highest value in the county series. The neighboring counties have shorter than average total face height. Total facial index is very leptoprosopic (91.40 as against 90.20 in the complete county series). Upper face height is also excessive, yielding an upper facial index of 52.76—the maximum of the series. Nevertheless, nose height is significantly below average. The fronto-parietal index is high; as is also the zygo-frontal index. Because the bigonial diameter is sharply depressed, the fronto-gonial index is low.

Pink skins are in slight excess in E. Cavan-Monaghan-Armagh, but pronounced vascularity is less than ordinarily common. There is an 8.3 per cent excess of straight hair. Black, dark brown and medium brown hair shades show an aggregate excess of more than 10 per cent. All of the hair colors that show red-gold pigment are correspondingly deficient. Eye color features pure blue with 51.4 per cent, a proportion exceeded nowhere else in the series. Scalloped iridical patterns are correspondingly high. There is a 14.7 per cent excess of slight upward obliquity of the eyes. The development of brow ridges in E. Cavan-Monaghan-Armagh is nearly the least of any Irish county (11.6 per cent pronounced or very pronounced), and exceeds only West Galway (11.3). Pronounced forehead height is in excess more than 12.9 per cent. Absent and submedium slope of the forehead are correspondingly high. Nasal roots are predominantly of medium height but tend toward pro-

nounced breadth; whereas the bridge is pronouncedly high as well as broad. Straight or concave septa rank second in the total series. Thick nasal tips are unusually common.

Teeth in this subseries are better than average: in resistance to wear, amount of loss, and dental caries. Attached ear lobes, large ear lobes, and pronounced aural protrusion are more than usually frequent. Pronounced occipital protrusion reaches the series maximum (29.0 per cent). Correspondingly, lambdoid flattening is relatively uncommon. The excess of occipital flattening amounts to 12.9 per cent. Facial asymmetry is a little below average.

Men of inferior size and weight with narrow deep chests, high heads, and very long narrow faces feature this county subgroup. Dark hair with blue eyes, small brow ridges, and steep, high foreheads, projecting occiputs and long narrow faces with slightly broad noses are the outstanding physical features of E. Cavan-Monaghan-Armagh.

ANTRIM-DOWN

Antrim, in the northeastern corner of Ireland, is hilly, especially in the east, where a range runs north and south. The shores are precipitous, but the slope inland is gradual. Most of the interior of the county is a basaltic plateau of relatively recent geological origin. There are also glacial drifts, and the southeastern coast is fringed by marine clays of postglacial date and raised beaches. The soil varies according to district. In some places it is a rich deep loam, in others a chalky marl, while still other areas have a thin coating of peat. The climate is temperate and agriculture is advanced. Linen manufacture is the principal industry. Belfast is the metropolis of the region.

County Down to the south of Antrim is indented by many loughs and bays, the largest of which is Lough Strangford. The shores are low and wooded and there are numerous forested islets. In the southwest are the Mourne Mountains of Eocene granite. The foundation of the country is Silurian slates and sandstone. There are many basaltic dykes and the northwest of the county includes a part of the basaltic plateau. The soil is mostly shallow and stony, but differs considerably in various regions. There are frequent bogs. Agriculture is fairly advanced. The breeding of horses is important, and pigs, sheep, and poultry are raised. Fishing is one of the coastal occupations, but linen manufacturing and brewing are the chief industries.

The series from Antrim-Down is one of our smallest county subgroups, since it contains only 152 individuals. The majority of men measured in these two counties belong either in the Presbyterian or the Church of Ireland series, rather than in the Catholic County series.

This subgroup has but one illiterate and in educational ranking is third in the series. There is only one individual who speaks Irish (0.6 per cent), and only 13.8 per cent have studied it at school. Agriculturalists and farm dependents are deficient to the extent of 11.2 per cent. It includes 9.0 per cent of fishermen, an excess of 6.4 per cent. Navvies are 5.8 per cent fewer than in the total series. Semi-skilled workers total 15.3 per cent, the highest in the series, and 7.3 per cent more than the total Irish percentage. Transport workers are slightly in excess and the series leads in factory operatives with 4.2 per cent. Tradesmen are less than ordinarily represented, clerks rather more so. The professional class totals 4.9 per cent, second highest in the series.

The men of Antrim-Down average 33.60 years in age, 2.10 years below the county mean. Average weight (154.50 pounds) is 2.80 pounds below that of the total series. Mean stature (171.51 cm.) is 0.39 cm. below the total Irish figure. Absolute span is correspondingly low, but shoulder breadth is ordinary. Chest dimensions are on the small side, but the thoracic index is only insignificantly elevated. Both sitting height and relative sitting height are low. Head length (194.97 mm.) is below par for the series. Head breadth is also sharply reduced, so that the cephalic index does not deviate significantly from the total series average. Head circumference is the lowest in Ireland. Head height is high, but the deviation is not statistically valid. Both length-height and breadth-height indices are well above total series value, but, again, because of the small size of the county sample, the differences are not significant. Face breadth is proportionately small, as is

also total facial height. Upper facial height (73.60 mm.) is 0.80 mm. above average for the total series. The upper facial index is also high. Noses are slightly shorter and considerably narrower than average, so that the mean nasal index (64.10) is among the lower values recorded for Irish county groups. Forehead breadth is small, as is also jaw breadth. The fronto-parietal index is low.

Pronounced vascularity or ruddiness is in excess in this series to the extent of 8.7 per cent, making this group the second in rank in the series. Freckles are in excess to nearly the same amount (8.3 per cent). The proportion of curly hair (6.6 per cent) is 3.3 per cent above average, and the highest in the county series. In combined categories of curved hair, Antrim-Down ranks fourth. Head hair quantity is slightly more than average and beard hair (10.5 per cent of pronounced quantity) is heavier than in any other Irish county series. The percentage of men with heavy body hair is also highest (7.9), but at that small. Slight deficiences of graying are doubtless attributable to the relatively low mean age of the subgroup. This group has the second highest percentage of dark brown hair (46.7 per cent) and is low in red-brown and red shades. Gray-brown eyes are also at a maximum here (6.6 per cent) as are green-brown with 7.9 per cent. In combined light eyes this group is fifth highest in the series. There is a marked deficiency of blue-brown irides. Mixed eyes in this group tend to be unusually dark. Scalloped patterns (presumably in blue eyes) are slightly in excess. A slight upward slant of the eye slits is found in an excess of 17.7 per cent. Antrim-Down is lowest in horizontal eye slits.

The subseries ranks second only to the Arans in percentage of large brow ridges. There is an excess of 13.4 per cent of high foreheads. Next to the western Ulster block (N. Fermanagh, etc.) these counties take first rank. This subgroup leads also in percentage of pronounced nasion depressions (37.5 per cent), with an excess of 14.6 per cent. The bridge of the nose inclines toward pronounced breadth. Straight or concave septa are unusually common and so are thick tips. The highest proportion of thick integumental lips is recorded for this subgroup (8.6 per cent).

This is true also of membranous lip thickness (7.9 per cent). The Antrim-Down men rank second in pronounced lip eversion with 9.2 per cent. Slight excesses of a submedium amount of mid-facial and alveolar prognathism are possibly worthy of mention.

Tooth wear, loss, and caries are less than average, possibly because the group is well below mean age. The caries index is second best in the Irish series. Some degree of crowding of the teeth is found in 65.6 per cent— second highest frequency in the entire series. Jaw angles are more than usually prominent. A pronounced roll of the helix of the ear reaches its highest series frequency in Antrim-Down (9.2 per cent). Ear lobes tend toward large size. Excessive ear protrusion is found in 31.6 per cent, the second highest proportion among the county subgroups. Occipital protrusion is above average. Lambdoid flattening is here most rare of all the subseries, with only 29.8 per cent. The highest total incidence of occipital flattening also occurs (55.9 per cent). Facial asymmetry seems more than ordinarily common.

General reduction of body and head size with almost incredibly long upper faces are then characteristic of the Antrim-Down subseries. Morphologically, the men of Antrim-Down are outstanding among Irish counties in the following important features: ruddiness, freckles, pronounced beard and body hair, dark brown hair color, high foreheads, big brow ridges, pronounced nasion depressions, thick membranous and integumental lips and strongly everted lips, teeth good but often crowded, ear protrusion, and occipital flattening.

Comparative Data (Table V-50). Two small samples of the population of County Antrim are available for comparison with our data. These series represent the studies of D. P. Gamble, T. Walmsley, and J. M. Mogey (see References), as installments of their survey of the peoples of Northern Ireland. They include a sample of 155 males measured in the Ballycastle region of Antrim and another of 115 males from Ballymoney. Dupertuis measured 197 men of Antrim from 13 different

places, including 15 from Ballycastle and 18 from Ballymoney. Again, in our data the men from County Antrim have been combined with those measured in County Down. Furthermore, our Antrim-Down subseries consists of Catholics only, whereas the Protestants are included in two separate series: Presbyterians (almost all from Ulster), and Church of Ireland (the majority of Ulster origin, but with a scattering of subjects from many other Irish counties). In table V-50 are listed the observations on eye color and hair color, and the means of measurements of the two Antrim samples measured by Gamble *et al.* in juxtaposition to the similar data of our Catholic Antrim-Down subseries and our Presbyterian series.

It is painfully apparent that the standards of pigmentation grading adopted by the Ulster anthropologists differ so radically from ours that there can be little if any utility in discussing them. The relatively small proportions of light eyes and other divergences found in the Ballycastle and Ballymoney series must be in considerable measure referable to differences of technique which cannot be resolved here. It should be noted, however, that the strict localization of their two series would inevitably bring out considerable differences from our samples which consist of individuals taken from much wider areas.

It is possible to discuss the measurements and indices with less felling frustration. The head lengths of the Ballycastle and Ballymoney men considerably exceed the means of both our Antrim-Down Catholic and of our Protestant series. Head breadths are closely similar in all of the four groups. Head height was measured by the Ulster anthropologist by use of a head spanner inserted in the ear holes of the subjects. Ours was a direct vertical measurement from the tragion. The former technique regularly yields values from 6 to 12 mm. higher than the tragion measurement.[1] However, it would seem that both the Ballycastle and Ballymoney means of head height exceed those of our series somewhat more than would be expected even from the differences in technique and instruments used.

---

[1] For a discussion of this problem and tables of means yielded by the two different techniques, *see* Hooton, 1939, pp. 60–61.

All of the means found in the different series for minimum frontal diameters are closely similar, and there is no great difference in the bizygomatic diameters. Bigonial diameters in the more recently measured Ballycastle and Ballymoney series are lower than in those of Dupertuis. This measurement can vary several millimeters according to the amount of pressure exerted by the measurer in compressing the soft parts over the gonia. The anthropologists of Northern Ireland found nasal lengths approximately two mm. shorter than did Dupertuis. This difference again may well be connected with the location of nasion by different techniques. Those who measure nasion from the deepest part of the depression of the root always get nose lengths that are shorter than anthropometrists who locate nasion (as we think it ordinarily should be located) by palpating the nasofrontal suture. It is usually above the deepest depression of the nasal root. Dupertuis gets slightly higher means of nose breadth also than do the later workers.

The range of stature in the different subseries is similar, but Gamble *et al.* find average spans much lower than did Dupertuis. As frequently mentioned in this report, Dupertuis took special care to get the maximum extension of arms in measuring span. Chest breadths are about the same in all of the subseries, but Dupertuis' chest depths are slightly higher. This again is a measurement subject to a good deal of personal equation. Sitting heights are about the same in all of the series.

The means of cephalic index in both the Ballycastle and Ballymoney samples are lower than those of the Antrim-Down Catholics measured by Dupertuis, and slightly lower than Dupertuis' Ulster Presbyterians. The differences arise from the greater head lengths of the Ballycastle and Ballymoney men.

The Antrim samples studied by Messrs. Gamble, Walmsley, and Mogey (1946, vol. 5) are probably for the most part Presbyterians. Ballymoney, at least, is stated by them to be a district mainly Protestant, but with certain subareas in which Catholics predominate. Metrically their series are somewhat closer to Dupertuis' Ulster Presbyterian than to the Antrim-Down Catholic sample. It is possible that a subdivision of the Ballycastle and Bally-

money samples into Protestants and Catholics would bring their means closer to those of the Dupertuis subseries.

The Ulster anthropologists have divided their two small samples into a considerable number of "types" empirically established. These types appear to be closer to the subjective types recognized by Coon than to the sorted morphological types utilized in this work. In view of the limitations of space in this monograph and the very small numbers of individuals included in the types of the Ulster anthropologists, it seems unpractical to discuss them here, valuable as the type analysis undoubtedly is.

N. FERMANAGH-E. DONEGAL-TYRONE-LONDONDERRY

This north-central series includes the whole of Tyrone and Londonderry, Fermanagh north of the Erne, and Donegal east of a line drawn from Donegal Bay to Lough Swilly. It is, in general, a hilly or mountainous area. The basic geological formation in the north and west is the Dalradian series of metamorphic rocks, consisting of mica-schist with some quartzite. In the south of Tyrone there are long ranges of hills of the Old Red Sandstone. Lower Carboniferous sandstone and limestone also occur to the north of Lower Lough Erne. The area varies greatly in fertility. In general the soil of the hilly regions is poor and thin, but fertile and workable in the valleys. The region around the city of Londonderry is an industrial center for the manufacture of linen, and there are also shipbuilding yards, iron foundries, distilleries, breweries, and other manufactures. Salmon and deep sea fisheries are important. The interior regions of this area are agricultural and stock-grazing country.

The N. Fermanagh-E. Donegal-Tyrone-Londonderry series (hereinafter referred to as the North Central county series) consists of 317 men. Illiteracy is low in this subseries (2.5 per cent), but the proportion of the well educated scarcely exceeds that of the total Irish county series. The subseries ranks sixth in educational ratio. Of this group 1.9 per cent are Keltic speakers and 21.4 per cent have studied it at school. The counties of Antrim-

Down and this North Central group may be said to have the least Keltic strength, inasmuch as almost no persons speak Irish, and comparatively few have studied it. In the counties of the Free State are many in which no one, or practically no one, speaks Irish, but even in these English-speaking regions our samples reveal that considerably more than a third have had school Irish which is a required subject. The North Central county series has a slight deficiency of hired laborers and tinkers, a 4.8 per cent deficiency of farmers and herdsmen, and a 3.3 per cent deficiency of farm dependents. It is also low in fishermen, but these are, except in 5 counties, a virtually negligible occupational group so far as our series is concerned. Again, navvies are represented by 11.1 per cent less than in the total series. The excess occupations are semi-skilled (excess 5.8 per cent), transportation (excess 3.0 per cent), factory (excess 2.6 per cent), skilled trades (0.8 per cent), shopkeepers and assistants (excess 8.9 per cent), and clerks (excess 0.6 per cent). Evidently then our North Central Ulster sample is more urban than rural in occupation.

The North Central county group averages only 33.90 years, which is 1.80 years below total series value. It is the fourth youngest group. Weight is down 1.70 pounds from the Irish county average. A deficiency of this amount may be due to low mean age. Stature is only very slightly and insignificantly below the mean. The thoracic index is slightly elevated. Head height (126.74 mm.) is the largest average of the series by a full millimeter. Hence length-height and breadth-height indices also attain their maxima. Total face height is low (rank 18), yet upper face height is significantly high, and this elevates the upper facial index. Noses are insignificantly short but above the total series mean breadth, so that the nasal index is significantly elevated and ranks highest of all the county subseries.

Vascularity in this series is a little high. Freckles are excessively common and moles are rare. There is a 10.3 per cent excess of straight hair, in which this subseries ranks second. This corresponds to a deficiency spread among the curved varieties. Graying and balding are a little low, in accordance with mean age. The marked excess in hair shade is in flat brown

(3.3 per cent) and there are deficiencies of small percentages in red-brown and red. Blue eyes (50.0 per cent) rank second in proportional occurrence among all of the Irish county series, and first rank is attained in combined light eyes. In this county subgroup are found also the highest frequencies of scalloped irides (32.8 per cent). Upward eye slant is more common here than anywhere else in Ireland. Eyebrow concurrency seems more than usually pronounced. Brow ridges run small. Correspondingly, this series ranks second in high foreheads (66.7 per cent)—an observation agreeing with the superiority in measured head height. Steep foreheads prevail. There is a strong excess of pronounced nasion depressions. Nasal roots incline more to great breadth than to pronounced height. The same is true of the nasal bridge. Nasal septa are in the majority of cases straight or concave. Tips are thick more often than usual. Straight nasal profiles predominate over convex varieties. Lip eversion shows a trend to the pronounced which is exceeded nowhere else in the series. This North Central group seems somewhat deficient in well-marked chin projection, but has the lowest percentage of median chins.

A high percentage of the North Central county group have partially erupted teeth (29.9 per cent). Tooth wear and loss are less than average. Wear is least of the series. The group has less caries than any other subseries. Gonial angles tend to be prominent. Attached ear lobes predominate over free forms. Marked ear protrusion reaches here its highest Irish frequency (36.2 per cent as against 21.9 per cent in the total series). Excess of pronounced occipital protrusion amounts to 6.3 per cent. Lambdoid flattening is in excess to the extent of 25.6 per cent, a proportion exceeded only in Antrim-Down.

The important feature of the anthropometry of the North Central group is the great head height (comparatively speaking) and the consequently hypsicephalic and acrocephalic tendencies manifested in the length-height and breadth-height indices. Freckles, blue eyes, high foreheads, pronounced nasion depressions, occipital protrusion and occipital flattening, and good teeth are the most important of the morphological excesses.

IN THE following section, an attempt has been made to combine the 19 county blocks of the Irish Catholic series into geographic areas that exhibit within themselves anthropological uniformities. In the beginning we naively delimited a northern area, an east central area, a west central area, a southeastern area and a southwestern area. These five areas seemed to "make sense" geographically and it was hoped that they would prove to be more or less unified anthropologically, each within itself.

When these areas were analyzed with respect to the homogeneity of each, having regard to the metric and morphological characters of their constituent county blocks, serious doubts arose as to the validity of the area classifications. In some areas there appeared to be morphological or metric directional trends either from the center outward or from one end to another, but these were usually inconsistent. A county block put in some given area often appeared to show striking resemblances to some other county block, geographically rather remote, which had been assigned to quite another area. No area appeared to be homogeneous anthropologically to the extent that its geographical limitation was fully justified.

It was then decided to attempt an over-all measure of metric and morphological resemblance of each county block to every one of the 18 others in Ireland (tables VI-1 through VI-19). A simple method of rating such resemblances was desirable. Such devices as the coefficient of racial likeness, Mahalanobis' positional index, the simpler measure of the average differences between means, are not only laborious but unsatisfactory. They are further less suitable for morphological observations (attributes) than for measurements (variables). The method of measuring resemblances here adopted was by rank affinity position of the means of measurements and indices and by similar ranking of percentages observed in the several blocks of a large number of the more important categories of morphological observations.

Thus 34 metric features and 41 morphological observations were ranked for each of the 19 county blocks. Resemblances of one county block to another were rated solely on the basis of the number of adjacent rankings in the two blocks involved. Thus, if Antrim-Down had a ranking of 12 in stature, the two closest county blocks to Antrim-Down were N. Fermanagh-E. Donegal-Tyrone-Londonderry 11, and W. Donegal 13. Adjacent rankings for morphological observations had to be a little more elaborate. Sometimes only the leading category of an attribute was ranked; sometimes the excess of that category over other categories.

It is assumed that if Antrim-Down, e.g., has as its mode 13 adjacent rankings to E. Cavan-Monaghan-Armagh and 12 to N. Fermanagh-E. Donegal-Tyrone-Londonderry, it is these blocks which Antrim-Down most closely resembles morphologically. If Antrim-Down shows but one adjacent ranking to Tipperary-Kilkenny, there is little morphological affinity between the blocks.

Of course it is very easy to raise objections to such a method. In the first place the means were ranked without reference to the significance of differences between them, but on absolute figures down to the second decimal place, and the percentages of attributes similarly. Such a method may lead to the selection of blocks for the favored position of adjacent rankings which are statistically no nearer the block under consideration than some others. Most of the other objections are those that apply equally to the various other schemes which have been used for a similar purpose. The C.R.L. measures probability of mean difference rather than extent of it. The simple mean difference of means neglects the significance of differences also. All such devices lump together measures of differing magnitudes and observations of differing importance without any proper weighting of the various components. No one knows how to make such a weighting, and, if it were made, it might be valid for one race or group and invalid for another.

Considering everything, the method here employed has the virtue of simplicity and probably no more vices than other methods mentioned, most of which involve endless computations.

The results of these resemblance ratings on the basis of adjacent rankings have been discussed briefly under the analysis of each area. The rank tables are also appended. The sole effect upon the previously delimited areas was to demonstrate the superfluity of the region called southeastern, which consisted of Waterford-Wexford, Tipperary-Kilkenny, and Wicklow-Carlow. The adjacent rank method showed that these counties could just as well be put with the main eastern central area.

Otherwise, not another county block was shifted from one area to another on the basis of rankings. Usually no such shift was indicated from the resemblances thus determined. If a county block was closer morphologically to a member block of another area than that to which it had been assigned, usually the resemblance did not stand up metrically. In a few instances the shift could not be made without violating the principle of geographical continuity.

NORTH IRISH AREA

The North Irish geo-ethnographically delimited area includes W. Donegal, N. Fermanagh-E. Donegal-Tyrone-Londonderry, and Antrim-Down. The counties of Ulster that it excludes are S. Fermanagh-W. Cavan and E. Cavan-Monaghan-Armagh. None of these fits anthropologically with the North Irish Area. The southern boundary of the North Irish Area begins at the west of Donegal Bay along the line of the southern delimitation of Donegal, and thence follows the course of the river Erne and Lower and Upper Loughs Erne. From there it proceeds along the boundaries between Fermanagh and Cavan, Monaghan and Tyrone, Armagh and Tyrone, following the course of the Blackwater River for the greater part of the way up to its mouth in Lough Neagh. It runs along the southern shore of this Lough and then follows the boundary between Armagh and Down south to Carlingford Lough.

The western and central part of this region is, for the most part, the old Dalradian series of metamorphic rocks, but in the south of Tyrone it includes a considerable region of Old Red Sandstone hills, and some Lower Carboniferous limestone and sandstone with coal measures. The northeastern part (Antrim) is a basaltic plateau fringed with chalk. The southeastern corner (Down) is Silurian slate and sandstone, with the Eocene granite of the Mourne mountains in the extreme southwestern corner.

The affinities of the blocks constituting the North Irish area are, on the basis of adjacent rankings, as follows:

N. FERMANAGH-E. DONEGAL-TYRONE-LONDONDERRY

Metric. West Donegal 9, Antrim-Down 9, Wicklow-Carlow 8.

Morphological. Antrim-Down 13, E. Cavan-Monaghan-Armagh 12, Wicklow-Carlow 8.

ANTRIM-DOWN

Metric. Waterford-Wexford 10, Wicklow-Carlow 9, N. Fermanagh-E. Donegal-Tyrone-Londonderry 8, West Donegal 7.

Morphological. E. Cavan-Monaghan-Armagh 13, N. Fermanagh-E. Donegal-Tyrone-Londonderry 12, Meath-Louth-Dublin 10.

WEST DONEGAL

Metric. Tipperary-Kilkenny 9, Antrim-Down 8, N. Fermanagh-E. Donegal-Tyrone-Londonderry 8.

Morphological. Mayo 10, Kerry 9, Cork 9, Limerick 9.

On the basis of the above rankings, the central block, N. Fermanagh- E. Donegal-Tyrone-Londonderry, is metrically closest to its neighbors to the east and west, and morphologically closest to Antrim-Down, but much nearer to the E. Cavan block than to West Donegal. Antrim-Down has its closest metric affinities to geographically remote counties and is closer to E. Cavan than to N. Fermanagh morphologically. West Donegal shows secondary metric affinities to the other subseries of the north, but its morphological resemblances are mostly elsewhere and far afield.

This area, then, is not well integrated on the basis of rankings. It can be said only that to tear any of its constituent blocks from the geographical setting and put them elsewhere would not improve matters anthropologically.

The educational rankings in the area are Antrim-Down 3, N. Fermanagh-E. Donegal-Tyrone-Londonderry 7, West Donegal 16. The last named county is a stronghold of the Keltic language, ranking third in percentage of native speakers. The other two counties have little acquaintance with the ancient tongue. The Antrim-Down group is at the Irish county minimum in this respect.

Since this area includes the industrial region surrounding Belfast and Londonderry, the population sample tends to be less rural than most other Irish areas, with the exception of West Donegal which has its full quota and more of agriculturalists, herdsmen and farm dependents. In the area, as a whole, there tend to be excesses of semi-skilled and transport workers, factory operatives, shop keepers and assistants, clerks and professional men.

The total anthropometric sample from the area is 672 men. All of the subseries are below the Irish county age mean to the extent of approximately 3 years.

All are below the average weight of the total series (deficiencies: Antrim-Down 3 pounds, West Donegal 2 pounds, N. Fermanagh-E. Donegal-Tyrone-Londonderry 1.7 pounds). They are all slightly under mean Irish stature, but not significantly so. Antrim-Down alone is significantly low in absolute span, but all three subseries are virtually the same in relative span, and conform closely to the Irish mean. Shoulder breadth and relative shoulder breadth are closely similar in the three, and little divergent from the series mean. Each of the three subseries is slightly low in chest breadth but close to average in chest depth. In the thoracic index they form a block virtually at the series mean, with West Donegal a little below and the two others slightly above. Antrim-Down is a little low in absolute and relative sitting height, but not signficantly so; the other two are very close to the total county mean. The west and east counties are somewhat short in head length and the central county a little higher, but still slightly below the total series mean. Head breadth is highest in West Donegal and a little above average. It declines somewhat from the middle to the east with both of the latter county subgroups slightly below par. The cephalic index is also a little higher than average in West Donegal, with the other two lower and straddling the series mean. All are below average in head circumference, but above it in head height, with the center of the block (N. Fermanagh-E. Donegal-Tyrone-Londonderry) achieving the Irish maximum. In the height-length index all three county series are well above mean Irish values and the same is true of breadth-height except that West Donegal's excess over the series mean is trifling. So the entire northern block shows tendencies toward hypsicephaly and acrocephaly when contrasted with the total Irish county series. These tendencies are exaggerated in the central of the three subseries.

All fall below average in face breadth (lowest in Antrim-Down) and they are all insignificantly low in the cephalo-facial index. Total face height in West Donegal is at the Irish mean, and in the other two counties insignificantly lower. Total facial indices cluster about the Irish average. But upper face heights in these counties are all elevated, differences increasing from insignificance in West Donegal to certain statistical validity in Antrim-Down. In consequence of long and narrow upper faces, all of these three subseries have elevated upper facial indices. Yet noses are rather short in this region, perhaps partly because of low mean age. Nasal breadths are low in Antrim-Down and West Donegal, but average in the central block. In consequence there is some diversity of the means of the nasal index with N. Fermanagh-E. Donegal-Tyrone-Londonderry at the Irish county maximum (65.14), Antrim-Down close to the total series mean with 64.10 and West Donegal quite low with 63.78, which places it seventeenth in the 19 county subseries.

The three blocks are again at variance in the minimum frontal diameter, which is high in West Donegal, at the mean in the central group, and definitely low in Antrim-Down. The fronto-parietal index behaves accordingly, decreasing from west to east. The same is true of the zygo-frontal index. Bigonial diameters in these three subseries are all low, and so is the zygo-gonial index, which decreases from west to east in a manner consonant with the gradations of the previous two indices.

We must now consider the morphological resemblances and differences.

West Donegal has slightly more swarthy skins than total Irish (1.9 per cent), whereas the central block and Antrim-Down have none at all. Again, West Donegal is a trifle low in pronounced vascularity, which increases in the center and reaches a notable high in Antrim-Down. All three regions are high in freckles, but West Donegal leads all Ireland in this feature, the frequency of which diminishes from west to east. The greatest excess of straight hair occurs in the central block; West Donegal is slightly high, and Antrim-Down a little low. West Donegal is high in deep waved hair, Antrim-Down in curly hair. Coarse hair increases from west to east as do quantities of head hair, beard hair, and body hair. In hair color there is a diminution of black from west to east; an increase in dark brown. Flat brown and golden brown are highest in the central block; red hair is most frequent in the west. On the whole, then, dark hair diminishes from west to east.

The central block leads in combined light eyes, ranking first in the Irish counties, whereas Antrim-Down is fifth and West Donegal away down at seventeenth. The last named county is especially high in the mixed blue-brown eyes, in which the center and east are deficient. The western block is darkest in eye color. External eyefolds are much commoner in the center and in the east, and eye slant in these two subseries (Antrim-Down and N. Fermanagh-E. Donegal-Tyrone-Londonderry) is nearly the most pronounced in Ireland. On the other hand, West Donegal is very low in eye slant. The last has fewer large brow ridges than the total Irish series. The reverse obtains in the more easterly blocks.

The first notable morphological agreement comes in the great predominance of high foreheads in the whole region, but this is less marked in West Donegal than in the other two subareas. Submedium and medium forehead heights decrease from west to east and high foreheads increase. But pronounced forehead slope is less common in West Donegal

than in the center and east. Pronounced nasion depressions also increase from west to east, achieving the Irish maximum in Antrim-Down. This is in conformity with the increase in the proportion of large brow ridges from west to east.

The noses of West Donegal also appear to be different from those in the two more easterly county subgroups. Nasal roots tend to be a little higher and narrower in West Donegal than in the other two subseries, and the nasal bridges definitely lower and narrower, with more convex septa, thinner tips, and more convex profiles. Straight nasal profiles increase from west to east; convex and concave profiles decrease. Curiously, however, to the east of West Donegal nasal wings flare more.

Thick integumental and membranous lips are commoner in the eastern blocks, although medium developments overwhelmingly predominate in both. Both submedium and pronounced lip eversion are less common in West Donegal than in the other two blocks. Alveolar prognathism is practically absent in West Donegal, but occurs in very small proportions farther east, with Antrim-Down insignificantly the highest. Incomplete tooth eruption is rarer in Antrim-Down than in the more westerly subseries, although all three blocks are of approximately the same mean age. Since this mean age is well below the total Irish average, it may or may not account for the better than average teeth which characterize the entire region.

Pronounced lateral projection of the malars tends to be below average in Antrim-Down, above average in the central block and even higher in the west. All have more than ordinary projection of gonial angles. There is no marked regional homogeneity in morphological details of the ear. Development of the helix decreases from east to west; large ear lobes similarly diminish; aural protrusion is far more marked in the two central blocks than in West Donegal.

Extremes of temporal fullness and occipital protrusion are far less common in West Donegal than in the two eastern blocks. Antrim-Down is very high in medium developments of these features. However, all three counties rank high in excess of pronounced occipital protrusion over submedium protrusion. Lambdoid flattening is above average in West Done-gal, and by far the most rare in all Ireland in the two eastern blocks. Exactly the reverse obtains in occipital flattening.

SUMMARY OF SOCIOLOGICAL FEATURES

The region is sociologically diverse, although the eastern block and the central block present many resemblances.

SUMMARY OF METRIC FEATURES

UNIFORMITIES	EXCEPTIONS
Below average age	—
Below average weight	—
Below average stature	—
Par in relative span	—
Par in shoulder breadth	—
Par in relative shoulder breadth	—
Low in chest breadth	—
Par in chest depth	—
Par in thoracic index	—
Below average head circumference	—
Above average head height	—
Above average length-height index	—
Above average breadth-height index	—
Below average face breadth	—
Low in cephalo-facial index	—
Par in total facial index	—
Above average in total face height	—
Above average total facial index	—
Below average nose length	—
Below average bigonial diameter	—

SUMMARY OF MORPHOLOGICAL FEATURES

UNIFORMITIES	EXCEPTIONS
Generally dark hair	—
High in freckles	—
Excess of high foreheads	—
More than ordinary gonial projection	—
Excess of occipital protrusion	—

The metric data of the northern area show some impressive uniformities. Some of these are probably referable to the coincidence that all of the blocks are below mean age.

Taking all of the morphological data together, regional homogeneity is notable by its absence. West Donegal usually stands apart from the other two subseries. Of course, all three blocks have excesses of high foreheads and pronounced gonial angles, together with generally dark hair. But skins are oftener dark and freckles more greatly in excess in the west than in the east. Black hair and the more rufous shades are also commoner in West Donegal. So are blue-brown mixed eyes; whereas blue eyes prevail in the east and the center, with more external folds and more upward slant of the eyes. Brow ridges are smaller in the west and foreheads less sloping; nasion depressions less marked, noses less prominent but more often convex; lips thinner and less everted, alveolar prognathism more consistently absent, lambdoid flattening commoner and occipital flattening far more rare.

It is of great interest that many of the morphological features in which West Donegal departs strongly from the two other blocks of the area ally the former with the western peninsular areas of Mayo and Kerry, and with Cork and Limerick, which are adjacent to the last two. However, metrically, West Donegal is as remote from those counties as it is geographically.

EASTERN IRISH AREA

The eastern geo-ethnographical area lies between the Shannon and Lake Erne on the west and the Irish Sea on the east. Northwestward, its boundary runs from Upper Lake Erne to the southern shore of Lough Neagh. Its northwestern boundary is the county line between Armagh and Down which runs south from Lough Neagh to Carlingford Lough. In the southwest it is irregularly delimited by the boundary lines between Tipperary and Limerick and between Waterford and Cork. It thus includes the whole eastern half of the island with the exception of Antrim-Down, the two most northerly counties.

The greater part of this region lies in the rich Carboniferous limestone central plains of Ireland. On the northwest, however, and also on the northeast, the three Ulster counties of E. Cavan, Monaghan and Armagh are principally upon the hilly southwest-northeast Silurian axis of slates, shales, and sandstones with outcroppings of granite and extensions into the Carboniferous limestone plain and the Tertiary clays of Lough Neagh. Also in the southwest, in counties Offaly, Leix, and Kildare, the limestone central plain is broken by domes of Old Red Sandstone, sometimes worn through so that the tops are exposures of Silurian slates and shales. An enormous tract is covered by the Bog of Allen. In general, the lowlands of this area are covered with a deep rich loam and are excellent for agriculture when properly drained. In the hilly regions the soil is thinner and poorer, but suitable for pasturage. Wicklow, Carlow, Wexford, and the eastern part of Waterford are Silurian beds of slates and shales. The high range of the Wicklow Mountains running northeast and southwest exposes a continuous core of granite from Dublin south to New Ross, a distance of 70 miles. Most of this region is moorland. In northern and western Waterford the ridges are Devonian Old Red Sandstone, often heather-clad. The synclines, covered with fertile soil are Carboniferous limestone. Kilkenny is largely an extension of the central limestone plain, but the southeastern part belongs to the Wicklow-Carlow Silurian axis and in the north is a high synclinal coal field which yields anthracite. There are also Silurian crests flanked by the Old Red Sandstone. The coal measure plateau and the synclinal axis of Upper Carboniferous slates and shales are also found in the eastern part of Tipperary. This county is largely Carboniferous limestone plain, but broken up with massive elevations of the Old Red Sandstone. Everywhere in this area of the limestone plain, or in valleys lying in the synclines on limestone beds, the land is most fertile. In the north are encroachments of the Bog of Allen; the higher districts, where the soil is thin and poor, are suitable only for pasturage. Here and there coal is mined, together with some lead, silver, and other minerals. Waterford and Wexford are important centers of fishing.

The affinities by adjacent rankings of the county blocks included in this area are as follows:

E. CAVAN-MONAGHAN-ARMAGH

Metric. Offaly-Leix-Kildare, 11, Tipperary-Kilkenny 8, Wicklow-Carlow 7.

Morphological. Waterford-Wexford 13, Antrim-Down 10, N. Fermanagh-E. Donegal-Tyrone-Londonderry 10, Wicklow-Carlow 7.

The morphological affinities of this group lie with the counties to the north as markedly as with those to the south, but the metric resemblances are so clearly with the latter that the block must be placed in the eastern area.

MEATH-LOUTH-DUBLIN

Metric. Wicklow-Carlow 9, Offaly-Leix-Kildare 7, Longford-Westmeath 6.

Morphological. Wicklow-Carlow 13, Antrim-Down 10, Waterford-Wexford 9.

LONGFORD-WESTMEATH

Metric. Antrim-Down 9, E. Cavan-Monaghan-Armagh 7, Sligo-Leitrim-S. Fermanagh-W. Cavan 8, Meath-Louth-Dublin 8.

Morphological. Arans 15, Offaly-Leix-Kildare 10, Mayo 10, E. Galway-Roscommon 9.

Although this county morphologically goes better with the central western group, its metric relations and geographical position seem to justify its inclusion in the eastern area.

OFFALY-LEIX-KILDARE

Metric. Wicklow-Carlow 9, Waterford-Wexford 8, West Donegal 8.

Morphological. E. Galway-Roscommon 9, Longford-Westmeath 8, Wicklow-Carlow 8.

WICKLOW-CARLOW

Metric. Offaly-Leix-Kildare 10, Waterford-Wexford 8, E. Cavan-Monaghan-Armagh 8, Antrim-Down 8.

Morphological. Meath-Louth-Dublin 13, Waterford-Wexford 10, Tipperary-Kilkenny 8.

WATERFORD-WEXFORD

Metric. Antrim-Down 10, Offaly-Leix-Kildare 8, Wicklow-Carlow 7.

Morphological. E. Cavan-Monaghan-Armagh 13, Wicklow-Carlow 10, Meath-Louth-Dublin 9.

TIPPERARY-KILKENNY

Metric. West Donegal 9, E. Cavan-Monaghan-Armagh 8, N. Fermanagh-E. Donegal-Tyrone-Londonderry 6, Cork 6.

Morphological. Wicklow-Carlow 8, Meath-Louth-Dublin 8, Waterford-Wexford 7, E. Cavan-Monaghan-Armagh 7, Kerry 7.

The closest metric affinities (rank method) of both Waterford-Wexford and Tipperary-Kilkenny lie far afield, with Antrim-Down in the former case and with West Donegal in the latter. In metric features, however, Waterford-Wexford's secondary affinities are with the eastern area, and Tipperary-Kilkenny shows second closest relationship to E. Cavan-Monaghan-Armagh. Morphologically, Waterford-Wexford and Tipperary-Kilkenny are solidly a part of the eastern area.

This large eastern area with its seven blocks

of counties, comprising altogether 16½ counties, is educationally diversified. In educational ranking we have the following array: Longford-Westmeath 2, Tipperary-Kilkenny 9, Meath-Louth-Dublin 10, E. Cavan-Monaghan-Armagh 14, Wicklow-Carlow 15, Waterford-Wexford 17, Offaly-Leix-Kildare 18. Illiteracy is especially high in Waterford-Wexford and Wicklow-Carlow, possibly to some extent because the samples from these blocks are well above mean age. For the opposite reason (youth), the Longford-Westmeath sample ranks very high educationally. Otherwise this area (with the exception of Tipperary-Kilkenny) is educationally far below the Irish average.

The eastern area is also very low in Irish speakers except Waterford-Wexford, which has 5.8 per cent (as against an average of 13.8 per cent in the total Catholic county series of 19 blocks). In this eastern area, individuals who have "no Irish" constitute from 61.2 to 66.1 per cent of the county samples.

Most of the county blocks in this area are excessively high in hired laborers and tinkers, the lowest occupational class. Thus in this category, Wicklow-Carlow ranks first in all Ireland with 22.8 per cent; E. Cavan-Monaghan-Armagh is second with 17.3 per cent; Offaly-Leix-Kildare third with 16.5 per cent; Meath-Louth-Dublin sixth with 14.6 per cent. Longford-Westmeath is very low in this class (2.8 per cent).

On the other hand, all of the county blocks in this area are decidedly low in herdsmen, farmers, farm stewards, and gardeners, except Wicklow-Carlow, which is only a little below average. All are also low in farm dependents except Longford-Westmeath, which is decidedly high.

Waterford-Wexford alone in the area is very high in fishermen. Navvies tend to be strongly in excess in Longford-Westmeath, but elsewhere slightly above average, or close to average. Semi-skilled trades are over-represented only in Tipperary-Kilkenny, transportation in Waterford-Wexford, factory workers are in general very rare. Except in Wicklow-Carlow the urban occupations are more strongly represented than the rural.

The age range in this area includes a spread from the lowest in the Irish county series (Longford-Westmeath, 30.25 years) to the highest (Waterford-Wexford, 40.90 years). The Wicklow-Carlow sample is also decidedly above mean age.

All county blocks in this area are below mean weight except Tipperary-Kilkenny. The Longford-Westmeath sample is the lightest in Ireland and the Meath-Louth-Dublin group second lightest. This area takes the six lowest places in stature rankings with only Tipperary-Kilkenny ranking tenth, nearly up to the Irish mean. A similar situation prevails in the case of span. Relative span is comparatively variable in this area, although it is consistently high everywhere in Ireland. There is nothing remarkable about the area as regards biacromial diameter and relative shoulder breadth.

Chest breadths run consistently below total Irish series means, but chest depths are quite erratic with the elderly sample from Waterford-Wexford at the Irish maximum and Longford-Westmeath, the most juvenile group, next to the minimum. All of the groups except Longford-Westmeath are notable for high thoracic indices, with Wicklow-Carlow and Waterford-Wexford ranking first and second in all Ireland, and the other four counties occupying the third to sixth places. But Longford-Westmeath ties for seventeenth place. Age disparity may have a good deal to do with this wide variability (see Hooton and Dupertuis, 1951, p. 17).

Sitting heights are low throughout the area, except in Tipperary-Kilkenny. Wicklow-Carlow has the highest relative sitting height in Ireland with Meath-Louth-Dublin second, but in the other counties there is no consistency of rank order.

In head length there is a clear decrease in this area from north to south, with the Irish minimum reached in the Waterford-Wexford sample. In head breadth, Tipperary-Kilkenny is exactly at the Irish county mean, but the other six counties occupy the last rankings of the Irish counties. Generally speaking, this area is noted for dolichocephaly and for relative scarcity of brachycephals (except in Tipperary-Kilkenny). Longford-Westmeath, Meath-Louth-Dublin and E. Cavan-Monaghan-Armagh are (except the Arans) the most consistently dolichocephalic regions of Ireland. Head circumferences diminish from north to south and are usually below Irish averages (except Tipperary-Kilkenny). Head heights are all above mean values except in Longford-Westmeath, which ranks eighteenth among the Irish counties. The length-height means are widely spread, with the southern counties showing high rankings, Meath-Louth-Dublin and E. Cavan-Monaghan-Armagh at the Irish mean, but Longford-Westmeath away down in eighteenth place.

Breadth-height indices are similarly high, except in Longford-Westmeath. With the exception of Tipperary-Kilkenny (which is insignificantly below the total Irish average), bizygomatic diameters in this area are very low. Total face heights range from the series minimum in the youthful Longford-Westmeath sample to the third ranking achieved by E. Cavan-Monaghan-Armagh. There is no areal homogeneity in this measurement, which is largely affected by age composition.

Facial index means run consistently high with the maximum in E. Cavan-Monaghan-Armagh, grading down to Tipperary-Kilkenny, which is still above the total Irish mean. Upper face height shows a wide spread, with Tipperary-Kilkenny tied for second place in Irish county averages and Longford-Westmeath at the bottom of the ranking. However, upper facial indices average very high except in Longford-Westmeath. Bottom and top rankings in this index occur within the area.

Nose heights are also widely diversified. The Longford-Westmeath sample ranks nineteenth or lowest among the Irish counties, perhaps in part because of its similar ranking in age. However, the Waterford-Wexford and Wicklow-Carlow series rank seventh and eighth in nose height, although they are the oldest in mean age. Nose breadths also show a wide range (considering the restricted range of the total 19 blocks of counties). The nasal index yields the following rankings: Meath-Louth-Dublin 3, Offaly-Leix-Kildare 5, E. Cavan-Monaghan-Armagh 6, Longford-Westmeath 10, Wicklow-Carlow 11, Waterford-Wexford 13, Tipperary-Kilkenny 19. This distribution merely suggests some slight decrease of the index from north to south.

There is no uniformity in minimum frontal diameter, nor in the fronto-parietal index, although the highest rankings of this index occur in this area. Longford-Westmeath ties for sixteenth place.

With the exception of Longford-Westmeath, the whole area shows high values of the zygo-frontal index. It holds 6 of the 7 first rankings in this measure (West Donegal is second).

Bigonial diameters run well below Irish means except in Tipperary-Kilkenny and Waterford-Wexford. Zygo-gonial indices are high except in Longford-Westmeath, and E. Cavan-Monaghan-Armagh. However, the fronto-gonial index shows no uniformity.

This area presents no uniformity in skin color. Longford-Westmeath and Meath-Louth-Dublin are among the darkest skinned, as is Offaly-Leix-Kildare. Waterford-Wexford and Wicklow-Carlow are medium. E. Cavan-Monaghan-Armagh is one of the lighter-skinned county blocks. The area as a whole is low in pronounced vascularity, with Wicklow-Carlow alone slightly above par. All blocks are low in freckling.

There is no homogeneity in hair form. The southern blocks are high in straight hair, as is also E. Cavan-Monaghan-Armagh in the north. Longford-Westmeath and Offaly-Leix-Kildare lead in curved hair. There is more baldness in this area than elsewhere, but Longford-Westmeath has the least in Ireland. This feature is largely dependent upon age. A similar situation obtains in the case of grayness. The area is on the whole very high in dark hair, with Longford-Westmeath the only divergent block, ranking eighteenth in combined dark hair. It is also very low in combined brown and red hair, except again Longford-Westmeath. All blocks of the area are high in combined light eyes except Tipperary-Kilkenny, which is insignificantly below the total Irish mean. All blocks are low in mixed eyes, save again Tipperary-Kilkenny.

All of the areas except Longford-Westmeath are high in obliquity of the eye-slits. There is no uniformity in size of brow ridges nor in forehead height. Pronounced forehead slopes are commonest in the southern blocks of the area.

Pronounced nasion depressions are in evidence except in E. Cavan-Monaghan-Armagh and Longford-Westmeath. Pronounced nasal root heights increase strongly from north to south. Nasal root breadths are generally pronounced except in Longford-Westmeath. Bridge heights are great in the south, but diminish to the north and reach the total series minimum in Longford-Westmeath, with Offaly-Leix-Kildare below par. Nasal bridges also tend to run wide except, again, in Longford-Westmeath. The same is true of tip thickness. Nasal profiles show no homogeneity and no clear trend. The whole area is high in midfacial prognathism.

The area is also high in tooth loss but shows no uniformity in the caries index. Except in Tipperary-Kilkenny, lateral malar projection is below the Irish mode. Projection of gonial angles also runs low except in Wicklow-Carlow. Pronounced occipital protrusions tend to exceed the Irish mean except in Longford-Westmeath. Lambdoid flattening is relatively infrequent except in Longford-Westmeath. Occipital flattening is unduly common except in Longford-Westmeath.

SUMMARY OF SOCIOLOGICAL FEATURES

The area ranks very low educationally (except Longford-Westmeath), and is very low in persons with a knowledge or speaking ability of Irish. It is high in the lowest occupational class (hired laborers and tinkers), except in Longford-Westmeath, where this class excess is replaced by a superabundance of "navvies" and farm dependents. Otherwise the area is low in agriculturalists. By and large, the occupational status of this area is low.

SUMMARY OF METRIC FEATURES

UNIFORMITIES	EXCEPTIONS
Low mean weight	Tipperary-Kilkenny
Low mean stature	Tipperary-Kilkenny
Low mean span	Tipperary-Kilkenny
Low mean chest breadth	—
High mean thoracic index	Longford-Westmeath
Low mean sitting height	Tipperary-Kilkenny
Low mean head breadth	Tipperary-Kilkenny
Marked dolichocephaly	Tipperary-Kilkenny
Low mean head circumference	Tipperary-Kilkenny
High mean head height	Longford-Westmeath
High mean breadth-height index	Longford-Westmeath
Low mean bizygomatic diameter	Tipperary-Kilkenny
High mean total facial index	—
High mean upper facial index	Longford-Westmeath
High mean zygo-frontal index	Longford-Westmeath

Low mean bigonial diameter	Tipperary-Kilkenny and Waterford-Wexford

TRENDS, NORTH TO SOUTH, OR VICE VERSA
Head length—decrease north to south
Head breadth—increase north to south
Head circumference—decrease north to south
Cephalic index—decrease north to south
Length-height index—increase north to south
Bizygomatic diameter—increase north to south
Bigonial diameter—increase north to south
Zygo-gonial index—increase north to south

The county blocks which tend to mar the unity of the area are Tipperary-Kilkenny and Longford-Westmeath. The former block has widely scattered and geographically far flung metric affinities, as has the latter. Neither can be put more naturally or satisfactorily in any other area.

SUMMARY OF MORPHOLOGICAL FEATURES

UNIFORMITIES	EXCEPTIONS
Low in pronounced vascularity	Wicklow-Carlow
Low in freckling	—
High in dark hair	Longford-Westmeath
Low in combined brown and red hair	Longford-Westmeath
High in combined light eyes	Tipperary-Kilkenny
Low in mixed eyes	Longford-Westmeath
High in eye obliquity	Longford-Westmeath
High in pronounced nasal root breadth	Longford-Westmeath
High in wide nasal bridges	Longford-Westmeath
High in nasal tip thickness	Longford-Westmeath
High in mid-facial prognathism	—
High in tooth loss	—
Low in lateral malar projection	Tipperary-Kilkenny
High in pronounced occipital protrusion	Longford-Westmeath
Low in lambdoid flattening	Longford-Westmeath
High in occipital flattening	Longford-Westmeath and Offaly-Leix-Kildare

TRENDS, NORTH TO SOUTH, OR VICE VERSA
Pronounced nasal root heights—increase north to south
Nasal bridge heights—increase north to south

Here again, Longford-Westmeath and Tipperary-Kilkenny tend to dissociate themselves frequently from the area as a whole. However, they would be even more at variance with other areas if therein included.

SOUTHWESTERN AREA

The Southwestern Area consists of the focal subarea, County Kerry, the peripheral subareas, Cork and Limerick, and the transitional subarea, Clare. Kerry is mountainous, barren, and damp. The hills and rocks are mostly of the Old Red Sandstone from the Devonian. Carboniferous limestone underlies some of the valleys. The western part of Cork is of geological formation identical with that of Kerry and the country is similarly wet and sterile. However, that part of Cork which is north of the Blackwater is more level and more fertile. There are anticlinal ridges of sandstone and synclinal limestone valleys. Also the southern part of the county is Lower Carboniferous sandstone and shale and is lower lying and perfectly suitable for agriculture. Limerick is mostly in the central limestone plain, but has outcroppings of the Old Red Sandstone. It is, on the whole, a very fertile county. Western Clare is covered with Upper Carboniferous strata, consisting of alternate shales and sandstones. On the north are barren limestone terraces, and on the east, masses of Old Red Sandstone with Silurian cores. Almost the only good land is found in the southern part, along the low banks of the Fergus and the Shannon.

The affinities by adjacent rankings of the county blocks included in this area are as follows:

KERRY

Metric. Cork 11, Clare 9, E. Galway-Roscommon 8, Limerick 3.

Morphological. West Donegal 10, Cork 9, Limerick 9, Clare 8, Tipperary-Kilkenny 8.

CORK

Metric. Clare 16, Kerry 7, Limerick 7.

Morphological. West Donegal 10, Clare 8, Kerry 8, Limerick 8, N. Fermanagh-E. Donegal-Tyrone-Londonderry 8.

CLARE

Metric. Cork 16, Mayo 10, Kerry 8, Limerick 8.

Morphological. West Galway 12, Sligo-Leitrim-S. Fermanagh-W. Cavan 8, Kerry 8, Cork 7, Limerick 6, E. Galway-Roscommon 6.

LIMERICK

Metric. West Donegal 9, Cork 7, Clare 7.

Morphological. Cork 11, Kerry 9, West Donegal 9.

On the whole, the four county blocks above named go together, although occasional aberrant similarities crop out such as morphological similarities of Cork and Kerry with West Donegal, and both metric and morphological similarities of Limerick with the same county.

Educationally, the only backward county of the Southwestern Area is Kerry, which is tied for eleventh place with the Sligo group. Clare ranks fourth, Cork fifth, Limerick sixth.

All of the counties except Limerick are strongholds of Keltic speech. Kerry with 44.2 per cent of Irish speakers, has nearly three times the proportion found in Clare, and nearly 3½ times as many as Cork. Limerick has only 3.2 per cent of Irish speakers as compared with 13.8 per cent for the total series.

The low occupational class of hired laborers and tinkers is somewhat high in Limerick (10.7 per cent), a trifle above average in Kerry (8.2 per cent), but very low in Clare (3.8 per cent) and in Cork (4.1 per cent).

The whole area is markedly deficient in herdsmen, farmers, farm stewards, gardeners, and farm dependents except Clare, which is only a little below average in these occupations. Kerry, with 13.4 per cent of fishermen, leads all of the Irish counties in this occupation. Cork is fairly high in fishermen, but the other counties are very low. Navvies are excessively common in Clare (34.7 per cent) and in Limerick (31.5 per cent) but somewhat below average in the other two counties. All are moderately high in semi-skilled trades except Kerry, which is insignificantly below average. Cork has about 3 per cent excess of transport workers; the other areas are average. Shop workers are a little in excess in Cork and Limerick and deficient to approximately the same amount (2 per cent) in the other two counties. Clare leads all of the Irish county blocks in clerks (4.4 per cent) and these are well represented in the other counties of the area except Kerry. Except in Limerick, the professions are above average. Cork leads all Ireland with 5.4 per cent. The area is also somewhat high in students, except, again, Limerick. Soldiers are in excess in Cork but markedly deficient in Clare.

Our anthropological sample from this geo-ethnographical region includes 2400 men, of whom 946 come from County Clare. A special effort was made to secure a big series in this county because it was the focus of our social anthropological studies. Three of the four subgroups of this area are above mean age (Cork, Clare, and Kerry) with excesses ranging from 1.55 years to 1.65 years. Limerick men are only 0.10 years above mean age.

All are above mean weight, with excesses ranging from 0.6 in Limerick to 3.2 pounds in Kerry. Rankings in mean weight for the total Irish county series are Kerry 4, Cork 5, Clare 6, Limerick 8. All the counties of the area are also above mean stature, with the exception again of Limerick which is at the Irish mean. Shoulder breadth is very high in Clare and Kerry, average in Cork, and insignificantly low in Limerick. In relative shoulder breadth Clare is rather high, Limerick slightly low. Clare has definitely high chest breadth and the other three counties are somewhat above average. All except Limerick are also above mean chest depth. In thoracic index Cork is slightly high, Kerry close to average, and the other two counties somewhat low. Sitting height in Kerry is highest for all Ireland; it is slightly to moderately elevated in the other counties. Relative sitting height is a little high throughout the area.

Kerry is the only county of the area which falls distinctly below the mean of Irish head length. All of the counties of the area have marked excesses of head breadth. The rankings for all Ireland are Kerry 1, Clare 2, Cork 3, Limerick 4. Similarly, all counties are more brachycephalic than the Irish average and occupy the first four rankings in this index. Circumference is high in Clare and Cork, but low in Kerry and Limerick. The last named is significantly high in head height, but the other counties cluster around the total series mean.

The length-height index is slightly elevated in Cork and Limerick, but all of the counties are definitely low in the breadth-height index. All have marked excesses of facial breadth. Kerry, Clare and Cork occupy the first 3 places in the Irish rankings of this measurement. Limerick is sixth. However, there is no unanimity of total face height. Kerry (127.45 mm.) is insignificantly high: Cork is

at the Irish mean; the other counties are low. The total facial index in this region is lower than anywhere else in Ireland. The constituent counties occupy the four lowest Irish rankings. Upper face height is well above average in Kerry and Cork, but not in Clare and Limerick. Clare has a mean upper facial index insignificantly below that of the total series; Limerick is insignificantly low.

All of the counties in this area except Limerick have very long noses. Rankings in Irish series are: Kerry 2, Cork 3, Clare 4, Limerick 12. However, the mean nose height of Limerick is not significantly low. There is no homogeneity of nose breadth but nasal indices average slightly low except in Cork.

Minimum frontal diameters are high in Clare and Cork, but near average in the other two counties. Precisely the opposite obtains in the fronto-parietal index. Bigonial diameters are high except in Limerick. Kerry is divergent in showing a very high fronto-gonial index.

All of the counties are slightly high in pink skin. All are high in freckles except Clare, which is definitely low. The region is heterogeneous in hair form, hair quantity and hair color. All counties, however, are high in blue-brown eyes and low in pure blue eyes. Clear iridical patterns are deficient, and diffuse patterns unusually common in all four counties. High foreheads are in excess except in Clare, where they are notably deficient. The whole region has an overwhelming excess of convex nasal septa and convex nasal profiles. Integumental lip thickness is not often pronounced in any part of the area, which, as a whole, is unusually deficient in mid-facial and alveolar prognathism. This feature may be related to dental loss which is excessive throughout the region. Furthermore these are the worst Irish counties for caries. Crowding of the teeth is also somewhat more common than in the series as a whole. The high mean age of the samples from this area is not irrelevant to the conditions described above. Furthermore, excess chin projection (except in Clare) may to some extent be influenced by falling in of the lips and alveolar borders—a consequence of dental loss and resorption.

In the observations of malars the region shows no uniformity but gonial angles are excessively prominent in Limerick, Kerry, and to a lesser degree, Cork.

All of the counties are low in roll of the helix and, except Clare, high in development of the antihelix. Darwin's point is less frequent than in the Irish series generally. Attached ear lobes are in notable excess, except in Clare. The last county is also distinct from the others in failing to show a surplus of large ear lobes. The whole region runs high in marked aural protrusion. Occipital protrusion is a little less than average. All counties are very high in lambdoid flattening, and all deficient in occipital flattening except Limerick which is just below average. Facial asymmetry is more than ordinarily common, but the excess is least in Kerry.

SUMMARY OF SOCIOLOGICAL FEATURES

UNIFORMITIES	EXCEPTIONS
Good educational status	Kerry
Strong in Keltic speech	Limerick
Deficiency in agriculturalists	—
High in clerks	Kerry
High in professional workers	Limerick

SUMMARY OF METRIC FEATURES

UNIFORMITIES	EXCEPTIONS
High mean age	Limerick
High mean weight	—
High mean stature	Limerick
Above average chest breadth	—
Above average chest depth	Limerick
Above average sitting height	—
Above average relative sitting height	—
High head breadth	—
Excess of brachycephaly	—
Low breadth-height index	—
High bizygomatic diameter	—
Low total facial index	—
Great nose height	Limerick
Slightly low nasal index	Cork
High bigonial diameter	Limerick

SUMMARY OF MORPHOLOGICAL FEATURES

UNIFORMITIES	EXCEPTIONS
High in pink skin	—
High in freckles	Clare
High in blue-brown eyes	—
Low in blue eyes	—
Low in clear irides	—
High in diffuse irides	—
Excess of high foreheads	Clare
Excess of convex nasal septa	—
Excess of convex nasal profiles	—
Deficiency of mid-facial prognathism	—
Deficiency of alveolar prognathism	—
Excessive dental loss	—
Excessive caries	—
More than usual tooth crowding	—
Low roll of the helix	—
Prominent antihelix	Clare
Reduced frequency of Darwin's point	—
Excess of attached ear lobes	Clare
Excess of marked aural protrusion	—
Less than average occipital protrusion	—
Excess of lambdoid flattening	—
Deficient in occipital flattening	—
Common facial asymmetry	—

There is no particular sociological uniformity in the area. However, metrically there are strong intercounty similarities with Limerick frequently diverging from the others. On the morphological side, Clare is most likely to diverge from the other counties. Morphological similarities are fairly impressive except in hair form and hair color.

WEST CENTRAL AREA

The West central geo-ethnographic area consists of Mayo, West Galway, the Aran Islands, E. Galway-Roscommon, Sligo-Leitrim-S. Fermanagh-W. Cavan. The masses of mountains which project westward into the Atlantic are, for the most part, old Dalradian metamorphic rocks, schists, quartzite, with intrusions of granite. Here and there they are overlaid with Silurian strata. Further to the east in the area, the mountains give way to the Carboniferous limestone plain. The sub-area in the northwest part of this plain, Sligo-Leitrim-S. Fermanagh-W. Cavan, is a country which is, generally speaking, wooded, but includes many outcroppings of rocky ridges. The climate is very moist, the soil a stiff, cold clay; there are plenty of lakes and bogs. Further south in Roscommon some of the level land, when drained, is very fertile. The Aran Islands are three elevated islands of Carboniferous limestone lying across Galway Bay.

The affinities by adjacent rankings of the

county blocks included in the West Central Area are as follows:

MAYO

Metric. Clare 13, Limerick 8, W. Galway 7, Cork 7, E. Cavan-Monaghan-Armagh 7.

Morphological. Sligo, etc. 7, West Donegal 8, West Galway 7, Longford-Westmeath 7, Arans 6, E. Cavan-Monaghan-Armagh 6.

SLIGO-LEITRIM-S. FERMANAGH-W. CAVAN

Metric. E. Galway-Roscommon 12, Longford-Westmeath 7, Tipperary-Kilkenny 7, Arans 6, Offaly-Leix-Kildare 6, Antrim-Down 6.

Morphological. E. Galway-Roscommon 13, Mayo 9, Clare 8, West Galway 7, Limerick 7.

WEST GALWAY

Metric. Arans 10, E. Galway-Roscommon 7, Mayo 7.

Morphological. E. Galway-Roscommon 14, Clare 11, Mayo 8, Sligo-Leitrim-S. Fermanagh-W. Cavan 7, Longford-Westmeath 7.

ARAN ISLANDS

Metric. West Galway 13, Sligo, etc. 10, Longford-Westmeath 8.

Morphological. Longford-Westmeath 17, E. Galway-Roscommon 9, Mayo 8.

E. GALWAY-ROSCOMMON

Metric. Sligo, etc. 12, West Galway 11, Kerry 8.

Morphological. Sligo, etc. 13, W. Galway 13, Offaly-Leix-Kildare 9.

Rank affinities in the area show the usual contradictions and inconsistencies. Sligo-Leitrim-S. Fermanagh-W. Cavan, West Galway, E. Galway-Roscommon show their closest rank affinities within the area both metrically and morphologically. Mayo is closest morphologically to the Sligo group, but shows nearer metric relationship with Clare. The Arans are closest metrically to West Galway, but are closer morphologically to Longford-Westmeath than to any other block. This resemblance may be due in part to the fact that the Arans and Longford-Westmeath are the two most juvenile county blocks. On the whole, any attempt to shift one of the county blocks to some other area would result in even greater confusion.

The total anthropometric sample from this area is 2352 men. The region runs the entire educational gamut. West Galway is the most illiterate county group in Ireland, whereas the Aran sample has no illiterates and therefore heads Ireland in educational ranking. However, only one of 139 of the Aran men has attended a secondary school or a university. Thus the Aran primacy in the educational ratio is somewhat illusory. E. Galway-Roscommon ranks eighth, Sligo-Leitrim-S. Fermanagh-W. Cavan twelfth, Mayo thirteenth, and West Galway nineteenth.

The area is just as heterogeneous linguistically. The majority from West Galway and the Arans speak Keltic (West Galway 78.3 per cent, Arans 95.7 per cent). Mayo is also an Irish speech stronghold with 24.1 per cent. However, E. Galway-Roscommon has but 12.7 per cent of Keltic speakers and the Sligo block with 0.4 per cent is virtually devoid of men who speak Irish (only 3 of 715).

The region is also occupationally diverse. Mayo is the only block with the ordinary proportion of hired laborers and tinkers. There are none at all in the Arans. On the other hand, there are huge excesses of herdsmen, farmers, farm stewards, and gardeners in all of the counties in the area and big surpluses of farm dependents, except in Sligo-Leitrim-S. Fermanagh-W. Cavan and E. Galway-Roscommon. These classes together constitute 88.5 per cent of the Aran subseries, 52.9 per cent of West Galway, 46.6 per cent of the Sligo block and lesser but still inordinately large proportions of the other blocks. The Arans are highest in fishermen with 5.8 per cent, but this proportion is also illusory, since most Aran men fish in addition to their other occupations. The whole region is also very low in navvies, but otherwise not remarkable.

From the point of view of age, the series is not too heterogeneous. E. Galway-Roscommon is 1.3 years below average; the Arans are 1.2 years below mean county age. Mayo is only a little low (0.45 years) and West Galway insignificantly high (0.65 years).

Every subgroup substantially exceeds the mean weight of the Irish county series, except the Arans, which are one pound light. This deficiency and an excess in the Sligo group are statistically insignificant, but all of the other subareas are significantly heavy. The E. Galway-Roscommon men with an average of 161.0 pounds lead all Ireland with a mean weight of 3.7 pounds above average.

The Mayo and Sligo subgroups are nearly at the Irish average of stature, but the other three subgroups are excessively tall, with the Arans topping all the Irish county series. Nowhere else in Ireland, save in Kerry, do we find mean county stature groups exceeding 173 cm. Absolute span, of course, behaves like stature. In the Mayo subseries and in the Sligo group relative span is significantly high, but in West Galway and excessively in the Arans it is low. In E. Galway-Roscommon it is virtually at the series average. Shoulder breadth is somewhat low in the Arans, about average in Mayo and the Sligo group, but well above the total county mean in West Galway and E. Galway-Roscommon. All relative shoulder breadths are close to the total Irish mean except that of the Arans, which is significantly low. Chest breadths are all high except those of the Sligo group and the Arans, which are near mean value. Chest depths in the area are somewhat variable. They are indubitably high in Mayo, but certainly low in the Arans where they are lowest in the total series. All thoracic indices are low, least so in Mayo, most remarkably in the Arans.

Sitting height is certainly high in E. Galway-Roscommon. The other subareas do not deviate significantly from the total series mean. Relative sitting height is very low in the Arans, significantly low in the Sligo subseries and in West Galway; close to average in the other two subareas.

The leading rankings in head length in Ireland occur in this area with the Arans achieving the Irish maximum (198.36 mm.). Only Mayo is insignificantly low in this measurement, all other subareas have excessive head lengths. Head breadth in Mayo is elevated over the total series mean one whole millimeter; all the other blocks are about average, and occupy adjacent rankings. Mayo is also well above the Irish average in cephalic index (rank 5), while the other blocks are low. The Arans tie with Meath-Louth-Dublin for the lowest mean cephalic index in Ireland.

In head circumferences this area has the first four rankings in Ireland, with Mayo dropping to seventh place in the Irish counties and alone failing to show a significant excess. Head height is low throughout, and in the Arans by far the least in Ireland. Except in the Arans and the Sligo group, the deficiencies in

the other blocks are not statistically significant. Again, all of the groups except Mayo show marked depression of the length-height index, with the Arans far below the range of the other Irish means. The same situation prevails in the breadth-height index, with the Arans far the lowest in Ireland, but in this measure Mayo conforms to the other blocks of the area.

All the subgroups except Sligo and the Arans have significantly high face widths. In this diameter they agree with but do not equal the Southwestern Area. Cephalo-facial indices tend to be high, but hardly significantly so. The Arans and West Galway occupy the two highest rankings in total face height; the other blocks of the area are a trifle over average. The total facial index is low in Mayo and E. Galway-Roscommon, average in Sligo-Leitrim-S. Fermanagh-W. Cavan, high in West Galway, and at the maximum Irish mean in the Arans. Upper face heights in this area tend to be among the shorter values or near the Irish mean (ranks 11 to 18). Even West Galway and the Arans with leading rankings in total face height achieve only low ratings in the upper face height. All upper facial indices are low (thirteenth to nineteenth rankings).

The rankings in mean nose height demonstrate the wide range of the area relative to the spread of county means. They are: Arans 1, West Galway 6, Mayo 9, E. Galway-Roscommon 13, Sligo-Leitrim-S. Fermanagh-W. Cavan 18. Nose breadth varies from the series maximum in West Galway to a tie for thirteenth ranking in E. Galway-Roscommon and the Sligo group. However, the total Irish county range of means is only from 35.24 mm. to 36.59 mm. In conformity with the wide variation of nasal measurements, the nasal index shows a considerable spread in its means. West Galway (rank 2) is very high; Sligo (rank 4) is also high. The lowest value in the area (Arans, 63.90, rank 16) is not significantly below the total Irish mean.

Minimum frontal diameters are also extremely heterogeneous, ranging from significantly high in Mayo (rank 2) to significantly low in the Arans (rank 16). The fronto-parietal index is highest within the area in West Galway (mean 71.35, rank 6) and lowest in the Arans (mean 70.36, rank 19). The zygo-frontal index again reaches its minimum in the

Arans and most of the subregions of the area are in the lower half of the rankings.

Bigonial diameter is highest of all Ireland in the Arans, next in West Galway, and significantly elevated in Mayo, but E. Galway-Roscommon is average and the Sligo group, significantly low. In the zygo-gonial index, Sligo and E. Galway-Roscommon are low; Mayo is middling and the Arans (rank 1) and West Galway (rank 3) are definitely high. The fronto-gonial index shows a range of only one unit in county means. Most of the subareas run a little high, but Mayo varies a little in the opposite direction.

The Aran Islands have an excess of brunet skins (14.4 per cent, second highest in Ireland). All other subareas are as light-skinned or even lighter than the Irish average. West Galway is especially high in vascularity; Mayo and the Arans slightly so; the Sligo and E. Galway groups are somewhat low.

Mayo is a heavily freckled area and the others tend to show more than average of this feature, except West Galway, which has a slight deficiency. All of the subareas are moderately deficient in straight hair except the Arans, which show a marked excess. Elsewhere in the area the straight hair deficiencies are compensated, usually, by concentration of low waved hair. Mayo alone has a significant excess of curly hair, but its total is only 6.4 per cent. Mayo is also conspicuous in the area for a moderate surplus of dark-haired individuals. All of the other subareas are deficient in black and dark brown. In the Arans and in E. Galway-Roscommon the notable excess is in medium or flat brown hair. All subareas are high in red-brown with Mayo least so. The last is the only subarea also which is not high in golden brown hair. Sligo, the Arans, and E. Galway-Roscommon have excesses of red hair.

The area, taken as a whole, is highest in rufosity in Ireland and (except Mayo) lowest in dark hair.

In combined light eyes this area is about in the middle of the Irish distribution, occupying ranks 7 to 15. In combined mixed eyes, Mayo and the Arans are high (tied for fourth ranking); the other subareas rank as follows: West Galway 9, the Sligo group 10, E. Galway-Roscommon 12. There is thus no distinctive position of the area in eye color. However, all of the subareas are notably deficient in eye obliquity. Sligo, the Arans, and E. Galway-Roscommon are somewhat high in pronounced eyebrow concurrency. Brow ridges are irregularly distributed as to size. The Arans lead all Ireland in proportions of large (pronounced and very pronounced) brow ridges. On the other hand, West Galway has fewest big brow ridges in Ireland, and Mayo is also very low in these categories.

Pronounced forehead heights are deficient, except in Mayo. The Arans have by far the fewest high foreheads in Ireland. On the whole, the area is not notable for steep foreheads except Mayo and to a lesser degree Sligo. Moderate forehead slopes tend to prevail.

All of the subareas except Mayo occupy very low rankings in pronounced and very pronounced nasion depressions, but this areal position is not referable to excesses of slight or medium depressions but rather to strong predominance of the medium category. High nasal roots are in strong excess in the Arans and E. Galway-Roscommon, but this feature is not conspicuous elsewhere in the area. Throughout the area, nasal bridges tend to be predominantly of medium height and breadth. Marked excesses of convex septa occur in Mayo, Sligo, and West Galway, whereas the Arans are high in straight and concave septa. Except in Mayo, the proportions of thick nasal tips run low. There is no homogeneity of nasal profile distribution. Mayo has the highest proportion of the relatively uncommon concave noses; the Arans lead in straight nasal bridges at the expense of convex. Sligo and E. Galway-Roscommon are, with the Arans, rather low in convex nasal profiles. Sligo is curiously high (9.9 per cent) in flaring nasal alae; E. Galway-Roscommon is above average. The Arans lead in pronounced frontal visibility of nostrils, but this is a character often associated with juvenility and the Arans are one of our youngest groups.

All of the subareas of this region are low in mid-facial prognathism. Partial tooth eruptions are in notable excess in the Arans and in Sligo; they are deficient in a small degree in West Galway which is the oldest of the subgroups. E. Galway-Roscommon and Sligo are below average in tooth wear. Throughout the area tooth loss is considerably below the Irish average, and much less than can be ascribed reasonably to the somewhat reduced mean age. Caries, however, are notably less frequent than average only in Sligo and the Arans.

The Sligo and West Galway subgroups are conspicuous for pronounced frontal projection of the malars. Mayo and West Galway also have great excesses of lateral projection of malars, whereas Sligo and E. Galway-Roscommon are not remarkable, and this feature is least developed in the Arans of all Irish county subseries. Mayo again is divergent in showing a high ranking (3) and a notable excess of pronounced and very pronounced gonial angles, while the Arans again are at the very bottom of the ranking list.

In Mayo, also, submedium helix rolls are in notable excess, although they are deficient in the other subareas. The distribution of Darwin's point is also rather erratic. It has the lowest frequency in all Ireland in the Arans, and is also below average in Mayo. On the other hand in the Sligo and E. Galway subareas it is found in fair excess. In all of the subareas except Mayo, free ear lobes are in excess. Throughout the area ear lobes tend to be medium in size rather than large.

Pronounced temporal fullness is in excess in all subareas except the Arans, which show a substantial deficit (in fact ranking nineteenth in this feature). The whole area ranks low in occipital protrusion—as an area the lowest in all Ireland. Lambdoid flattening, however, is unusually prevalent, being least marked in Sligo and most pronounced in the Arans. In spite of low rankings in occipital protrusion, the entire area shows a rarity of occipital flattening. Facial asymmetry is rarest in the Arans of all Ireland and below average occurrence also in West Galway.

SUMMARY OF SOCIOLOGICAL FEATURES

This area tends to present extremes sociologically. It has no uniformities.

SUMMARY OF METRIC FEATURES

UNIFORMITIES	EXCEPTIONS
Low mean age	West Galway
High mean weight	Aran Islands
Excessive head length	Mayo
Average head breadth	Mayo
Low cephalic index	Mayo
High head circumference	Mayo
Low head height	—
Low length-height index	Mayo
Low breadth-height index	—
Low upper face height	—
Low upper facial index	—

SUMMARY OF MORPHOLOGICAL FEATURES

UNIFORMITIES	EXCEPTIONS
Prevalence of light skins	Aran Islands
Excess of freckles	West Galway
Deficiency of straight hair	Aran Islands
Excess of low waved hair	Mayo
Deficiency of dark hair	Mayo
High percentage red-brown hair	—
High percentage golden brown hair	Mayo
Deficiency in eye obliquity	—
Deficient pronounced forehead height	Mayo
Low in mid-facial prognathism	—
Low in tooth loss	—
Low in pronounced gonial angles	Mayo
Deficiency in submedium roll of helix	Mayo
Excess of free ear lobes	Mayo
Excess of pronounced temporal fullness	Aran Islands
Low in occipital protrusion	—
High in lambdoid flattening	—
Low in occipital flattening	—

The West Central Area presents little to justify its delimitation except geographically. However, on the anthropological side, not one of its constituent blocks would fit better into any other area previously described. In sociological features this area usually runs the whole range, or nearly all of it, in most characters tabulated. There are some fairly impressive metric uniformities, but usually one of the subareas, commonly Mayo or the Arans, diverges from the others even in these few congruities. The morphological agreements are no more impressive.

CONCLUSIONS

Anyone who has read carefully the foregoing attempt at dividing Ireland into geoethnographical areas will conclude that the areas thus delimited are, in nearly every instance, composed of county blocks which do not cohere anthropologically in any satisfactory way. In other words, the attempt has been a failure.

One reason for the failure might be an erroneous carving up of the island from the point of view of geography. The original combinations of subseries into county blocks (e.g., Antrim-Down) made by Dupertuis were based upon contiguous counties and upon his field impressions of anthropological resemblance within such county blocks. Of course, any county subseries is primarily a geographical subseries, but a county may be quite diversified geographically. A better job of delimiting geo-ethnographic areas might conceivably be done by dividing up the country on the basis of soils, or climate, or vegetation, and breaking down county subseries so as to put each individual on the basis of residence in the area thus delimited. I doubt if anything but chaos would result from such an effort. Soil areas are patchy, not continuous, and the same applies to vegetation areas.

Even if we grant that a better set of geo-ethnographical areas could have been made out of Ireland (and we are wholly willing to have this demonstrated), it seems probable that faulty geographical delimitation is not the villain of the piece.

The whole method of attempting to describe races or groups by combinations of isolated arrays of means and measurements and modes of attributes is, in our opinion, obsolete, fallacious, and downright erroneous. It results in the setting up of hypothetical and entirely supposititious racial or group abstractions, so that a population is described in terms of a non-existent individual characterized by fictional average dimensions and combinations of modal morphological features which in reality may never occur together.

We had thought that physical anthropology was through with this hoary sinner—the fictitious average type—but unfortunately such is not the case. There has arisen a group of geneticists who are interested in physical anthropology, but know little about it, and another group of physical anthropologists who are interested in genetics without knowing much about that, who have revived the old idea of talking about "populations" as if they were races or subspecies. These workers concern themselves with isolated variables and attributes because they are afraid to study individual combinations allegedly for fear that

they will "mistake phenotypes for genotypes." Actually they are afraid to use the term "race" in any except the most generalized application, lest they be accused of "racial discrimination" or of being "racists." They are willing to have "races," but they are loathe to assign any individual to a race, because they think of "races" as being "populations" or "groups." This is absurd. If there is a Negro race, there must be Negroes. The same thinkers, if they can be so designated, are equally opposed to individual constitutional "types"— and for the same reasons.

Now it has seemed crystal clear to me for many years that the first task of physical anthropological science, or of zoological taxonomy, is to describe what goes with what and its second task is to find out why. Let us not dodge the fact that a person with frizzly or woolly hair, black skin, broad nose, thick and everted lips is a Negroid type, a member of the Negro race—in short, a Negro.

If we wish to describe the different physical strains in Ireland, we can describe them intelligibly only by taking individuals who have the same combinations of anatomical features—who "look alike," and delimiting them as "types," "breeds," "subraces" or what will you.

The reason why the adjacent ranking method of similarities yields such chaotic and contradictory resemblances is that morphological modes do not necessarily go with metric averages. In West Donegal the closest affinity in hair coloring, eye color, freckling may be to Mayo, whereas in size and proportions the West Donegal people are closest to the group from Tipperary-Kilkenny. But it is quite possible that if we were to pick out in West Donegal only the individuals of a certain pigmentation combination, they might resemble the similar individuals in Mayo, not only morphologically but also metrically.

Now, for the moment, it matters not a whit whether the people who look alike because they have the same pigmentation, hair form, face and nose shape, body build and stature, owe these similarities to genetic or environmental causation. The important question is "What kinds of Irishmen are there?" And we shall never discover this by studying isolated characters rather than looking at groups of individual whole Irishmen.

PART II

COMPARISON OF CATHOLICS AND PROTESTANTS

INTRODUCTION

COMPOSITION OF THE PROTESTANT SERIES

OUR Protestant Irish series includes a Church of Ireland sample numbering 508 men and a Presbyterian group consisting of 321 men (table VII-1). These two series have been tabulated separately, and also combined to make a total Protestant series of 829 men to be compared with the total Catholic County series of 8909 individuals.

Of the Church of Ireland series, 346 individuals (68.1 per cent) were born in the counties of Ulster. Sligo-Leitrim-S. Fermanagh-W. Cavan, Wicklow-Carlow, and Cork are the strongest Free State contributors to the series. Of the Presbyterian series, 302 men (94.0 per cent) were born in the Ulster counties. County subgroup Antrim-Down is the heaviest contributor to the Presbyterians and N. Fermanagh-E. Donegal-Tyrone-Londonderry is the heaviest contributor to the Church of Ireland series.

SOCIOLOGICAL OBSERVATIONS

Education (Table VIII-1). The Presbyterian series is slightly better educated than the Church of Ireland series, since the former includes no illiterates and no persons who have not received some formal education. The Presbyterians also have an insignificantly higher percentage of university trained men than the other Protestant group. Both Protestant series are better educated than the total Catholic county series. Their superiority does not lie in university men, but in persons who have attended secondary school, and also in the dearth of illiterates. The education ratio, whereby *illiterates* and *read and write only* are divided into *secondary school* plus *university*, gives for Protestants a figure 13.9 as against 3.1 for Catholics in the total county series.

Language (Table VIII-2). There are only two native Irish speakers or persons who speak only Irish in either of the Protestant series, while the Catholic series includes 14.8 per cent of these combined categories. More than twice the proportion of Presbyterians who have studied Irish in school is found in the Church of Ireland series (4 to 9.7 per cent), presumably because more members of the latter series are resident in Eire. However, the percentage of Total Protestants who have had school Irish is only 7.5, as against 30.4 per cent in the large Catholic county series.

Occupation (Table VIII-3). The occupational status of both Protestant series is far superior to that of the combined Catholic county series. In the lowest occupational grade (*hired laborers and tinkers*) the differences between the Presbyterians and the Church of Ireland, and between both combined and the Catholics, are small. The Church of Ireland group has 2 per cent less of hired laborers and tinkers than has the Catholic series, but the Presbyterians exhibit only a one per cent deficiency. Both Protestant groups are slightly higher (about 2 per cent) than the County series in agricultural and pastoral occupations, but the deficiency is

more than overbalanced by the larger proportion of farm dependents found in the Catholic series (7.7 per cent as against 3.5 per cent for total Protestants). If we add both of these two classes together, we find that Protestants have 20.1 per cent and the Catholics 22.3 per cent of farmers, herdsmen, gardeners, stewards, farm dependents, etc.

There are more *fishermen* among the Catholics than Protestants, but this is a small occupational category in both. One of the largest occupational differences is found in the proportions of *navvies* in the respective series. The Presbyterians have 7.9 per cent, the Church of Ireland 9.0 per cent, and the combined Protestants 8.6 per cent. This figure is to be contrasted with the 23.2 per cent in the Catholic series. In *semi-skilled workers* there is practically no difference between Presbyterians and Church of Ireland men, but total Protestants have 12.8 per cent and total Catholics only 8.0 per cent.

In the categories of *transportation, factory workers,* and *skilled trades* the Protestants show interesting excesses. However, in the mercantile class (*shop assistants, small shopkeepers, and merchants*), the Protestants with 21.1 per cent are twice as numerous as the corresponding category in the Catholic series (10.2 per cent). The difference in this category between Presbyterians and Church of Ireland communicants is trifling. Again, the *clerks* among the Protestants are more than twice as numerous as among the Catholics (4.1 per cent and 1.8 per cent respectively). In the very small professional class, the Catholic series has a slight superiority, although conditions are reversed in the case of *students*. A more important difference is the proportional superiority of the Catholic series in *soldiers* (11.6 per cent, as against 4.2 per cent in the combined Protestant series).

In summary it may be said that the main occupational differences between the two series (total Protestants and Catholics) lie in

126

the great excess of navvies among the Catholics and also of soldiers; in the much larger proportions of mercantile workers and semi-skilled workers in the Protestant groups, together with small excesses of nearly all of the more skilled and educationally more demanding occupations. Probably these differences in large measure reflect the more industrial character of Ulster, as compared with Southern Ireland. Evidently the Ulsterites enjoy an occupational superiority which is consistent with their better educational status. On the whole, there is little occupational difference between the two Protestant series, but the small divergences suggest that the Church of Ireland men are more largely rural and agricultural; that the Presbyterians have a very slight superiority in most of the higher occupational grades.

Age (Table IX-1). The Church of Ireland series is 0.9 years older on the average than the total County series, while the Presbyterian series is 0.35 years older. The total Protestant series has a superiority in age over the Catholics amounting to 0.70 years. The difference is statistically insignificant.

Weight. The Presbyterians are 2.70 pounds heavier than the Church of Ireland men and 3.00 pounds heavier than the Catholics. Whereas the Church of Ireland men are insignificantly heavier than the Catholics of the County series, the Presbyterians weight the total Protestant group to a superiority of 1.30 pounds, which is, however, insignificant. The standard deviation of weight is lowest in the Presbyterian series.

Stature. The Church of Ireland series is insignificantly taller than the Catholic series, but the Presbyterians (173.31 cm.) are very tall indeed, and by their inclusion in a total Protestant series give the latter a definite stature superiority over Catholics amounting to 0.66 cm. The only County subgroup that exceeds the stature of the Presbyterians is that of the Aran Islands.

Span and Relative Span. The Church of Ireland span is almost exactly that of the Catholics, but, again, absolute span of the Presbyterians is so much greater that it weights the Protestant series to a definite span superiority over the Catholics. Relative span, as has been remarked, is very high for all of Ireland. The Church of Ireland group differs very little from the Catholic group, but, again, the Presbyterians with a relative span of 105.68 are definitely high, exceeding the total Catholic series by 0.36 units. The total series differences are very small. The relative span of the Presbyterian series is equalled by one Catholic county subgroup and exceeded by another.

Biacromial Diameter and Relative Shoulder Breadth. Absolute shoulder breadth (biacromial) offers the same comparison as span. It is highest in the Presbyterians by a significant margin, and lowest in the Church of Ireland series. Total Protestant and Catholic series differ very little. Relative shoulder breadth is virtually identical in all three series.

Chest Breadth, Chest Depth, and Thoracic Index. Average chest breadth in the Presbyterians is ahead of that of the large Catholic county series, but the Church of Ireland series is the lowest, and weights the Protestant series total to an insignificant deficiency. There is no significant difference in chest depth between Church of Ireland and Presbyterian groups. Both definitely exceed the total Catholic county mean. The thoracic indices of both Protestant series are higher than that of total Catholics, and the Church of Ireland group definitely exceeds the Presbyterian group. Thus the Protestants have relatively narrower and deeper chests. Waterford-Wexford and Wicklow-Carlow are the only Catholic subgroups that equal or exceed the Church of Ireland index, but Cork, Offaly-Leix-Kildare, Meath-Louth-Dublin, Tipperary-Kilkenny, and E. Cavan-Monaghan-Armagh equal or exceed the Presbyterian mean. These comparisons align the Church of Ireland men with the middle east and southeast coastal chest proportions and the Presbyterians with the east central and southwest peninsula thoracic type.

Sitting Height and Relative Sitting Height. The Presbyterians have absolute sitting heights exceeding those of the Church of Ireland series and of the Catholic county series. However, several Catholic county subgroups exceed or virtually equal the Presbyterian figure (Clare, Kerry, Cork, Limerick, E. Galway-Roscommon, etc.). Relative sitting height is lower in both Protestant series than among the Catholics, but Antrim-Down, West Galway, and the Arans all have means lower than those of the Presbyterians. In the case of the Arans the difference is significant. The Arans have a superiority of stature over the Presbyterians.

Head Length. Head length of the Church of Ireland group is insignificantly higher than that of the Catholic series, whereas the mean head length of the Presbyterians is markedly superior to both. The total Protestant series thus has a higher average. The Aran Islanders considerably exceed the Presbyterian mean, and West Galway and E. Galway-Roscommon slightly exceed it.

Head Breadth. Both of the Protestant series are markedly inferior in mean head breadth to the total of the Catholic County series. Yet many counties of the eastern half of Ireland yield subgroup means that approximate the rather low values found in the Protestants. The broad heads of Western Ireland seem to be missing from the Protestant series.

Cephalic Index. There is little difference between the Church of Ireland and Presbyterian groups in cephalic index, but both fall below the total Catholic mean by a significant amount. Among the Catholic subgroups that equal or exceed the Protestants in dolichocephaly are the Arans, Longford-Westmeath, and Meath-Louth-Dublin.

Head Circumference. Head circumference of the Church of Ireland series is inferior to that of the Presbyterians, which, in turn, is insignificantly inferior to that of the Catholics. The total Protestant series is thus inferior in this measurement.

Head Height, Length-Height, and Breadth-Height Indices. Head heights of the Church of Ireland group definitely exceed those of the total Catholic series, while those of the Presbyterians are even higher. The Presbyterians mean (126.22 mm.) is surpassed only by the N. Fermanagh-E. Donegal-Tyrone-Londonderry Catholic subgroups. A number of the Catholic subgroups approach or equal the Church of Ireland mean (West Donegal, Wicklow-Carlow, Tipperary-Kilkenny, Limerick, and Antrim-Down). Length-height indices are approximately equal in both Protestant series, and insignificantly higher than total Catholic values. Many Catholic county subgroups equal or exceed the Protestant mean (64.13). These include, among others, all of the Ulster county groups in the Catholic series except E. Cavan-Monaghan-Armagh. The mean breadth-height index is considerably higher among the Protestants than in the generality of Catholic subgroups. Only three of the Catholic county subgroups attain or exceed the Protestant means. These are Wicklow-Carlow, Meath-Louth-Dublin, and N. Fermanagh-East Donegal-Tyrone-Londonderry.

Bizygomatic Diameter. Facial breadth is deficient in both Protestant series as compared with the Catholic county mean, to the extent of 1.55 mm. in the Church of Ireland series, and 0.75 mm. in the Presbyterian series. The counties of Eastern Ireland present means of bizygomatic diameter that are approximately those of the Protestant groups. In fact, the Catholic county series from this area cluster around the Protestant values.

Cephalo-Facial Index. Presbyterians show the highest mean in this category, with the Church of Ireland lowest, and the Catholics in the intermediate position. Most of the Catholic county subgroups are clustered around the total Protestant mean and differences are slight and insignificant.

Total Face Height. In total face height, the Church of Ireland group is definitely inferior to the Catholic county total; the Presbyterian series insignificantly so. Consequently, the total Protestant series falls below the Catholic value. No single Catholic county subgroup has so low a mean of total face height as is shown by the Church of Ireland series (125.85 mm.). The closest approximation is Longford-Westmeath (126.35 mm.). The Presbyterian figure (126.75 mm.) is slightly higher than Catholic county values of Central Ulster and Antrim-Down. Most southern and western Irish have longer faces.

Upper Face Height. Both Protestant groups exceed the means of the total Catholic series. Average upper face height of the Presbyterians is prodigious (73.80 mm.). It is only exceeded by Kerry in the Catholic county subgroups, but Cork and Tipperary-Kilkenny are close behind. Thus the southwest peninsula area shows the longest upper faces geographically, while from a sectarian viewpoint, the Calvinists are the extreme.

Facial Index. Both Church of Ireland and Presbyterian series are slightly more leptoprosopic than the total Catholic county series, but the differences can scarcely be regarded as significant. The Protestant values are between the extremes of the county subgroups.

Upper Facial Index. The upper facial indices of both Protestant series are higher than the total Catholic mean, but similar values are common in East and North Ireland among the previously discussed County subgroups.

Nose Height, Nose Breadth, Nasal Index. Church of Ireland nose heights are slightly shorter than the Catholic county values, but the Presbyterians have longer noses than the total Catholics. The differences are insignificant. Many of the southern and western Catholic county subgroups exceed the Presbyterian means of nose height. Similarly, the Church of Ireland and Presbyterian means of nose breadth straddle the total Catholic average. The nasal index averages 64.54 in the total Protestant series. This figure is slightly and insignificantly above the Catholic mean (64.38).

Minimum Frontal Diameter. Forehead breadth is least among the Presbyterians (possibly the most narrow-minded), but also small in the Church of Ireland group as compared with the Catholic total. Longford-Westmeath is the only Catholic subgroup that falls below the Presbyterians in minimum frontal diameter, but three of the county subgroups fall below the Church of Ireland mean of 108.46 mm. (Antrim-Down, Offaly-Leix-Kildare, and Longford-Westmeath).

Fronto-Parietal Index. The Church of Ireland mean equals that of the Catholic county subgroups while the Presbyterians are 0.48 lower in this category. The Presbyterian mean, 70.57, falls about midway in the means of the county groups that have the lower fronto-parietal indices: the Arans, Kerry, Sligo, etc., Limerick, E. Galway-Roscommon, Longford-Westmeath, Antrim-Down.

Zygo-Frontal Index. Church of Ireland men lead in value of this index with the Presbyterians lowest and the Catholic county mean intermediate between the two. The Arans and Kerry are the only two county subgroups showing lower values than the Presbyterians. More than half of the Catholic county subgroups are well above the Protestant total.

Bigonial Diameter. Both Protestant series are inferior to the Catholic total in bigonial diameter. The Church of Ireland mean of 108.14 mm. is lower than any Catholic county subgroup except Longford-Westmeath (107.62 mm.). The Antrim-Down group with a mean of 108.18 mm. is virtually the same. All Northern Irish appear to have narrow jaws. The broad jaws go with the western and southwestern subbrachycephals.

Zygo-Gonial Index. The Protestant and Catholic series present practically identical values of this relationship.

Fronto-Gonial Index. This index in the Presbyterian series is 100.50, a relatively very high value (due to narrow foreheads). The Church of Ireland mean does not differ significantly from Catholic totals.

MORPHOLOGICAL OBSERVATIONS

Skin Color, Inner Arm. Although there is little difference in skin color between Presbyterians and Church of Ireland men, the Protestant series show slight deficiencies of brunet skins as compared with the Catholic County series (5.9 per cent as against 7.8 per cent, table X-1).

Vascularity. Pronounced vascularity is excessive in the Presbyterian series as compared with both the Church of Ireland men and the Catholics. The combined Protestants in this category lead the Catholics by over 3 per cent. Correspondingly the Catholic excess over the combined Protestant groups in medium vascularity is exactly 3 per cent.

Freckles. The Presbyterians exceed the Church of Ireland series in total percentage of persons showing freckling. However, the Church of Ireland men resemble the total County series and diverge from the Presbyterians in the higher percentage of medium to pronounced freckling. In the large Catholic County series, freckling is slightly less common than in the combined Protestant series, but the freckling is, on the whole, heavier.

Moles. Moles are considerably less common among Presbyterians than among Total Catholics, with the Church of Ireland series presenting an intermediate status, closer to the Catholics than to the Presbyterians.

Hair Form. On the face of the evidence of our two small Protestant series, the Presbyterians have 3.6 per cent more deeply waved hair and more pronouncedly curly hair than have the Church of Ireland men. The divergence between the combined Protestant series and the Catholic county series is very great. The Protestants have 44.6 per cent of straight hair and the Catholics only 28.7 per cent. Every grade of curved hair is more heavily represented in the latter, but especially low-waved and deep-waved hair. The differences are ethnic and regional rather than religious, of course.

Hair Texture. Differences in hair texture between the Protestant groups are virtually nil. The Catholics seem to have a trifle more coarse hair than either of the Protestant groups, but the excess is probably negligible.

Hair Quantity, Head; Baldness. Differences between the three series in the amount of head hair are not impressive. Taking the evidence at face value, the Protestants seem to have more individuals with abundant (pronounced) head hair than do the Catholics. We have seen that both Protestant series slightly exceed in mean age the Catholic county series. Naturally, baldness is then somewhat more prevalent in the Protestant series than in the large Catholic series. The excess of baldness in the total Protestants amounts to 5.9 per cent. This result does not square with the slight superiority in head hair thickness found among the Protestants. However, the Church of Ireland men, although somewhat below the mean age of the Presbyterians, are more inclined to baldness than the latter. Since the physical characteristics of the Church of Ireland men are closer to the average and mode of the County series than are those of the Presbyterians, it is curious that they diverge so far from their Catholic congeners in the matter of baldness.

Hair Quantity, Beard and Body. Beard hair is heavier in the Presbyterians than in the Church of Ireland men, and the latter again approach the figures found in the Catholic series. The same relative status is held in amount of body hair.

Grayness, Head and Beard. Between the various series there is no important difference recorded in the amount of graying of head hair. This is also true in the case of graying beard. (Submedium graying of the beard shows a 5 per cent excess in Protestants over Catholics. This may be an observational accident, or may be caused by the slight age superiority of the Protestants.)

Hair Color, Head. The Protestants have somewhat lighter hair than the Catholics, on the average, and the Presbyterians run higher in golden brown hair than do the Church of Ireland men. Differences in the very rare

131

shade of black are negligible. The Presbyterians have considerably less of dark brown hair than the Catholics, and the Church of Ireland men slightly less. Correspondingly, flat brown is more frequent in both Protestant series than among the Catholics. Red-brown is more common in the latter. Golden brown is in excess among the Presbyterians as compared with Church of Ireland and Catholic men, and red hair is deficient. It is quite evident that the Presbyterians diverge in hair color from the large county series more markedly than do the Church of Ireland men. The latter differ from Catholics only in having more flat brown and less dark brown and red-brown hair.

Eye Color. Gray-brown and green-brown eyes are more common among the Protestants than among the Catholics and the most prevalent mixed eye shade—blue-brown—although heavily represented, falls below the Catholic county series by a dependable amount. In this shade the Church of Ireland men are intermediate between Presbyterians and Catholics, although still much behind the latter. Gray and gray-blue eyes are slightly more frequent among the Protestants than among the Catholics. The Presbyterians have nearly a 3 per cent excess of blue eyes over the Catholics, but the Church of Ireland men are slightly deficient in this shade which is dominant, nevertheless, in both Protestant series. In the Catholic series, blue-brown eyes are in first place. On the whole, eye color is a little lighter among the Protestants, but the excess of light eyes belongs mostly to the Presbyterians.

Pigment, Mixed Eyes; Iris. In view of the somewhat lighter eye shades prevalent among the Protestants, it is curious that our recorder should have found mixed eyes among these Ulsterites decidedly more heavily pigmented than among the Catholics. Both Presbyterians and Church of Ireland men exceed the Catholics in every grade of the darker mixed eyes and fall well below them in the very pronouncedly light eyes. Thus it seems that mixed eyes, though slightly less common among the Protestants, are, on the average, more heavily pigmented. Iris pattern shows differences between Catholics and Protestants that are not altogether intelligible. Clear iris forms without

pattern are less frequent among the Protestants than among the Catholics. Rayed eyes are rarer among Church of Ireland men than among Catholics, but the Presbyterians differ only very slightly from the Catholics. Scalloped patterns (usually found in pure blue or gray eyes) are considerably in excess among both groups of Protestants.

Eyefolds, External, Median, and Internal. Both Protestant series have more external eyefolds than the Catholics, and the excesses are more marked in the Presbyterians than in the Church of Ireland men. Median and internal folds are recorded so infrequently as to be negligible in all of the series.

Eye Obliquity and Eye Opening Height. An upward slant of the eye slits is found in approximately 21 per cent more Protestants than Catholics. The excess lies mainly in the category of submedium upward slant. Absence of eye-slit obliquity is especially a West Irish trait which goes with the broader faces and heads. Differences between the two Protestant series in eye slant seem trivial. The Protestants appear to have more low palpebral openings and fewer high eye openings, but the differences are small and unimportant.

Eyebrow Thickness and Concurrency. Protestants have thinner and less markedly concurrent eyebrows than Catholics, although the differences are, on the whole, minute.

Brow Ridges. Absence of brow ridges and small brow ridges are more frequent in both Protestant series than among the Catholics. The latter largely exceed the Protestants in brow ridges of medium development. However, both Presbyterians and Church of Ireland men have relatively more individuals with pronounced brow ridges and the Presbyterians have a relatively high excess of very pronounced brow ridges, although there is not one example of this among the Church of Ireland men. Thus the combined Protestant excess in these categories amounts to 5.7 per cent.

Forehead Height and Slope. One of the most striking observational differences between the Catholic and Protestant series is the far greater prevalence of high foreheads among the latter. The combined excess of Protestant high-brows amounts to 14.5 per cent and is about equally marked in Presbyterians and

Church of Ireland adherents. Steep foreheads or foreheads of submedium slope are also somewhat commoner in the Protestants, but extremely sloping or receding foreheads are also significantly more prevalent in both the Church of Ireland and the Presbyterian series.

Nasion Depression. The nasion depression is oftener deep in both series of Protestants than in the Catholic series. The Presbyterians slightly exceed the Church of Ireland men in depth of nasion depression.

Nasal Root, Height and Breadth. Although the Presbyterians seem slightly to exceed the Church of Ireland men in pronounced height of the nasal root, the position of the total Catholic series is intermediate to the two Protestant series. However, both Presbyterians and Church of Ireland men have definitely higher proportions of individuals than Catholics with pronouncedly and very pronouncedly broad nasal roots.

Nasal Septum. Straight or concave septa are commoner in both Protestant series than among the Catholics.

Nasal Bridge, Height and Breadth. Nasal bridges are, on the average, higher among the Protestants than among the Catholics, but the larger part of the excess is in the Presbyterian series. On the other hand, both Protestant series definitely surpass the Catholics in proportions of individuals with broad and very broad nasal bridges.

Nasal Profile. Concave noses are slightly and perhaps insignificantly rarer in both Protestant series than among Catholics. The Presbyterians and Church of Ireland men are definitely at variance in other categories of nasal profile. The Presbyterians have a strong excess of convex noses, whereas the Church of Ireland men have straight noses as the predominant form. In this respect they resemble the Catholic series.

Nasal Tip, Thickness and Inclination. The nasal tip tends to be pronouncedly thick in a definitely higher proportion of Protestants than of Catholics. This tendency toward thick tips is much more marked in Presbyterians than in Church of Ireland men. Nasal tips are less pronouncedly upward inclined in both Protestant series than among the Catholics and horizontal tips are slightly commoner among the former.

Nasal Wings. Both Protestant series tend toward medium development of the nasal wings rather than to compressed or flaring forms. These latter appear in small excess in the Catholic series.

Nostril Visibility, Frontal. Frontal visibility is oftener absent in Protestant than in Catholic men of these series, presumably because nasal tips are less markedly uptilted in the former.

Lips, Integumental and Membranous Thickness; Eversion. The data suggest no dependable differences between the Protestant and Catholic series in thickness of integumental lips. The Protestants seem to show larger proportions of both thin and thick membranous lips than the Catholics. The same increased tendency toward extreme Protestant variation is shown by the data on lips eversion.

Prognathism, Mid-facial and Alveolar. Mid-facial prognathism is slightly more common in both Protestant series than in the Catholic series, but, again, it is recorded so rarely in all three series that deviations seems unimportant. There is also a very small deficiency in alveolar prognathism in both Protestant series.

Chin Prominence. The data on chin prominence indicate an unimportant superiority in pronounced chin projection on the part of the Presbyterians only.

Teeth: Eruption, Bite, Loss, Wear, Caries, Crowding. Pronounced tooth loss is definitely greater among the Protestants than among the Catholics. Although both of the subgroups of the former are somewhat higher in mean age, the excess of pronounced tooth loss seems a little greater than would be expected from that factor. On the other hand, both Protestant series show much less tooth wear than is found in the large Catholic series. Medium and pronounced caries are also considerably less among the Protestants. The Catholics show a very slight excess of pronounced tooth crowding.

Malars, Frontal and Lateral Projection. The Catholics strongly exceed both Protestant series in both frontal and lateral malar projection. Between the Protestant series differences are negligible.

Gonial Angles. There are no important differences in gonial angle prominence between the respective series.

Ear: Helix, Antihelix, Darwin's Point, Lobe

Attachment, Lobe Size, Protrusion. Presbyterians appear to have a greater proportion of pronouncedly rolled helices than Church of Ireland men and Catholics. Both of the Protestant groups, and their combination tend more to extremes of helix development than do the Catholics. The Protestant series agree in showing also slightly more development of the antihelix than is recorded for the large County series. A slightly greater development of Darwin's Point also characterizes the Protestants. The latter have more attached and soldered ears than the Catholics, and their ear lobes run slightly larger, perhaps in the latter feature because of higher mean age. Pronounced ear protrusion is also greater in the Protestants and especially among the Presbyterians.

Temporal Fullness. Pronounced temporal fullness is markedly less in both Protestant groups than among the Catholics, most notably so in the Church of Ireland men.

Occipital Protrusion. Both Protestant series exhibit much more pronounced occipital protrusion than does the total Catholic county series. This feature and lack of temporal fullness are, of course, associated with the more prevalently dolichocephalic type of Ulster.

Lambdoid Flattening. The lambdoid flattening which is extraordinarily prevalent among the Catholic series is vastly deficient in both Protestant series. It is much rarer among the Presbyterians than among the Church of Ireland men, although the latter show, again, far less flattening than the Catholics.

Occipital Flattening. Flattening of the occiput in various grades is more frequent among Presbyterians than among Church of Ireland men, and far more common in both than among the Catholics.

Facial Asymmetry. Presbyterians show slightly more facial asymmetry than do Catholics and Church of Ireland men slightly less. However, the differences are not impressive.

SUMMARY

SOCIOLOGY

The Protestants, most of whom are natives of Ulster, are far better educated than the average of the Catholic county series. The Presbyterians slightly exceed the Church of Ireland men in educational status, since the former include no illiterates. The educational ratio, a rough measure devised by dividing the number of well-educated by the number of totally uneducated, reveals that the combined Protestants are about four times as well-educated as the average of the Catholic county series.

Only two men, both Church of Ireland, in the whole Protestant series are native Keltic speakers and very few of the Protestants have studied Gaelic in school. The Presbyterian series is superior to the Catholic series in occupational status, notably in the far greater proportions of persons engaged in skilled occupations and in mercantile work, and in the far smaller proportion of navvies.

SUMMARY OF METRIC DIFFERENCES

In tables IX-2 to IX-5 the metric features of Church of Ireland men and Presbyterians have been computed separately and also as a combined Protestant series for comparison with the total Catholic county series. However, an inspection of the arrays of means of two Protestant subgroups in comparison with those of the Catholics makes it perfectly obvious that the three groups must be regarded as samples from somewhat different anthropological universes. There is little justification for combining the Church of Ireland men with the Presbyterians, because these two Protestant subgroups differ from each other in more features than they as individual members of a Protestant pair agree to differ from total Catholics.

Thus the Church of Ireland men and Presbyterians both differ from the total Catholics in the same direction in 9 metric features (6 measurements and 3 indices). However, the Church of Ireland series differs from the total Catholic series in 5 metric features in addition to the above (making a total of 14 metric differences), while the Presbyterian series differs from the total Catholic series in 11 features in addition to those differences shared with the Church of Ireland men, so that the total Presbyterian differences from total Catholics is 20.

There are also 12 metric features in which the Church of Ireland series differs significantly from the Presbyterians. Thus the former is nearly as different from its companion Protestant series as it is from the total Catholic series. In half of the characters in which the two Protestant subseries differ significantly, the Church of Ireland men are intermediate between the Presbyterians and the Catholics, but in 4 of 12 instances the Church of Ireland men are on the deficiency side of the total Catholics, and in two cases, the Church of Ireland men are on the excess side of the Presbyterians. The former are, on the whole, metrically and indicially nearer the Catholics than to the Presbyterians. Thus, anthropometrically it would be more reasonable to combine Church of Ireland with total Catholics than with the Presbyterians.

Some further commentary on the intergroup differences is desirable. The Church of Ireland men have absolutely and relatively deeper chests than either Presbyterians or Catholics. They exaggerate the high thoracic index found in total Catholics. In their narrower head breadths and lower mean cephalic index, on the other hand, they exaggerate the Presbyterian difference from Catholics. In narrower bizygomatic diameter, smaller total face height, they are again at the extreme from the Catholics, with the Presbyterians in the middle. This statement also holds for hinder breadth of the jaws (bigonial diameter). The general metric features of the Church of Ireland men relate them to the Ulster Catholics, and apparently to the physical types prevalent in the middle eastern coastal part of Ireland—Meath-Louth-Dublin, and, to some extent, Longford-Westmeath.

135

They seem to have very small representation of the massive brachycephalic type found in the southwest (Cork, Kerry, etc.).

The metric features in which both Church of Ireland and Presbyterians differ from total Catholics are generally speaking of the same nature—smaller, narrower and higher heads, smaller and narrower faces, but higher and narrower upper faces. These again give the impression of being regional differences largely conditioned by the absence of broad-headed, broad-faced men in the east.

The Presbyterians, of course, are of mainly northeastern Irish (Ulster) origin. As a series they are bigger, heavier, longer-limbed men than total Irish Catholics, with much longer and narrower heads, higher heads, longer upper faces, and broader noses than those of the Catholics, but narrower foreheads. Their differences from total Catholics are not only regional differences, such as would be expected to occur from their geographical concentration, but in part, also, ethnic differences, presumably because of mainly Scottish origin. The Church of Ireland men, coming from all over Ireland, although mainly from Ulster, have probably more English strains, but are also, putatively, more mixed with the Irish types which constitute the total Catholic county series.

SUMMARY OF MORPHOLOGICAL DIFFERENCES

Morphological differences (tables X, 2-5 and XI-1) appertaining to the head and face can be grouped in the following general categories of features: skin, hair, eyes, eye slits, eyebrows, forehead, nose, lips, prognathism, teeth, malars, ears and cranial shape. Each of these 13 general categories has a number of graded subcategories which may exhibit significance in differences between any two groups. The number of these subcategories is 63.

CHURCH OF IRELAND AND TOTAL CATHOLICS

The Church of Ireland series differs from the total Catholic series in 10 of 13 general features and in 44.5 per cent of total subcategories. Generally speaking, the Church of Ireland men have less curvature of the hair,

more baldness, more grayness, and more brown hair. Blue-brown mixed eyes are fewer and their mixed eyes seem more heavily pigmented than those of the Catholic series. The Church of Ireland foreheads seem to be higher and steeper and equipped with larger brow ridges. Noses and lips are somewhat thicker. Although caries appear to be fewer, tooth loss is more pronounced. In the Church of Ireland series, malars are flatter, the shape of the head more narrowly elliptical. Ears protrude more.

PRESBYTERIANS AND TOTAL CATHOLICS

The Presbyterians differ from the total Catholic series in 11 of 13 general features, and in 49.20 per cent of the subcategories. Their differences from total Catholics are sometimes in a different direction from those displayed by the Church of Ireland men. The Presbyterians tend to have more pronounced skin vascularity, more golden brown hair, smaller brow ridges, and higher and steeper foreheads, more convex nasal profiles, less pronounced malars.

TOTAL PROTESTANTS AND TOTAL CATHOLICS

The paired Protestant series differs from the total Catholic series in 10 of the 13 main features, but in only 38.09 per cent of subcategories. It is thus clear that the bulk of the differences between Presbyterians and Catholics and between Church of Ireland men and Catholics, respectively, are in features in which both sects of Protestants present an united front against the Catholics.

CHURCH OF IRELAND AND PRESBYTERIANS

The differences between Presbyterians and Church of Ireland men are limited to 3 general features and only 12.70 per cent of the morphological subcategories. They have to do mostly with beard and body hair, in which the Church of Ireland men are less well endowed, and in the lower and straighter-bridged noses of the latter. We have, then, the rather paradoxical situation that morphologically the Protestants might reasonably be considered a single group as contrasted with the Catholics, whereas metrically, they differ from each other much more markedly (although not in as many characters as each of them differs from the total Catholics).

SUMMARY OF TOTAL SIGNIFICANT DIFFERENCES BETWEEN CHURCH OF IRELAND, PRESBYTERIANS, AND CATHOLICS

DIFFERENCES BETWEEN CHURCH OF IRELAND AND TOTAL CATHOLICS

The tabular summary (table XI-2) of metric differences indicates that the Church of Ireland men tend to be smaller than the total Catholics in 8 of 10 measurements which exhibit significant differences. Gross metric differences are noticed in more than half of the dimensions studied, but significant differences in indices (proportions) are found in only one-sixth of cases.

When the subcategories of morphological trait differences are grouped so that only whole features such as skin, eyes, and nose are considered, it is notable that some significant difference between the series representing the two sects occurs in every feature except skin, eyebrows, and prognathism. The totalling of the subcategories indicates that the Church of Ireland men are different from the Catholics in some 44.45 per cent of morphological observations. It is quite apparent, then, that these samples have been derived from distinct anthropological universes.

DIFFERENCES BETWEEN PRESBYTERIANS AND TOTAL CATHOLICS

Differences in gross dimensions between Presbyterians and Catholics are more numerous than between Church of Ireland men and Catholics (table XI-3), totalling 72.22 per cent of all measurements studied. In most significantly differing measurements, the Presbyterians are larger than the Catholics. Indicial differences are also more numerous than in the preceding comparison.

Morphological differences between Presbyterians and Catholics total 49.20 per cent of all observed traits, which is a little more than in the case of the Church of Ireland and

Catholic differences. Eyebrows and prognathism are the only features in which the Presbyterians do not show some significant difference from the Catholics.

DIFFERENCES BETWEEN COMBINED PROTESTANTS AND TOTAL CATHOLICS

Combining the two Protestant sects into a total and comparing that with the Catholic county series (table XI-4) reduced the total of significant differences to 33.33 per cent of measurements, 20 per cent of indices, and 38.09 per cent of morphological traits. The combined series, when contrasted, are still statistically differentiated to an overwhelming degree.

DIFFERENCES BETWEEN CHURCH OF IRELAND AND PRESBYTERIANS

The Church of Ireland men are smaller than the Presbyterians in 44.44 per cent of measurements, larger in none (table XI-5). Since they are also smaller than total Catholics in the same proportion of measurements, it is clear that the Catholics are intermediate between the two Protestant sects in size. Indicially, the Church of Ireland series differs from the Presbyterian series in the same per cent of proportions as it differs from Total Catholics. Nevertheless, in the total of metric features, the two Protestant groups differ from each other in fewer means than either of them differs from the Catholics.

When we come to morphological features, it is perhaps surprising to find that the Presbyterians and Church of Ireland men though very diverse from each other in size, present a total of only 12.59 per cent of significant differences in morphological traits. These few differences pertain to hair, nose, lips, and cranial shape.

The Presbyterians and Church of Ireland men ought to be more nearly alike than either is like to the total Catholic county series, because the bulk of the Protestants are derived from the Ulster counties. But that this likeness should be mainly morphological and accompanied by great differences in size is, at least, remarkable.

PART III

MORPHOLOGICAL (SUBRACIAL) TYPES

SORTING CRITERIA

THE sorting criteria for establishing "morphological types" were set up in about 1930 by the senior author with the help of Dr. Carleton S. Coon. They were devised particularly for dividing up American criminals, then being studied, into subracial or ethnic types. The whole scheme was an endeavor to get away from the time-worn method of talking about "racial types" based upon arbitrary abstractions from isolated means and modes in a population. There was at that time, as there still is, a great deal of discussion of "races" or "subraces" within the white stock, with little or no work done on the actual occurrence within such population of individuals who showed the putative criteria of "Nordics," "Alpines," "Mediterraneans," or what will you.

In this scheme, no attempt was made to set up new "races." It was designed merely to apply to individuals the conventional "racial" features more or less agreed upon by anthropologists and established in the literature.

However, it was necessary to rig a scheme whereby every person fell into some "race" or type, whether or not he conformed to classic race definitions.

The conventional primary criteria used for dividing up the white race are hair color, eye color, and head form (notably as expressed by the length-breadth or cephalic index). Sometimes stature and the nasal index are used as secondary criteria.

Not wishing to overstress the importance of the threadbare cephalic index, we decided to split it two ways—80 and above, and 79 and below. Thus all of our Irish were divided into those whose heads were more or less round and those who were more or less long-headed. Individuals whose length-breadth index was on the brachycephalic side were invariably put into a different category from those who fell into the other division of head form, but the subcategory to which they were assigned depended upon the associated pigmental criteria.

We began with the notorious "Nordics"—supposedly long-headed, fair-haired, blue-eyed. Because of the frequent inclusion in the supposedly "Nordic races" of individuals whose hair is not strictly blond, it was decided to include as "Pure Nordics" only such persons as actually had blue eyes, and really blond hair—either ash or golden—along with cephalic index under 80.

This left for the "Predominantly Nordic" group all "near blonds" who were long-headed and had either blue or mixed eyes. There are four categories as listed below.

The term "Keltic" was applied to long heads with a combination of blue eyes and darkish hair or red hair. There is perhaps no set and conventional designation for this combination, but it is so common in those parts of Northwestern Europe where Keltic languages are spoken that it seemed a fairly appropriate name. As will be seen in later discussions, it turns out to be a linguistic misnomer. However, the physical type thus crudely defined is a reality and nothing hypothetical.

"East Baltics" were blond or red-headed round-heads with either light or mixed eyes. The definition is in accordance with common practice in European racial classification. The secondary nasal index criterion is also conventional.

The term "Dinaric" has usually been referred to brachycephals of varied pigmentation with long faces and usually long, hooked noses. Into this classification were dumped no less than ten categories of round-heads mostly of mixed pigmentation but invariably with nasal indices under 63. This last secondary criterion usually was effective to catch the long faces and convex noses. The group is somewhat heterogeneous, but the data to follow perhaps justify its delimitation.

Traditionally, a Mediterranean is a pure brunet dolichocephal, and individuals conforming to such a description were classified as "Pure Mediterranean." There are but 33 in our huge Irish sample.

All of the darkish and pigmentally mixed dolichocephals were put in the "Nordic Mediterranean" class with the occasional use of a differentiating secondary criterion based on stature. Long heads with red hair and mixed eyes with statures above 170 cm. were assigned to "Predominantly Nordic" but if stature fell below 170, they were assigned to "Nordic Mediterranean." The assumption is that long-heads who are obviously a mixture of blond and brunet strains may reasonably be called "Nordic Mediterranean" or "Predominantly Nordic" according to the weight of the pigmental features and the supposed difference in stature between "Nordics" and "Mediterraneans."

Pure Alpines, theoretically, should be all round-headed with dark eyes and dark hair. There is not a single individual of this description in our sample of nearly 10,000 Irish males. Therefore, all persons with round heads, more or less darkish or intermediate pigmentation and with relatively broad noses for Ireland (nasal indices over 63, to differentiate them from Dinarics) were lumped together as "Nordic Alpines."

After the lapse of about one-quarter of a century the senior author still does not consider as invalid the sorting scheme here briefly explained and detailed below. In fact, he makes bold to assert that no better scheme for dividing up whites on the basis of combinations of pigment, and head form, with sparing use of other criteria, has been brought to his attention as having been rigorously applied to a very large sample of European males and then elaborated as to its metric associations and its sociological implications. The senior author does not pretend that these crudely delimited "types" are "races." Perhaps they are "subraces," perhaps only "breeds." Let us not worry for the moment about the taxonomic designations, but find out rather what the sorting out of these types can teach us about the Irish population.

Details of Sorting Criteria

Pure Nordic—55 individuals; 0.6% of the total series. Ash blond, golden hair, blue eyes, cephalic index under 80, all statures.

Predominantly Nordic—649 individuals; 6.8% of the total series.

Red hair and mixed eyes, cephalic index under 80, stature over 170 cm.

Ash blond, golden hair, mixed eyes, cephalic index under 80.

Light brown hair, mixed eyes, cephalic index under 80.

Light brown hair, blue eyes, cephalic index under 80.

Keltic—2408 individuals; 25.3% of the total series.

Dark hair and blue eyes, cephalic index under 80, all statures.

Red hair and blue eyes, cephalic index under 80, all statures.

East Baltic—105 individuals; 1.1% of the total series.

Red hair and blue eyes, cephalic index over 80, nasal index over 63.

Red hair and mixed eyes, cephalic index over 80, nasal index over 63.

Ash blond, golden hair, blue eyes, cephalic index over 80.

Ash blond, golden hair, mixed eyes, cephalic index over 80.

Dinaric—1768 individuals; 18.6% of the total series.

Dark hair and dark eyes, cephalic index over 80, nasal index under 63.

Dark hair and blue eyes, cephalic index over 80, nasal index under 63.

Dark hair and mixed eyes, cephalic index over 80, nasal index under 63.

Red hair and blue eyes, cephalic index over 80, nasal index under 63.

Red-brown hair and blue eyes, cephalic index over 80, nasal index under 63.

Light brown hair and blue eyes, cephalic index over 80, nasal index under 63.

Red-brown hair and mixed eyes, cephalic index over 80, nasal index under 63.

Red-brown hair and dark eyes, cephalic index over 80, nasal index under 63.

Light brown hair and dark eyes, cephalic index over 80, nasal index under 63.

Light brown hair and mixed eyes, cephalic index over 80, nasal index under 63.

Nordic Mediterranean — 2749 individuals; 28.9% of the total series.

Dark hair and mixed eyes, cephalic index under 80, all statures.

Red hair and mixed eyes, cephalic index under 80, stature under 170 cm.

Red-brown hair and mixed eyes, cephalic index under 80.

Light brown hair and dark eyes, cephalic index under 80.

Pure Mediterranean—33 individuals; 0.3% of the total series.

Dark hair and dark eyes, cephalic index under 80, all statures.

Red-brown hair and dark eyes, cephalic index under 80.

Nordic Alpine—1754 individuals; 18.4% of the total series.

Dark hair and blue eyes, cephalic index over 80, nasal index over 63.

Dark hair and mixed eyes, cephalic index over 80, nasal index over 63.

Red-brown hair and blue eyes, cephalic index over 80, nasal index over 63.

Light brown hair and blue eyes, cephalic index over 80, nasal index over 63.

Light brown hair and mixed eyes, cephalic index over 80, nasal index over 63.

Red-brown hair and mixed eyes, cephalic index over 80, nasal index over 63.

Light brown hair and dark eyes, cephalic index over 80, nasal index over 63.

These eight subracial types have the following ranking in the total Irish study:

RANK	TYPE	% OF TOTAL SERIES
1	Nordic Mediterranean	28.9%
2	Keltic	25.3%
3	Dinaric	18.6%
4	Nordic Alpine	18.4%
5	Predominantly Nordic	6.8%
6	East Baltic	1.1%
7	Pure Nordic	0.6%
8	Pure Mediterranean	0.3%

DISTRIBUTION OF MORPHOLOGICAL TYPES BY COUNTY SUBGROUPS

THE county distribution of morphological types by nativity is really the crux of the investigation of these types. If they occur in each county in roughly the proportion in which they are found in the entire series, it is obvious that they have little or no regional, geographic, or even racial significance. They would then represent merely the more or less common physical combinations which are segregated out of the general Irish ethnic complex. If, however, they tend to show geographical grouping, we may assume that they are something more than arbitrary sorting combinations. Several methods of studying the birthplaces of individuals belonging to the eight morphological types have been tried. Each county or county combination (there are 19 in all) contributes so small a proportion to the total series that the percentage occurrence of any given type in that county, when compared with the total contribution of that county to the series, can show only apparently small and usually statistically insignificant differences. This method of treatment and analysis has been carried out in table XIII-1. (See also figs. 39-85.)

For the purpose of mapping distributions, a different method has been adopted (table XIII-3). The percentage occurrence of each morphological type in a county or county group is expressed as a ratio of the total contribution of that county or county group to the entire morphological type series. Thus if West Donegal constitutes 2.3 per cent of the county series, and 2.6 per cent of the Nordic Mediterranean type is found in West Donegal, it is evident that the ratio 1.1 indicates that slightly more of this type are found in West Donegal than would be expected. A ratio of unity would indicate an approximately normal distribution of the type in that county as compared with all of Ireland. As the ratio surpasses unity, the type is over-represented; as it approaches zero, the reverse is the case.

A third method is to list the actual percentages of the various types comprising the total in each county (table XIII-4). This method tends to obscure the variations in occurrence of the numerically large and numerically scanty types.

The distributions will be analyzed firstly from the point of view of county series; secondly, from the point of view of the types themselves.

DISTRIBUTION BY COUNTY

West Donegal. West Donegal is the birthplace of only 2.3 per cent of the total type series. It is apparent from table XIII-3 that the principal types in this county are of the following order in frequency of occurrence: Nordic Mediterranean, Dinaric, Keltic, Nordic Alpine. The other types are almost unrepresented. Table XIII-3 shows quite simply that the Dinaric and Nordic Mediterranean types with a ratio of 1.1 are over-represented in West Donegal. The Keltic type is normal with a ratio of 1.0. Other types have indices or ratios below unity and therefore are under-represented. Thus the Nordic Alpine type with an index of 0.9 is a little scarce in this county, although table XIII-5 shows that members of this type actually constitute 17.0 per cent of the West Donegal natives in the type series. It is evident that the outstanding features of the West Donegal natives are a slightly heavy over-representation of the brachycephalic Dinaric type and of the long-headed, mixed brunet, Nordic Mediterranean type (the most numerous type in all Ireland), and rarity or absence of all of the blond types and of the very rare Pure Mediterranean type. The dominant West Donegal types are Dinaric and the ubiquitous Nordic Mediterranean.

Mayo. Mayo contributes 6.0 per cent to the morphological type series of nativities. Table XIII-3 reveals that here the Keltic type with an index of 0.8 is markedly deficient as are also the Predominantly Nordic type (0.5) and the Pure Mediterranean type (0.5). All other types attain or surpass their series quota. Most notably, the Pure Nordic type has in Mayo an index of 1.5. Although this represents only 5 men, it marks this county as one of the highest in production of this rare type. Again, the round-headed, blond or rufous East Baltic type has an index in Mayo of 1.3, while the Dinaric and Nordic Alpine types each attain 1.2, and the Nordic Mediterranean with 1.0 is at par. It is clear enough that, proportionately, the leading types in Mayo are long-headed blond pure Nordics, round-headed blond East Baltics, and brachycephalic mixed Dinarics and Nordic Alpines. The sparsity of the Keltic type is important.

Sligo-Leitrim-S. Fermanagh-W. Cavan. This district contains every Irish morphological type with no marked excess, except in the case of the scarce Pure Mediterranean type which here attains an index of 3.1 (only 8 persons). The Pure Nordic and Dinaric types are slightly deficient.

West Galway. West Galway has its highest proportional representation in the Pure Nordic and Predominantly Nordic types (indices of 1.2 each). Of course, these two types actually constitute only 8.8 per cent of the type natives of West Galway. East Baltics, Dinarics, and Pure Mediterraneans are deficient.

Aran Islands. Pure Nordics and Pure Mediterraneans do not occur at all in the small Aran series. Here the dominant type is Keltic, with a slight over-representation also of Nordic Mediterraneans. All other types are deficient.

Clare. The notable feature of Clare is a heavy over-representation of Dinarics (index 1.5). Nordic Alpines slightly exceed their quota (1.1). Thus the round-headed types are dominant. Keltics, Nordic Mediterraneans, and all other long-headed types are deficient.

Kerry. Kerry is the leading brachycephalic county and shows the highest index in East Baltics (2.3). The other round-headed types— Dinaric and Nordic Alpine—also markedly exceed their normal proportions. Pure Nordic and Pure Mediterranean do not occur. Here the strongest Irish types, Nordic Meriterranean and Keltic fall far below their expected occurrence.

Cork. Cork has excess of the blond East Baltic and Pure Nordic types and is slightly

high also in Nordic Alpines and Dinarics. The Keltic type is very poorly represented. Nordic Mediterraneans are at par.

Limerick. Limerick is a county with a fairly even type distribution. Pure Nordics are markedly high, Dinarics and Nordic Alpines moderately so. The most important deficiency is that of the Keltic type. Nordic Mediterraneans are at par.

E. Galway-Roscommon. E. Galway-Roscommon is a strangely neutral district. The heaviest Irish types—Nordic Mediterranean and Keltic—are at their normal quotas; Predominantly Nordic a little above par, and all other types slightly low.

Longford-Westmeath. This central county block is anthropologically the most peculiar in Ireland. In the case of two of the numerically smallest morphological types—Pure Nordic and Pure Mediterranean—maximum indices of 2.2 and 2.4 respectively are attained. It also has the highest Predominantly Nordic index (1.7). One suspects here the influence of juvenile blondness, since this group is far the youngest of all county groups in mean age. Nordic Mediterraneans are somewhat high, Keltic and East Baltics at par, and Dinarics and Nordic Alpines are low.

Offaly-Leix-Kildare. This south central block is very high in the rare Pure Mediterraneans (index 2.2), and moderately high in Keltics and Nordic Mediterraneans. All other types are deficient.

Tipperary-Kilkenny. Tipperary-Kilkenny is highest in Dinarics, followed by the East Baltic type. All other types are very slightly deficient or about normal in occurrence.

Waterford-Wexford. Probably the most important feature of Waterford-Wexford is its weakness in the basic Nordic Mediterranean and Keltic types (0.9). It is strangely high in Pure Nordic, Predominantly Nordic, and Nordic Alpine.

Wicklow-Carlow. Wicklow-Carlow is a geo-ethnographic focus and very important in its type distribution. It has a Keltic index of 1.4; Pure Mediterraneans are at par, and all other types are below par.

Meath-Louth-Dublin. This group has a high index for the rare Pure Mediterranean type (1.8). More importantly, it has a high Keltic index (1.3) and is slightly above normal in Nordic Mediterranean. Brachycephalic types are deficient.

E. Cavan-Monaghan-Armagh. This southeastern Ulster block has a high Keltic index (1.4) and is normal in Pure Nordic, Predominantly Nordic, and Nordic Mediterranean. It is entirely bereft of Pure Mediterraneans.

Antrim-Down. Antrim-Down has an eccentric Pure Mediterranean index (2.1). Its most important excess, however, is in the Predominantly Nordic type (1.2). It is slightly high in Nordic Mediterranean and Keltic. Round-headed types are deficient.

N. Fermanagh-E. Donegal-Tyrone-Londonderry. This north central block has a high Pure Nordic index (2.1) and also strongly exceeds in East Baltics (1.6) and slightly in Keltics, Predominantly Nordics and Nordic Alpines.

DISTRIBUTION BY TYPE

Pure Nordic. This small and scattered type includes only 55 men. Its greatest excesses are in Longford-Westmeath, N. Fermanagh-E. Donegal-Tyrone-Londonderry, Waterford-Wexford, Limerick, Mayo, Cork, West Galway. It is at par in E. Cavan-Monaghan-Armagh, and deficient in other county series. Its only truly isolated region of strength is in Waterford-Wexford. There seems little doubt that this type is an immature variant, for the most part, of the Predominantly Nordic type with which it has been combined in the mapping of types.

Predominantly Nordic. This type, consisting of 649 men, is in excess in the following county groups: Longford-Westmeath, Waterford-Wexford, West Galway, Antrim-Down, Sligo-Leitrim-S. Fermanagh-W. Cavan, E. Galway-Roscommon, and N. Fermanagh-E. Donegal-Tyrone-Londonderry. It is represented in all of the other county subgroups, but is most deficient in West Donegal and Mayo. It is, then, found in the north and west central areas with an outlier in the southeastern corner.

Keltic. This type includes 2408 individuals and is the second largest in Ireland. It is most strongly represented (in order) in the following counties: Wicklow-Carlow and E. Cavan-Monaghan-Armagh, Aran Islands and Meath-Louth-Dublin, Offaly-Leix-Kildare and N. Fermanagh-E. Donegal-Tyrone-Londonderry, West Galway and Antrim-Down. It is most strongly deficient in Kerry, Cork, Limerick, Mayo, and Clare. It is evidently weak in the southwest and in the extreme west.

East Baltic. This rufous brachycephalic type is in most marked excess in Kerry, followed by Cork and N. Fermanagh-E. Donegal-Tyrone-Londonderry, Mayo, Sligo-Leitrim-S. Fermanagh-W. Cavan and Tipperary-Kilkenny. It is markedly deficient in E. Galway-Roscommon and West Galway. Evidently it is concentrated in southwest and north central Ireland.

Dinaric. This sizable type numbers 1768 individuals. It is strongest in Clare, then Kerry, Tipperary-Kilkenny, Limerick, Mayo, Cork and West Donegal. It is thus concentrated in the extreme west and southwest.

Nordic Mediterranean. The thickest stratum of the Irish population is made up from this type which numbers a total of 2749 men (28.9 per cent of the type series). On the whole, this type is evenly distributed throughout Ireland. The range in indices is from a high of 1.1 in several counties or county subgroups to 0.8 which low occurs in Clare.

Pure Mediterranean. This type includes only 33 men and can scarcely be termed a perceptible constituent of the Irish population. However, it is concentrated in a specific area. Thus it has an index of 3.1 in Sligo-Leitrim-S. Fermanagh-W. Cavan, followed by Longford-Westmeath (2.4) and Offaly-Leix-Kildare (2.2), Antrim-Down (2.1), Meath-Louth-Dublin (1.8). It is entirely absent from West Donegal, the Arans, Kerry, Limerick, Cork, E. Cavan-Monaghan-Armagh.

Nordic Alpine. This type with 1754 men ranks fourth numerically. It is most heavily represented in Kerry with an index of 1.4, Waterford-Wexford (1.3), Mayo, Cork, and Limerick (1.2). It is most deficient in the Arans (0.6) and Longford-Westmeath, Tipperary-Kilkenny, and Meath-Louth-Dublin (0.7). This again is an extreme western and southwestern type with an outlying group in the southeast.

GEOLOGICAL AND GEOGRAPHICAL CORRESPONDENCES OF MORPHOLOGICAL TYPES

GEOLOGY, SOIL, GEOGRAPHY

THE correspondence between the distribution of morphological types and geological features is moderate. The poorest areas, from an agricultural viewpoint, are probably those of the igneous rocks and the metamorphic rocks. These are particularly Donegal, with parts of Tyrone and Londonderry, the western part of Mayo, and West Galway. Other poor areas are the Old Red Sandstone, the Carboniferous sandstones and grits. These are found especially in the southwestern peninsular area (Clare, Kerry, Cork) and in the southeastern corner, Waterford-Wexford.

In general it may be said that all three brachycephalic morphological types show greatest concentrations in the above-named areas. There are some exceptions. Both West Donegal and West Galway are refuge areas of the dolichocephalic dark-haired mixed-eyed Nordic Mediterraneans, with strong Keltic minorities. So are the Arans (which are upper Carboniferous limestone).

The interior Central Plain of Ireland, on the Lower and Middle Carboniferous limestone, is the most fertile area, and here we find concentrations of Keltic and Nordic Mediterranean types east of the Shannon, with strong infusions of Nordic west of the Shannon.

We may now deal more specifically with the concentration of the general types with respect to geological and soil areas. Let us begin with the Dinaric type, the most numerous and widely distributed of the brachycephals.

The heaviest concentration is in Clare, which is geologically very diverse, with Upper Carboniferous limestone in the northwest, Old Red Sandstone in the northeast, Lower and Middle Carboniferous limestone in the southeast, and Carboniferous grit, shale and sandstone in the southwest.

To the southwest a secondary concentration of Dinarics is found in Kerry, mostly Carboniferous grits and Old Red Sandstone and, east of Clare, in Tipperary-Kilkenny, largely limestone formations and extensions of the Central Plain. The only useful generalization about the geographical distribution of this type is that it is focused in Clare with great strength in the county groups to the southwest and southeast of Clare, moderate strength in Limerick, Cork, Mayo and West Donegal, and comparative weakness in all north central and northeastern areas.

The Nordic Alpine type, a shorter-faced, broader-nosed brachycephalic type, is distributed more in accordance with geological features than is the Dinaric. While its strongest concentration is in Kerry, it is greatly in excess in all regions of granite and metamorphic rocks of Old Red Sandstones. It is interesting to note that it is nowhere really strong in the Central Plain or along the east coast north of Wexford. In the west it is weak only in the Arans. One of the stronger concentration regions of the Dinaric type—Tipperary-Kilkenny—is weak in Nordic Alpines, but N. Fermanagh-E. Donegal-Tyrone-Londonderry is a region of strength in the Nordic Alpine type, but of weakness in Dinaric. This is also true of West Galway. On the whole the Nordic Alpine types appear concentrated on poorer geological formations than the Dinarics.

The East Baltic type (numerically very weak) is also on the barren rock to a great extent. Its heaviest concentrations in Cork and Kerry, in the southwest and in N. Fermanagh-E. Donegal-Tyrone-Londonderry are widely separate. It is sparse on the sterile rocks of West Galway and the Arans and West Donegal, but strong in Mayo. It has some strength in the rich limestone counties of Tipperary-Kilkenny, a Dinaric stronghold, but is a little weak in Waterford-Wexford, a very strong Nordic Alpine region.

On the whole the East Baltic concentration is on the poorer western and southwestern geological formations, but it really offers no convincing geological correlations.

Of the three dolichocephalic types it may be said in general that they tend to be concentrated in the central limestone plain, on the basaltic rocks of Antrim and the slates and grits of County Down.

More specifically the Nordic Mediterranean type of darkish hair and mixed eyes conforms to the above statement but also shows concentration on the igneous and metamorphic rocks of West Donegal and on the Upper Carboniferous limestone of the Arans. These last two are barren areas. This type, however, has the widest and most even distribution in Ireland. It is actually well below par (0.8) only in Clare. It can hardly be stated to have any marked geological, as contrasted with general, geographical concentration. For that

matter, even in its mean of concentration its index never reaches 1.2.

The Keltic type, second in numerical strength in Ireland, has a clear geographical concentration along the middle of the east coast, but it does not particularly relate to geological formations, since the middle of the area is central limestone plain and the north and south are Cambrian, Ordovician and Silurian grits with granite outcrops.

The numerically weak Pure and Predominantly Nordic type is weak in West Donegal, Mayo, Clare and Kerry but strong in West Galway. Its concentrations are not clearly related to geological formations. In summary the morphological types seem to show no clear and consistent relationship to geological formations, apart from a tendency of all brachycephals to occur in excess on those formations which are poorest for agriculture.

Education (Tables XIV-1 and XIV-2). Illiteracy is entirely absent from the small Pure Nordic type series (consisting of young men) and is virtually absent also from the Predominantly Nordic and East Baltic types. But these also are well below mean age. By far the highest percentage of illiterates occurs in the Keltic type and there is little reason for doubting that the high mean age of this type is responsible for the inclusion of a considerable proportion of older men who have not had the advantages of education. Nevertheless, it is remarkable that this numerically enormous type is also markedly deficient in men who have enjoyed the advantages of secondary school and university education. The Pure Nordic type leads in men who have attended secondary schools, but has no university men at all. The East Baltic type leads in university men and also has a marked excess of secondary school men. The Dinaric type is also one of the better educated types, whereas the Nordic Mediterranean type is distinctly inferior.

Table XIV-2 gives the educational ratios of the several types (the proportion of well educated to illiterate and poorly educated individuals). The Pure Nordic type has no ratio because it includes no illiterates and no persons who have not been to school. It hardly deserves first ranking, since the East Baltic type is relatively highest in university men, whereas the Pure Nordic type includes none at all. The Predominantly Nordic type is also well educated, the Dinaric type only about half as well educated as the Predominantly Nordic type, and so on down to the Keltic type, which is considerably the most ignorant. (It should be mentioned that the Keltic type is actually the least Keltic in linguistic proficiency, and that the East Baltic type is highest in Keltic speakers. Thus, paradoxically, the Keltic type not only speaks the least Keltic, but is also the most generally ignorant, whereas the East Baltic type, which includes the most native Irish speakers is, on the whole, the best educated.)

Because of the very small numbers of individuals that comprise several of the types —notably the Pure Mediterranean, Pure Nordic, and East Baltic—the ratios and ranking are somewhat illusory. Actually, 91.2 per cent of our Irish series falls into four of the eight morphological types in the following order of magnitude: Nordic Mediterranean, Keltic, Dinaric, Nordic Alpine. These four large Irish types rank in educational ratio respectively sixth, eighth, fourth, and fifth. The two round-headed types—Dinaric and Nordic Alpine—are numerically inferior to the long-headed types, but educationally superior.

Language (Table XIV-3). In the total series, 57.6 per cent of individuals have no acquaintance with the Irish language. It is a rather amusing commentary upon the appropriateness of the name "Keltic" as applied to a morphological type that this type has the largest proportion of individuals who are completely ignorant of the Irish tongue (63.6 per cent). The excess amounts to 6.0 per cent. A very small deficiency of Keltic speakers or students is also to be noted in the Nordic Mediterranean type which is numerically the strongest of our eight morphological types. However, the four most numerous types (as listed above) comprise 92.7 per cent of Keltic speakers.

The most important part of table XIV-3 is the column which gives the percentage of native Irish speakers for the several types. There are, in the total type series, 12.3 per cent of native Irish speakers and another 0.9 per cent (86 persons) who can speak nothing but Irish. Considerably the highest combined proportions of native speakers and speakers of Irish only are found in the rufous, brachycephalic, East Baltic type (15.2 per cent) and in the Nordic Alpine type (14.2 per cent). The Pure Nordic, Predominantly Nordic, and Pure Mediterranean types have deficiencies. Thus the round-headed types include proportionately more Keltic speakers, though absolutely fewer. Unfortunately, the East Baltic type is so small in numbers that we cannot feel assured of the significance of the finding. This is also the case in the deficiencies shown by the Pure Mediterranean and, possibly, of the Pure Nordic types. It is interesting to note also that the Keltic type has the smallest proportion of persons who have studied Irish at school.

On the whole, the relationship between Keltic language and morphological type is very tenuous. It amounts to a little more than an indication that Pure Nordics, Predominantly Nordics, and Pure Mediterraneans are somewhat less likely to be Keltic speakers than are men of the other morphological types and that, in particular, the name "Keltic" is an egregious misnomer for the type to which we have applied that designation, so far as language is concerned.

Occupation (Table XIV-4). The lowest occupational class is that of hired laborers and tinkers. This constitutes 7.6 per cent of the morphological series. Notably deficient in this category is the East Baltic type. There are no Pure Mediterraneans in this occupation, but they are so few that their occupational distribution is unreliable. By far the highest proportion in this occupation belongs to the Keltic type (10.8 per cent). All other types are slightly, but usually insignificantly deficient. In the general herdsman and agricultural class the Keltics also lead and Pure Mediterraneans and Nordic Alpines also show an excess. In the farm dependent class, Pure Nordics, Predominantly Nordics, East Baltics, Nordic Alpines, show excesses. Other types are slightly low. The differences are not great in any case. Fishermen constitute too small an occupational class to merit much discussion. All types except those which are very small in numbers have nearly proportional representation of fishermen.

Navvies constitute 22.1 per cent of the entire series. In this lowly occupation are excesses of Nordic Mediterraneans and Keltics, but the excesses are not large. Notable deficiencies of navvies are found in the East Baltic and Nordic Alpine types.

Semi-skilled trades constitute 8.3 per cent of the series. The Pure Nordics lead with 17.3 per cent and the Pure Mediterraneans have none in this occupational group. Their marked excess is in another small occupational

category—transportation. Here they lead with 12.1 per cent. A more important though smaller excess in this class is found among the Nordic Alpines. Pure Nordics and Dinarics are low in this group.

Factory workers constitute only 1.6 per cent of the series. East Baltics have a slight lead in this class. In the skilled trades group, again, numbers are small. The most interesting points of the distribution are the leading position of Pure and Predominantly Nordics and the low rankings of Keltics and East Baltics.

The mercantile or shop-keeping class comprises 11.1 per cent of the series. Notably, but possibly insignificantly high, are the Pure Mediterraneans and Pure Nordics. Keltics are very low in this grouping. In clerical work the leading type is Predominantly Nordic, followed by Nordic Mediterranean. Keltics are low. In the professional group the leading types are East Baltic and Pure Nordic. Dinarics and Nordic Alpines are also somewhat high. Keltics and Nordic Mediterraneans are low. Among the soldiers, Keltics are notably deficient. The leading types are East Baltic, Pure Mediterranean, and Pure Nordic, but these types are all numerically inadequate. East Baltics also lead among the students with nearly twice as many proportionately as any other type. Predominantly Nordic, Nordic Alpine and Dinaric types are slightly high; Keltics and Nordic Mediterraneans are low.

The Pure Nordic type consists of so small a sample that its occupational distribution is unreliable. Its notable crude excesses are in farm dependents, semi-skilled trades, skilled trades, and shop assistants.

The Predominantly Nordic type, which has an adequate representation, is also high in farm dependents and in skilled trades. Its other excesses are in clerks and students.

The inadequate East Baltic type is interestingly low in such menial occupations as hired laborers and tinkers, navvies, and quite remarkably high in soldiers, professional men, and students. The excesses and deficiencies are hardly reliable.

The handful of Pure Mediterraneans (33) has to be assigned to no less than 14 occupational categories.

In the four main groups (Nordic Mediterranean, Keltic, Dinaric, and Nordic Alpine) we find that the outstanding fact is the inferior situation of the Keltic type. All of the more menial occupations are well represented, while the more skilled occupations are deficient. This correlates with their educational ranking, which is the lowest of all eight types. The Nordic Mediterraneans, although they are the largest group numerically, show nothing outstanding occupationally. Their excesses are in navvies, semi-skilled trades, clerks and soldiers. They seem to represent occupationally a step up from the Keltics. The Nordic Alpines seem definitely higher in the occupational scale. Although they are slightly over-represented in agricultural pursuits, they are ahead in transportation, professional workers, and students. The Dinarics show up occupationally best of the four major types. They have fewer agricultural workers on the whole than the Nordic Alpines and they are well represented in skilled trades, shop workers, the professions and among students. Taking these data at face value, it appears that the round-heads have the edge on the long-heads, occupationally speaking. The most interesting fact brought to light is that the above ranking bears out exactly the educational ranking of the four types. Of the smaller types, the East Baltic makes the best occupational showing, but the distribution is unreliable.

Occupation, Rural and Urban (Table XIV-5). Occupationally the most distinctively rural type is the Keltic, closely followed by the Nordic Alpine. The blond Pure Nordics, Predominantly Nordics and East Baltics appear rather more urban. The distinction between urban and rural occupation is probably not important.

Religion (Table XIV-6). More than 91 per cent of the total Irish series adheres to the Catholic religion. Our interest in dividing up physical types according to religious affiliation is merely based upon the supposition that discrimination between Protestants and Catholics would help to separate the persons of recent Scottish and English descent from these of more ancient Irish lineage. This supposition seems to have been partly verified. The small sample of Pure Nordics shows a slight deficiency of Catholics and excesses both of Church of Ireland members and of Presbyterians. Lesser, but statistically more reliable, excesses of the same kind occur in the Predominantly Nordic type. The large Keltic type has virtually the same sectarian distribution as occurs in the total series. The East Baltic type has the normal dominance of Catholics, but also a dubious excess of Church of Ireland members and a deficiency of Presbyterians. The Dinaric type is excessively Catholic. The Nordic Mediterraneans have a small excess of Church of Ireland members. The Pure Mediterranean type is high in Presbyterians, but the sample cannot be adjudged reliable. The very large Nordic Alpine type has a small excess of Catholics.

On the whole, there is very little relationship between morpological types and religious affiliation. Perhaps it may be asserted, tentatively, that the blonder types include more Protestants.

Age Groups (Table XV-1). Because of the dependence of morphological typing upon hair color, the distribution of the eight types through the 14 age groups has to be interpreted with caution. Blond hair and some shades of light brown darken with age up to the point where graying sets in. In very old individuals the hair color during youth and maturity often cannot be determined because the hair has turned completely white or has disappeared.

The Pure Nordic type with ash blond and golden hair disappears before 50 years, but this fact probably does not mean that the individuals who had this blond hair color could not survive through middle age, but only that their hair color did not survive. The types with the lightest hair are Pure Nordic and East Baltic. Those with intermediate hair shades (at least in part) are Predominantly Nordic, Nordic Mediterranean, Nordic Alpine, and Dinaric. The darkest haired types are Keltic and Pure Mediterranean.

If the reader will take the trouble to compare the individual type distributions within each age group with the total series percentage in that age group, he will see at once which types are in excess and in deficiency in the successive age groups and what the age trends of the several types are.

Thus Pure Nordics are in enormous excess from 15–19 through 20–24, become definitely deficient at 40–44, and have only one survivor at 45–49 years. The equally light haired but round-headed East Baltics show their huge excess at 20–24 years. They begin to be deficient from 35–39 onward, but a few linger on in middle age and the last survivor is at 70–74 years. There happen to be twice as many East Baltics as Pure Nordics and so one might expect that they would show a later age group survival.

Predominantly Nordics are in strong excess through the first three age groups, begin to show deficiency at 35–39, and thereafter are always relatively scarce.

Dinarics have an age group distribution not widely divergent from the series total, although they tend to be slightly deficient from 40–44 years onward.

Nordic Mediterraneans are also close to the series total but they tend to be slightly in excess from 35–39 years onward.

Nordic Alpines show slight excesses in the first two groups and slight deficiencies in nearly all groups from 40–44 onward.

The three types just mentioned have in them some individuals with the lighter shades of brown hair in addition to dark shades. The complexity of hair shades included in these mixed categories probably contributes to their close approximation to the general series distribution.

The Pure Mediterranean has solely dark hair but includes only 33 individuals and its distribution through 14 age groups cannot be expected to be representative. It may be worth while to note that its excesses are in 45–49, 50-54 and 60-64.

The Keltics with mostly dark hair but sometimes red-brown or red hair are deficient up to 35–39, and thereafter in slight to moderate excess throughout every age group. Their most impressive strength in relation to other types is from 50–54 years onward.

The Keltic type, which for the total series is numerically the second strongest, is thus the greatest survival type in the advanced age groups. It predominates in numbers in age groups from 50 onward except in 75–79 years, in which the Nordic Mediterranean exceeds it slightly. The very old Irish males are thus mostly long-headed with medium dark to dark hair.

Age (Tables XV-2 and XV-3). The sorting criteria, of course, do not include any age selection. Yet in Ireland, as in the United States, the blond and near-blond types turn out to be much younger in mean age than the brunets or the intermediates. Thus our handful of Pure Nordics with golden or ash blond hair average 26.10 years, which is 8.80 years below mean age. Predominantly Nordics are 6.95 years below mean age and East Baltics

4.95 years. Dinarics and Nordic Alpines, of intermediate pigmentation, are, respectively, 1.50 years and 1.40 years below mean age. The brunet types exceed mean total morphological series age.

There can be little doubt that blond hair is, generally speaking, impermanent. It darkens with age in such a way as to transfer many young "Pure Nordics" into "Predominantly Nordics"; "East Baltics" into "Nordic Alpines."

Weight (Table XV-4). The following table shows roughly the regression of mean weight upon mean age in the morphological types:

Type	Mean Weight	Mean Age
Nordic Alpine	158.80	33.50
Nordic Mediterranean	157.30	35.50
Dinaric	157.30	33.40
East Baltic	156.70	29.95
Keltic	156.60	38.55
Predominantly Nordic	155.50	27.95
Pure Nordic	151.10	26.10
Pure Mediterranean	150.30	39.10

It is evident that the only effect of age deficiency upon mean weight is exhibited in the Pure and Predominantly Nordic groups, if anywhere. Incidentally, Nordic Alpines are usually the heaviest morphological type elsewhere, as in Ireland. Brachycephalic groups are likely to exceed dolichocephalic groups in mean weight, since the former include many more men with dominant endomorphic or mesomorphic components in body build, while long-heads are likely to have a predominance of ectomorphy.

The only morphological types that display clearly significant weight differences from the Irish totals are the Nordic Alpine with an excess and the Predominantly Nordic with a deficiency.

Stature (Table XV-5). The only statural sorting criterion throws men with red hair and mixed eyes who are under 170 cm. into the Nordic Mediterranean type rather than the Predominantly Nordic, and vice versa. This discrimination tends to weight Predominantly Nordic for tallness against Nordic Mediterranean. It is unimportant because of the comparatively few persons falling into the categories in question. There are only 39 red-haired Nordic Mediterraneans.

Actually, the Predominantly Nordic is by far the tallest of our morphological types, since it is 1.20 cm. above mean stature. Dinarics are next in statural ranking with 0.42 cm. excess. No other type is significantly tall. The shortest type is the numerically insignificant Pure Mediterranean (as would be expected). Nordic Alpines with a mean deficiency of 0.69 cm. are also significantly short.

Span and Relative Span (Tables XV-6, XV-7). Absolute span runs closely in correlation with absolute stature and requires little or no comment. Span relative to stature is of interest. All Irish, according to these data, have very high relative spans. The average of the morphological series, 105.32, is prodigious. Significantly low relative spans are found in the Predominantly Nordics, and even lower, although not significantly so, in the Pure Nordics.

Biacromial Diameter and Relative Shoulder Breadth (Tables XV-8, XV-9). The variations in means of biacromial diameter are very small. The narrowest shoulders are found in the Pure Nordic and Pure Mediterranean types, but the samples are so small that the deficiencies hardly attain statistical significance.

Relative shoulder breadth again finds the Pure Mediterraneans and the Pure Nordics strongly deficient, with the Predominantly Nordic also well below average. The Nordic Alpine group has a possible significant excess in relative shoulder breadth.

Chest Breadth, Chest Depth, and Thoracic Index (Tables XV-10, XV-11, XV-12). The highest chest breadths are found in the Nordic Alpines and Dinarics, deficient breadths in Pure Nordic, Pure Mediterranean and Predominantly Nordic. The only type in which chest depth is surely excessive is the Keltic. Chest depth is deficient in Pure Nordic, East Baltic, and Predominantly Nordic types.

Thoracic index in Ireland is an important means of differentiating anthropological types. It is clear that the Keltic type is marked by a relatively narrow and deep chest. This is true, to a lesser extent, of the Nordic Mediterranean type. The Pure Mediterranean type has the highest relative chest depth, but its excess is statistically insignificant. On the other hand, relatively wide and shallow chests characterize the East Baltics, Dinarics, and Predominantly Nordics.

Sitting Height and Relative Sitting Height (Tables XV-13, XV-14). Absolute sitting height correlates closely with stature and requires no commentary. Relative sitting height is not markedly variable in the morphological types. It is somewhat high in East Baltics and in Nordic Alpines. It is uncertainly low in Pure Mediterraneans and Pure Nordics.

Head Length (Table XV-15). Since sorting is based primarily upon cephalic index, head lengths are, naturally, strongly differentiated among the types. There is, however, no particular reason in the selection that would militate in favor of differences between the various long-headed types taken among themselves, and similarly with the broad-heads. Actually, we cannot be sure that any of the dolichocephalic types differs significantly from any other in head length. Crudely, the Pure Nordics have the shortest heads in this group. The brachycephals group themselves roughly about a mean of approximately 192.50 mm. and the dolichocephals around a mean nearly 5 mm. higher. The Dinarics certainly have the shortest heads of the brachycephals.

Head Breadth (Table XV-16). Head breadths are subject also to the sorting criteria. The long-heads generally fall around a mean of 151.50 mm., whereas the brachys range around 157.75 mm. Thus the differences in head breadth on the whole are greater than in head length. No certain differences occur within the two main categories of narrow heads and broad heads.

Head Circumference (Table XV-17). Head circumference is dubiously high in East Baltics and Pure Mediterraneans and uncertainly low only in Pure Nordics and Dinarics.

Cephalic Index (Table XV-18). Of the five long-headed groups, the Pure Mediterraneans alone exceed 77 in mean index and their excess is statistically insignificant over those of the other dolichocephalic groups. Nor are there any clear differences between the three groups of round-heads.

Head Height, Length-Height, and Breadth-Height Indices (Tables XV-19, XV-20, XV-21). Head height is definitely low in the Pure Mediterranean and Keltic types, but significantly so only in the latter. It is uncertainly high in East Baltics and possibly so in the other brachycephals. The dolichocephals cluster round length-height indices of about

63.30. The Pure Mediterraneans and Keltics are clearly inferior among the long-headed groups. The three round-headed groups range around 65.12 in this index. Among the dolichocephals the breadth-height index runs very low in Pure Mediterraneans and Keltics and rather high in Pure and Predominantly Nordics.

Minimum Frontal Diameter (Table XV-22). The brachycephals naturally have wider foreheads than the dolichocephals. The differences in the two groups run about 2 mm. The long-heads seem to group themselves in two categories of forehead breadths—the narrow group (Keltics and Pure Mediterraneans) and the broader group (Pure Nordics, Predominantly Nordics, and Nordic Mediterraneans). The Dinarics have the narrowest foreheads among the round-heads, and the Nordic Alpines the widest.

Fronto-Parietal Index (Table XV-23). The relation of forehead breadth to maximum head breadth runs lower in brachycephals than in dolichocephals. In the long-head group the minimum occurs among Pure Mediterraneans, followed in ascending order by Keltics, Nordic Mediterraneans, Predominantly and Pure Nordics. Dinarics have the lowest fronto-parietal index among the brachycephals.

Zygo-Frontal Index (Table XV-24). The highest relationship of forehead breadth to face breadth is found in the Pure Nordics (78.50). Predominantly Nordics, Nordic Mediterraneans, and Keltics also run high. The minimum index (76.74) occurs in the Pure Mediterraneans. Thus there is no consistent difference between dolichocephals and brachycephals in the mean values of this index.

Bizygomatic Diameter (Table XV-25). Face breadth is naturally greater in round-heads than in long-heads, assuming no marked differentiation in gross size. The Dinarics, who have longer and narrower noses, naturally have the least facial breadth among the brachycephals. In the long-headed types, the Nordic and Predominantly Nordic groups seem slightly inferior in face breadth.

Cephalo-Facial Index (Table XV-26). The cephalo-facial index is the relation of face breadth to head breadth. It is ordinarily lower in brachycephals than in dolichocephals. In the former category the minimum is reached in Dinarics. The highest index among the long-heads is found in the Nordic Mediterranean type.

Total Face Height (Table XV-27). The Dinaric type alone is indirectly selected for long faces, since it is sorted for the occurrence of long and narrow noses. The Nordic Alpine type, in which nasal indices are high, gets the reverse selection. None of the long-headed types receives any discriminative attention in the sorting as regards face height. Actually, the Dinaric type has considerably the greatest total face height, although it is a round-headed type. The crude minimum face height occurs in the Pure Mediterranean type, but the mean is of uncertain value. East Baltics certainly have short faces. The young Pure Nordic group falls considerably below the Predominantly Nordic, Keltic, and Nordic Mediterranean types in face height.

Upper Face Height (Table XV-28). Upper face height attains a maximum among the Dinarics, as a result of their having been selected for long and narrow noses. Next in order come the Keltic long-heads and the Nordic Mediterraneans, whose upper faces are distinctly long. Relatively short upper faces are found in East Baltics, Pure Nordics, and Nordic Alpines. The short upper faces of the Pure Nordics may be related to their juvenility.

Facial Index (Table XV-29). We expect relatively longer and narrower faces in dolichocephals than in brachycephals. However, the Dinaric type is round-headed and long-faced. It is, however, below the dolichocephalic types except the Pure Mediterraneans in total facial index. Unfortunately, the sample of Pure Mediterraneans is inadequate and the mean unreliable in its deviation.

Upper Facial Index (Table XV-30). The upper facial index of the Keltic type is significantly higher (i.e., the maxilla is relatively longer and narrower) than in any other morphological type, dolichocephalic or brachycephalic. This distribution is independent of the criteria used in sorting. The lowest and broadest upper faces occur in the East Baltics and the Nordic Alpines.

Nose Height (Table XV-31). By sorting, the Dinarics have the longest noses (58.22 mm.) and the East Baltics the shortest (54.22 mm.). The nose is also rather short in another round-headed group, the Nordic Alpines (54.42 mm.).

Nose Breadth (Table XV-32). In this measurement, again, sorting by nasal index has affected the means of the several types. The Dinarics with a mean of 34.13 mm. are lowest, the Nordic Alpines with 37.37 mm. considerably the highest. Pure and Predominantly Nordics run somewhat low.

Nasal Index (Table XV-33). The Dinarics with a mean index of 58.86 are far below any other type. The Nordic Alpines with 69.02 are correspondingly high. East Baltics are also high (68.42), partly on account of discriminative sorting.

Bigonial Diameter (Table XV-34). We expect jaw breadths to be greater among brachycephals than among dolichocephals. This expectation is realized. The maximum bigonial diameter among the round-heads occurs in the Nordic Alpine type. Among the long-heads, Nordic Mediterraneans and Keltics definitely exceed the other groups in jaw breadth.

Zygo-Gonial Index (Table XV-35). This index is very low in East Baltics and high in Keltics.

Fronto-Gonial Index (Table XV-36). The relation of jaw breadth to forehead breadth is much reduced in Pure Nordics and East Baltics (the two types with lightest hair). The Keltic type is outstanding for high value of this index.

SUMMARY OF METRIC DIFFERENCES OF THE MORPHOLOGICAL TYPES

PURE NORDIC CHARACTERS INDEPENDENT
OF SORTING CRITERIA

- lowest mean age
- low mean weight
- low mean shoulder breadth
- low mean chest breadth
- low mean chest depth
- high breadth-height index
- high fronto-parietal index
- high zygo-frontal index
- low bizygomatic diameter
- low upper face height
- low nose height
- low nose breadth
- low bigonial diameter

CHARACTERS INVOLVED IN SORTING CRITERIA
>high mean head length
>low mean head breadth
>low mean cephalic index

SUMMARY OF METRIC DIFFERENCES OF PURE NORDIC TYPE

The only metric differentia of this type clearly involved in the sorting criteria and thus axiomatic, are high head length, low head breadth, and low cephalic index. Most of the independent metric criteria detailed above seem to us to be related to the very low mean age of these long-headed blonds, and consequent failure to achieve full adult body size. In other words, sorting for blonds seems to select many subadult and very young adult subjects who are therefore likely to fall short of fully mature dimensions and proportions in many characters, since growth often proceeds up to middle age.

PREDOMINANTLY NORDIC CHARACTERS INDEPENDENT OF SORTING CRITERIA
>low mean age
>low mean weight
>high mean stature
>low relative span
>low relative shoulder breadth
>low chest breadth
>low chest depth
>high sitting height
>low length-height index
>high breadth-height index
>low minimum frontal diameter
>high fronto-parietal index
>high zygo-frontal index
>low bizygomatic diameter
>high cephalo-facial index
>high facial index
>high upper facial index
>high nose height
>low bigonial diameter

CHARACTERS INVOLVED IN SORTING CRITERIA
>high head length
>low head breadth
>low cephalic index

SUMMARY OF METRIC DIFFERENCES OF PREDOMINANTLY NORDIC TYPE

Apart from the differences of measurements directly included in the sorting criteria or indices derived therefrom, there are many distinctive features of the Predominantly Nordic type. Those of the body seem again related to tender mean age. Those of the head and face are to some extent correlated with dolichocephaly although not necessarily entirely dependent upon long-headedness. For example, a dolichocephal does not necessarily have a long narrow face and a low bigonial diameter, although, on the whole, the latter combination is more likely to occur with a long head than with a round head.

The greater number of features distinguishing the Predominantly Nordic as contrasted with the Pure Nordic is probably referable, for the most part, to the adequate size of the sample of the former and the inadequate size of the latter.

KELTIC CHARACTERS INDEPENDENT OF SORTING CRITERIA
>high mean age
>high mean chest depth
>high thoracic index
>low head height
>low length-height index
>high breadth-height index
>low minimum frontal diameter
>high fronto-parietal index
>low bizygomatic diameter
>high cephalo-facial index
>high upper face height
>high facial index
>high upper facial index
>high nose breadth
>high zygo-gonial index
>high fronto-gonial index

CHARACTERS INVOLVED IN SORTING CRITERIA
>high mean head length
>low mean head breadth
>low cephalic index

SUMMARY OF METRIC DIFFERENCES OF KELTIC TYPE

Some of the independently differentiated characters of the Keltic type may possibly be indirectly involved in the sorting criteria, e.g., low minimum frontal diameter and high upper facial index. On the other hand, it must be emphasized that these features, though rather strongly correlated with a sorting based upon the cephalic index, are not incapable of independent variation.

High nose breadth of the Keltics is quite

contrary to expectation when faces are long and narrow. A low bizygomatic is not inevitably implied by prevalent dolichocephaly of the population.

EAST BALTIC CHARACTERS INDEPENDENT OF SORTING CRITERIA

low mean age
low mean chest depth
low mean thoracic index
low mean fronto-parietal index
high mean bizygomatic diameter
low cephalo-facial index
low mean total facial height
low mean upper facial height
low mean facial index
low mean upper facial index
low mean zygo-gonial index
high mean length-height index
low mean breadth-height index

CHARACTERS INVOLVED IN SORTING CRITERIA

low mean head length
high mean head breadth
high mean cephalic index
low mean nose height
high mean nose breadth
high mean nasal index

SUMMARY OF METRIC DIFFERENCES OF EAST BALTIC TYPE

Selection of high nasal indices to differentiate the East Baltic from the similarly round-headed Dinaric and Nordic Alpine types involves many facial measurements and indices in the sorting criteria.

It might be argued, indeed, that only low mean age, low mean chest depth and low mean thoracic index of this type are entirely independently differentiated—characters which may in themselves stem from the blondness of the type.

No distinctive features of this type in head measurements and indices can be claimed to be entirely free of correlation with the selectional criteria of high cephalic and nasal indices.

DINARIC CHARACTERS INDEPENDENT OF SORTING CRITERIA

low mean age
low mean thoracic index
high mean length-height index
low mean breadth-height index
high mean minimum frontal diameter

low mean fronto-parietal index
low mean zygo-frontal index
high mean bizygomatic diameter
low mean cephalo-facial index
high mean total face height
high mean upper face height
high mean upper facial index
high mean bigonial diameter
low mean zygo-gonial index

CHARACTERS INVOLVED IN SORTING CRITERIA

low mean head length
high mean head breadth
high mean cephalic index
high mean nose height
low mean nose breadth
low mean nasal index

SUMMARY OF METRIC DIFFERENCES OF DINARIC TYPE

Apart from age and the thoracic index, few metric characters that distinguish this type can be said to be completely independent of the sorting criteria, although those so listed are not directly involved in the selection by cephalic and nasal indices. Sorting in these indices involves more or less direct selection of head length, head breadth, nose height and nose breadth, and indirect involvement of all measurements significantly correlated with the above.

NORDIC MEDITERRANEAN CHARACTERS INDEPENDENT OF SORTING CRITERIA

low mean minimum frontal diameter
high mean fronto-parietal index
low mean bizygomatic diameter
high mean cephalo-facial index
high mean facial index
high mean upper facial index
high mean zygo-gonial index
low mean length-height index
high mean breadth-height index

CHARACTERS INVOLVED IN SORTING CRITERIA

high mean head length
low mean head breadth
low mean cephalic index

SUMMARY OF METRIC DIFFERENCES OF NORDIC MEDITERRANEAN TYPE

The metric features of this type are nearly all directly or indirectly involved in the sorting criteria.

PURE MEDITERRANEAN CHARACTERS
INDEPENDENT OF SORTING CRITERIA
   high mean age
   low mean total face height

CHARACTERS INVOLVED IN SORTING CRITERIA
   low mean cephalic index

SUMMARY OF METRIC DIFFERENCES OF PURE MEDITERRANEAN TYPE

Lack of significant metric differentiae of this type is undoubtedly due in part to the inadequate size of the sample (only 33 men).

NORDIC ALPINE CHARACTERS INDEPENDENT OF SORTING CRITERIA
   low mean age
   high mean weight
   low mean stature
   high mean relative sitting height
   high mean length-height index
   low mean breadth-height index
   high mean minimum frontal diameter
   low mean fronto-parietal index
   high mean bizygomatic diameter

   low mean cephalo-facial index
   low mean total face height
   low mean upper face height
   low mean facial index
   low mean upper facial index
   high mean bigonial diameter
   low mean zygo-gonial index
   low mean fronto-gonial index

CHARACTERS INVOLVED IN SORTING CRITERIA
   low mean head length
   high mean head breadth
   low mean cephalic index
   low mean nose height
   high mean nose breadth
   high mean nasal index

SUMMARY OF METRIC DIFFERENCES OF NORDIC ALPINE TYPE

The distinctive Nordic Alpine features particularly involve weight, stature, relative sitting height. Most metric features of the head and face that are distinctive are involved directly or by correlation with the sorting criteria.

CONCLUSIONS ON METRIC DIFFERENCES OF THE MORPHOLOGICAL TYPES

The reader who desires to carp at the sorting of individuals into types on the basis of combination of metric and morphological characters will find in the preceding sections abundant evidence that a few basic metric sorting criteria such as differences in the cephalic and nasal indices carry with them many other differentiae in the groups sorted, partly or largely because of correlations of these latter with the initial sorting criteria. So it may be argued by such persons that secondary correlated differences are virtually as arbitrary as those upon which the sortings were initially based. It seems to us, however, that the manifestation or demonstration of such secondary characters actually reinforces and validates the concept of the several types.

If there were no distinctive metric features of the "types" apart from those actually sorted, it might reasonably be argued that said types are purely arbitrary and largely fictitious. The fact that many secondary differences appear (even if correlated) shows that the several types possess some integrity and homogeneity and are not merely theoretical. If the initial sorting criteria carry with them correlated features, they are so much the better as sorting criteria for types.

In the summaries above it will be noted that many distinctive metric features of the eight types are concerned with the trunk dimensions and proportions such as stature, weight, shoulder breadth, chest diameters, and chest indices. These bodily differentiae, which are in general quite remote from the cephalic index, the nasal index, etc., are particularly in evidence in the case of the Pure Nordics, the Predominantly Nordics, the Keltics, and the Nordic Alpine types. These are all types which show marked average age deviations in one direction or the other. It can hardly be argued that the age differences are directly correlated with the initial sorting criteria apart from hair color. It is also doubtful that the body differences in dimensions and proportions are particularly in turn the result of an age selection which came about through hair color sortings.

In all cases significance of difference is between an individual type and the total Irish series of which it forms a part. That is a much more rigid test of distinction than if the differences were estimated type against type.

If the type differences depended only upon cephalic index and nasal index sortings, such groups as Predominantly Nordic, Keltic and Nordic Mediterranean should show a nearly uniform array of distinctive metric features. A perusal of the summaries above will convince the reader that such is not the case, although of course, there are many coincidental differences in the same direction.

It is of interest to note that the largest type numerically—the Nordic Mediterraneans, sup-posedly pigmentally intermediate dolichocephals—show on the whole the fewest differentiae from the total series of which they form 28.9 per cent. On the other hand the Keltics, who are second in strength with 25.3 per cent of the total series are comparatively marked in their metric differentiation.

The most complicated sortings were carried out to differentiate the East Baltic, Dinaric, and Nordic Alpine types. It could be claimed that the discrimination of the nasal index to some extent explains the wide diversity of these three somewhat brachycephalic types.

The fact that our eight types show many distinctive differences can hardly be charged to a fault in the method of sorting, because the object of typing is to establish combinations of differences in individuals.

Skin Color, Inner Arm (Table XVI-1). Naturally, the selection of hair color types influences skin pigmentation. Thus the Pure and Predominantly Nordic types are almost wholly pink in skin color as are the East Baltics. The Keltics have fewer dark-skinned persons than the Dinarics and the Dinarics than the Nordic Alpines. The Nordic Mediterranean type has still more heavily pigmented skins (13.4 per cent). Finally, the Pure Mediterranean type is two-thirds dark-skinned.

Vascularity (Table XVI-2). Pronounced vascularity grades well with skin color. The maximum percentages occur in the East Baltic and Pure Nordic blonds. Then there is a vast falling off to the Predominantly Nordics, Keltics, Dinarics, Nordic Alpines, Nordic Mediterraneans and, finally, to the Pure Mediterraneans, who include 12.1 per cent of individuals with pronouncedly vascular skins.

Freckles (Table XVI-3). The matter of the association of freckles with morphological types is important. We expect the brunet Pure Mediterraneans to have the fewest freckles and they, accordingly, lead in absence of freckles with 69.7 per cent. It is rather surprising that next in absence of freckling should be the prevailingly dark-haired, blue-eyed Keltic type with 64.0 per cent absent. The most freckles are found in the rufous East Baltic type (32.4 per cent absent), perhaps because of small size of the sample. The second place is held by Predominantly Nordic with 50.4 per cent of absence. It is clear enough, however, that the freckles seem to go with the red-haired and light-haired types.

Moles (Table XVI-4). Moles are least common in the dark Pure Mediterraneans (3.0 per cent) and, consistent with freckles, are next scarcest in the Keltics (4.4 per cent). Moles are commonest in the light-skinned Predominantly Nordics. This finding is rather surprising, in view of the supposition that moles are ordinarily more frequent in dark-skinned individuals.

Hair Form (Table XVI-5). The correlation of hair form with morphological type is weak. The tiny Pure Nordic group seems to be highest in straight hair and low in curved varieties (except deep waves). The Predominantly Nordic type is, on the contrary, slightly high in deep waves, but low in low waves. The Keltic group, one of the largest, tends to some slight excess of straight hair.

The small East Baltic group has the most deep-waved and curly hair. The Dinarics are notable for low waves. The Nordic Mediterraneans are close to series total distribution in hair form. Pure Mediterraneans are too few for reliable judgment. They seem to be very high in deep waves. The large Nordic Alpine group has slightly more curved hair than is found in the total series.

Hair Texture (Table XVI-6). Here, again, is a remarkable fact, in that about the only notable deviations from general distribution in hair texture are found in the Pure Nordic group which has a large excess of fine hair, and the East Baltic group which has an even greater excess of coarse hair. These data, together with those from hair form, seem to demonstrate that fine hair is more inclined to be straight (as shown by Pure Nordics) and coarse hair to be curved (as in East Baltics). In fine hair the Predominantly Nordic group ranks second.

Hair Quantity, Head, Beard, and Body (Tables XVI-7, XVI-8, XVI-9). Body hair quantity ordinarily increases with age, but the tabulation by morphological types reveals no important differences whether by age or by type. Beard quantity shows little except an absence or scarcity of pronounced growths in the under-aged. Pure and Predominantly Nordics, and something of an excess in these categories in the brunet Nordic Mediterraneans. There is a surprising but undependable excess of weak beards in our few Mediterraneans, who also rate high in submedium body hair.

Baldness (Table XVI-10). Although baldness is principally controlled by genetic factors, it increases with age. Therefore the following rankings in baldness and in mean age are interesting.

Type	Rank	Total Baldness	Rank	Mean Age
Keltic	1	46.5	2	38.55
Nordic Mediterranean	2	41.2	3	35.50
Dinaric	3	38.8	5	35.40
Pure Mediterranean	4	36.4	1	39.10
Nordic Alpine	5	35.7	4	33.50
East Baltic	6	30.5	6	29.95
Predominantly Nordic	7	25.3	7	27.95
Pure Nordic	8	20.0	8	26.10

Since the blond types are youngest, they show the least balding. However the Pure Mediterranean type (too small) is out of line with its high mean age in its relative scarcity of baldness. On the whole, age ranking fits well with rank in baldness. There is no suggestion of any type peculiarity, apart from age, except in the Pure Mediterraneans. Incidentally, the Keltic and Nordic Mediterranean types lead not only in total baldness but in medium and pronounced degrees of baldness.

Grayness, Head and Beard (Tables XVI-11, XVI-12). In general, ranking of grayness in head and beard go with mean age rather than with morphological type. Less graying of beard hair as compared with head hair may be due in part to the difficulty of detecting grayness in clean-shaven individuals.

Type	Head	Beard	Rank in Age	Mean Age
Pure Mediterranean	54.5	33.2	1	39.10
Keltic	53.8	42.7	2	38.55
Nordic Mediterranean	47.5	35.3	3	35.50
Dinaric	42.6	29.7	5	33.40
Nordic Alpine	40.1	29.4	4	33.50
East Baltic	21.9	16.3	6	29.95
Predominantly Nordic	17.3	12.2	7	27.95
Pure Nordic	10.9	9.1	8	26.10

Hair Color, Head (Table XVI-13). Hair color is one of the most important sorting criteria of the morphological types. However, each type tends to have some latitude of variation permitted in hair color, so that it is important to study the distribution of hair shades in each type. Thus the Pure Nordic type can be either golden blond or ash blond, and turns out to be 81.8 per cent golden. Incidentally, the 18.2 per cent of ash blonds in this type represent 10 persons out of the 15 in the 9,521 Irish males of the type series who have ash blond hair. Predominantly Nordics may have

a wide assortment of light hair going with light or mixed eyes. Actually, 81.5 per cent of this large type group have golden brown hair, and 12.6 per cent have red hair, the other shades being ash brown (4.8 per cent), golden (0.9 per cent) and ash (0.2 per cent). Thus this type is distinctly rufous (in that golden brown hair has a great deal of red-gold pigment).

The Keltic type must have blue eyes, but may have any shade of hair from black to red-brown and red, excluding golden brown, ash brown, golden, and ash. In reality, it has 46.9 per cent of flat brown hair (the largest proportion in any type) and 39.7 per cent of dark brown hair. This type includes the largest numbers of men with red-brown hair and with red hair found in any morphological type, but the percentages in the total composition of the type (6.2 and 5.7 respectively) are quite small.

The East Baltic type is round-headed and must have ash, golden, or red hair with blue or mixed eyes. It turns out to have the strongest representation of red hair in any type—no less than 72.4 per cent. It has 23.8 per cent of golden hair, and the rest is ash.

The Dinaric type has every shade of hair except golden and ash, but it is predominantly dark brown (41.0 per cent) and brown (37.3 per cent). This type also has a strong representation of golden brown (10.6 per cent).

The Nordic Mediterranean type must have darkish hair and mixed or lightish eyes, but it may have red hair and mixed eyes if stature is under 170 cm. This last minor category includes only 1.47 per cent. The Nordic Mediterranean type is dominantly dark brown in hair color (52.4 per cent) with a strong minor of flat brown (36.2 per cent). Nearly half of the black-haired men in the whole morphological type series are Nordic Mediterraneans, but black hair comprises only 4.7 per cent of the type.

The Pure Mediterranean type is so insignificant in numbers as to be practically negligible. It has, of course, the darkest hair, but even in this type the dominant shade is dark brown (72.7 per cent), rather than black (9.1 per cent).

The large Nordic Alpine series falls behind Pure Mediterraneans and Nordic Mediterraneans in darkness of hair, but is still dominantly dark-haired. Its modal shade is dark brown. It has nearly the same distribution of hair color as has the Dinaric type.

The order of the morphological types in general increasing intensity of hair pigmentation is Pure Nordic, East Baltic, Predominantly Nordic, Keltic, Dinaric, Nordic Alpine, Nordic Mediterranean and Pure Mediterranean.

The most interesting phenomenon in hair shade distribution among the types is the occurrence of red hair, which amounts to 3.9 per cent in the total series—not an inordinately high proportion. In the first place, many physical anthropologists and textbooks assert that red hair belongs in the dark hair series and this is certainly incorrect. Red hair is an intensification of the red-gold pigment found in golden blonds. Red hair belongs with golden, and ash blond hair with flat brown and with darker shades of brown. Our East Baltic type is a brachycephalic type which is predominantly red-haired. The eyes are blue or mixed.

The data suggest that red hair in Ireland is more likely to be associated with brachycephaly than is golden hair or even ash hair. Black hair tends to go with dolichocephaly in preference to brachycephaly. This is true also of dark brown hair. On the whole, flat brown hair is more likely to be found in the long-headed types. But it is clear that hair shade is not strongly correlated with head form.

Eye Color (Table XVI-14). There are only 43 distinctly brown-eyed men in our morphological type series of 9,521 Irishmen. Of these, 33 (100 per cent) are Pure Mediterranean and the rest Dinaric. It is extraordinary, to say the least, that only 43 men with purely brown eyes should be found in this large Irish series. Grey-brown is not a common shade of mixed eyes in Ireland (5.2 per cent). The highest proportional occurrence of this type is among the Nordic Mediterraneans (11.1 per cent). Green-brown is even more rare (3.8 per cent), but again most heavily represented in the Nordic Mediterranean type (7.6 per cent). On the other hand, blue-brown with 43.8 per cent is the commonest shade of eyes in Ireland. Again,

it is overwhelmingly a Nordic Mediterranean eye shade, with 81.3 per cent of persons in that type having this eye shade. This is nearly two times the representation of blue-brown in the other types, where by selection, it is permitted to occur.

Gray and gray-blue are very rare eye colors. Both are especially strong in the Keltic and Pure Nordic types. Blue eyes, with 42.1 per cent, are the second commonest shade in Ireland. The Pure Nordic and Keltic types, with 90.9 per cent and 89.9 per cent respectively of this eye shade, are the principal carriers. However, except in the Pure Mediterranean and Nordic Mediterranean types, from which blue eyes are excluded, no Irish morphological type falls below 38.5 per cent of pure blue eyes.

We may now sum up eye color from the point of view of type distribution. Pure Nordics are almost wholly blue-eyed; the residue having gray or gray-blue eyes (9.1 per cent). Predominantly Nordics have more than half of their number with pure blue eyes (52.1 per cent). Nearly all of the remainder have blue-brown eyes. Almost 90 per cent of Keltics have pure blue eyes and the other 10 per cent have gray or gray-blue eyes. East Baltics have slightly more than one-half of their numbers with blue-brown eyes and nearly all of the rest have blue eyes. Dinarics have every shade of eye color, with blue-brown predominant (45.4 per cent), and blue a strong second (41.8 per cent). Blue-brown is an overwhelming majority in the Nordic Mediterraneans, with gray-brown and green-brown subsidiary shades. All of the Pure Mediterraneans have brown eyes. In the Nordic Alpine type, blue-brown leads blue and there are scatterings of other mixed eye shades.

Ireland is perhaps the most remarkable country in the world for the general predominance of dark hair in association with light eyes.

Pigment, Mixed Eyes (Table XVI-15). The bulk of the mixed eyes in Ireland (76.0 per cent) have much more iridical area in light background than in the superficially pigmented pupillary zone. The darkest mixed eyes are found in Nordic Mediterraneans, Nordic Alpines, and Dinarics. The lightest occur in East Baltics and Predominantly Nordics.

Iris (Table XVI-16). Clear unpatterned irides are naturally commonest in the types with predominance of pure dark (Pure Mediterranean, 72.7 per cent) or pure light eyes (Pure Nordic, 54.6 per cent). Rayed irides (usually the commonest pattern in mixed eyes) are reported, curiously enough, in only 21.6 per cent of the Irish. It is remarkable that they appear at all in the Pure Nordic and Keltic eyes which are restricted to blue, gray, and gray-blue eyes. Zoned irides are still rarer. There is an uncertain excess among the East Baltics. Spotted eyes seem unusually common among the Nordic Mediterraneans. Diffuse irides (unpatterned or otherwise unclassifiable) occur in about one-third of Irish and are in notable excess among the Nordic Mediterraneans. Scalloped patterns (usually going with very light eyes) are excessively present among the Keltics and the Pure Nordics.

Eyefolds, External, Median, Internal, Eye Obliquity, and Eye Opening Height (Tables XVI-17 through XVI-21). Eyefolds are reported in a remarkably small percentage of individuals and their occurrence among the morphological types reveals nothing of interest. Obliquity of the eye slits is, however, apparently an important Irish feature. An upward slant is crudely most common among the Pure Mediterraneans, although the observation may be unreliable on account of the small size of the series. Otherwise, upward slants are significantly commonest among the Keltics and Nordic Mediterraneans, definitely deficient among East Baltics, Pure Nordics, and Predominantly Nordics. Submedium or low palpebral openings are unusually prevalent among the Keltics and the Nordic Mediterraneans. High openings are in excess in Dinarics only.

Eyebrows, Thickness and Concurrency (Tables XVI-22, XVI-23). Pronouncedly thick eyebrows are possibly in excess among the Nordic Mediterraneans, but medium developments are prevalent in each type. Pronouncedly concurrent eyebrows are in excess in the Predominantly Nordic and Nordic Mediterranean types. Submedium concurrency seems to be a feature of the Keltic and the small series of Pure Mediterranean types.

Brow Ridges (Table XVI-24). Size of brow ridges seems not to bear any intimate relationship to morphological type. Brow ridges run slightly small (submedium) in Dinarics and Predominantly Nordics. Keltic and Nordic Mediterranean types seem to have somewhat more pronounced brow ridges. However, all differences are small.

Forehead, Height and Slope (Tables XVI-25, XVI-26). Nearly 56 per cent of Irish are recorded to have pronouncedly high foreheads and three and one-half per cent to have low foreheads. The types with notable excesses of high foreheads are East Baltic, Pure Nordic, and Nordic Alpine. Deficiency of high foreheads is greatly marked in the dubious Pure Mediterranean type, and slightly but significantly in the Keltic and Nordic Mediterranean types. Foreheads tend to be less sloping (submedium) in Nordic Alpine, East Baltic, Pure Nordic and Dinaric types; more sloping (pronounced) in Keltic and Nordic Mediterranean types. The small groups of Pure Nordics and Pure Mediterraneans show foreheads with the most forward slope.

Nasion Depression (Table XVI-27). Nasion depressions are least marked (submedium) in the East Baltic, Dinaric, and Predominantly Nordic types; most pronounced in Keltic and Nordic Mediterranean types.

Nasal Root, Height and Breadth (Tables XVI-28, XVI-29). Height of nasal root seems largely independent of morphological type. However, high nasal roots seem to be somewhat in excess in Dinarics, and certainly deficient in Nordic Alpines and possibly in East Baltics. Pronouncedly broad nasal roots are clearly deficient among the Dinarics and excessively prevalent in Pure Nordic and Nordic Alpine types.

Nasal Bridge, Height and Breadth (Tables XVI-30, XVI-31). The great majority of nasal bridges of every type are of medium height. The Dinaric type has a considerable excess of pronouncedly high bridges and a deficiency of bridges of submedium height. Pronouncedly high bridges are most deficient in Pure Nordics and East Baltics, but insignificantly so also in Nordic Alpines. Pronouncedly broad nasal bridges show up most notably in Pure Mediterraneans (insignificant), Nordic

Alpines, and Pure Nordics (also insignificant). Notable deficiencies are apparent in the Dinaric and possibly in the East Baltic types.

Nasal Profile (Table XVI-32). Straight noses are slightly more common than convex noses in the total series and concave noses are rare. East Baltic and Nordic Alpine types show the highest proportions of concave noses, while this nasal profile is most uncommon among the Dinarics. Straight noses are most excessively present in the Pure and Predominantly Nordic and Nordic Alpine types. The Dinarics have an overwhelming lead in convex noses with 53.2 per cent. This type of nose is notably deficient among Pure Nordics and Nordic Alpines. It is also somewhat deficient in East Baltics and Predominantly Nordics.

Nasal Septum (Table XVI-33). Exactly 61 per cent of Irish have convex nasal septa. These are most excessively represented in the Pure Mediterranean, East Baltic, and Dinaric types. They are least common among the Pure Nordics. Keltics and Pure Nordics are notable for excess of straight or concave septa.

Nasal Tip, Thickness (Table XVI-34). Submedium thin tips are so uncommon that their distribution among the types means nothing. The highest percentages of pronouncedly thick tips are found among the Pure Mediterraneans and Nordic Alpines. They are most markedly deficient in the Dinarics, moderately so in East Baltics.

Nasal Tip, Inclination (Table XVI-35). The vast majority of nasal tips (82.6 per cent) are recorded as having a submedium upward inclination; 11.3 per cent have a medium upward inclination. Horizontally directed and downward directed tips are very rare. Medium upward inclination of the tip is in marked excess in the East Baltic type, which is richest in concave profile. The nose in the Dinaric and Keltic types is less likely to have the medium upward tilt.

Nasal Wings (Table XVI-36). Nasal wings are oftenest compressed and most rarely flaring in the Dinaric type, which was selected for long narrow noses. Flaring alae occur most frequently in Pure Mediterranean and Nordic Alpine types.

Lips, Integumental and Membranous Thickness, Eversion (Tables XVI-37, XVI-38, XVI-39). The thickness of the integumental lips has been rated as medium in 94.4 per cent of the Irish types. Variations of the small residue seem unimportant. Membranous upper lips are of medium thickness in 72.8 per cent. Submedium (thin) membranous lips are in notable excess among Pure Mediterraneans and Keltics. In general, thick lips are rare, but they occur in slight excess in East Baltics, Pure Nordics, and Predominantly Nordics.

Submedium lip eversion is notably excessive in the Pure Mediterranean and Keltic types, notably deficient in Pure Nordic, Predominantly Nordic, and East Baltic types. Fuller lips, of course, are most likely to occur in the younger age groups to which many members of these types seem mainly to belong. Thus pronounced lip eversion is commonest in the same three types. Pronounced eversion is very rare in Keltic and Dinaric types.

Mid-Facial Prognathism and Alveolar Prognathism (Tables XVI-40, XVI-41). Only a little more than 8 per cent of the series are recorded as showing some amount of mid-facial prognathism. The Predominantly Nordic type leads in this feature. It occurs most rarely in the Nordic Alpine type. Alveolar prognathism is even rarer than mid-facial prognathism. Type variations in the few occurrences are unimportant.

Chin Prominence (Table XVI-42). Least proportion of prominent chins and the most of submedium prominence are found in the Pure Nordic type. Predominantly Nordics are also slightly deficient in chin prominence.

Teeth: Eruption, Loss, Caries, Wear, Crowding, Bite (Tables XVI-43 through XVI-48). Incompletely erupted dentitions are commonest in the younger blond types and less frequent in the older types. The regression seems purely dependent upon age. Amount of tooth loss seems similarly age conditioned. The same applies to caries. In fact, tooth observations show little or no relation to morphological types apart from age.

Malars, Frontal and Lateral Projection (Tables XVI-49, XVI-50). Pronounced frontal projection of the cheek bones is not uncommon in Irish subjects, but the data suggest no certain association of the feature with morphological type. Lateral projection is pronounced or very pronounced in 34.2

per cent. It finds its greatest excesses in the East Baltic, Dinaric, and Nordic Alpine types, which are broad-headed. The dolichocephalic types show deficiencies of pronounced lateral projection.

Gonial Angles (Table XVI-51). The Nordic Alpine and East Baltic types also show marked excesses of prominent gonial angles. The Dinaric type shows only a moderate excess. Deficiencies of pronounced gonial angles occur in Pure Mediterranean, Predominantly Nordic, Keltic, and Nordic Mediterranean types.

Ear: Helix, Antihelix, Darwin's Point, Lobe, Size, Protrusion (Tables XVI-52 through XVI-57). The types are not certainly differentiated in amount of roll of the helix, nor in the development of the antihelix. Medium roll of the helix and pronounced roll of the antihelix is noteworthy in the Pure Mediterraneans, but again paucity of numbers in the sample makes the data of dubious value. Some development of Darwin's Point seems to occur excessively in the Pure Nordic type —a feature which agrees with an uncertain deficiency of roll of the helix observed in this same numerically inadequate group. However, the Pure Mediterranean group shows most development of Darwin's Point. Darwin's Point appears to be unduly rare among the Nordic Alpines. Free ear lobes are in great excess among the Pure Mediterraneans but again the data cannot be regarded very seriously. All of the Pure Mediterraneans who have not free ear lobes are recorded to have attached ear lobes. Attached ear lobes are in marked excess among the Pure Nordics. Nordic Mediterraneans, Keltics, and East Baltics seem to have small excesses of the free variety.

Pronouncedly large ear lobes are in great excess in Pure Mediterraneans and to some extent in Keltics, possibly because these types are well above mean age. For the same reason they are deficient in East Baltic, Pure Nordic, and Predominantly Nordic types. They are unduly rare also in the Dinaric type. Marked protrusion of the ear is somewhat more than ordinarily frequent in the Keltic and Pure Nordic types.

On the whole, morphological details of the ear seem to bear very little relationship to the types here studied.

Temporal Fullness (Table XVI-58). Pronounced temporal fullness is a marked feature of the East Baltic, Nordic Alpine, and Dinaric types in the descending order of excesses named. These are brachycephalic types and such fullness is expected of them. Submedium temporal fullness is especially characteristic of the Keltic type, but the Nordic Mediterranean type also has a notable excess of hollow temples.

Occipital Protrusion (Table XVI-59). Excessive proportions of persons with submedium occipital protrusion occur in the three brachycephalic types, whereas all of the long-headed types, except the Pure Mediterranean, show excesses in the opposite direction.

Lambdoid Flattening (Table XVI-60). Some degree of lambdoid flattening occurs in 77.2 per cent of all individuals comprising the aggregate of types. If we can trust our small samples, lambdoid flattening is most common in the East Baltic and Pure Mediterranean types. It is apparently most pronounced among the Dinarics.

Occipital Flattening (Table XVI-61). Occipital flattening occurs oftenest in the brachycephals and is rarest among the Pure Mediterraneans and Pure Nordics.

Facial Asymmetry (Table XVI-62). In about 25 per cent of cases, one or other side of the face is larger to the extent of causing the recorder to observe facial asymmetry. The bulging side is the side indicated. The right side is larger than the left more than twice as often as the left side is larger than the right. Facial asymmetry is least common in the Pure Mediterranean and Pure Nordic types. It is somewhat in excess in the Nordic Alpine and East Baltic types. The Dinaric type, however, is an easy leader in this facial lopsidedness. Thus facial asymmetry seems to be linked with brachycephaly.

SUMMARY OF TYPES

PURE NORDIC TYPE

THE Pure Nordic type consists of only 55 men, mostly young. It is found principally in Longford-Westmeath and N. Fermanagh-E. Donegal-Tyrone-Londonderry and the western peninsular area of Mayo and West Galway (figs. 28, 29). It occurs also in the southeastern corner. Areas which have yielded none of this type are Kerry, the Aran Islands, and West Donegal.

Sociology

This type has no illiterates and no persons who are literate but have not attended school. It is highest in secondary school men, but includes no university men. It cannot be ranked by the educational ratio, but in general, must be placed very high—probably first. It is below average in proportion of Keltic speakers. Occupationally, this type is high in mercantile workers, semi-skilled trades, professional men, and soldiers. It is also high in farm dependents—perhaps because of the low mean age of the group. It has none of the other and perhaps lower agricultural groups and is low also in tinkers, fishermen, transport workers, and has no clerks or factory workers. It

is to be rated as one of the most highly placed types in occupation. This type has an uncertainly significant excess[1] of Protestants—both Church of Ireland and Presbyterian.

Physical Characteristics

The Pure Nordic type is by far the youngest of all the morphological types, averaging only 26.10 years; 8.80 years below the mean age. The oldest man in it is aged only 49 years. It must be assumed that many of its sociological and physical attributes are conditioned by its tender mean age. Its weight is at the type series minimum (with the exception of the even tinier sample, Pure Mediterranean). This weight inferiority is probably due only in part to youth. Stature is approximately at the mean, while span and relative span are insignificantly low. Were the deficiency significant, it might be charged to age, since arm length is attained late. The type is relatively and absolutely narrow-shouldered, as Irish types go. The chest is significantly narrow and shallow, but the thoracic index is at the mean of the series. Head length is insignificantly above average, but head breadth definitely below average. The

Figure 28

Distribution of Pure plus Predominantly Nordic Morphological Types in Ireland. Pure Nordics plus Predominantly Nordics are concentrated in relative distribution in an S-shaped band from Antrim-Down through West Galway. There is an isolated concentration in Waterford-Wexford (probably due to Norse and Danish settlements) and a focus in Longford-Westmeath (probably connected with the juvenility of that county subsample). Note that greatest relative scarcity of the combined types is in the western peninsular areas in the following order: West Donegal, Mayo and Clare, Kerry and the Arans.

[1] In consideration of the sorting methods used for distinguishing the morphological types, it seems unnecessary to make detailed calculations of the critical ratios of differences between means of measurements and indices. In any event, the publication of such tables of differences is not worth the cost. However, a quick comparison of the probable errors of means of subtypes with those of the total series, or of the means of one subtype with another, enables one to draw a correct conclusion as to significance (if one is conservative and does not attempt to squeeze out differences down to the smallest level of possible significance). If the differences between the means of the subgroup

and of the total series is more than three times the sum of the respective probable errors, the significance is sufficiently certain. This is a rough-and-ready test based upon the ordinary formula of the square root of the sums of the squares of the errors. A more elaborate and perhaps more precise formula could be employed, but this method is near enough for our present purpose. The actual error of differences ordinarily works out as a figure slightly in excess of the larger of the two subtype errors, but somewhat less than their sum. To take the sum of the two errors as the actual error of the differences is erring, if at all, on the safe and conservative side.

166

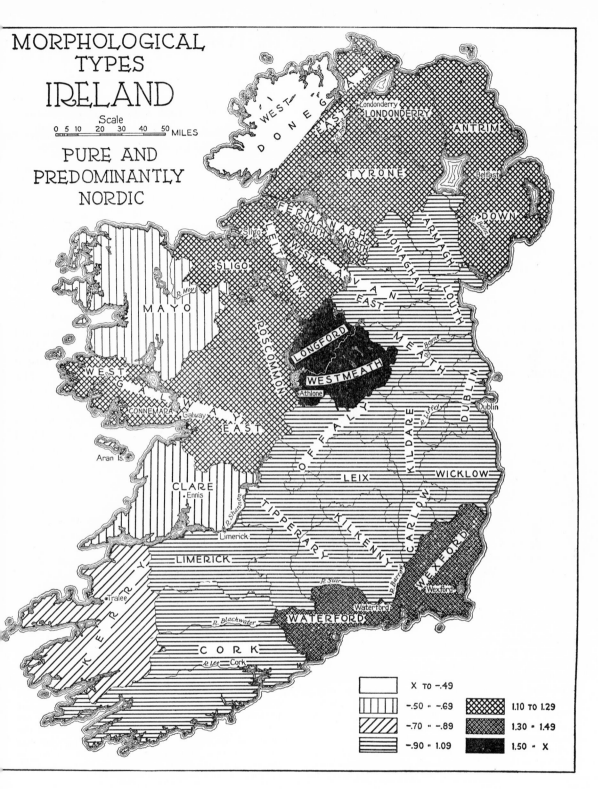

MORPHOLOGICAL
TYPES
IRELAND

Scale
0 5 10 20 30 40 50 MILES

PURE AND
PREDOMINANTLY
NORDIC

	X TO -.49
-.50 " -.69	1.10 TO 1.29
-.70 " -.89	1.30 " 1.49
-.90 " 1.09	1.50 " X

FIGURE 28

cephalic index (76.65) is approximately that of all the dolichocephalic types and well below the series average. The breadth-height index achieves the series maximum, but all long-headed types are elevated in this index. The forehead is narrow and the fronto-parietal index is highest of all types. The minimum bizygomatic diameter is achieved by this type and the maximum zygo-frontal index. The bigonial diameter is very small, and the fronto-gonial index depressed. Total face height is below average, but the facial index is high. The upper facial index, however, is insignificantly low. Noses are short and narrow, but the nasal index is not distinctive.

All of the Pure Nordics have pink skins and they exceed all other groups save the East Baltic in pronounced vascularity. Freckles are slightly more than ordinarily common, but so also are moles. All kinds of hair form occur (except frizzly or woolly), with an excess of the straight variety. Fine hair is commoner than in any other type. Pronounced head hair is in great excess but body hair is not excessive; baldness is least common of all types—an age effect. The same stricture applies to excess absence of graying of head and beard. Hair color is 81.8 per cent golden and the rest ash blond (by sorting). Eye color is 90.0 per cent pure blue and the rest blue-gray. Clear and scalloped irides are in great excess. Submedium external eyefolds are a little above average, but medium and internal folds of any degree are rare. There is the least obliquity of eye opening found in any type. Eyebrows show a marked excess of medium thickness. Brow ridges are medium in most cases, but tend to be more than ordinarily frequent in the extreme categories (*absent* and *very pronounced*). Foreheads tend to pronounced height and medium slope. Low broad nasal roots seem common, and also rather low and broad nasal bridges. Nasal tips are universally directed upward. The nasal profile is most

often straight of any Irish type. The septum is also less often convex than in any other type. Thick integumental lips are in uncertain excess—a fact which may be due either to sampling or to tender mean age. Membranous upper lips are inclined to be thick—again a feature of youth. Correspondingly, eversion of lips is more marked than in any other type. There is very little prognathism, either mid-facial or alveolar. Chins are less than ordinarily prominent. Tooth eruption is incomplete in 47.3 per cent of cases (an age phenomenon), relating usually to third molars. Tooth loss is at the series minimum as is also caries. This dental superiority is attributable to low mean age. Pronounced malar projection is less than ordinary for Irish, but jaw angles are well up to average prominence. The ear shows more than average submedium roll of helix, presence of Darwin's Point, noteworthy percentage of attached lobes, and ears are of medium size. Ears show the highest percentage of pronounced protrusion of any group. Temporal fullness is medium, but occipital protrusion is most pronounced of any type. Medium lambdoid flattening is excessively present, and occipital flattening is unduly rare. Facial asymmetry is at the series minimum.

PREDOMINANTLY NORDIC

DISTRIBUTION

This sizable type consists of some 649 men and is distributed somewhat similarly to the Pure Nordic type, with the difference that it is deficient in Mayo and in slight excess in Antrim-Down. It is, then, west central with outliers in the northeast and southeast corners. It is notably deficient in the southwest and northwest corners.

SOCIOLOGY

This type is well educated, ranking third among the eight morphological types. It is,

FIGURE 29

PURE NORDIC MORPHOLOGICAL TYPE DISTRIBUTION IN IRELAND. The mapping of this handful of strictly Pure Nordics is merely added as a supplement to that of Pure and Predominantly Nordic, with which it should be compared. It is of interest to note that Mayo, which in its total sample of the combined types is poor, is yet rich in Pure Nordics. The reverse is true of Waterford-Wexford. Cork is another area comparatively high in Pure Nordics, but scarcely up to par in the combined group.

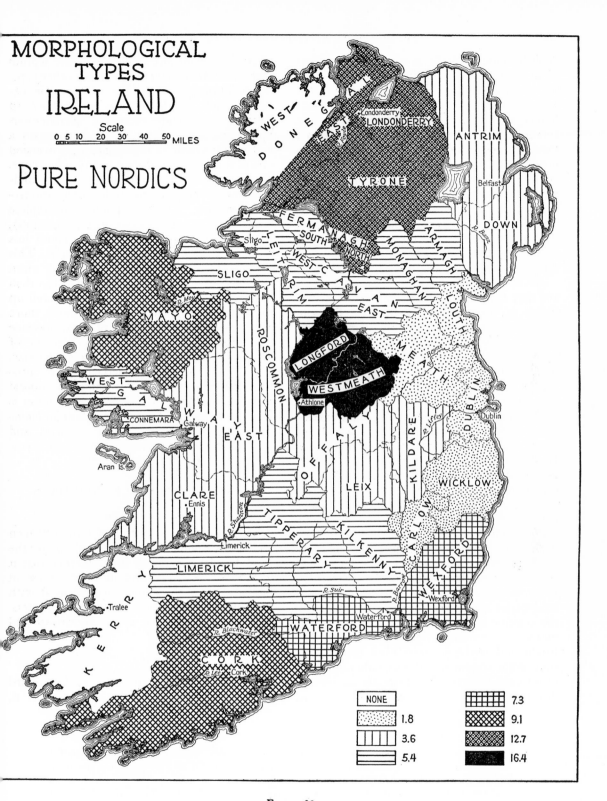

MORPHOLOGICAL
TYPES
IRELAND

Scale
0 5 10   20   30   40   50 MILES

PURE NORDICS

NONE		7.3
1.8		9.1
3.6		12.7
5.4		16.4

FIGURE 29

like the Pure Nordics, notably deficient in Keltic speakers. Also like the Pure Nordics, it has an excess of Protestants, considering the dominance of Catholicism in all types. Occupationally, this type does not diverge markedly from the total distribution of the county series. It leads in clerks and is slightly high in students. It is quite high in farm dependents, but, like the Pure Nordics, this may be due to low mean age. It is quite low in other agricultural groups, slightly below in hired laborers and tinkers, navvies, fishermen, and is somewhat high in skilled trades.

PHYSICAL CHARACTERISTICS

The Predominantly Nordic type is second youngest of the series, with a mean age deficiency of 6.5 years. It is 1.7 pounds below average weight and is easily the tallest Irish type. Relative span is slightly low, as are also absolute and relative shoulder breadth. Chest diameters are inferior and the thoracic index is low, describing a relatively shallow chest. Heads are very long and narrow, with a cephalic index (by selection) averaging 76.62 (falling between the closely grouped Pure Nordics and Keltics). Head height is insignificantly above the Irish average. The length-height index is definitely low, the breadth-height index significantly high. The minimum frontal diameter is inferior, and the fronto-parietal index unusually high. The bizygomatic diameter is reduced and the cephalo-facial index elevated. The zygo-frontal index is elevated, the bigonial diameter depressed. The fronto-gonial index is also low. Total face height is above the mean of the Irish, but not markedly so. The total facial index (91.50) makes this type the most leptoprosopic in Ireland. However, the upper face is shorter than ordinary, although the upper facial index is above the total series mean. Noses are shorter than average. Metrically, this type is probably only a fully adult edition of the Pure Nordic type previously described.

This type is practically as pink-skinned as the Pure Nordics, but not so strongly vascular. Freckles are even more excessively common. Moles are also in slight excess. Hair form differs from that of the Pure Nordic in that the definite excess is in deep waves rather than straight. This type also has a tendency toward fine hair texture. Beard hair and body hair tend to be submedium in quantity and there is more baldness than in the Pure Nordic type. Graying of head and beard is only less rare than in the Pure Nordics. Hair color is 81.5 per cent golden brown—a shade often replacing golden blond in adults. Small amounts of ash brown (but highest of any type), golden, and ash are to be noted and 12.6 per cent of red. More melanotic pigment in the hair and more rufosity distinguishes this type from the Pure Nordic. Eye color is 52.1 per cent pure blue and the rest mixed—mostly blue-brown. Thus some pigment is also added to the iris. The pigment in mixed eyes is very scanty. Eye slant, as in the Pure Nordics, is excessively rare. Eyebrows are of medium thickness, but concurrence is marked. Features of forehead and nose are mostly medium, but this type, like the Pure Nordic, has an excess of straight nasal profiles. Nasal wings tend to flare. Membranous lips tend slightly to thickness and eversion. Slight mid-facial prognathism is more than usually prevalent. Chin prominence is normal. Since this type is also below mean age, tooth eruption is often incomplete, tooth loss is reduced, as are also wear and caries. Crowding is deficient. Malar projection is only slightly above the Irish average; gonial angles are less pronounced than average. The ear differs from the Pure Nordic ear in a high percentage of free lobes. This is probably not an age effect. Occipital protrusion is excessive, although not to the extent found in the Pure Nordics. Lambdoid flattening is even more prevalent and more pronounced. Occipital flattening is correspondingly rare. Facial asymmetry is less than ordinarily common.

There can be little doubt that the Predominantly Nordic type is an adult variation of the Pure Nordic, with, however, some slight admixture of a brunet strain which is possibly alien to the Pure Nordic.

KELTIC

DISTRIBUTION

The Keltic type, consisting of 2,408 men, is numerically the second strongest in Ireland. It is weak only in the extreme southwest and west (Kerry, Cork, Limerick, Mayo, Clare). It is strongest in the eastern half of Ireland (see fig. 30).

Sociology

The Keltic type is by far the most poorly educated type in Ireland. It has the highest proportion of illiterates and the highest proportion of persons who know no Keltic. It is slightly deficient in persons speaking Keltic and Keltic only, but its greatest deficiency comes in the group studying Irish at school (23.7 per cent). Occupationally, also, it is the most lowly type. It leads in hired laborers and tinkers; is second in navvies. It also leads in farmers and herdsmen and is high in factory workers. It is notably deficient in the mercantile class, in clerks, professional men, soldiers, and students. This type has the proportions of Catholics and Protestants which are approximately average for our entire Irish morphological series—90.34 per cent of Catholics.

Physical Characteristics

The Keltic type is the second oldest in Ireland—3.36 years above the mean age. The type is 0.60 pounds below mean Irish weight, but does not deviate significantly from average stature. The thoracic index in this type is significantly high, because the chest is deep relative to its width. It is exceeded in this index only by the small Pure Mediterranean group. Head circumference is markedly low since head breadth is meager and head length, although large, falls below that of the numerically strong Nordic Mediterranean type. The cephalic index (76.59) is the minimum for Irish types. Head height is lower than that of any other type save only the Pure Mediterranean. The length-height index is next to the Irish minimum, while the breadth-height index is significantly high although exceeded by two Nordic types and the Nordic Mediterranean type. The forehead is very narrow and the fronto-parietal index high. The bizygomatic diameter is depressed, but significantly higher than the average values found in the Nordic types. The cephalo-facial index is higher than that of any other type save only the Nordic Mediterranean. The bigonial diameter is somewhat low and the fronto-gonial index is highest for Ireland. The zygo-gonial index is moderately elevated. The high facial index (91.10) is exceeded only by that of the Predominantly Nordic type. The upper face is particularly long. The upper facial index average demonstrates that this type has relatively the longest and narrowest upper face. Noses are a trifle long, probably in part an effect of advanced mean age and also they are a trifle broader than average. Thus the nasal index is also a little above average.

The Keltic type is very light-skinned, although exceeded in this respect by the three blond types. It falls below these types only in pronounced vascularity. The type is relatively low in freckling and also has fewer than average moles. All kinds of hair form occur, with low waves in the modal position. However, the Keltics present the strongest assemblage of straight-haired individuals to be found in any Irish type, save the Pure Nordic. Baldness and graying of head and beard are excessive in this type—doubtless because of the high average age. The modal hair color (46.9) is flat brown, but a strong minority (39.7 per cent) has dark brown hair, and a red-haired contingent amounts to 5.7 per cent. In darkness of hair pigmentation, this type is exceeded only by the small group of Pure Mediterraneans and by the large Nordic Mediterranean group.

All Keltics have pure blue or gray-blue eyes. Almost 54 per cent of Irish blue eyes belong to members of this Keltic type, although the type constitutes only 25.3 per cent of the Irish type series. Irides with scalloped patterns reach their Irish maximum and clear irides are greatly in excess. External eyefolds are slightly more than ordinarily common in this type. Upward slant of the eye slits is more frequent in the Keltic type than in any other except the Pure Mediterranean. Variations from medium height of eye openings, when they occur at all, are low more than is ordinarily common, but these are not characteristic. This type has a higher percentage of persons with pronounced brow ridges than any other Irish morphological type. Foreheads incline toward the more sloping forms. Nasion depressions tend to be deep; straight nasal profiles slightly exceed the convex form. Membranous lips are rather more than ordinarily thin. Teeth loss, wear, face shortening by tooth wear, and caries are at the maxima in these Keltics, but, reasonably, this condition must be attributed to the high mean age of the type. The Keltic type is average in frontal projection of the malars and is high in medium lateral projection. Gonial angles are infrequently prominent. Hollowness of the temporal region is a distinct feature as is also marked occipital protrusion. Although lambdoid flattening occurs in nearly three-fourths of the Keltics, this feature is less common in the Keltic morphological type than in any other. Occipital flattening is relatively infrequent.

EAST BALTIC

DISTRIBUTION

This small type group includes only 105 men, all brachycephalic blonds or red-heads. It is concentrated in Kerry and the southwest with outliers through the central west and northwest (see fig. 31). However, it is markedly deficient in West Donegal, West Galway, the Aran Islands, and in East Galway-Roscommon. In Eastern Ireland it is everywhere deficient.

SOCIOLOGY

The East Baltic type is well educated and ranks at least second in educational rating—perhaps first. The highest percentage of university men is found among this group and it also includes the highest percentage of Keltic speakers found in any type. Occupationally, there are only 2.9 per cent of hired laborers or tinkers in the East Baltic type. A small (and statistically insignificant) excess of farm dependents, as in Pure and Predominantly Nordics, may be connected with low average age. Navvies are definitely deficient. Professional classes are markedly above average and it is first in students. It is in excess also in soldiers. Occupationally, as educationally, this type seems to be the most highly placed. It has the normal 90 per cent of Catholics, is high in the remainder in Church of Ireland and low in Presbyterians.

PHYSICAL CHARACTERISTICS

The East Baltic type with a mean age of 29.95 years is 4.95 years below the average of the Irish type series. It is 0.50 pounds below the mean weight of the series. Its stature is insignificantly below that of the total series. Most bodily dimensions are insignificantly below the series total, but chest depth is definitely diminished, so that the thoracic index is lower than that of any other type, indicating a relatively shallow chest. Sitting height is elevated, both absolutely and relatively. Head circumference attains the maximum of the Irish series. Head length is far below the series average, but the head breadth (157.96) is prodigious and accounts for the high horizontal circumference. The cephalic index (by sorting) is frankly brachycephalic (82.08). Head height attains the Irish maximum (125.54 mm.) and, of course, length-height index is elevated and breadth-height index is depressed. The minimum frontal diameter is large, but the fronto-parietal index is low. Bizygomatic diameter (142.80 mm.) is the largest in Ireland, but the cephalo-facial index is quite low. The zygo-gonial index is considerably the lowest of the Irish type series. Total face height is sharply diminished and the total face index achieves the Irish minimum (87.25). Upper face height is also small and the upper facial index (49.79) is far below that of any other type. Noses are short, but only moderately

FIGURE 30

KELTIC MORPHOLOGICAL TYPE DISTRIBUTION IN IRELAND. This type, with 25.4 per cent, is second in frequency among Irish types. This map shows its highest concentration in the middle eastern coastal counties (with an outlier in the Aran Islands). However, these most concentrated areas have ratios of only 1.3 to 1.4. Even the thinnest occurrence in Cork and Kerry has a ratio of 0.6 and in Mayo of 0.8. Secondarily above par ratios (1.10–1.29) occur in Antrim-Down, N. Fermanagh-E. Donegal-Tyrone-Londonderry, Offaly-Leix-Kildare, and West Galway. The distribution suggests an initial settlement on the middle of the east coast with isolated outliers in the Arans and West Galway. At any rate, whether or not the east coast Keltic band represents a primary settlement, it is clear that to the west and southwest this type (which occurs plentifully in every region of Ireland) has either been supplanted by others or has achieved a limited penetration.

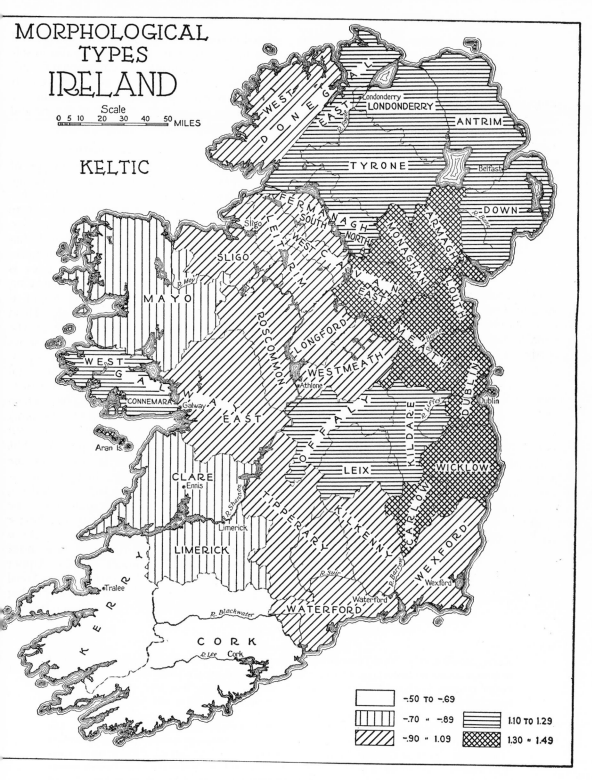

MORPHOLOGICAL
TYPES
IRELAND

Scale
0 5 10   20   30   40   50 MILES

KELTIC

-.50 TO -.69
-.70 " -.89   1.10 TO 1.29
-.90 " 1.09   1.30 " 1.49

FIGURE 30

broad. The nasal index, though very high for Ireland, falls below that of the large Nordic Alpine brachycephalic group. It should be recalled that narrow-nosed brachycephals, by sorting, are segregated into the Dinaric type.

In this small sample of 105 men, all except one are pink in skin color of unexposed areas. One is pale (1.0 per cent). The percentage of pronounced vascularity (47.1) exceeds even that found in the Pure Nordic type. Freckles achieve their Irish maximum with 67.6 per cent. The least straight hair of the various types is found among the East Baltics. The largest proportion of East Baltics (46.2 per cent) has low waved hair, but this type includes the second highest percentage of deep waves (26.9 per cent) in the Irish type series and also the largest percentage of curly hair (4.8 per cent). Coarse hair (16.2 per cent) is more than three times as common as in any other morphological type. Baldness is unusually rare, perhaps because of low mean age of the sample. Graying is much less than ordinarily frequent, probably for the same reason. The most remarkable fact about the East Baltic type is that it has 72.4 per cent of red-haired men. Of course, by the sorting criteria hair shades were limited to ash blond, golden, and red, but the predominance of red in this type was wholly unexpected. The East Baltic type comprises only 1.1 per cent of our Irish type series, but more than 36 per cent of the men with red hair and about 33 per cent of the men with golden hair and about 25 per cent of the ash blonds are East Baltics. Eye color in this type is 51.4 per cent blue-brown and nearly 43 per cent pure blue. Gray-blue comprises 3.8 per cent and the rest are mixed. The mixed eyes are very lightly pigmented. Upward eye slant is comparatively uncommon in this type and downward inclination, always rare, attains the series maximum of 10.5 per cent.

The East Baltic type is excessively characterized by individuals with pronouncedly high foreheads, but a low percentage with pronounced slope. The largest proportion of concave noses (12.5 per cent) is found in this type, although straight and convex noses predominate. The upward inclination of the nasal tip is more pronounced in this type than in any other. Membranous lip thickness tends toward pronounced and marked lip eversion is more than ordinarily common. Tooth loss, wear, and caries are below average in this type, perhaps because it is also below mean age. Lateral projection of the malars in the East Baltic type exceeds that of any other type except that of the Nordic Alpine. Gonial angles are also prominent in unusual proportions. Pronounced temporal fullness in this type is far more common than in any others, even the other two brachycephalic types. Occipital projection tends to be submedium in an excessive percentage, but is, on the whole, average, as in every other type. Some lambdoid flattening occurs in all but about 15 per cent of East Baltics.

DINARIC

DISTRIBUTION

The Dinaric type includes some 1,768 individuals, or 18.6 per cent of the type series. Its concentration by nativity closely parallels that of the allied Nordic Alpine type. In most cases these two types are under-represented and over-represented in the same counties. The heaviest concentration of the Dinaric type is in Clare, followed by Kerry, Tipperary-Kilkenny, Limerick, Mayo, and Cork (fig. 32). Thus it is mainly a far western and southwestern type. It is low in the east and northeast and also low in the area west of the Shannon which we call the Sligo-Galway crescent.

One of the principal features of this summary will be the comparison of the Dinaric with Nordic Alpine and East Baltic types with a view of ascertaining whether or not these are really distinct population strata. With respect to distribution, it may be stated that the East Baltic type differs from the Dinaric in being weak in West Donegal, and strong in Sligo-Leitrim-S. Fermanagh-W. Cavan, in Longford-Westmeath, and in the north central Ulster block. This amounts to a strength of the East Baltic type in the areas of blondness and rufosity.

SOCIOLOGY

The Dinaric type is, on the whole, well educated. In the educational ratio it ranks fourth among the eight Irish morphological types. Contrary to the condition found in the East

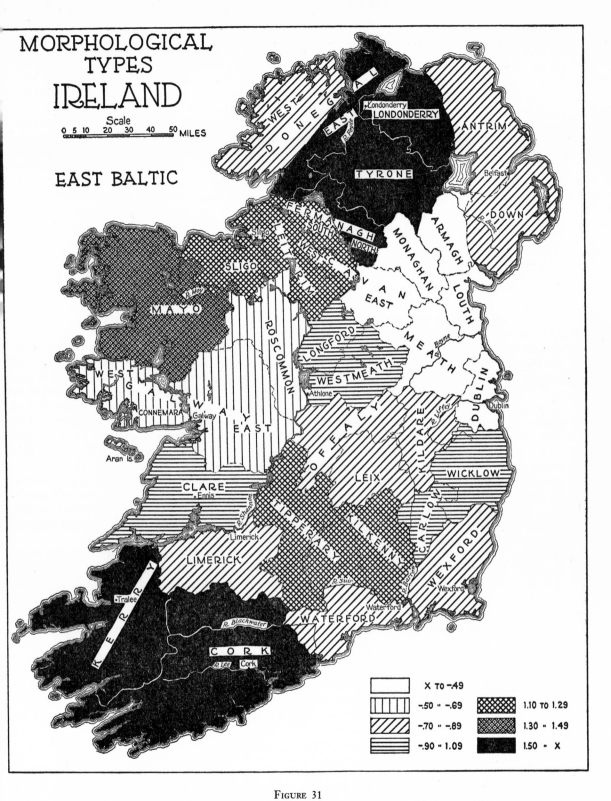

MORPHOLOGICAL TYPES IRELAND

Scale
0 5 10 20 30 40 50 MILES

EAST BALTIC

	X TO -.49			
	-.50 " -.69		1.10 TO 1.29	
	-.70 " -.89		1.30 " 1.49	
	-.90 " 1.09		1.50 " X	

FIGURE 31

DISTRIBUTION OF THE EAST BALTIC MORPHOLOGICAL TYPE IN IRELAND. This is essentially a map of rufosity associated with the broader-nosed brachycephals. The two widely separated islands of East Baltic concentration are intriguing.

Baltics and Nordic Alpines, this type is slightly deficient in Keltic speakers. Occupationally, it is somewhat deficient in hired laborers and tinkers, and also in agriculturalists and in navvies. It is slightly high in skilled trades, shop-keepers and their assistants, professional workers, soldiers, and students. Thus, like the other round-headed types, it seems to have a higher occupational status than is characteristic of most of the long-heads. The Dinaric type rivals the Nordic Alpine in its high proportion of Catholics. These two types lead, each with approximately 93.5 per cent.

PHYSICAL CHARACTERISTICS

Age of the Dinaric type is virtually identical with that of the Nordic Alpine type, 1.5 years below the general mean. Weight is at the mean of the total Irish series and Dinarics are 1.5 pounds lighter than Nordic Alpines and 0.5 pounds heavier than East Baltics. The Dinaric type averages slightly more than total Irish in stature and in this respect diverges from both of the other brachycephalic types. Absolute span is actually higher in this type than in any other except the much taller Predominantly Nordic type. It significantly exceeds that of the other two brachycephalic types. The Dinaric type equals in absolute shoulder breath (biacromial) the Nordic Alpine type—both exceeding all other morphological types. Relative shoulder breadth is less than that of the East Baltics and Nordic Alpines. In chest breadth also the Dinaric type virtually equals the Nordic Alpine, which stands at the top of Irish types. Chest depth is above that of the East Baltics, but inferior to that of the Nordic Alpines. The thoracic index of this type is below the Irish mean; it is insignificantly lower than that of the Nordic Alpine type, but significantly higher than that of the East Baltics. Actually, the East Baltics and the Dinarics have relatively the broadest

and flattest chests of the Irish morphological types.

Head circumference in Dinarics is the least of all Irish types except pure Nordic, but only insignificantly lower than that of the Keltic type. Head length is the series minimum and head breadth, although large, is slightly inferior to the means of the other two brachycephalic types. The mean cephalic index (82.20) is slightly higher than that of the other two round-headed types. Dinaric head height is slightly lower than that of the East Baltics and Nordic Alpines. The length-height indices of all three are substantially similar, but the Dinarics have slightly lower breadth-height indices. Minimum frontal diameter is above the Irish mean, but well below that of the other two round-headed types. The fronto-parietal index is the minimum of the series, but only insignificantly lower than the value found in East Baltics. Bizygomatic diameter is smaller than the means of the East Baltics and Nordic Alpines, but higher than that of any dolichocephalic type. The cephalo-facial index is at the Irish minimum, but the difference between the Dinaric mean and that of the East Baltic type is not significant. Bigonial diameter is above the series mean, but lower than that of the Nordic Alpines and East Baltics. Both Dinarics and Nordic Alpines have low zygo-gonial indices, but they far exceed in this index the East Baltic type, which averages nearly an entire index unit below the total Irish mean.

Total face height in the Dinarics (128.30 mm.) is nearly a millimeter above the mean face-height of the next longest-faced type—the Predominantly Nordic type. The facial height of the Dinarics exceeds that of the Nordic Alpines by 3.20 mm. and that of the East Baltics by 3.9 mm. The total facial index of this (90.30) markedly exceeds that of the East Baltics and Nordic Alpines, but falls

FIGURE 32
DISTRIBUTION OF THE DINARIC MORPHOLOGICAL TYPE IN IRELAND. This type, with 18.6 per cent, is third in frequency in Ireland. The map suggests a very uneven distribution, but the thinnest areas have ratios of 0.7 or 0.8, and the thickest are Clare, with a ratio of 1.5, Kerry, with a ratio of 1.4, and Tipperary-Kilkenny, with a ratio of 1.3. Thus the Dinarics are nowhere rare, although definitely concentrated in the southwest and south, with outlying strength in Mayo and West Donegal, but a curious weakness in West Galway and the Aran Islands, where the type yields to the Keltic, Nordic Alpine, and Nordic types.

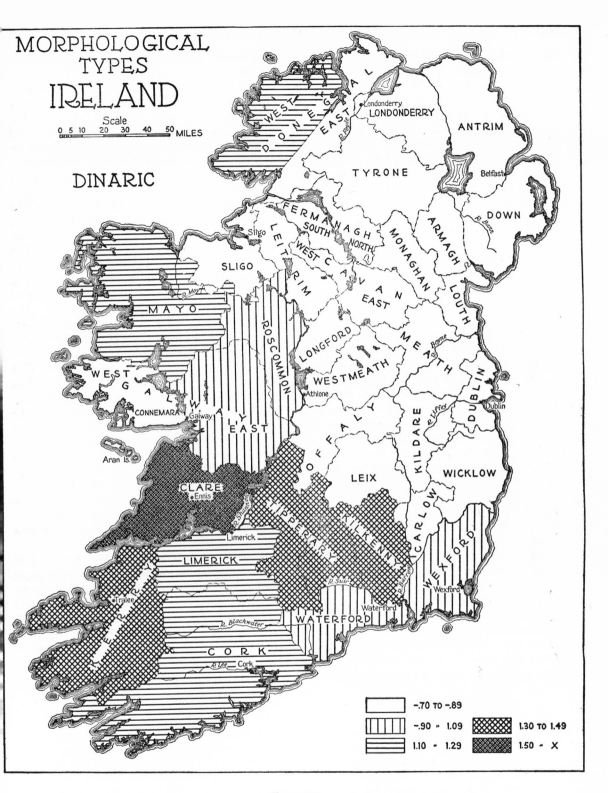

MORPHOLOGICAL TYPES
IRELAND

Scale
0 5 10 20 30 40 50 MILES

DINARIC

☐	-.70 TO -.89	
⫿⫿ -.90 " 1.09		▨ 1.30 TO 1.49
☰ 1.10 " 1.29		▦ 1.50 " X

FIGURE 32

significantly below those of the Predominantly Nordic, Nordic Mediterranean, and Keltic types. The decreased leptoprosopy of the Dinaric type, as compared with the principal dolichocephals, is due to high average facial breadth. Upper face height in the Dinarics is also the maximum of the series and far greater than that of the comparatively short-faced Nordic Alpines and East Baltics. The upper facial index of Dinarics is superior to that of the other brachycephalic types, but falls within the range of means of the long-heads. Nose height is at the Irish maximum among the Dinarics. The greatest contrasts with the Dinarics are found in East Baltics and Nordic Alpines (and Pure Nordics). The Dinaric nose is also the narrowest of the series and contrasts in this respect most extremely with the Nordic Alpines, but also to a lesser degree with the East Baltics. The nasal index (by sorting) is far lower in the Dinaric type than in any other and is more than 10 units lower than that of the Nordic Alpines, 9.56 units lower than that of the East Baltics. However, both of these latter brachycephalic types are selected, to some extent, for high nasal indices.

The Dinaric type includes about the proportion of brunet skins found in the total Irish type series. It is slightly lighter in skin color than the Nordic Alpines, but, of course, far darker than the East Baltics. Vascularity is close to average for all Ireland. Freckles are about the same as in Nordic Alpines and far fewer than among the East Baltics, who are the most freckled of Irish types. The Dinaric type is slightly low in straight hair and leads all other types in low-waved hair. Deep-waved hair and curly hair are at approximately the total series average. Tendency to curl is slightly more emphasized in the Nordic Alpine type, more so among the East Baltics, who lead all types in deep waved hair. Baldness is less frequent than among Nordic Alpines, although the two types are practically identical in mean age. On the other hand, graying is

slightly more prevalent among the Dinarics, both with respect to head and to beard. There is comparatively little difference in hair color between the Dinarics and the Nordic Alpines. The principal distinction is that the Dinaric type has 2.2 per cent of red hair, while the Nordic Alpines have none.

Only ten men of the Dinaric type have dark eyes, none of the Nordic Alpines. Otherwise there is little difference in eye color between the two types, both of which have all sorts of mixed eyes, about 46 per cent of which are blue-brown. The Dinaric type has 41.8 per cent of blue eyes, the Nordic Alpine 38.5 per cent. Mixed eyes are somewhat lighter in the Dinarics than in the Nordic Alpines. Distribution of iris patterns in the two types is practically identical. Eyefolds of all types are commoner in the Nordic Alpines than in the Dinarics. Eyebrow concurrency is somewhat less marked in the Dinarics; brow ridges are also smaller. The Nordic Alpines have higher and less sloping foreheads. Nasion depressions are less often pronounced in the Dinarics, who also have higher and narrower nasal roots and bridges, many fewer concave noses and straight noses, far more convex noses. In these nasal characteristics the East Baltics are close to the Nordic Alpines. Nasal tips are thinner by far in the Dinarics than in the Nordic Alpines, the East Baltics being intermediate in this character. The upward turning of the nasal tip is less often pronounced in the Dinarics than in either of the two other round-headed types. Nasal wings are oftener compressed, less often flaring. In membranous lip thickness there is little or no difference between Dinarics and Nordic Alpines. However, mid-facial prognathism is much commoner in Dinarics than in East Baltics or Nordic Alpines.

There is practically no difference in tooth loss and caries between Dinarics and Nordic Alpines. Crowded teeth are considerably commoner in the Dinarics than in the Nordic Alpines, but there is very little difference be-

FIGURE 33

NORDIC MEDITERRANEAN MORPHOLOGICAL TYPE DISTRIBUTION IN IRELAND. This is the most evenly distributed type in Ireland, and the most numerous. It has a pronounced deficiency only in Clare. The heavy excesses are seen to stretch in a band along the east coast as far as Wicklow with an extension in the midlands as far as the Shannon. There are also isolated concentrations in West Donegal and the Arans.

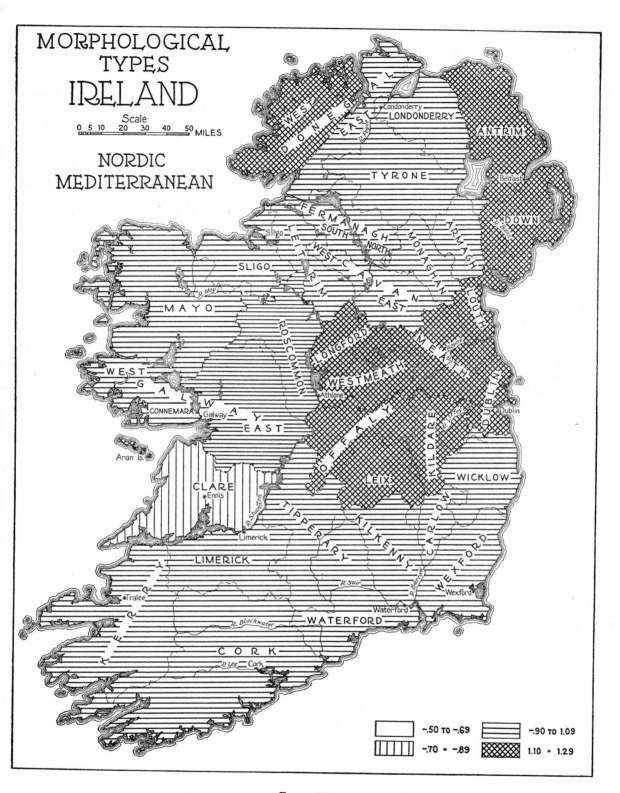

MORPHOLOGICAL
TYPES
IRELAND

Scale
0 5 10 20 30 40 50 MILES

NORDIC
MEDITERRANEAN

☐	-.50 TO -.69	▤	-.90 TO 1.09
⊞	-.70 " -.89	▩	1.10 " 1.29

FIGURE 33

180 THE PHYSICAL ANTHROPOLOGY OF IRELAND

tween East Baltics and Dinarics in this feature. Lateral projection of the Dinaric malars is less than in the Nordic Alpines or the East Baltics. Gonial angles are far less often pronounced. The helix of the ear is less rolled in the Dinaric than in the Nordic Alpine type and the presence of Darwin's Point is recorded in a higher percentage of the former type. Free ear lobes are slightly more common in the Dinarics, but ear lobes are smaller than in the Nordic Alpines. They are still smaller among the East Baltics, but the latter group is considerably below the other two in average age. Dinaric ear protrusion seems, on the average, to exceed that observed in the other two types. Temporal fullness is more frequently pronounced in Dinarics than in any long-headed type, but occurs far less often than in either of the other two round-headed types. Lambdoid flattening is found less often than in the East Baltic type (which has the maximum of this feature), but it is rather more common than in the Nordic Alpines. Occipital flattening occurs in the Dinarics in approximately the same percentage as in Nordic Alpines. Facial asymmetry is more frequent in this type than in any other. On the whole, the Dinaric type is profoundly different from the other brachycephals, and, for that matter, from all other Irish types.

NORDIC MEDITERRANEAN

The Nordic Mediterranean type consists of 2749 men and is the most numerous Irish type. It constitutes the thickest and most evenly distributed stratum of the Irish population, ranging from 0.8 to 1.1 in its ratio in the various Irish county groups. It attains its minimum in Clare, but is also low in Kerry, Waterford, Wicklow-Carlow, N. Fermanagh-E. Donegal-Tyrone-Londonderry (fig. 33). Its maximum ratio of 1.1 is achieved in several county groups. The relative and absolute type predominances are shown in figures 37 and 38. It is rather difficult to interpret the maps themselves, but the accompanying legends, which need not be recapitulated here, show that the Nordic Mediterranean type is *absolutely* the most numerous or the second most numerous in every Irish county group and that it is most commonly found in combination

with the Keltic type to constitute from about 55 per cent to about 67 per cent of the male population. Its *relative* predominances are in combination with the Keltic only in three county subgroups. Such relative predominances also are found with the combined Nordic type in two county groups, and with the Dinaric type in one group. Hence this modal Irish type cannot be linked in its distribution with the Keltic type or any other single type to the exclusion of others.

SOCIOLOGY

The Nordic Mediterranean type is below the median in education, ranking sixth of the 8 types. It has about the normal quota of Keltic speakers, but is rather low in students of school Irish. Occupationally, the type is close to average Irish distribution. Although it leads in navvies, it is not occupationally depressed. It is rather high in semi-skilled trades, clerks and soldiers, slightly low in tinkers, and various kinds of agriculturalists, and definitely low in professional workers. The type has a deficiency of Catholics and an excess of Church of Ireland.

PHYSICAL CHARACTERISTICS

The Nordic Mediterranean type is 0.60 years above mean age, ranking third. It is virtually at the all-Irish mean of weight, and, in fact, nearly average in most bodily dimensions.

The chest index is somewhat elevated, signifying a relatively deep and narrow thorax. However, the Keltic type exhibits this feature in a much more pronounced degree. The longest heads in Ireland are found in this Nordic Mediterranean type. Head breadth, though narrow, exceeds that of other dolichocephalic types, except the Pure Mediterraneans. Head height is superior to that of the Keltics and the Pure Mediterraneans. The length-height index is very low and the breadth-height index high, as in other long-headed types. Face breadth in this type is far inferior to that of the round-headed types, but higher than that of other dolichocephals. The cephalo-facial index reaches its Irish maximum. Total face height is well above the Irish average, as is also the total facial index. Upper face height is also high. Naturally both total facial and upper facial indices are on the high side and align this type with the other dolichocephalic leptoprosopic types and with the Dinaric type (which has been selected for long narrow noses). In the Nordic Mediterranean type the nose is about of average length, but a little more than ordinarily wide. Hence the nasal index is somewhat above the Irish mean, but it is exactly the same as that of the Predominantly Nordic type and really differs very little from the mean nasal index of any other of the long-headed types.

Although skin color in the Nordic Mediterraneans is darker than in any other Irish type save the small Pure Mediterranean, yet 86.2 per cent of this type have pink skins. Pronounced vascularity is deficient; freckles are slightly less than ordinarily common. The modal hair form is low waved (as in every other Irish type). Hair color is much darker than in any other sizable type, with 4.7 per cent of black hair and 52.4 per cent of dark brown. Nevertheless, more than one third of the type has medium brown hair. All of the eyes are mixed—81.3 per cent blue-brown. Mixed eyes are a little more heavily pigmented in this type than in any other. Yet 74.7 per cent of the mixed eyes are recorded as "pronouncedly light" or "very pronouncedly light." The most prevalent iris pattern is "diffuse" or without marked patterning (by far the most common in Nordic Mediterraneans). Brow ridges are a little larger than ordinary; foreheads least often high, and a little more sloping than in any other except the Keltic type. Nasion depressions tend toward pronounced depth. The nasal profile is a little oftener straight than convex as in all Irish types except the Dinaric.

Tooth loss, wear, and caries in the Nordic Mediterranean type are somewhat above the Irish average—possibly because of an elevation in mean age. Frontal projection of the malars is slightly high, but pronounced lateral projection is less than average. The same stricture applies to prominence of gonial angles. The ear presents no distinctive features. Pronounced temporal fullness is well below the Irish average. Occipital protrusion, as in other dolichocephalic types, is inclined to be marked. Lambdoid flattening is very common, but its occurrence hardly deviates from that of the total Irish series. Occipital flattening is deficient.

PURE MEDITERRANEAN
Distribution

The Pure Mediterranean type is composed of all individuals with cephalic index under 80, pure dark eyes, and black, dark brown, medium brown, or red-brown hair. There are only 33 such individuals in our Irish series of 9521 men. This handful is concentrated in Sligo-Leitrim-S. Fermanagh-W. Cavan but with comparative strength also in Longford-Westmeath, and in Offaly-Leix-Kildare. However, at least one individual of this type occurs in every county group with the following exceptions: West Donegal, Aran Islands, Kerry, Cork, Limerick, E. Cavan-Monaghan-Armagh. The map distribution of this small type is somewhat U-shaped, with the heaviest concentration in the left leg of the U and the lightest in the eastern coastal strip which comprises the right leg. This U of dark eyes coincides with a similar U-shaped concentration of dark mixed eyes, which is given in figures 34 and 35. There are no less than 603 Irishmen in our series with pronouncedly dark or very pronouncedly dark eyes. Of these 364, or 60.3 per cent belong to the Nordic Mediterranean type of long heads. The rest are divided nearly equally between the Nordic Alpine and Dinaric types. The map of the distribution of the darker shades of mixed eyes includes a couple of concentrations that are not found in the U-distribution to which we have just alluded. These are in Waterford-Wexford and in West Donegal. The former group represents a concentration of the round-headed Nordic Alpines, and the latter is especially strong in Nordic Mediterraneans. There is some suspicion that a sorting which combined the "Pure Mediterraneans" with the Nordic Mediterraneans of very dark mixed eye color might segregate a Mediterranean type in a more liberal sense, of which the core is our Pure Mediterranean group. It must be noted, however, that our great Nordic Mediterranean type is not over-represented in the Sligo-Leitrim-S. Fermanagh-W. Cavan county group, which contains the core of the Pure Mediterraneans. In general, the Pure Mediterranean type is practically lacking in the southwest of Ireland and quite rare in the west.

Sociology

This little group is so small as to be unreliable for sampling purposes. It is not well educated; it ranks next to the last in educational ratio. It includes only 2 men who are Keltic speakers. It happens to lead occupationally in shop-workers, transportation, and soldiers, but the numbers of individuals concerned are so small that no importance can be attached to these facts.

Physical Characteristics

The Pure Mediterraneans are the oldest type group in Ireland with an age excess of 4.20 years. They are lightest in body weight, shortest in stature, lowest in absolute span and highest in relative span, low in absolute shoulder breadth, lowest in relative shoulder breadth. They have the highest average thoracic index (i.e., their chests are deepest relative to their breadth). They seem then to be small men with narrow shoulders, narrow, deep chests, and relatively long arms. Other absolute lows are in sitting height and relative sitting height. However, their heads are significantly long, but somewhat broader than those of the other long-headed types. The mean cephalic index (77.01) is above that of the other long-headed types, and they have absolutely the lowest mean head height and the lowest mean length-height index. The minimum frontal is lowest of all the Irish types, as is also the zygo-frontal index. Total face height is the minimum of the Irish types and the total facial index is below the Irish mean, but exceeds that of two of the brachycephalic types (the East Baltic and the Nordic Alpine). The noses are rather long, possibly because of the high mean age of the type group, and also above average breadth. The nasal index is lowest of all of the types except the Dinaric (which is selected for low nasal index).

The Pure Mediterranean type has 63.6 per cent of swarthy skin and is thus by far the most heavily pigmented of the Irish types. Among the other types dark skins are far the most numerous among the Nordic Mediterraneans. The Pure Mediterranean type is the most deficient in pronounced vascularity; has fewest freckles, and, perhaps accidentally,

FIGURE 34

Distribution of 33 Pure Mediterraneans, and of mixed eyes, very pronouncedly dark plus pronouncedly dark (fig. 35). The distribution of this pitiful handful of long-headed men with pure dark eyes is possibly of significance only in the consideration of Irish prehistory. This group is concentrated around Sligo Bay with an outlying extension southeastward including Longford-Westmeath and Offaly-Leix-Kildare. If this may be compared with that of very pronouncedly dark and pronouncedly dark mixed eyes, it will be noted that these dark mixed eyes are distributed in a roughly U-shaped area which includes the concentration of Pure Mediterraneans. But there are two other isolated concentrations of dark mixed concentration— Waterford-Wexford and West Donegal, which are virtually devoid of Pure Mediterraneans. Most of these dark mixed eyes occur in Nordic Mediterraneans, but there are a number also among the Nordic Alpines and the Dinarics. The Waterford-Wexford and Antrim-Down sections are both county groups with an absolute predominance of Nordic Mediterraneans as is also West Donegal.

There is little doubt that less meticulous observers than Dupertuis would have classified many of these dark mixed eyes as pure darks, thus greatly increasing the number of Pure Mediterraneans, mostly at the expense of Nordic Mediterraneans. However, it is not our opinion that our tiny Pure Mediterranean group is merely a segregate from the large Nordic Mediterranean type.

These dark mixed eyes and the Pure Mediterranean distribution do not coincide with the areas in which light eyes are least frequent (with the exception of West Donegal which is low in light eyes but quite devoid of Pure Mediterraneans). The relatively dark-eyed areas in the west and southeast occur in regions where Nordic Alpines and Dinarics are concentrated, and all of the pure dark (homogeneous) brown eyes that occur outside of the Pure Mediterraneans belong to Dinarics.

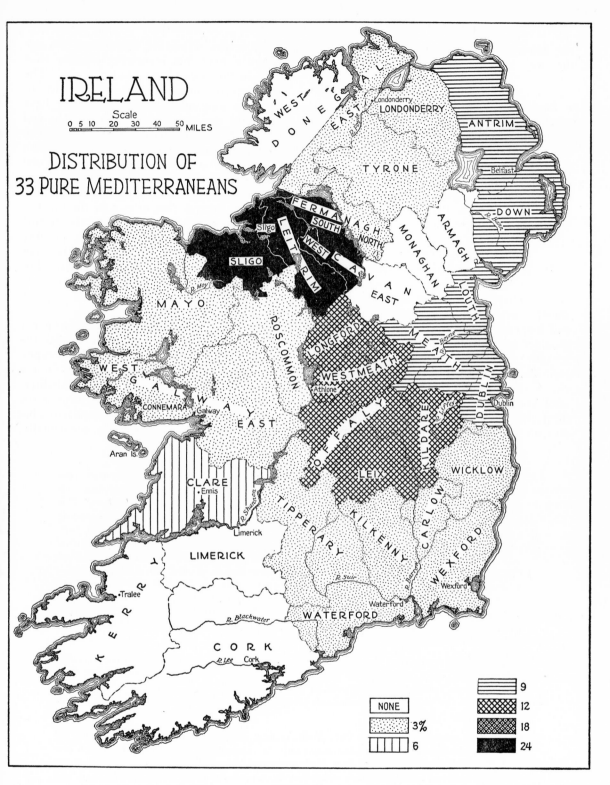

IRELAND

Scale
0 5 10 20 30 40 50 MILES

DISTRIBUTION OF
33 PURE MEDITERRANEANS

NONE		9
3%		12
6		18
		24

FIGURE 34

fewest moles. It has an excess of deep-waved hair, but, curiously, includes none of the few individuals with curly or frizzly hair. Beard and body hair are most poorly developed in this type. In spite of high mean age this small group is also somewhat deficient in baldness. It is slightly high in the graying of hair, but not in the graying of beard. The 9.1 per cent of black hair found in this type represents the maximum, by far, in Ireland! Yet the dominant shade is dark brown (72.2 per cent), which is again an Irish maximum. Eye color, by the sorting criteria, is invariably dark. Of the 43 dark eyes found among our Irish males, all are found in this type except 10 that belong to Dinarics. (There are no pure Alpines in Ireland among the males.) External eyefolds are perhaps over-represented and the upward slant of the eyes is considerably more common than in any other Irish type. Thin eyebrows and absence or small development of concurrency also seem to be marked in this type. There is a deficiency of foreheads of pronounced height, and forehead slope is prevailingly medium.

Observations on the nose show very little that is distinctive. There is an uncertain excess of broad nasal bridges, but no homogeneity of nasal profile and no strong trend toward any particular variety of profile. Intriguing suggestions of predominance of thick lips, convex septa, and flaring alae must be regarded with skepticism, since the numbers involved are so inadequate. Similarly, the great excess of membranous lips with submedium eversion and the excess of alveolar prognathism and of prominent chins are of uncertain validity. Tooth loss in this type is greater than in any other, but it will be recalled that this inadequately represented type is the oldest (in mean age) in Ireland. The crude figures also indicate that the Pure Mediterranean type leads in frontal projection of malars, but lateral projection is less than ordinarily pronounced, and gonial angles that are prominent are deficient. A slight development of Darwin's Point is excessively prevalent and great excesses of free ear lobes of pronounced size are features to be associated with high mean age. This type, along with the Keltic, most rarely shows marked temporal fullness, but its occipital protrusion is not exceptional. Lamb-

doid flattening seems to be commoner than in any other type except the East Baltic, and occipital flattening is at the Irish minimum.

It is, of course, possible to dismiss nearly all of the distinctive features of this Pure Mediterranean type as random variations without statistical significance and hence without anthropological significance. This will, without doubt, be the point of view of anthropologists who entertain a sort of religious bias against the recognition of types in populations, presumably because they believe that such recognition is in some way discriminative, anti-democratic, and "racist." However, such anthropologists will object equally to the rest of our morphological types, however adequately they are represented and however distinctive their characteristics. There is no point in arguing with those prejudiced against racial or morphological type differences, any more than with those who, without any real basis of fact, have set forth statements and theories purporting to establish racial hierarchies in a morphological, metric, and cultural context.

But it may be worthwhile to say a few words here to the reader who is open-minded about the matter of "type," but reluctant to accept as types selected samples of such inadequate size that their distinctiveness and internal homogeneity cannot be demonstrated by the use of ordinary statistical devices such as the critical ratio. Standard errors and such paraphernalia are of great utility in safeguarding the anthropologist against overestimating the significance of crude differences in samples of adequate size. They are of no use whatsoever in appraising the differences between samples so small that a random distribution of variations cannot be postulated. In the present instance our tiny Pure Mediterranean type cannot be validated by any statistical device. It is quite possible, however, that it has more reality than some of the huge groups whose statistical differentiation in numerous metrical and morphological features is facilitated by their small standard errors. Take, for example, Neanderthal man, as represented by skeletal remains. Although individuals referred to the Neanderthaloid race, or subspecies, or whatever we may care to call it, are comparatively numerous—certainly to be counted by the dozens—there are not enough of them to es-

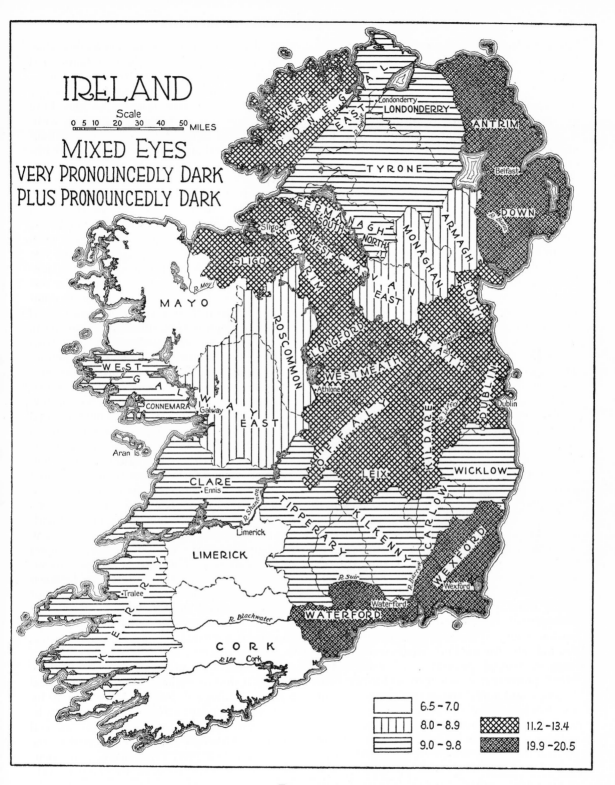

IRELAND

Scale
0 5 10   20   30   40   50 MILES

MIXED EYES
VERY PRONOUNCEDLY DARK
PLUS PRONOUNCEDLY DARK

	6.5 – 7.0
	8.0 – 8.9
	9.0 – 9.8
	11.2 – 13.4
	19.9 – 20.5

FIGURE 35
DISTRIBUTION OF MIXED EYES, very pronouncedly dark plus pronouncedly dark. This map
is supplemental to figure 34, and is discussed in the commentary on that map.

tablish a satisfactory sample that can be analyzed statistically. Yet no physical anthropologist doubts the validity of the conception of Neanderthal man as a zoological group. It is true of course, that some feel that Neanderthal man should be divided into the classic or conservative type and the progressive type, but that is a matter of no importance here. What is pertinent is that a very small number of human individuals, presenting in common an assemblage of morphological and metrical variations, may establish a breed or a type as an anthropological reality with the implication of close genetic relationship. We are inclined to think that our insignificantly small, but rather sharply distinguished Pure Mediterranean type represents the residuum of an important population stratum of Ireland—possibly surviving only in scattered individuals by Mendelian recombination. Here is probably one of the basic elements in the larger Nordic Mediterranean type which is undoubtedly the result of the intermixture of several racial substrains.

NORDIC ALPINE

DISTRIBUTION

The Nordic Alpine type includes 1754 men, or 18.4 per cent of the Irish county series. It is widely distributed in Ireland, and nowhere very weak except in the Arans and to a lesser extent in the east, north of Waterford-Wexford (fig. 36). However, it is most strongly concentrated in the south (especially Kerry and Waterford-Wexford) with a general over-representation in nearly all parts of Ireland west of the Shannon.

SOCIOLOGY

In education this type ranks fifth in Ireland. It is above average in proportions of Keltic speakers. The Nordic Alpine type is not very distinctive occupationally. It is rather high in agriculturalists and farm dependents, but low in navvies. Other small excesses occur in

transport workers, the professions, and students. In general its occupational status is higher than average.

PHYSICAL CHARACTERISTICS

This numerous type is 1.4 years below mean Irish type age. It is the heaviest of the Irish types, with mean weight 1.6 pounds above average. Stature, however, is 0.69 cm. below the Irish mean and inferior to that of every other type save the numerically inadequate Pure Mediterranean. Shoulder breadth duplicates the Irish maximum achieved by the Dinarics. Relative shoulder breadth is a trifle higher than in any other type. Chest diameters are large, but the thoracic index is close to the Irish type mean. Relative sitting heights are a little high, although this index shows comparatively small variations among the Irish types. By virtue of the sorting criteria used, head length is significantly low and head breadth high. Head height is also high, and the length-height index is the highest of the series. Breadth-height indices are, of course, reduced. Minimum frontal diameter is the largest of the types, and the mean fronto-parietal index exceeds that of the other brachycephalic types. Bizygomatic diameter is second only to that found in the small East Baltic type. The cephalo-facial index is significantly low. Total face height and the total facial index, with upper face height and the upper facial index, are all low. The nasal diameters are naturally involved in the sorting for nasal index. Therefore the nose height is short; the nose breadth achieves the maximum among the Irish types. Bigonial diameters also are at the type maximum, but the zygo-gonial index is lowest in Ireland.

Exactly 10 per cent of Nordic Alpines have dark skins. Consequently, they rank third among the Irish types in brunetness. However, pronounced vascularity is above the Irish average. There are slight excesses of all of the curved varieties of hair. Deficiencies of bald-

FIGURE 36

NORDIC ALPINE MORPHOLOGICAL TYPE DISTRIBUTION IN IRELAND. No area except the Aran Islands has a ratio of less than 0.7. The highest concentrations (Kerry, Waterford-Wexford) are 1.3 and 1.4. The relative weakness of this type in the eastern half of Ireland (except Waterford-Wexford) is related, of course, to the Nordic Mediterranean and Keltic concentration in this area.

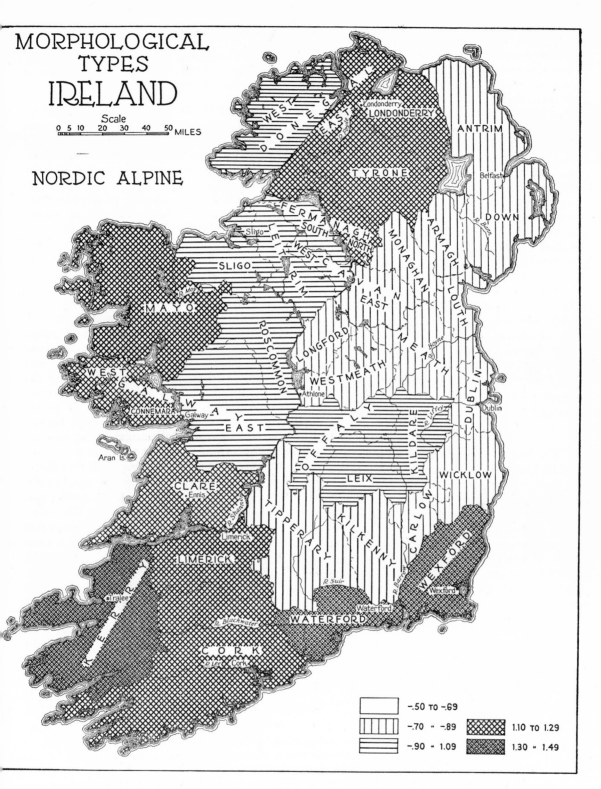

MORPHOLOGICAL
TYPES
IRELAND

Scale

0 5 10 20 30 40 50 MILES

NORDIC ALPINE

	-.50 TO -.69
	-.70 " -.89
	-.90 " 1.09
	1.10 TO 1.29
	1.30 " 1.49

FIGURE 36

ness and graying may be attributable in part to low mean age.

By our sorting criteria, the Nordic Alpine type may have any shade of hair color except golden, ash blond, and red. Actually, its modal hair color is dark brown, with medium brown a close second. Red-brown and golden brown shades are moderately well represented. Only a few men have black hair. The Nordic Alpine type falls well below the Nordic Mediterranean and the Pure Mediterranean in darkness of hair, and is also somewhat lighter than the Dinaric type. Blue eyes are fewest here in any of the Irish types except in those from whom blue eyes have been excluded by sorting criteria. Yet 38.5 per cent of Nordic Alpines have blue eyes and 5.1 per cent gray or gray blue. At this advanced state of the analysis of the Irish series we are unwilling to face the labor of sub-dividing the Nordic Alpine type, but it seems to us now that it would have been interesting to split off the blue-eyed and gray-eyed individuals as a brachycephalic sub-

type more or less paralleled by our long-headed Keltic type. Mixed eyes are more light than dark in 76.2 per cent of the Nordic Alpine type.

Foreheads are of pronounced height in an excess percentage of cases and forehead slope is less than average. Noses are not extraordinary, but low bridges and broad bridges and roots are a little commoner than in most Irish types. Straight profiles of the noses are more than ordinarily common and concave noses are also in excess. Similarly convex profiles are deficient. All of these nasal features are involved indirectly in the sorting criteria. Nasal tips tend to be thick and alae are flaring oftener than usual. A slight superiority of the dental conditions of this type may be attributable to the low average age of the type. Lateral projection of the malars tends to be pronounced or very pronounced more often than in any other Irish type. Gonial angles also achieve the Irish type maximum in prominence. In the ear there is a single feature

FIGURE 37

ABSOLUTE TYPE PREDOMINANCES IN IRELAND. The absolute type predominances yield a map more likely to induce astigmatic headaches in the reader than to give an immediately clear picture. The heavy horizontals always mean that the basic Nordic Mediterranean is the leading type; the heavy verticals, the Keltic; the heavy diagonals northeast to southwest are the areas in which Dinarics lead. The actual listings of areas by combined occurrences of the two leading types are:

Nordic Mediterranean and Keltic

Antrim-Down	61.0%
Offaly-Leix-Kildare	61.0%
West Donegal	58.3%
E. Galway-Roscommon	57.4%
Longford-Westmeath	57.1%
West Galway	56.4%
Sligo-Leitrim-S. Fermanagh- W. Cavan	55.4%

Keltic and Nordic Mediterranean

Arans	67.4%
Meath-Louth-Dublin	66.3%
Wicklow-Carlow	63.6%

E. Cavan-Monaghan-Armagh	63.4%
N. Fermanagh-E. Donegal- Tyrone-Londonderry	54.4%

Dinaric and Nordic Mediterranean

Clare	52.1%
Kerry	51.6%

Nordic Mediterranean and Dinaric

Mayo	52.3%
Limerick	51.5%

Nordic Mediterranean and Nordic Alpine

Cork	52.9%
Waterford-Wexford	48.7%

Note that Nordic Mediterranean is always the leading type or the second type. The Keltic type is a fairly close second, and leads along the central part of the east coast. Absolute Dinaric predominance is found only in Clare and Kerry. If this map be compared with that of relative type excesses, it will be clear to the student that the basic Nordic Mediterranean type, with excesses notable only in the north and central part of the east coast, really represents the thickest population stratum in all but a north central and east coast band, in which it yields to Keltic, and in a very small southwestern area of absolute Dinaric predominance.

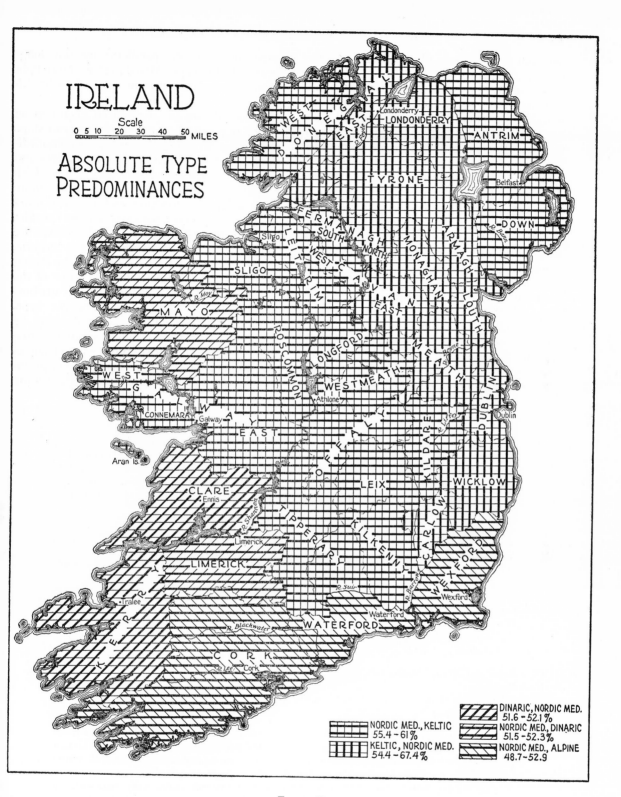

IRELAND

Scale
0 5 10   20   30   40   50 MILES

ABSOLUTE TYPE
PREDOMINANCES

NORDIC MED., KELTIC
55.4 – 61%

KELTIC, NORDIC MED.
54.4 – 67.4%

DINARIC, NORDIC MED.
51.6 – 52.1 %

NORDIC MED., DINARIC
51.5 – 52.3%

NORDIC MED., ALPINE
48.7 – 52.9

FIGURE 37

worthy of mention. Darwin's Point is less common than in any other type. Marked temporal fullness and deficiency of occipital projection are naturally a feature of this brachycephalic type. Lambdoid flattening is about as common as in any other type, and occipital flattening reaches its type maximum.

FIGURE 38

RELATIVE TYPE EXCESSES IN IRELAND. This map shows in each county group the one or two morphological types that are found in excess of their total Irish county representation. The following are the excesses:

Keltic only—Wicklow-Carlow.
Keltic and Nordic Mediterranean—Offaly-Leix-Kildare; Arans; Meath-Louth-Dublin.
Nordic and Nordic Mediterranean—Antrim-Down; Longford-Westmeath.
Nordic and Keltic—E. Cavan-Monaghan-Armagh; E. Galway-Roscommon.
Nordic and East Baltic—Sligo-Leitrim-S. Fermanagh-W. Cavan; N. Fermanagh-E. Donegal-Tyrone-Londonderry.
Nordic and Nordic Alpine—West Galway; Waterford-Wexford.
Dinaric and East Baltic—Tipperary-Kilkenny.
Dinaric and Nordic Alpine—Mayo; Clare; Limerick.
Dinaric and Nordic Mediterranean—West Donegal.
East Baltic, Dinaric, and Nordic Alpine—Kerry; Cork.

This map has to be studied in detail to enable the patterning to be discerned. Attention should be called to the band of Nordic concentration (in combination with other types), sweeping from the north and northeast to the Bay of Galway; to the northern and southwestern islands of East Baltics, combined in the north with Nordics, but in the southwest with Nordic Alpines and Dinarics. Note the curious coincidence of Waterford-Wexford with West Galway in Nordic and Nordic Alpine strength. Note also that Keltic type excesses usually occur with Nordic Mediterranean along the center of the east coast, but with Nordic in the E. Galway-Roscommon, and E. Cavan-Monaghan-Armagh groups. In studying this map, remember that the excesses are only relative; the absolute type predominances are represented in figure 37.

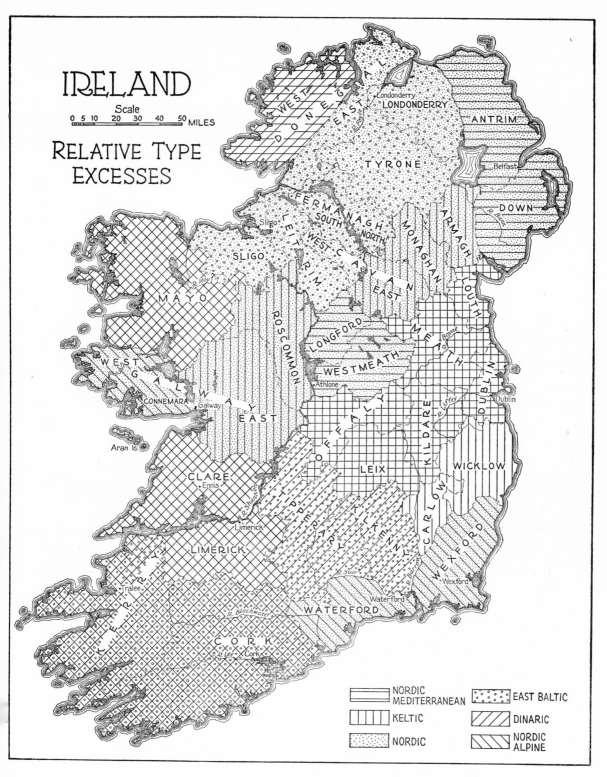

IRELAND

Scale
0 5 10   20   30   40   50 MILES

RELATIVE TYPE
EXCESSES

NORDIC
MEDITERRANEAN

KELTIC

NORDIC

EAST BALTIC

DINARIC

NORDIC
ALPINE

FIGURE 38

CORRELATION OF MORPHOLOGICAL TYPES WITH ARCHÆOLOGICAL FINDS, ESPECIALLY OF SKELETAL MATERIAL

THERE is no secure evidence of the occupation of Ireland during Palaeolithic times. Therefore, any talk of "Palaeolithic survivors" in the modern population would seem to imply that they came of stocks which survived the Palaeolithic in some region outside of Ireland, and entered that island as carriers of some later culture. The most comprehensive description of the skeletal remains in Ireland from earliest times down to the present is that of Cecil P. Martin (1935), and in this section we shall first consider the data and conclusions of that careful worker as they bear upon the present distributions of morphological types.

One much discussed skull of alleged Palaeolithic age was found in Kilgreany Cave in Waterford. It seems quite improbable that this skull (Kilgreany B) is Palaeolithic, but Martin thinks that it may be late Palaeolithic, or at any rate, very early Neolithic. For our purposes, it is only necessary to note that it is a large skull, very long and narrow, relatively low in the vault, quite short and wide in the face, with a high nasal index. Martin may be right in supposing that it would be hard to match among modern Irish skulls. In the living Irish this combination of a long, low, narrow, skull with a short, broad face and wide nose would also be exceptional, although we could probably run down a few examples of these associated proportions in our Nordic Mediterranean type. (We have not sorted for this particular combination of features.)

The first well attested inhabitants of Ireland are the Mesolithic people of the Twenty-five-foot Raised Beach. Martin lists measurements of 8 skulls which he attributes with more or less certainty to the Raised Beach people, although Movius is skeptical of the validity of these identifications. For our purposes it matters little whether they are Mesolithic or Neolithic. All of these skulls, except one (which is mesocephalic), are relatively very long and narrow, with cranial indices between 70 and 73. Some are small and some are large,

but all are high in the vault (markedly hypsicephalic). Only two of these crania have measurable faces, one of which has a somewhat short and broad upper face, the other (from the measurements) a relatively long face. Both have high nasal indices. Long bones associated with two of the crania indicate short stature.

None of our dolichocephalic Irish types of today yields average proportions which are close to those described above, particularly as respects great height relative to breadth and length. Nor do any of the types as a whole manifest high nasal indices. Here again, it is probable that a search through the individual records would turn up a few men with the cranial features attributed to these Raised Beach people, but they would certainly be atypical.

Some 9 skulls are listed by Martin as belonging to the people of the Megalithic monuments, presumably of late Neolithic date, but possibly of Early Bronze Age. These, with one exception, are dolichocephalic to mesocephalic, but they are relatively lower and broader and have higher length-breadth indices than the earlier series. Also, the faces are quite long and the noses much narrower. Statures are variable, but none especially high. These are very much more like the skulls of our modern Irish dolichocephals and could be duplicated quite easily in the Nordic Mediterranean, Keltic, and probably in the Predominantly Nordic types. The one brachycephalic skull in this series of Martin (that of a female) is possibly intrusive and of later date. It is an out-and-out Alpine, with a short, broad face and an extremely high nasal index. Doubtless it could be matched among the Nordic Alpines (female) in our modern living series.

Martin records the measurements of some 12 Short Cist skulls of the Bronze Age. There are also a few other skulls which he has seen but of which no measurements are given. Of the 12 skulls listed 8 are brachycephals, quite short-headed, moderately broad to broad, with considerable variation in height. Three of these brachycephalic crania have short, broad faces and relatively very broad noses. The others have long and relatively narrow noses. The short-faced, broad-nosed skulls are identified as probably female, the long-faced as male. At least two of the males were very tall, approximating or exceeding 6 feet. While the sexes assigned to these skulls may be correct, it is relevant to note that these two types are clearly identifiable with our Dinaric and Nordic Alpine (or East Baltic) types, respectively, and that they occur in about equal proportions among the living males. In the case of the Crooked Wood skulls illustrated by Martin (1935, pl. VI, opp. p. 100), the long-faced skull certainly appears to be that of a male, but the skull with the short broad face is not unmistakably female, although, from the plate, its appearance is more female than male. Martin notes that the mesocephalic skulls in the Short Cists are, except in one case, those of females, and belong to the same type as was characteristic of the Megalithic monuments. He suggests that the Bronze Age brachycephals may often have married women of the Neolithic stock.

Some 7 skulls have been recovered from Middle to Late Bronze Age finds with mixed cremated and inhumed burials. Martin records measurements of 5 skulls, the other two having been lost. However, the features of the 2 lost skulls are known from an earlier report. Of the skulls 4 are brachycephalic and the other 3 dolichocephalic. The brachycephalic skulls are of the long-faced, narrow-nosed type (Dinaric)—at any rate, the three published by Martin. The long-heads, however, have cranial heights that are similar to the skulls of the people of the Raised Beach rather than to the lower heads of the Neolithic stock. These long-heads are thought to have been taller than the Neolithic men.

The correlations of the scanty skeletal material with existing types, up to this point, are as follows: the very narrow, long hypsi-cephalic and presumably wide-nosed crania of the Raised Beach period do not conform to the general proportions of any of our dolicho-cephalic types, but probably (and almost certainly) these proportions could be found in individuals or even sizable groups within the present long-headed morphological types, by sorting for the required combinations of characters. The lower-headed and wider-headed dolichocephals and mesocephals of the Megalithic burials, with their long, narrow faces and narrow noses, are well within the range of our Nordic Mediterranean and Keltic morphological types, and probably also of the somewhat higher-headed Predominantly Nordic type. The two types of Bronze Age brachy-cephals, one with a long narrow face and a narrow nose, the other with a short, broad face and a broad nose, are essentially our Dinaric and Nordic Alpine (or East Baltic) types. In short, by the end of the Bronze Age the few and fragmentary skulls that have been recorded for the several periods seem to exhibit a sufficient range of type combinations to include almost anything that we have in the modern population.

Martin lists some 9 skulls of Iron Age burials which are well enough preserved to permit the taking of most standard measurements. The length-breadth index in these skulls ranges from 74.2 to 79.4. They are all long-headed, or at least on the dolichocephalic side of the arbitrary division we have made at 80. But they are by no means as relatively narrow as the Raised Beach skulls, or even as the Megalithic skulls. The face varies from long and narrow to fairly broad, and so do the noses. The height of the skull vault is comparatively low, or even very low. The forehead is invariably narrow. Stature seems to have been moderate. All of these requirements are fulfilled quite accurately in our Keltic type, and even in our tiny Pure Mediterranean type.

A few skulls of indeterminate, but probably much later, dates, from the Irish crannogs, present a range from marked dolichocephaly to brachycephaly, but nothing at all distinctive. Presumably, all previous elements in the Irish population were represented in these artificial lake-dwellings.

Martin has also recorded measurements of some 21 Early Christian skulls, of which 19 per cent are brachycephalic, 38.1 per cent mesaticephalic, and 42.9 per cent dolicho-cephalic. He also discusses another series of 49 skulls from a burial mound near Dublin which were measured by Frazer. Of these 25 per cent were brachycephals, 65 per cent mesaticephalic, and 10 per cent dolichocephalic. Martin comments that the people of this age "had in general slightly long faces and narrow noses. In most cases the skulls are of moderate height, . . . [and] are well-filled and capacious-looking." He states that the angular outline so common in earlier ages has disappeared (1935, pp. 140–141).

In his valuable work, Martin lists also the measurements of skulls of 6 indubitable Norsemen, and of 10 more crania that are probably Norse. They are all dolichocephalic or mesocephalic and are relatively high with long and narrow faces. The skulls look well-filled; the nasal bones are narrow and prominent, and the whole nose often markedly narrow. The forehead is broad or medium, and slightly retreating; the zygomatic arches are well developed in breadth; the mandible is strong with prominent chin, and the face invariably orthognathous. These specifications fit our Predominantly Nordic type very well and our Pure Nordic type, which consists in large measure of immature individuals, not quite so well. The Predominantly Nordic type leads the other long-headed types in head height and the Pure Nordic and Predominantly Nordic types also lead the dolichocephals (but not the brachycephals) in length-height index. These two types also rank first and second among all the types in the breadth-height index. In total face height the Predominantly Nordics rank second only to the Dinarics (who are selected for long noses with which are normally associated long faces). The Predominantly Nordic and Pure Nordic types are also first and second in total facial index (i.e., they have relatively the longest and narrowest faces). Finally, the Predominantly Nordic type leads all others in stature.

The most complete and penetrating analysis of Irish craniometry has been made by W. W. Howells (1941, pp. 103-219), as part of the Harvard Anthropological Survey of Ireland, in connection with his study of approximately 140 skeletons of Early Christian Irish discovered in the course of archæological excavations at Gallen Priory in Ferbane, Co. Offaly. The life of the monastery was about A.D. 700–1600.

The Gallen Priory skulls are moderately large and rugged and slightly bigger than most of the other British series, particularly in length. The means of the series are mesocranial, orthocranial, and metricranial, but the skulls tend to be relatively low. Reconstruction of stature from the long bones indicates that it averaged approximately 167 cm. or 65¾ inches. The ranges of stature were only from 150.5 cm. to 176 cm. Evidently these Early Christian monks were considerably shorter than the average of any of the morphological types of the modern population.

Howells does not break down this series into types, but deals with it as a single unit, comparing means, etc., with those of all of the British series available. This method is valuable in a comparison of the total Gallen series with others, but it does not help us greatly in trying to ascertain whether the same types occur in the mediæval Irish monks as in our modern population. The result of pooling all of the individuals, regardless of type disparity, is to throw the means into an intermediate position between the type extremes, if these happen to show bimodality. Our own method of dividing the cephalic index at below 80, and 80 and above, tends to divide the intermediates or mesocephals equally between the long-heads and the round heads, and to some extent it exaggerates differences in its use of two rather than three classes of the length-breadth index of the head.

Howells studied the variability of his Irish cranial series and ascertained it to be in general slightly less homogeneous than some of the well-known series of English crania, but he did not consider that the heterogeneity manifested was enough to lead to the supposition that some foreign type was included in the group. Nevertheless, most of the measurements and indices have fairly large ranges, such as occur when a total population consists of a number of diverse types (as is usually the case). The cranial or length-breadth index, for example, ranges from 68 to 84, although the mean is 76.38. The height-length index with a mean of 70.93 has a range from 59 to 77. The total facial index has a general mean of 85.92, but a range of 74–101. The nasal index, which averages 47.52, varies from 39 to 57. There is certainly enough of a spread in the ranges of Howells' measurements and indices of the Gallen crania to provide for the segregation of all of the morphological types recognized in the modern population. However, since pigmentation of hair and eyes, together with the cephalic and nasal indices, are the main criteria used for our type differentiation, it would obviously have been impossible for Howells to employ these criteria in his craniological studies. We could take all of the purely metric and indicial features in which our present morphological types are differentiated from each other and use them as a basis for resorting Howells' crania into morphological types. But this would involve the very difficult and precarious task of attempting to reduce measurements and indices on the living to their equivalents on dried crania. There actually exists no adequate basis for making such translations. No one knows, for example, exactly how to convert the nasal index on the living to the nasal index on the dried cranium.

We shall have to content ourselves with a crude comparison of our total series means with those found by Howells on the Gallen crania. However, before we do this, it is more important and interesting to consider the results Howells achieved in comparing his total cranial population with that of apposite cranial series from Britain and elsewhere.

Howells, who is a most ingenious investigator, found, on the basis of thorough comparisons of means of measurements and indices, mean differences of the aggregates of measurement and indices and also of the variabilities, that his Gallen series closely resembles: (a) a series of British crania from Dunstable, Redfordshire, datable to the fifth or sixth century A.D. and comprised of burials scattered over the slopes of a Bronze Age barrow, probably of Britons; (b) a series of Anglo-Saxon crania pooled by Morant and called the London Museum series. However, the Dunstable and British Anglo-Saxon series do not closely resemble each other. Howells then took another series (Schuster's Round Barrow crania) which is plainly a conglomerate of Neolithic and Bronze Age types and compared his Irish series with it. He found that the Irish series is closest of all to this Bronze Age British series of mixed Bronze and Neolithic type. He then

took the means of the cranial index of "typical" British Neolithic series, and of "typical" British Bronze Age series, and weighted each in a proportion to give the mean cranial index of the Gallen skulls. Thus he used 51.25 per cent of Neolithic skulls (with a mean index of 71.7) and 48.75 per cent of Bronze Age skulls with a mean index of 81.3, to derive a blend that would produce a mean index of 76.38, which is that of the Gallen skulls. Using these proportions of measurements from the two British series all down the line, he produced a theoretical "Gallen Cross" which proved to be much closer to the real Gallen figures than any other comparable cranial series and was in fact virtually identical with the actual Gallen mean dimensions. He then rigged a similar set of figures to weight the means of a hypothetical "Dunstable Cross" by using appropriate percentages of Neolithic and Bronze Age measurements. This gave a close approximation to the actual Dunstable means, but not quite so close as in the case of the Gallen figures. From this brilliant experiment he concluded that both the Dunstable and the Gallen series could be explained as a cross of Neolithic and Bronze Age crania—in the Gallen series composed of about equal numbers of Neolithic and Bronze Age elements, and in the case of the Dunstable series, in an approximate ratio of 3 Neolithic to 8 Bronze. Thus he concluded that the Early Irish cranial series was probably the result of amalgamating a population of Neolithic and Bronze Age elements.

In England the Iron Age crania more closely resemble those of the present population than do those of previous periods. Morant thought that the Iron Age invaders displaced the earlier peoples and fathered the present population. Certain features of the English Iron Age crania (notably the low vaults) make it difficult to derive the latter from a Neolithic-Bronze Age cross and the same holds true of the modern population. The small and random sample of Irish Iron Age skulls to some extent presents a similar difference. Howells points out that variations of the different series, mostly of strictly local origins, are to be expected, and that Gallen Priory, in the middle of the Central Plain, presents no features that result in a general type requiring the participation of

Iron Age invaders. He cites the opinion of Mahr that in point of numbers the Iron Age immigration to Ireland was small and unimportant.

It is at this point that we may introduce a comparison of our modern total Irish series with the means of measurements derived from the Gallen Priory crania. To this comparison may be added the means of our subsample from the combined counties of Offaly, Leix, and Kildare, which is as near as we can come to paralleling in the modern population the local character of the Gallen series (table XVIII-1).

Various anatomists and anthropologists have grappled with the difficult task of attempting to relate measurements on the living to those on dried skeletons. Perhaps the best source for a summary of this work is a monograph by W. M. Krogman (1939). Dr. J. Lawrence Angel of Jefferson College Medical School, Philadelphia, has kindly put at our disposal his experience and conclusions from utilizing the Todd-Krogman data as to allowances to be made from the drying and shrinking of the bones and the loss of the soft tissues. Here we shall employ Dr. Angel's corrections which add nothing for tissue dehydration on the ground that in standard anthropometric practice it seems probable that pressure of the caliper points would offset such an effect. Table XVIII-2 gives the total Gallen Priory means, the Angel corrections, the restored totals, and the comparison of the means of the total Irish county series of the present investigation.

For the restoration of glabello-occipital length, Angel recommends an addition of 6.9 mm., which is certainly conservative. This figure raises the Gallen Priory means to an average of 1.55 mm. above our total Irish county series. The suggestion is that the Catholic monks may have had slightly longer heads than the present male population of Ireland. Angel's addition of 9.1 mm. for head breadth is again on the conservative side and raises the Gallen mean to a value of 0.25 mm. over our total. However, this difference between the reconstructed monks and the modern Irishmen is virtually nil. Angel's correction of auricular height, amounting to 8.5 mm. brings the Gallen total to a mean 0.98 mm.

below that of our modern Irish—certainly a sufficiently close approximation. The horizontal circumferences of our modern series fall below the Gallen mean by 1.91 mm., which is again a very small difference.

Minimum frontal diameter, after an addition of 7.6 mm. for soft parts, still leaves the Gallen mean 5.4 mm. below that of the modern Irish—the largest discrepancy encountered in the two series and hardly explicable on the basis of differences involved in the reconstruction. On the other hand, the addition of this same amount, recommended by Angel for the bizygomatic diameter, puts the Gallen monks 2.44 mm. above the modern Irish. The same amount added to restore the bigonial gives the Gallen men an excess of 1.01 mm. over the modern total county series. Angel suggests the addition of 6.4 mm. for nasion-menton or total facial height, but this addition leaves the Gallen mean 2.92 mm. below that of our total Irish of today. Contrariwise, the one mm. addition for upper facial height gives the monks 0.53 mm. of mean excess.

The nose height addition suggested by Angel is only 2.0 mm., and this seems to us grossly inadequate when we consider nasal elongation in old age, which probably involves the septum as well as the tip. In point of fact this correction leaves the Gallen monks 2.94 mm. short on nasal length. Angel very tentatively suggests 11 mm. as the addition to be made for nose breadth, which involves, of course, the entire thicknesses of the alae. This actually brings our Gallen monks to a mean only 0.79 mm. below the modern average.

If we take the reconstructions at par value and consider the comparisons of measurements of the head and face, we have to conclude that the monks had slightly lower and longer heads, with circumferences a trifle higher; narrower foreheads, wider faces, slightly wider jaws, much shorter total face heights, but upper faces slightly longer than the men of today; shorter noses that were virtually of the modern breadth.

Now if we have sufficient faith or credulity to compare the reconstructed indices of the Gallen material with the total Irish means (using the reconstructed means of measurements to derive a reconstructed index of means), we find that the Gallen monks had a slightly lower cranial index (0.60), a somewhat lower length-height index, very much lower indices in all of those that involve the minimum frontal diameter; much lower facial indices, and slightly higher nasal indices.

The total result of this labored and dubious comparison of reconstructions of skeletal material with measurements on the living leaves us substantially with the same differences that are exhibited by the crude comparison of skulls with heads. Thus, after reconstructions, the Gallen monks still have longer and lower heads, narrower foreheads, wider faces, shorter total faces, broader jaws, with corresponding differences in the indices in which these diameters are involved.

The stature of the Gallen monks reconstructed by the use of the Pearson formulae averages, according to Howells, is 167 cm. Recent improved formulae for the reconstruction of stature from postcranial bones indicate that the Pearson formulae, which were based upon the utilization of old data on a short French population, give unsatisfactory results when used upon tall populations. One of us has investigated this matter thoroughly (Dupertuis and Hadden, 1951; Trotter and Gleser, 1952). Dr. Dupertuis recommends that we use for reconstruction the formulae most recently published by Trotter and Gleser. He considers that these formulae are based upon better data than were available to him. Accordingly, we have ascertained that the stature of the Gallen series based upon the humerus may be reconstructed at approximately 171.6 cm., and, on the basis of the femur at 170.4. Tibial lengths yield a mean stature of 171.5. Our total Irish Catholic County series has a mean of 171.90 cm., while the Offaly-Leix-Kildare group is 171.42. It appears that the Gallen monks were little, if any, shorter than the present population of males.

By and large, the Early Christian monks could hardly be regarded as a random sample of the present Irish population because of their narrower foreheads, broader and shorter faces. Yet we should have little difficulty in picking out of our series of living Irish a sample of men who would conform to the Gallen means. The most intriguing deviation of the modern Irish from the skeletal measurements and their reconstructions is in the greater depth of the modern mandible, which imparts a considerable increment of face height, and in their wider foreheads and narrower faces. It is a curious fact that our study of age changes in the Irish males (published elsewhere) shows that the metric features whereby the Gallen monks are particularly differentiated from the modern total series of Irish males, are, for the most part, displayed in the age groups of the latter from 60 years onward. This leads to the suggestion that some of the differences may be due to age composition of the Gallen Priory series. On the basis of various cranial criteria, Howells estimated that 13.4 per cent of his 127 male skulls belonged to young adults (21–35 years), 59.1 per cent to middle aged adults (35–55 years), 26.8 per cent to old adults (56–75 years) and only one skull (0.8 per cent) to a very old individual. Our county series includes no less than 56.2 per cent of males under 35 years of age, including 9.8 per cent of subadults (15–19 years); 28.9 per cent of middle aged persons, 13.7 per cent of old adults and 1.3 per cent of the very old. Thus it is evident that most of the metric deviations between the two series are probably referable to age disparity. If it seemed worth while, we could calculate from our age group studies of modern Irish males the means and measurements of a sample of roughly the same age composition as that of the Gallen Priory series. Such a selected sample would certainly be much closer to the means of the measurements and indices of the Gallen monks. It would be longer-headed, wider in bizygomatic diameter and shorter in total face height. It would also be narrower in the forehead, but would not reach down to the reconstructed means of minimum frontal diameter found in the Gallen monks. The labor of such a procedure would hardly be justified by the results. For us it is sufficiently clear that the Gallen monks probably differed very little, if at all, from a group of modern Irishmen of comparable ages.

Incidentally, the subseries from Offaly-Leix-Kildare, which was brought into the comparison, is closer to the Gallen Priory than to the total Irish county series in 12 of 22 measurements and indices tabulated, but the 10 closer resemblances of the total series tend to be concentrated in indices rather than measurements. In this connection, Dr. Dupertuis has remarked that in all probability the Gallen monks were learned men drawn from all parts of Ireland and perhaps from the outside, so that there is no particular reason why they should resemble a local modern population more than they resemble the Irish at large. It is to be supposed, or at any rate, piously to be hoped, that the Gallen monks measured by Howells contributed few if any genes to the modern Offaly-Leix-Kildare population.

Apart from the pitifully few crania and skeletons that have come to light in the course of archæological excavations, the latter have not yet contributed much to the elucidation of the sequence of physical types in Ireland and the identification of their origins. It might be assumed that the distribution of archæological sites, if well mapped, would provide indications as to the centers of population in the various periods, and even of the places of ingress and the direction of diffusion of the various cultures. Neither Dr. Hugh Hencken nor Dr. Hallam L. Movius, our local experts on Irish archæology, have much confidence in such use of the archæological data. Dr. Movius states that the exploration and mapping of sites are too incomplete to furnish reliable indications of culture distributions. Dr. Hencken feels that in such a small country as Ireland there is little chance of cultural isolation, and too great freedom of population movement throughout the island to promise anything in the way of a correlation of archæological sites with differences in the physical characteristics of ancient populations—much less with those of modern peoples who have moved about extensively in historical times.

Nevertheless, it seems worth while to summarize the archæological findings with reference to our problem of explaining the distributions of modern types. In this connection the archæological distribution maps of Dr. Joseph Raftery (1951) are of great interest, as well as his treatise on the archæology of the country. Professor R. A. S. Macalister's (1949) standard work provides another most useful source of information.

The earliest Mesolithic settlers, dating from about 6500 B.C., are represented exclusively by sites in Antrim and Down, mostly on the coast of the former county in the raised beaches. The archæologists agree that these settlers came across from Scotland and had a culture which was largely a Mesolithic survival of that of the Upper Palaeolithic Creswell folk of Britain. However, the culture of these earliest Irish settlers seems to have extended no farther west nor south than the line of the Bann. This eastern corner of Ireland is the only flint-bearing area in the island, so that it was naturally the place of concentration of the Mesolithic people who used flint for their implements. If they spread elsewhere, they would have been forced to use other kinds of stone for their tools, and their industries would be difficult to recognize. In any event, so far as is now known, the Mesolithic settlers were confined to this small part of Ireland. It is thus a little far-fetched to identify in the far west and southwest of Ireland certain "Palaeolithic survivors" among the modern types, since we do not know that the Mesolithic carriers of the Palaeolithic tradition penetrated to those relatively remote regions (Coon, 1939). This, of course, does not imply that certain physical types in southwestern Ireland do not resemble Palaeolithic types, but there is no present evidence that these resemblances are anything more than genetic recombinations of later inhabitants of Ireland.

The only skull found in connection with the Upper Palaeolithic Creswellian culture in Derbyshire, England, is that of the Langwith Man, described by Sir Arthur Keith (1925, vol. 1, pp. 127–35). It is a small, very narrow, low-vaulted skull of meager capacity which belonged to a male of middle age and probably of short stature. It is relatively and absolutely lower in the vault than any of the Irish skulls attributed to the Raised Beach people by Martin. There is the presumption, at any rate, that the Mesolithic settlers of Ireland were small-skulled dolichocephals, as the modern population of Antrim-Down is, predominantly, today.

We may accept Howells' opinion that the few Neolithic crania from Ireland, published by Martin (presumably the Raised Beach and Sand Hill series) are, so far as can be judged, undifferentiated from the Neolithic type in England. In all probability then, the earliest Irish population, whether it be called Mesolithic, Raised Beach, or simply "Neolithic" in Howells' sense of anything that is pre-Megalithic, came over from Britain. We have not attempted to isolate any very long, narrow, but high-headed type in our living series, but examples assuredly can be found very easily in our Predominantly Nordic, Pure Nordic, and Nordic Mediterranean types in that order. There are doubtless many of them also in our Keltic type, which, however, is generally lower-headed, although narrower than the Nordic Mediterranean. However, it seems quite improbable that the Raised Beach people were blond Nordics. It is much more likely that they were of the darker hair color and eye pigmentation found among our Nordic Mediterraneans, if they were not purely brunet.

The few Irish Megalithic crania are regarded by Howells as, like the Gallen series, a mixture of Neolithic and Bronze Age types, such as correspond to some of the Early Bronze Age or Round Barrow series of England. The question of interest here is whether archæology can reveal to us anything as to the origin of the Megalithic peoples and whether they came as a new wave of invaders, or were merely a mixture of Neolithic and later Bronze Age inhabitants. There seems to be a nearly general agreement among archæologists that the Megalithic culture was sea-borne along the Atlantic coasts and thence to Britain and Ireland. Ultimately it goes back to Spain and Portugal, from which it spread into France and Brittany. The clearest recent account we have consulted as bearing upon Irish Megalithic colonization, is that of Professor Stuart Piggott (1949, pp. 81–106). Rock-cut, communal tombs in the Mediterranean go back to the early third millennium and beyond, and in Southern France and Spain there are also stone versions built above ground. There was an early division into two types: "passage-graves" in which a more or less circular burial chamber is approached by a passage—the whole under a round cairn—and "gallery-graves"—merely elongated chambers, usually under a long mound. After a while these types become mixed up. The passage graves seem to have been carried by a sea-borne colonization from south Spain to Portugal, thence to Brittany, where the other type is present, apparently as a result of a land movement from the Gulf of Lyons and the region of the Pyrenees.

Piggott states that an important area of colonization for the bearers of the gallery-grave culture was at the head of the Irish Sea. It has been named the Clyde-Carlingford culture because its main ports of entry seem to have been around Carlingford Lough in Northern Ireland and in the Clyde estuary. This culture spread over the southern islands of the Hebrides, Aran, Bute, Kintyre, Galloway in Scotland, and southward to the Isle of Man and Anglesey. In Ireland it comprises most of Ulster with outlying colonies as far as Mayo and Sligo. The tombs undergo progressive degeneration as they go westward. The ancestors of these Clyde-Carlingford tombs belong to the gallery-grave group of south France and the western Mediterranean. The crescentic facades of these tombs are a conspicuous feature of chambered tombs in Sardinia. The pottery has a very close parallel in a class of Neolithic wares in south France. Therefore the origin of this colonization is to be looked for in France and the Pyrenees. A branch of the British Windmill Hill Neolithic culture, ultimately of Yorkshire origin, arrived in Ulster approximately at the same time as the Clyde-Carlingford culture and Piggott thinks it more probable that the Irish branch of this culture is due to a secondary colonization from Scotland than to a new move from Continental Europe.

Here, then, there seems to be some evidence of a Megalithic colonization. Whether it brought new physical types cannot be stated; it is only probable that if they were new types, they consisted of lower- and wider-headed dolichocephals or mesocephals than the earlier Neolithic peoples. But this is only a guess. The passage-graves in Ireland can be traced, according to Piggott, to a later colonization which made its first landfall in the neighborhood of Dublin. These grouped passage-graves have been classed as the Boyne culture, from the famous New Grange tomb near the Boyne. The culture can be traced spreading westward to Sligo Bay and northward into Antrim. Scattered sites have been found as far south as Limerick. However, Raftery states that the number of passage-graves in Ireland does not total more than 80. The pottery found and the ornamentation of the tombs go back to

Iberia and probably to Brittany as well.

There is a most intriguing similarity between the distribution of the passage-graves, as indicated by Raftery's map (1951, pl. V, opp. p. 80), and that of our tiny Pure Mediterranean type, which numbers only 33 individuals. There is a concentration of these tombs in Sligo and of the Pure Mediterranean type in our combined county series in Sligo-Leitrim-S. Fermanagh-W. Cavan. The earliest type of the passage graves, the *tholos* tombs, are found on the east coast from Carlingford Lough to Wicklow Head. Other passage-grave groups are found also in this area. The few scattered Pure Mediterraneans occur, often singly, in 13 of 19 of our county subgroups. None is found in West Donegal, the Arans, Kerry, Cork, Limerick, and E. Cavan-Monaghan-Armagh. Areas which have yielded more than one of these individuals are: Sligo-Leitrim-S. Fermanagh-W. Cavan—8, Longford-Westmeath—6, Offaly-Leix-Kildare—4, Meath-Louth-Dublin—3, Antrim-Down—3, Clare—2. Beddoe (1885, p. 267) makes the following interesting observation about the area in which our handful of Pure Mediterraneans is concentrated.

. . ."in the mountains about the battle-field of northern Moytura, between Sligo and Roscommon, I met with the swarthiest people I have ever seen. Seven out of thirty-three had quite black hair, and many had dark eyes. A few had handsome features of the so-called Kimbrian type, rather short heads, spade faces, and aquiline noses and might have been Walloons; but most of them approached the commoner types; still I was more reminded of the South Welsh than anywhere else in Ireland."

The fact that in the living population there are a few individuals of the Pure Mediterranean type born here and there, but especially in the Midlands where the passage-graves have a restricted concentration, may seem an unimportant coincidence. Its interest lies in the fact that, with all of the archæological evidence pointing to immigrations ultimately from such distant places as Spain and Sardinia, and with all of the persistent Irish lore about the early inhabitants being small, dark, long-headed people, these few Pure Mediterraneans furnish the only real indication that a population of this description ever existed in Ireland. The few skulls reported by Martin as of probably Megalithic origin are not at all

well attested as the actual primary interments of Megalithic tombs. Most burials found in the Megalithic, whether they are in passage-graves, gallery-graves, horned cairns, or simple dolmens, are cremations.

If our minute Pure Mediterranean group were composed of individuals whose sole distinction was the possession of pure dark eyes, the matter might be dismissed as a mere genetic accident, or they might be referred to casual aliens who have drifted into Ireland from time to time bringing genes for dark eyes. In fact, the latter is still a quite plausible explanation. But our little Pure Mediterranean group has a considerable number of peculiar features. It has the highest mean age, and the lowest average weight and stature of all morphological types. It has the relatively narrowest and deepest chests, the lowest relative sitting height, the highest cephalic index of the dolichocephalic types, the lowest head height, the lowest height-length index, the lowest mean minimum frontal diameter, the lowest zygo-frontal index, the shortest total face height, and the lowest facial index among the long-headed types. It also has quite a few outstanding morphological features which have been discussed elsewhere in this work.

The metric features of the Pure Mediterranean type accord very well with those that can be deduced from the measurements of the few dubiously Megalithic crania that have been preserved. We may then consider the possibility that our Pure Mediterraneans represent the surviving remnant of the Megalithic people. It is our opinion that the Carlingford-Clyde culture (that of the gallery-graves) and the passage-grave culture must have represented colonizations of considerable size. We take no stock in the theory that a few traders or Megalithic missionaries could have induced the preceding inhabitants of Ireland to build vast megalithic structures all over the island. If the passage-grave people or the gallery-grave people, or both, were small dark, dolichocephals, and if they indeed contributed a fairly large proportion of the strains that have gone into the composition of the present Irish population, the reader may well inquire why so very few of them (0.3 per cent of a sample of nearly 10,000 males) have survived in the contemporary Irish. The answer probably lies in the selective survival in Ireland of certain types and certain features. This subject has been treated extensively by the present writers elsewhere (Hooton and Dupertuis, 1951). Studies of this same sample of the Irish population by age groups clearly demonstrate that pure dark eyes, dark mixed eyes, and mixed eyes in general decline in frequency and ultimately disappear in the successively older groups of Irish males. So do dark skins and the more curved varieties of hair and also pigmented moles. While our tiny handful of Pure Mediterraneans is well dispersed through the age groups, there can be no doubt that some sort of selective influences have operated to eliminate from the Irish population, for the most part before late middle age, persons with dark skins and dark eyes. As one goes from age group to age group, it becomes increasingly apparent that the strongest Irish type in the matter of survival is the long-headed, dark-eyed, pure light-eyed Keltic type. It goes from strength to strength.

Pure dark eyes are supposedly dominant over light eyes in Mendelian inheritance, although this matter is not as simple as it once seemed. However, if there had been at some time or other, a ponderable proportion of dark-eyed people in the Irish population— say from 25 to 50 per cent—apart from selective factors operating against the survival of dark-eyed persons, we should expect that dark eyes would occur by Mendelian recombination in the mixed descendants in at least 12½ to 25 per cent. But if the dark-eyed persons always constituted a very small minority—say 5 to 10 per cent—it is conceivable that they would disappear entirely by accidental gene loss (the phenomenon known as "genetic drift"). Such a disappearance could occur if the few dark-eyed persons were dispersed in an overwhelming majority of light-eyed individuals. This would make an excellent explanation of the virtual absence of dark eyes in Ireland if we could suppose that the various immigrant stocks included very few with dark eyes. In consideration of the fairly high frequency of dark eyes in the population of Britain, which to a great extent is supposed to be the source of Irish colonization—Mesolithic, Neolithic, Iron Age, and historic—it is hardly conceivable that there were not many waves of immigrants which included very substantial proportions of persons with dark eyes.

It therefore seems that the evidence of selective survival of light-eyed persons and of progressive elimination of dark-eyed persons throughout the older age groups may afford us the best clue to a solution of the problem. Of course, this explanation raises the presumption that most of the dark-eyed Irish either die early in life or marry light-eyed mates and leave only mixed-eye progeny. (In this connection there should be introduced data having to do with the percentage of dark eyes in Irish females. Our recollection of the Dawson material is that they are considerably more common.)

Because it is perfectly clear that such previous observers of Irish pigmentation as Beddoe (1885, pp. 3–4) have classified dark mixed eyes as dark eyes, it has been desirable for us to map by county groups and to tabulate by morphological types the percentages of mixed eyes that have been classified as *very pronouncedly dark* and *pronouncedly dark*. These two categories in the morphological type series total 11.1 per cent, of which 3.4 per cent are very pronouncedly dark. The type in which these very dark mixed eyes are commonest is the Nordic Mediterranean with 13.3 per cent of the combined categories, followed by the Nordic Alpine with 11.3 per cent, and the Dinaric with 10.3 per cent. A few occur in the Predominantly Nordic type. In our Nordic Mediterranean type series there are 364 men who would be classified as dark-eyed by less meticulous observers than Dupertuis. The county distribution is instructive, because it shows a band of dark-mixed eyes in considerable strength stretching from West Donegal and Sligo Bay southeast to include Longford-Westmeath and the inland group of Offaly-Leix-Kildare together with the coastal Meath-Louth-Dublin group. This area again corresponds not only with the concentration of our Pure Mediterranean type, but also with the passage-grave area. However, the highest concentration of dark mixed eyes occurs in Antrim-Down with 19.9 per cent and in Waterford-Wexford with 20.5 per cent. The former is, of course, the Carlingford-Clyde cultural center and the latter is its most southerly extension. However, dark eyes in Waterford-Wexford are probably attributable to much later invasions than those of the Megalithic people.

There are certain other indications of brunet features extending through the Midland region, which are not caught in our type sortings but may be discerned from the study of various distribution maps of anthropometric and morphological features taken separately. Thus it is apparent that this is the region of Ireland where the most curly, deep-waved, and frizzly hair occurs (although the extremely curved forms of hair are lacking in our Pure Mediterraneans). It is an area of rather short faces, considering its prevalent dolichocephaly, and of slightly elevated nasal indices.

While we do not think that we have proved, by any means, the association of our Pure Mediterranean type with the descendants of the Midland and Ulster Megalithic colonists, we believe that we have, at any rate, established a reasonable probability of such identification.

We may now proceed to a consideration of the relation of Bronze Age archæological finds to our present distributions of morphological types. We have already seen that the very few Bronze Age crania from the Short Cists, recorded by Martin, correspond clearly enough to two of our main brachycephalic types—the Dinaric and the Nordic Alpine (and probably to the small East Baltic type, since pigmentation information on the basis of which the East Baltic and Nordic Alpine types are distinguished from each other is naturally unavailable for crania).

Raftery (1951, pl. IX, opp. p. 128; pl. XII, opp. p. 145) publishes two distribution maps showing the locations of Early and Late Bronze Age sites. The Early Bronze site maps are fairly evenly distributed over the island with the exception of sparsity in western Galway, northwestern Mayo, southwestern Clare, and the adjacent parts of Kerry and the Waterford-Wexford southeastern corner. There is, however, a tremendous concentration of Early Bronze Age sites in the valley of the Bann River and generally in Antrim-Down. This distribution makes no particular sense in relation to the concentrations of our brachycephalic morphological types. In fact, it may be said that, on the whole, the areas which are heaviest in brachycephaly today tend to be rather poor in the Early Bronze Age sites. The Bann River valley is in a region where

today the Dinarics are the strongest of the round-headed morphological types, but they are greatly in the minority.

The distribution map of the late Bronze Age sites is very much like the preceding, with a very similar concentration in the Bann River valley and generally in Antrim-Down. There are several other smaller concentrations—in the Lough Erne region, along the upper Shannon, and just south of Dublin. None of these seems significant in relation to brachycephalic modern type concentrations. If the Bronze Age settlers were Nordic Alpines and Dinarics or East Baltics, they were concentrated in areas far to the east and north of their present places of strength. Both of these distribution maps of Bronze Age sites look as if the cultures represented came in through Antrim-Down, were concentrated there, and spread out in scattering fashion to the south and west. We must here recall the skepticism of Drs. Movius and Hencken with regard to the relevance of incomplete archæological distribution plots to the arrangement of present morphological types in Ireland.

There seems to be a radical disagreement between authorities on Irish archæology as to the implications of changes in culture from period to period. Raftery (1951, p. 180) rather astoundingly maintains that "the first people who reached this country after the retreat of the ice were the only true immigrants in mass." He would ascribe all the successive cultural phases to this same people, and he even suggests the possibility that Keltic may have been spoken in Ireland from Stone Age times. On the other hand, Macalister, in common, we suppose, with most other students of the subject, attributes the principal cultural innovations, such as the beginning of the Megalithic cult and the introduction of a full Bronze Age, to new colonizations, whether of small groups or of masses. Leaving out of account the sudden appearance of brachycephals in the Bronze Age Short Cist burials, there is sufficient plain archæological evidence to support the supposition that at least two groups of invaders came into Ireland in this period. The first of these were the Beaker Folk whose incursions into lowland Britain are known by a very large number of burials (between 600 and 700 according to Piggott,

1949, p. 111), as well as a few habitation sites, with associated and extremely characteristic pottery. It is almost as well attested as any postulate in archæology that these people came from Holland and the Rhineland, although in the Rhineland their culture and they themselves seem to have been the result of intermixture of the Battle-axe people of the north and brachycephalic stocks of ultimately Iberian origin, who early acquired a knowledge of the use of copper. The Beaker Folk in Britain were usually tall, heavy-boned brachycephals, presumably mainly of the type that we call Dinaric. Some of them reached Ireland, certainly from Britain, although very few beakers have been found in the former country and these only in the north. While Raftery apparently thinks that these beakers are of various dates and imply nothing of importance with respect to invasions, Macalister (1949, pp. 82–88) is convinced that Ireland was not only invaded by the Beaker Folk but ravaged from one end to another with the consequent destruction of the Megalithic civilization. He ascribes the rarity of beakers in the archæological finds to the supposition that the Beaker Folk had given up making beakers, for the most part, at the time they invaded Ireland from Britain. He thinks that the brachycephalic Beaker men usually married dolichocephalic Irish women, citing Martin's opinion that most of the long-headed skulls in the epimegalithic tombs are those of females. The truth may lie between Macalister's conception of a mass conquest and Raftery's notion of a peaceful penetration of unaccompanied pots, but certainly the skeletal evidence in Ireland and all of the collateral evidence from Britain and elsewhere indicate that Macalister is more nearly right.

The second cultural incursion of the Irish Bronze Age is that of the Food-vessel people, whose burials in stone cists or in graves under barrows accompanied by characteristic pottery (partly in the Neolithic Peterborough tradition) occur in Yorkshire, in Scotland, and in Ireland itself. This group almost certainly came into north Ireland from Britain, probably after the Beaker Folk. Most of the Bronze Age brachycephals found in Irish tombs are of these Short Cist people, and they include both long-faced, and short, wide-faced brachy-

cephals (our Dinaric, Nordic Alpine and East Baltic types). Piggott states that certain cup-and-ring carvings, found on the slabs of several Food-vessel burials in Scotland, are concentrated in Ireland near the copper deposits of Kerry and Wicklow and have connections with similar carving in northwest Spain and Portugal. He suggests that this may indicate an Iberian origin of the physical type associated with the Food-vessels in Ireland, which he postulates (1949, p. 122) as ". . . a parallel and approximately synchronous event with the coming of the Beaker invaders to eastern Britain." Raftery divides the Food-vessels into two main types, the Bowl and the Vase types. The Bowl type is northern in Ireland, and in Britain is confined to the Highland Zone of Scotland. He thinks that most of the Bowl type of decoration is due to Beaker influence, while one or two motives are Neolithic B (Peterborough). The Vase type is found mainly in the Central Plain of Ireland, in the west, and in an area bordering on these two regions in the south. Foreign sources claimed for the origin of the Vase include northern Europe, Portugal, and the Pyrenees, but Raftery (1951, pp. 152–55), in accordance with his consistent hypothesis, regards the whole Food-vessel class as a local development.

The Early Iron Age in Ireland is variously dated as to its beginnings from 500 B.C. to 200 B.C. It is generally agreed that it ended about A.D. 450. Raftery's map of Early Iron Age sites (1951, pl. XIII, opp. p. 160) shows them to be much fewer than the Early Bronze or Late Bronze Age sites, but with not dissimilar concentrations. There is a clustering of sites in northern Antrim and in the northern part of the central plain. They are very rare in the peninsular areas, except West Donegal, and in general quite sparse below an east-to-west line extending from Galway Bay to the east coast just north of the Wicklow mountains. We have already pointed out the rough similarity of this distribution to the areas of concentration of Keltic type, our Nordic Mediterranean type, and, to some extent, of our Predominantly Nordic and Pure Nordic types. The Iron Age burials are usually in long cists, although some short cists of Bronze Age tradition were probably used into the first century B.C. There are also occasional cremations, and Raftery (1951, p. 206) cites a cairn in the full Passage-grave tradition, complete with typical decoration, and erected and used in the Iron Age. Further, there are cremations in small pits under mounds, often extended burials as secondary depositions in earlier mounds, and commonest of all, burials in flat earth, perhaps previously marked by Ogham stones or by wooden pillars.

On the whole, Iron Age finds are rare in Ireland and Iron Age culture was poor in comparison with preceding periods. Macalister (1949, p. 213) wishes to bring in as Iron Age invaders tall, yellow-haired people with narrow skulls, Teutonic or Scandinavian in blood. He regards the invasions as numerically small, and consisting chiefly of men. Raftery, according to his general conclusion about archæological cultures and invasions, sees no colonization, but for the most part, merely trade influences. He admits the coming of the Menapii, the Brigantes, and the Cauci of Ptolemy, but points out that all of these tribes who took refuge in Ireland were located in the southeast, where no Iron Age finds have been recovered. On this matter we must prefer the explanations and reconstructions of T. F. O'Rahilly, a full discussion of whose identifications follows in the next section.

CORRELATION OF MORPHOLOGICAL TYPES WITH LEGENDARY, HISTORICAL AND LINGUISTIC DATA

WHILE the authors of this monograph profess no competence in matters of Keltic linguistics and Irish legendary history, it is of considerable interest to see how the present distribution of morphological types in Ireland may relate to the reconstruction of Irish history by recent acknowledged authorities. The historical sketch below is based upon the views of T. F. O'Rahilly (1946), who argues convincingly that the old theory identifying the Bronze Age invaders of Ireland with Q-speaking Kelts is incorrect and that the Goidels were the last Keltic invaders and were preceded by three groups of P-speaking Kelts.

O'Rahilly advances reasons for believing that the names given in Ptolemy's description of Ireland are actually those recorded by Pytheas in his last geographical work dating back to about 325 B.C. Many of these names he regards as evidence that the Keltic spoken in Ptolemy's Ireland was of the Brittonic type (*p* instead of *q*).

The first Keltic invasion of Ireland, according to O'Rahilly, was that of the Priteni or Cruthin, who are thought to have come from Britain about the fifth century B.C. The Cruthin preserved their individuality best in the north of Britain, where they were known as the Picti. In early Christian Ireland remnants of the Cruthin survived in scattered communities, mainly in the northern half of Ireland, and especially in the northern half of Antrim and the west of Down. Presumably they were, at one time, spread over the larger part of Ireland. Since the Iron Age crania from Britain and Ireland are usually long-headed, it seems probable that the descendants of the Cruthin are to be identified with one of our dolichocephalic Irish morphological types, either the dark to medium brown-haired and mixed-eyed Nordic Mediterraneans, or the dark-haired, blue-eyed Keltics. They may belong to both of these types. We shall see below how the details of historical and legend-

ary location of tribes fit with this tentative identification.

The second Keltic invasion, according to O'Rahilly, was that of the Builg, Fir Bolg, or Bolgi, who are identified also with the Erainn. The last (like Ptolemy's Iverni) were especially those Builg who dwelt in the south of Ireland. They were already in a position of dominance in Ireland before 325 B.C. Although they were especially associated with Munster, they were ultimately widespread in Ireland, in districts as far apart as Antrim and Kerry. O'Rahilly thinks that they invaded Ireland from Britain, first landing in the south.

If these Irish Bolgi were anything like the historical Belgae of Cæsar, they were of mixed pigmentation and headform, presumably mainly of Nordic and Alpine descent. Their descendants may well be represented by our Nordic Alpine type, but they could also belong to any one of our morphological types, with the probable exceptions of the numerically insignificant Pure Mediterranean, Pure Nordic, and Predominantly Nordic types. However, as we shall see, there are vague indications that some of the Fir Bolg may have been long-headed.

The third invasion was that of the Lagin, who, according to O'Rahilly, came from Armorica about 300 B.C. The Lagin were accompanied by the closely related Domnainn and Gálioin. The Lagin landed on the east coast and seem to have conquered a considerable part of Leinster and Connaught, but made little impression upon Munster and Ulster. In pre-Goidelic times the province of the Lagin seem to have been a narrow strip of coast between Dublin and the Boyne, but one of the tribes of south Antrim was probably of Laginian origin and they were well established in Connaught. In early historical times the Domnainn were centered in northwestern Mayo, but, before the Goidelic invasion, O'Rahilly thinks that they were politically dominant in all of Connaught. The Lagin are supposed to have defeated the Fir Bolg and to have driven their remnants to the west of Connaught, and, especially, to the Aran Islands. There are two stone forts on the Arans which, according to legend, were constructed by the Fir Bolg. O'Rahilly accepts this tradition and conjectures that the forts were built about the second century B.C. The Fir Bolg were also supposed to be numerous to the east and south of Galway Bay.

The supposed province of the Lagin along the east coast of Ireland is a part of a belt extending from the Carlingford Lough to the northern boundary of Wexford and then inland to the Shannon, which is the area of our heaviest concentration of the long-headed, dark-haired, blue-eyed, Keltic type. There is more evidence for connecting this type with the Laginian Kelts which will be set forth later.

The fourth Keltic invasion was that of the Goidels. O'Rahilly (1946, pp. 147–53) identifies the Quariates, an Alpine tribe mentioned by Pliny, as a remnant of the Q-Kelts which survived in the Alpine region of Gallia Narbonensis in Roman times. From various linguistic evidence he infers that the Goidels came originally from the southeastern part of Gaul, where the Quariates resided. From that region a band of Q-speaking Kelts first migrated to the west coast of Gaul not later than 120 B.C., whence they invaded Ireland sometime before the rest of Gaul was brought under Roman rule in 50 B.C. (O'Rahilly, 1946, pp. 207–08). He thinks that the Irish evidence favors the second half of the period 150–50 B.C. as the date of the Goidelic invasion.

From the eighth century onward various learned Irishmen were reconstructing the history of their country in pre-Christian times in a compilation known as the Lebor Gabala, with a subsidiary purpose of unifying the country by obliterating the memory of the diverse ethnic origins of the earlier peoples. Since the earlier non-Goidelic Keltic tongues had already been extinguished, it was desirable to discount the view that the Goidels were comparatively recent comers. Hence the date of the Goidelic invasion was deliberately pushed back to somewhere in the second millennium B.C., and a few tribal names of

pre-Goidels (Fir Bolg, Gálioin, Domnainn) were assigned to settlers of non-Keltic origin whose invasions were pushed still further back. The later Keltic tribes, or such of them as had retained a modicum of independence, were endowed with fictitious Goidelic genealogies (O'Rahilly, 1946, pp. 193–208).

In legendary history the Goidels are supposed to have come from Spain, because it was believed that Hibernia was derived from Iberia. The reason for this belief also rested in part upon the ancient supposition that Ireland lay between Britain and Spain. According to tradition the Goidels landed in two parties, one in west Munster, the other in north Leinster. The Munster landing was in the estuary of Kerry known as the Kenmare river. According to legend Munster at this time was ruled by two kings of the Erainn. Subsequently, it may be deduced from the involved and contradictory mass of mythology, the Goidels acquired the rule of Munster. Traditionally this achievement was by agreement rather than by conquest.

The Midland Goidels were Conaught, "descendants of Conn," and established themselves in Tara, a short distance from the east coast. This remained their capital down to the seventh century. They also pushed westward across the Shannon and conquered the province now known as Connacht (Connaught). Ultimately the name Connachta was applied only to the men of the western province. As late as the fifth century A.D., the Goidelic conquest was still incomplete and the Ulster Ulaid (the Builg or Fir Bolg) were still challenging the rule of the Midland Goidels. Three of the sons of Niall, the second historical Goidelic king of Tara, finally overthrew the Ulaid and razed their capital, Emain, in Armagh. They then established for themselves kingdoms in northwest Ulster and founded a group of vassal states in Ulster known as the Airgialla. The Ulaid were driven eastward into County Down and their kinsmen, the Dal Riata, were confined to a small territory in the north of County Antrim. A body of the Cruithin of east Ulster, who had hitherto been vassals of the Ulaid, were formed into an independent state occupying the greater part of Antrim and the west of Down. The vassal states were in central and south Ulster and the kingdoms of the three sons of Niall corresponded more or less to the present Donegal.

The above is the historical reconstruction of O'Rahilly of the Goidelic conquest of Ireland. It is summarized here because it may throw light upon the present distribution of morphological types in Ireland. If the Goidels came from southeastern Gaul not long before 50 B.C. and were ultimately of Alpine origin, it is very likely that they were predominantly brachycephalic and of mixed pigmentation. The odds in favor of Goidelic brachycephaly are much higher than of Builg brachycephaly if the latter came from Armorica, or any where in the north of France where the Iron Age Kelts, on the basis of skeletal material, may be said to be predominantly dolichocephalic or mesocephalic, although doubtless with some brachycephalic admixture.

Kerry, the site of the landing of the Munster Goidels, with the neighboring counties of Cork, and Limerick, and Clare, constitutes the most brachycephalic area of Ireland. In the modern population of Ireland we have recognized three brachycephalic types which together comprise some 38 per cent of the modern male population. These types are concentrated in the west and especially the southwest, with extensions along the south coast and through Wexford. There is also a considerable representation of brachycephalic types in central Ulster. They are rarest in the Midlands and in eastern Ulster (Antrim and Down). One of these types, called Dinaric, is very narrow-nosed and usually long-faced, and may be of almost any pigmentation combination. There are even a very few individuals of this type who have pure brown eyes (10). This is the tallest of the brachycephalic types and is most heavily represented in Clare, but with secondary great strength in Kerry, Mayo, Tipperary-Kilkenny, and Limerick. It is less evenly distributed in the areas of brachycephalic strength than the second great round-headed type, the Nordic Alpine. This latter type is broader of nose and shorter of face, also somewhat shorter in stature. The third type, East Baltic, is really a subdivision of the Nordic Alpine, and includes all those round heads with nasal indices over 63 who have ash blond, golden, and red

hair, with light eyes. It is numerically very small, 1.1 per cent of the total Irish sample. The Nordic Alpine type is more clearly and evenly marginal in Ireland than the Dinaric or East Baltic types. It is very strong in all of the western peninsular areas and along the whole of the south coast. The few rufous East Baltics have two great areas of concentration, Kerry and Cork in the south, and central Ulster (West Donegal, Tyrone, Londonderry).

Some of these brachycephals must be descendants of the Bronze Age pre-Keltic invaders of Ireland, but it is impossible to state from the consideration of the few Bronze Age skulls available for study that the latter were exclusively Dinarics, Nordic Alpines, or East Baltics. They may have been all three. If all of our brachycephalic types represent only the descendants of the Bronze Age people, it is hard to see why they in particular should have been displaced so generally to the barren peninsular areas, as contrasted with the other pre-Keltic inhabitants—the Mesolithic and Neolithic peoples. It is also very difficult to explain why they have so tenaciously adhered to Keltic speech merely because of their geographical position. On the other hand, if, as now seems probable, the last Keltic-speaking invaders, the Goidels, were predominantly brachycephalic, the relationship between Irish speakers and round-headedness becomes, perhaps, more comprehensible.

In some areas of Ireland, such as all of the south coast and the southwestern counties, the prevalent brachycephaly (which in Clare exceeds dolichocephaly in the population and in Cork, Limerick, and Mayo nearly equals it) was presumably due not so much to the pushing of Bronze Age scions into this area as to the landings and colonization of the round-headed Goidels. The strength of the brachycephalic elements in Connaught (especially in West Galway and Mayo) and also in West Donegal is more plausibly referable to the retreat of the Late Iron Age Goidels to these fastnesses than to the displacement of Bronze Age invaders, although these may well have formed a part of the brachycephalic population here as elsewhere.

We are now in a position to attempt a correlation of the various Keltic invasions of

Ireland with the present distribution of morphological types, disregarding, for the moment, any attempt to reserve certain morphological types for allotment to the pre-Keltic inhabitants of Ireland, or to subsequent non-Keltic historical invaders.

We may list in each of four provinces of Ireland the names of the tribes of the four successive invasions assigned to various counties and bring forward for comparison the distribution in the same regions of our several modern morphological types.

MUNSTER

Cruthin or Priteni. O'Rahilly identifies no tribal names in Munster with the Cruthin. However, in Munster both the Nordic Mediterranean and the Keltic types are very strongly represented, although in most of Munster they are numerically inferior to other types.

Builg, Bolgi, Fir Bolg, Erainn. Ptolemy's Iverni occupied what is now County Cork. In early historical times the following branches of the Erainn were in Munster: the Corcu Loigde in the western half of Cork, the Corcu Duibne in Kerry, the Muscraige in scattered regions between the river Lee and the north of Tipperary, the Desi in Waterford and the south of Tipperary, the Corcu Baiscinn in West Clare, the Dal Cairbre in Limerick and Tipperary. The whole of Munster is a stronghold of brachycephalic types, but the Nordic Alpines are relatively more numerous along the south coast than the Dinarics.

The Lagin. No Laginian tribes are identified by O'Rahilly as settled in Munster. However, the dark-haired, blue-eyed, long-headed Keltics, although relatively weak in this area, rarely fall below 15 per cent of the total population. In other words, the physical type which is predominant in the traditional Laginian area is not at all uncommon in Munster.

The Goidels. The southern Goidels traditionally landed in Kerry and gradually became supreme in Munster. The centers of greatest concentration of brachycephaly, of present life of the Irish language, both correspond to southwestern Munster, but O'Rahilly does not record the names of any specific Goidelic tribes in particular regions of Munster except the Eoganacht in north Clare and in north Cork. There are so many Nordic

Alpines, Dinarics, and even East Baltics in the southwest peninsula that it would be entirely unreasonable to assign them all, or even the larger part of them, to Bronze Age brachycephalic ancestors.

Conclusions on Munster. If, as seems probable, the Cruthin and the Lagin were mainly dolichocephalic, the former, perhaps, predominantly of a Nordic Mediterranean type and the latter of the Keltic type, the reinforcement of Bronze Age brachycephaly in Munster may well be due to the Builg and the Goidel.

LEINSTER

Cruthin or Priteni. O'Rahilly thinks that the Ui Enechglais of southeastern Wicklow and Kildare may have been an isolated branch of the Midland Loiges who were Cruthin. The Loiges were in a part of Leix and the Fothairt scattered through Leinster, but with their most important settlements in the southeast of Wexford and in the barony of Forth in Carlow. Other Fothairt were in Offaly and in north Wexford or south Wicklow. One branch was as far north as the town of Armagh.

Although few tribal names or locations of the Cruthin have survived, the whole of Leinster is a very strong Nordic Mediterranean area, but nearly as strongly Keltic in morphological type.

Builg, Bolgi, Fir Bolg, Erainn. Among the Fir Bolg or Erainn tribes assigned to Leinster are: the Osraige in Tipperary and Kilkenny, the Cualainn in the south of Dublin and the north of Wicklow, whom O'Rahilly equates with Ptolemy's Cauci; the Manapii of Ptolemy in Wicklow, possibly to be identified with the Monaig who later survived in Ulster; the Brigantes in south Wexford, possibly to be identified with the Ui Bairrche, who were driven out of Wexford by the Lagin and in historical times were settled in the southeastern corner of Leix, in adjoining parts of Carlow and Kilkenny, and in isolated settlements farther north in Kildare; the Benntraige in Wexford, who may have been a remnant of Ptolemy's Coriondi; the Dal Mesin Corb in Wicklow, and the Ui Garrchon in Kildare and the adjacent part of west Wicklow; the Calraige in Westmeath and Longford, but also in Sligo, Mayo, and Roscommon. The Luaigni, or Luigni, are regarded by O'Rahilly as Ivernian. They were the defenders of Tara and apparently occupied a territory in Meath and a portion of southeastern Cavan.

These Bolgic tribes are mostly in the south of Leinster in areas with a fairly strong brachycephalic minority. Wexford is especially strong in Nordic Alpines.

The Lagin. The province of the Lagin was the part of Leinster lying south of the mouth of the Liffey. Here were the northern Lagin in Kildare and the south of Dublin; the Ui Fhailge to the west, occupying parts of Leix, Offaly, and Kildare; and the southern Lagin (Ui Chenselaig) in Wexford and Carlow. Another tribe of probable Laginian descent was the Gailing, who were later settled as vassals and fighting men of the Goidels in the north of Meath, and the north of County Dublin. At some time before the Goidelic conquest the Lagin apparently occupied a strip of territory along the coast from Dublin to the Boyne. Apparently, the Lagin landed on the east coast of Leinster and conquered most of the province from the Erainn.

The Lagin area corresponds quite accurately with the area of greatest concentration of the long-headed, blue-eyed Keltic type. There is also a strong Nordic Mediterranean concentration in most of this region. Wicklow and Carlow, seats of the southern Lagin, are the most strongly Keltic in type of any of our Irish county areas. Offaly, Leix, and Kildare, are approximately equal in Nordic Mediterraneans and in Keltics.

The Goidels. Tuathal Techtmar, according to legend, was a Goidelic warrior who landed on the east coast of Ireland, subdued the non-Goidelic tribes, became king of Tara, and carved out a kingdom for himself in the Midlands. According to O'Rahilly, from the seventh century onward, the Midland territory was divided into a western kingdom called Mide, which included Westmeath, Longford, and most of Offaly, and an eastern kingdom known as Brega, which comprised most of Meath, the southern part of Louth, and the northern part of County Dublin. The whole territory was conquered by the Goidels from the Lagin and the Erainn. The Midland Goidels established themselves in Tara, a short

distance from the coast, and this remained their capital down to the seventh century. The southern Goidels apparently moved up through Munster by peaceful penetration, until they finally made Cashel their headquarters, perhaps as late as the fifth century A.D.

Conclusions on Leinster. If the Goidels were brachycephals, they have left comparatively weak traces in northern Leinster, but stronger representation in the descendants in the southern part of the province. The existence of the Pale, which in the time of Henry VIII was bounded by a line drawn from Dundalk to Kells, thence to Naas, and from Naas east to Dalkey, included parts of the modern counties of Dublin, Louth, Meath, and Kildare. It varied from time to time according to the strength of the English. This may explain in part the scarcity of brachycephals in this region, if they are, in the main, descendants of Goidels. Again, the Cromwellian transplantation of the Irish across the Shannon may well have effected the displacement westward of more round-headed Goidels, who were presumably the dominant group, than of tributary pre-Goidelic Keltic peoples, who were perhaps mainly dolichocephals.

CONNAUGHT

Cruthin or Priteni. O'Rahilly thinks that the Sogain, who dwelt among the Ui Maine, a tribe of probable Laginian descent in the eastern half of Galway and the southern half of Roscommon, were Cruthin. In Connaught the Cruthin were probably mixed up with the other pre-Goidelic elements. They retained their identity longest in Ulster.

Builg, Fir Bolg, Bolgi, Erainn. Among the Erainn tribes settled in Connaught, O'Rahilly mentions the Calraige, who were in Roscommon, Mayo, and, especially, in Sligo, as well as across the Shannon in Westmeath and Longford. The Luigni, partly in Leinster, also occupied territory in Sligo. They, with the Laginian Gailing, probably got this territory as a reward for fighting with the Kings of Tara in the Goidelic conquest of Connaught. The Fir Bolg, according to tradition, were overthrown in a battle at Mag Tuired, Sligo, by the Lagin. In one legend they were allowed by their conquerors to retain possession of Connaught, but in others they are forced to take refuge in islands outside of Ireland. However, O'Rahilly is certain that one of their refuge places was the Aran Islands.

Another tradition deals with the sons of Umor, who ultimately were settled in the west of Connaught, mainly near the coast. A poem by Mac Liac mentions 17 places or districts, of which 4 appear to be in Mayo, 7 in Galway, and 3 in Clare, which in ancient times was considered a part of Connaught. O'Rahilly identifies these sons of Umor with the Fir Bolg, who were defeated and driven westward into Connaught by the Lagin. He judges from Mac Liac's lists that the Fir Bolg were especially numerous on the east and south coasts of Galway Bay. West Galway and Mayo are very strong in brachycephaly, the former especially in the Nordic Alpine type and the latter in all three types of round-headedness. But neither the east shore of Galway Bay nor the Arans is notable for brachycephaly. The Arans are, in fact, a great stronghold of the Nordic Mediterranean and Keltic types. However, the Aran population is known to have absorbed a sizable English garrison resident there for many years, and these English soldiers may well have contributed to the predominant dolichocephaly of the present Arans and to other peculiarities of physique exhibited by the present male population of those inbred islands.

Ptolemy's Auteini, whom he places approximately in Galway, are thought to be identical with the Uaithni, who in historical times were in the northeast of Limerick and the adjoining parts of Tipperary, but who, traditionally, had dwelt west of the Shannon in earlier times. They were certainly non-Goidelic and may have been, according to O'Rahilly, of mixed Cruthnian, Laginian, and Ernean (Fir Bolg) descent.

The Lagin. The Gailing, who were Laginian (according to O'Rahilly), aided the Goidels in their conquest of Connaught and were rewarded with a grant in Mayo. In Connaught, Laginian tribes were well established as a result of their previous conquest of the province. There is no trace of the Lagin, as such, but the Gálioin and Domnainn, their associated tribes, are represented by several place names in various parts of Connaught.

In early historical times the Domnainn were settled particularly in northwest Mayo, but O'Rahilly thinks that their association with this wild district is due mainly to the Goidelic conquest of Connaught, since their traditional capital in prehistoric times was Cruachain in the north of Roscommon. Elsewhere they are listed as inhabiting districts corresponding to the baronies of Carra, Erris, and Tirawley in Mayo and Tireragh in Sligo. The Cattraige and the Gabraige of the river Suck in East Galway and the Delbna Nudat have been classed as Domnainn. The Ui Maine, whose territory comprised approximately the eastern half of Galway and the southern half of Roscommon, are considered by O'Rahilly to have been of Laginian descent. The Conmaicne, dispersed in historical times in various parts of Connaught and northwest Leinster, are also regarded as of Laginian descent. They occupied parts of Counties Westmeath, Longford, Leitrim, Mayo, and Galway.

The Goidels. At a fairly early but indeterminate period some of the race of Conn (the Goidels), pushed across the Shannon and conquered Connaught and their name was applied to that province in ordinary usage as early as the latter half of the seventh century. In early historical times they were divided into the Ui Fhiachrach, the Ui Briuin, and the Ui Ailella, of which the former two tribes were widespread through the province and the last, of little importance, in Sligo.

Conclusions on Connaught. The distribution of Keltic tribes in Connaught, as derived from O'Rahilly, does not clarify to any extent the present day distribution of morphological types in Ireland. The Arans, with only 27.1 per cent of the brachycephalic types, are one of the weakest areas in Ireland in round-headedness. They are second strongest in all Ireland in Nordic Mediterraneans, and the proportional representation of Keltics is also one of the highest in Ireland. If we suppose that the Arans are principally peopled by descendants of the Fir Bolg who retreated thither, we should have to suppose also that the Fir Bolg were probably, in the main, long-headed. But we know that the Cromwellian settlement planned to clean out all of the Irish from the islands off the coast of Connaught. That this was accomplished in the

Arans is doubtful. Nevertheless the population of these islands has undoubtedly been modified by the absorption of English garrisons long maintained there. Englishmen are more likely to be long-headed than round-headed. If the Cruthin, the Fir Bolg, and the Lagin were all of mainly long-headed type, and if they all tended to be forced into the wildest westerly parts of Connaught, we might reasonably expect an excess of long heads in those areas. But this is not the case. Mayo and West Galway have less than one per cent of excess of Nordic Mediterraneans; West Galway has 1.5 per cent excess of Keltics, but Mayo has nearly 4 per cent of excess both of Dinarics and of Nordic Alpines and West Galway has 2.4 per cent excess of Nordic Alpines and a deficiency of 5.6 per cent of Dinarics. Of course, there are enough long heads in both of these counties to accommodate the ancestors of the three waves of pre-Goidelic Keltic refugees. If we suppose only the Goidels to have been principally brachycephalic, we have to conclude that they, the last dominant Keltic group retreated furthest to the west, carrying with them their Keltic speech. The displaced Fir Bolg, Lagin, and the absorbed Cruthin would then be commoner in the eastern and better areas of Connaught, contrary to historical tradition, and their conquerors the Goidels would be the ones who ended up in the far western wilds. This does not seem very probable, unless we argue that the Goidels who were the overlords and conquerors of the earlier Keltic peoples hated the English so much more than their Keltic predecessors, who by this time also spoke Goidelic, that they walked over their prostrate forms in eastern Connaught in order to squat among the rocks on the coast. This argument raises the very strong probability that the Fir Bolg, if not the Lagin, included substantial brachycephalic elements. About the only other recourse is to fall back upon the theory that all of western brachycephals are descendants of pre-Keltic Bronze Age inhabitants who, because of their geographical isolation, adhered more tenaciously to their acquired Goidelic speech than did the Goidels themselves. The same reasoning would have to apply to the refugee Fir Bolg of the Arans, but they may have been long-headed.

There is another way out of this dilemma but before we commit ourselves to it, let us consider the distribution of Keltic tribes in Ulster.

ULSTER

Cruthin or Priteni. The remnants of these people are supposed to have retained their identity longest in North Ireland. After the overthrow of the Ulidian (Fir Bolg) rule of Ulster, one band of the Cruthin was formed into an independent state under the name of Dal nAraidi in South Antrim and North Down. This is the only Cruthin group identifiable in Ulster in historical times, although the Cruthin formerly must have been widespread throughout the province.

Builg, Fir Bolg (Erainn). The Monaig or Manaig, regarded as representatives of Ptolemy's Manapii, survived in the early historical period in two communities, one in the west of County Down and the other in the neighborhood of Lough Erne, in what was later Fermanagh. They were Builg. Other historical branches of the Erainn were the Dal Fiatach, representatives of the ancient Ulaid, in the east of Down, and the Dal Riata, ancestors of the Scottish kings, in the north of Antrim. Ptolemy's Darini, located approximately in South Antrim and North Down, were also Erainn. By the beginning of the historical period they had been submerged in the Cruthinian state of Dal nAraidi. Also the Voluntii of Ptolemy are identified as the Ulaid, whose traditional capital was Emain, near Armagh. In historical times they retained their independence as the Dal Fiatach in eastern Down. These Ulaid gave their name to the whole province of Ulster and were at one time the leading power in North Ireland. How far west in Ulster they originally dwelt is not stated by O'Rahilly, but after the Goidelic invasion they were restricted to the east.

The Lagin. The Galioin of North Leinster were employed as fighting men by the Goidelic kings of Tara. They helped to overthrow the Ulaid and some of them were probably rewarded with grants of land in Ulster. O'Rahilly states that the Gailine or Gailinne, in the south of Antrim, were said to have been of Laginian origin. He thinks that the Lagin made very little impression upon Ulster. But the Cianacht, who were Gailing, aided the sons of Niall in the conquest of Ulster and were rewarded with land in Derry.

The Goidels. The sons of Niall (Goidelic king of Tara) are supposed to have defeated the Ulaid and established kingdoms for themselves in northwest Ulster more or less corresponding to the present Donegal. In central and south Ulster a number of vassal states, the Airgialla, were established. Presumably these states were composed of descendants or allies of the Goidels. O'Rahilly mentions the names of some of these tribes or septs but does not identify them. Probably some of them, or even most of them, were pre-Goidels. The Mugdornai, for example, may have been Erainn. Some details are available concerning the areas of the kingdoms of Niall's sons in northwest Ulster, but these are irrelevant for our purposes. The descendants of the three sons of Niall in Ulster were known as the Northern Ui Neill.

Conclusions on Ulster. Although the Cruthin, who are identified with the Picts of Scotland by O'Rahilly, presumably retained their identity longest in the north of Ireland, only one group of them has been recorded as surviving in the state of Dal nAraidi in Eastern Ulster, after the Goidelic conquest. The Nordic Mediterranean type is the predominant type in Antrim and Down and in West Donegal, but yields to the Keltic type in the central counties of Ulster. The Erainn, and especially the Ulaid in Ulster, are supposed to have been driven into East Ulster by the Goidelic conquest. If we suppose them to have been brachycephalic in part, there are plenty of brachycephals throughout Ulster to represent them in the modern population. But all round-headed types in Ulster are weakest in East Cavan, Monaghan, and Armagh, together with Antrim and Down. In West Donegal the long-faced Dinarics are very strong, but in the central block the Nordic Alpines are in excess. Probably the Builg or Erainn were not exclusively round-headed. If they included a dolichocephalic type, their Belgic origin might make it more probable that it was the lighter-eyed Keltic type than the mixed-eyed Nordic Mediterraneans, on the supposition that, like the historic Belgae, they had some Germanic admixture which would

tend to lighten the hair and eyes. The relatively heavy concentration of the very rare red-headed, or blonde-haired, light-eyed, brachycephalic East Baltic type in central Ulster corresponds with a similar concentration in Kerry and Cork, where many Builg tribes are listed. However, it would be reckless to attribute much importance to the distribution of a type which comprises only 1.1 per cent of our total Irish sample.

The Lagin are listed as surviving, or settled in historical times, only in parts of Antrim and Derry, but the dark-haired, blue-eyed, long-headed Keltic type is somewhat stronger in the central area of Ulster. If the Lagin belonged to that type, as seems probable in Leinster, there must have been many more of them who settled in Ulster with the Goidels than O'Rahilly's accounts imply. Alternatively, they may well have shared with the Builg, or even with the Cruthin, in belonging to this type.

O'Rahilly names few Goidelic tribes. He usually refers rather to Goidelic kingdoms or dynasties. He is of the opinion that the Goidels were always a minority group which utilized vassal tribes, such as the Lagin, in their conquests. West Donegal, which was more or less coterminous with the Goidelic kingdom of Conail, one of the three sons of Naill, has a strong Dinaric representation, although the Dinarics are only third in frequency of types in that area. It is also the only Ulster area of strong Irish speech survival, but that fact may be irrelevant in this particular context.

In summary, if any sense at all can be made in the matter of the comparison of presumed Keltic tribal occupation and present distribution of morphological types in Ulster, it is only the following: east and west Ulster are areas of strong Nordic Mediterranean typology and possibly of Cruthin absorption or survival; central Ulster is very conglomerate in typology and it was here, at least in part, that the Airgailla or vassal states were established. It is especially above par in Keltics, in spite of the fact that it is not supposed to have been an area of Laginian conquest, except perhaps under Goidelic leadership in fairly late times.

GENERAL CONCLUSIONS ON RELATION OF MORPHOLOGICAL TYPE DISTRIBUTIONS TO KELTIC INVASIONS AND DISTRIBUTIONS

Let us now appraise in general the tentative identifications of morphological types with O'Rahilly's Keltic invasions and tribal locations to see whether they have any modicum of evidence to support them.

The first Keltic invasion, that of the Cruthin or Pretani, supposedly from Britain, was identified provisionally with the long-headed, dark-haired, mixed-eyed Nordic Mediterranean type, principally because that type is most widely distributed in Ireland, most numerous except in a few areas, and because one might reasonably suppose that if the first Keltic invasion came through Britain, the chances for long-headedness and darker pigmentation of the eyes would be better than in the case of subsequent invasions more strongly adulterated by admixture with blue-eyed, round-headed, and blond peoples from the regions of continental Europe where such characters occur most frequently. Remnants of the Cruthin survived into historical times in parts of eastern Leinster and eastern Ulster, which are strongly long-headed areas, and, generally speaking, predominantly Nordic Mediterranean. They are also usually weak in brachycephaly. But most of these regions are also strongly Keltic. The Cruthin or some of them, might have had pure blue eyes. On the whole, the identification of the Cruthin with the Nordic Mediterranean type is, to say the best for it, not improbable.

The Builg or Bolgi are supposed to have come through Britain and to be identified ultimately with the Belgae. If they were physically anything like the historical Belgae, they would probably be mixed in head form with a good deal of brachycephaly, but with a considerable tendency toward lightness of pigmentation. One might therefore guess that they would be represented by one or more of our brachycephalic types, especially those carrying lighter shades of hair and eyes. These would be the East Baltics and the Dinarics (in part). They are supposed to have landed first in the south, where they were perhaps most numerous. This, of course, is the strongest area in brachycephaly. In Connaught they were dispersed westward by the conquest of

the Lagin, and in Ulster they were subjugated and driven eastward by the Goidelic conquest. Dinaric types are very strong in Mayo and in West Donegal, but not particularly so in West Galway or in the Arans. They are weak in most parts of Leinster, from which the Builg were supposed to have been dislodged by the Lagin. Identification of the East Baltic type with the Builg is not contravened by the distributions. It is relatively strongest in Kerry, Cork, central Ulster, and Mayo. Of course, some of the Builg were probably long-headed—and may have belonged to almost any of our types except Pure Mediterranean. Again, the Builg identification is possible and even probable, but nothing more.

The third invasion, that of the Laginian tribes who landed on the east coast, from Armorica according to O'Rahilly, and conquered Leinster and Connaught, can be identified somewhat more plausibly with the dark-haired, long-headed, light-eyed Keltic type. The main difficulty with this identification is that in Munster and Ulster, on which the Lagin are thought to have made very little impression, there are still heavy representations of the Keltic type which cannot reasonably be attributed to Laginian ancestry. In Connaught, where many of the Lagin were pushed to the far west in Mayo and West Galway, according to tradition by the Goidelic invasion, the distribution of the Keltics does not well accord with this supposed event, since in all places except the Arans the wild westerly coastal areas are centers of brachycephaly.

Finally, a tentative identification of the Goidels with one or all of the brachycephalic morphological types was based largely upon the acceptance of O'Rahilly's argument that they invaded from southwestern Gaul at a relatively late time, because invaders from such an area and at such a time ought to carry more Alpine strains of brunet, broad-faced brachycephaly than any of the previous groups alleged to have come through Britain or direct from the Armorica area. This argument fits in well enough with the reinforcement of brachycephaly in the southwest by the invasion of the southern Goidels. However, in order to accept it in Leinster, we have to suppose that the round-headed element in that province was driven westward, or eliminated in some way, to a far greater extent than the preceding Keltic long heads who had been conquered at a fairly late date by the Goidels. If we can bring ourselves to believe that more of the dominant military caste or aristocracy were expelled from Leinster than the long heads who had been their vassals, we can still adhere to the identification. In West Donegal and Mayo the long-faced Dinarics are represented in considerable strength, but in the latter county the Nordic Alpine and East Baltics are proportionately strong, whereas in West Donegal they are somewhat below par. Clare is the strongest Dinaric county, and some of the Eogonacht settled in north Clare, but the tall, heavy, long-faced round head of frequently lightish pigmentation fits Builg specifications better than those of the presumptively Alpinoid Goidels.

It must be confessed that the identifications proposed above are by no means satisfactory or convincing. The difficulties are not eliminated if we switch back to the old theory that the Goidels were Bronze Age invaders and the Cruthin, Fir Bolg, and Lagin various non-Keltic predecessors. We merely push back the shaky identifications a thousand years or more.

Suppose that we change our identifications, turning them more or less upside down. How would it work if we made the Cruthin Dinarics, the Fir Bolg Nordic Alpines, the Lagin Nordic Mediterraneans and the Goidels Keltics? We should then have to suppose that the Cruthin were the Bronze Age round heads, or, at any rate, that they reinforced brachycephaly brought in by non-Keltic round heads, coming also from Britain and through the north of Ireland. Then the strongest type of Cruthinian ancestry would be concentrated in Clare, Cork, Kerry, and that region, whereas the Cruthin are not identified by tribal names in Munster, but mostly in Leinster and east Ulster. Then the Fir Bolg coming also from Britain, but invading from the south, would reinforce the southern and western marginal brachycephaly

as in our previous identification. The Lagins would then have to be Nordic Mediterraneans (coming from Armorica). This identification would not fit badly in Leinster, where Keltics and Nordic Mediterraneans have overlapping concentrations. But it would not go very well in Munster, where there were only small Laginian penetrations, although the Nordic Mediterraneans are only relatively weak. It would be still less of a fit in Ulster in which Nordic Mediterraneans are very strong, but in which there are supposed to have been very few tribes of Laginian origin. Distributions in Connaught would accord all right with this identification, but we should always have to suppose that many Nordic Mediterraneans were of pre-Laginian origin, because there are so many of them everywhere—far too many to be accounted for on the basis of the Laginian invasion.

Then, if the Goidels are to be Keltic in type, we are forced to accept the paradoxical situation that their area of highest concentration—eastern Leinster—is precisely the spot where the Goidelic language has vanished entirely. Did the Goidels sit right on and learn English while their pre-Goidelic vassals decamped westward, taking with them the Irish language? The only place where Goidelic speech goes with a Keltic type plurality is in the Arans.

On the whole, the identifications just proposed offer many more difficulties and less plausibility than those originally made. The first set of identifications, although by no means satisfactory, is, at any rate, preferable. Of course, one of our troubles is that waves of invaders are not invariably of different subracial or morphological types and all of one wave are not necessarily homogeneous as to morphological type. Even if such conditions of individual homogeneity and mutual diversity were satisfied, which would be very improbable, the populations in succeeding generations would have to refrain from interbreeding and stay put in their positions as described in the historical reconstructions, if a perfect fit of modern morphological types to ancient tribal distributions were to be realized. Furthermore, they would have to be immunized against admixture with latercomers and preserve geographical immobility from the fifth century A.D. down to the present, in order to secure this ideal fit of modern morphological types with ancient Keltic groups and locations. Naturally we are not so simple as to have hoped that these impossibilities—anthropological and historical—could be surmounted. Nevertheless, it was regarded as a task that should be attempted and in our opinion the results are not wholly worthless.

Some measure of validity certainly seems to us to appertain to the striking correspondence of the Laginian spread to the area of concentration of the Keltic type, which is the most distinctively Irish. Again, the reinforcement of brachycephaly in the south and in some other areas, after much pondering of the evidence, still, seems to us, as originally conjectured, to have been due firstly to increments of Builg round-headedness, and secondly to further additions of brachycephaly by the invasions and conquests of the Goidels. Before we consign our attempts at correlation to the waste-basket, let us consider the effects of later movements of peoples into Ireland and displacements of the population within the country during historical times.

CORRELATION OF HISTORICAL EVENTS WITH PRESENT DISTRIBUTION OF MORPHOLOGICAL TYPES

THE VIKINGS

IRELAND escaped Roman invasion and domination, and also those of the Anglo-Saxons. In 795, the Vikings began, and continued to plunder, Ireland for nearly a century. There was practically no harbor or landing place without fleets of pirates. Apparently no part of the island escaped their raids. In 836, they established their first fortified stronghold in Dublin, and from then on they began to conduct their raids from various fortifications, the most important of which may have been Dublin. By this time, they seem to have made settlements at different places. As early as 826, the Ulster annals speak of strangers in Meath in such a way as to convey the impression that they were residents (Shetelig, 1940, p. 51). Similar references occur a little later relative to the heathens from Inver Dea (Arklow) and the Norse of Lough Neagh. By this time, however, the Irish were uniting against these Norwegians and some bloody battles were fought. In 849 the first Danish Viking raids occurred, and they in turn attacked the Norwegians. It is of importance to note that the Danes are referred to as "the black strangers" who landed at Dublin and inflicted a severe defeat upon "the white strangers." The Danes apparently allied themselves with the Irish and after three years the allied forces were victorious. Nevertheless, it is clear that after 853, Olav re-established Norwegian power in Dublin. Seemingly, the Danes left Ireland some time after this. Between 856 and 859, mention is made of the Gall-Gaidil ("foreign Irish"), mercenaries who seem to have been the result of mixture between the Norse and the Irish and who had one Norwegian and one Irish chieftain. Shetelig (1940, p. 58) thinks that the bulk of them were Irish who had adopted Norwegian religion and habits after the first generation of the Norse invasion. They are of interest as indicating the process of amalgamation that was going on

between the native Irish and the invaders, a process which continued until the Norwegians and Danes lost their ethnic identity.

In 871, Olav went back to Norway to help his father and never returned. It appears that during his 20 years' reign in Ireland the Norse were trying to organize a domination over considerable portions of Ireland, Scotland, and the west coast of England. Place-names in England and Scotland indicate that an extensive Norwegian colonization was going on at that time, and it was during this period that the Norse occupation of the Isle of Man took place. In Ireland, this colonization probably also proceeded, but Shetelig (1940, p. 61) says that place-name material fails us in Ireland, probably because the two languages were so different that Norwegian place names could not be adopted into Irish speech with the facility that characterized their adoption into English. In any event, it is clear that Ireland received a considerable Norwegian immigration from about the middle of the sixth century, and that the Norwegian element attained a powerful position that was to endure for three centuries.

The kingship of Dublin was taken over by Olav's brother, Ivar, who became the progenitor of a line of Norwegian kings which lasted for the next hundred years. The Dublin Norwegians were defeated by the Irish and expelled from the country in 901, but it seems probable that the settled Norse population was allowed to remain. Shetelig thinks that the Norse were mostly in the sea-ports—Dublin, Cork, Limerick, and Waterford—and were concerned with commerce and shipping whilst the native Irish were largely countrymen. After the fall of Dublin, there is little information about the Norse status in the towns, and none at all about their inland settlements of which there must have been some, since they were avid for the acquisition of land. Later on, some Irish clans are encountered who regard themselves as descendants of the Norse, but who have given up Norse language and habits of life. At the battle of Confey in 916 a king of the Fenechlais (in Arklow) fought on the Irish side. Fenechlais is "*Feni Ecclesiae*"—i.e., Norsemen of the church (Shetelig, 1940, p. 67 and footnote).

In 913, enormous fleets of Vikings once more sailed into Waterford, which was an old Viking stronghold. Shetelig states that this invasion might have found support from a Norwegian population resident upon the banks of the fjord and along the river on the province of Gall-tir (Gaultier), "land of the stranger." The Norse operations began by the plundering of the province of Ossory, the conquest of Cork and Lismore. They then ravaged Munster and Leinster, defeated the Irish at Confey in Ossory, and finally retook Dublin in 916. There followed a period of Irish history in which the Norse were everywhere rulers of the Irish, from whom they exacted tribute. While the Dublin kings were the leading power, there were also Norwegian settlements on the west coast, Strangford Lough, Carlingford Lough, and Lough Erne. They were also established at Waterford, Wexford, and Limerick. The last was the most powerful Viking town in the tenth century, after Dublin. The fortification of the Vikings in Limerick probably dated from 922. Thence they proceeded up the Shannon as far as Lough Ree and even made incursions into Offaly and Westmeath. Then began fights between the Limerick Vikings, the Waterford Vikings, and the Dublin Vikings, apparently terminated by the destruction of the Limerick force at Lough Ree in 937. From now on the Dublin Norse were supreme. They ruled as petty kings, intermarried with the Irish, and probably accepted Christianity to some extent.

It is in the period of 964–77 that Mahoun, the king of Cashel, and his brother Brian Boru were fighting the Limerick Norse along the Shannon and generally in Munster. In 969 Mahoun defeated the Limerick Norse near Tipperary, burned Limerick, killed the men, carried off the women and children, went all over Munster killing the foreign warriors quartered on the population, and took hostages in Cork. In a subsequent fight against the Shannon Norse, who were supported by allies from the Isle of Man, the Hebrides, and by some Irish, Mahoun was murdered, but eventually Brian beat them all and sacked Limerick again (977). Brian finally captured Dublin, turned his army against the high-king at Tara and with united forces from southern Ireland, including Waterford Norsemen, became high-king of all Ireland in 1002. In 1014 Brian defeated the Dublin forces, who were aided by levies from all of the Viking areas of Western Europe, at the battle of Clontarf. Nevertheless, the Irish did not then take Dublin. The Norse settlements remained as before, but the Dublin kings now adopted Christianity.

It has seemed worth while to go into all of these historical events involving the Norwegians in Ireland, not only because it entails the listing of the principal fortifications and settlements of these invaders, which we can check as to their present population with regard to morphological types, but also because history makes it perfectly clear that the Norse were gradually absorbed into the Irish population in which they still constitute an identifiable element.

So far as we can judge from the few well attested crania of Norsemen that have been found in Ireland in burials with Norse gravegear, our Predominantly Nordic and Pure Nordic types conform to the Norse specifications. These Norsemen were certainly Nordics, for the most part, although the Danes were probably something else. Our combined Pure Nordic and Predominantly Nordic types total 704 men, or 7.4 per cent of the total morphological type sample, which consists of 9,521 individuals. The weakest representations of the combined Nordic types are in West Donegal (2.8 per cent), Mayo (4.0 per cent), Clare (4.7 per cent), Aran Islands (5.4 per cent), and Kerry (5.6 per cent). Nordics are then comparatively rare in the extreme western peninsular and insular areas, with the exception of West Galway and, in the southwest, Cork. West Galway has 8.8 per cent of Nordics and E. Galway-Roscommon 8.1. They are therefore present in comparative strength in this area. We are not able to find any statement that the town of Galway was a fortified Norse settlement, but the Norse must have frequented Galway Bay and probably some of the Nordic strains in West Galway and East Galway may be due to settlements here. Of course, the notorious western Ireland settlement of the Norse was at Limerick on the Shannon, but the entire county of Limerick shows at present 7.3 per cent of Nordics, which is slightly below the normal quota. The Viking town of Limerick was repeatedly sacked and destroyed and it seems probable that under Brian Boru there was a considerable destruction of the Norse in Limerick and Cork. Apparently the Norse survived the Irish reconquests a good deal better further up the Shannon. The town of Cork was frequently pillaged by the Norse in the ninth century; it was burned by them in 820 or 821. From 845 onward it was stated to have been in the possession of the Danes, but in 1012 it again fell in flames. The new city was then founded by the Danes on the banks of the Lee. In view of the Danish and Norwegian occupations of Cork city and harbor, it is scarcely surprising that the entire county yields today 7.0 per cent of the Nordic type, which is a little below par for the country.

The Norse are also said to have occupied a fortified place in Fermoy, North Cork, soon after 800. Tipperary and Kilkenny and Offaly-Leix-Kildare each show 6.6 per cent of their present male population of Nordic type. This is about what would be expected from these inland counties, which were often ravaged by the Norse, but did not include, so far as we are aware, any extensive Norse settlements, although the Norse early occupied a stronghold at Dun Almain, Kildare. The southeastern counties, Waterford and Wexford, have the second highest proportional representation of Nordics in all of Ireland (9.6 per cent). Here, of course, was a Norse stronghold of old and Shetelig mentions the fact that the Norse fleets coming again to Waterford in 913 may have had help from a Norwegian population already resident there. But Waterford and Wexford were even more famous as Danish strongholds and remained so up to the coming of the Anglo-Normans. The latter city was captured by Strongbow in 1171, the former in 1169.

At this point we may discuss the probable racial antecedents and morphological types of the Danes. Whereas the Danish Iron Age crania are a homogeneous, long-headed, low-vaulted group of tall stature, the modern population shows a mean cephalic index of 80.6 which is not subject to much regional variation (Coon, 1939, p. 334). Coon thinks that there has been a resurgence of the brachycephaly characteristic of Denmark in the Neolithic period, which he attributes to the Borreby type, a rugged, big-skulled, short- and wide-faced, leptorrhine or mesorrhine type of tall stature which he believes to be of Mesolithic origin (1939, p. 123). In any event, both in the Neolithic period and in modern times (Danish Bronze Age burials are mostly cremated), brachycephaly has been commoner than dolichocephaly in Denmark. The pigmentation of the modern Danes is also mixed and, apparently, there is more medium and dark hair than light hair, although Coon appears to gloss over this situation.

Generally speaking, eye color is 38 per cent light, 58 per cent mixed, and 3 per cent dark. Correlations from the discrete Danish data cannot be made, but Coon (1939, p. 335) notes the presence in Sams of a tall, blond, brachycephalic type and thinks that brunet pigmentation is not associated with brachycephaly. However, it may be deduced from Coon's recapitulation of the uncorrelated data on cephalic index, hair color, and eye color in Denmark that there must be a considerable proportion of the contemporary Danes who are round-headed, short-faced and have medium to dark hair and either light or mixed eyes. The Danes of today are separated from those of the period of Danish settlement and domination in Waterford-Wexford (A.D. ca. 800–1200) by an interval of about 750 years and the Danish invaders of Ireland from those of the Early Iron Age (ca. 500 B.C.-A.D. 100) by roughly the same elapsed time. However, it is more likely that the Danish Vikings resembled the people of today than that they resembled the restricted number of Iron Age invaders of Denmark. The latter would have been at least partially absorbed in the preceding largely brachycephalic population of Denmark.

In addition to its great comparative strength in Nordics, Waterford-Wexford is an area of very strong concentration of Nordic Alpines (23.7 per cent). So is Cork, another area of localized Danish settlement, but so also are Kerry, Limerick, Mayo, and to a lesser extent West Galway and Clare. In these counties there is no evidence, as far as we are aware, of Danish settlement. There are earlier and later elements in this population of both Waterford-Wexford and Cork which must have contributed Nordic Alpine types, but it is very tempting and not at all unreasonable to suppose that the Danes are in part responsible for the Nordic Alpine type and even perhaps for some of the Dinarics (18.3 per cent) in the contemporary Waterford-Wexford males. On the other hand, the Nordic element in these counties is certainly attributable to the Norse, and perhaps in a very minor degree to the Danes also, since the latter may have included some of that type. Of course, the later conquest by the Anglo-Normans may well have reinforced the Nordic type here as elsewhere. But the Norse are the only colonists of whom we may be sure as to their fundamental blondness and long-headedness.

Wicklow-Carlow has only 6.5 per cent of Pure and Predominantly Nordic types. We know that the Norse often plundered Wicklow and they are stated to have occupied a stronghold at Dunlevin in the western part of the county. They also had some sort of a fortified place or settlement near Arklow in the south of Wicklow.

Our strongest Nordic representation in any county group is that of Longford-Westmeath with 12.7 per cent. Some slight allowance has to be made for the youth of this county sample (the youngest of all Ireland) because many immature individuals have golden hair which later darkens. However, our Predominantly Nordic type constitutes the larger part of the Nordic sample in this county group and Predominantly Nordics are by no means always juvenile. This element, as well as the smaller representation of Nordics in Carlow and Kilkenny, is probably referable to the expansion from the lower Shannon of the Limerick Norse. Lough Erne was captured in 932 and thereafter much of Longford was colonized, and probably Westmeath also. The heavy Nordic representation in Roscom-

mon and in Westmeath is also in part attributable to the Norse settlements around Lough Dee.

In Sligo-Leitrim-S. Fermanagh-W. Cavan, the proportions of Pure and Predominantly Nordics also are above par (8.8 per cent). This again is the region of the Lough Erne conquest and presumed Viking settlements. In Meath-Louth-Dublin, the combined proportion of Nordics is 7.3 per cent, which seems a little small, in view of the priority of Dublin as a Norse settlement and of its long predominance. The feeble representation in our sample may be due to the fact that Dupertuis did not measure to any extent in large cities such as Dublin, but it seems more probable that the Norse element in the eastern coastal region suffered displacement across the Shannon in Cromwellian times, or before that at the hands of the Anglo-Normans, to a somewhat greater extent than in the parts further to the north, south, and west. E. Cavan-Monaghan-Armagh also has 7.2 per cent of Nordics, although it is stated that the same Turgeis who, in about 830 sailed up the Shannon and built a stronghold on Lough Ree, eventually established himself in Armagh and usurped the abbacy, after repeatedly sacking the monastery. His wife Ota is said to have settled at Clonmacnoise, near the Shannon in Leix, and to have profaned the monastery there with pagan rites. Evidently the Norse "got around" and it is not surprising to find traces of them today wherever they raided and settled according to historical data.

In Antrim-Down the percentage of Nordic types is 8.5 which is well above normal. As early as 839 the Norse had a fortification at Lough Neagh and were raiding Louth from there. They also had another stronghold on Carlingford Lough. In 851 the Dublin Norse defeated the Danes in a three days' battle at Carlingford Lough. The defeated Danes under their leader Horne then took service with the king of Ossory. So there must have been a Danish element in Down. Antrim-Down includes 15.2 per cent of Nordic Alpines and 13.8 per cent of Dinarics, both of which proportions are below par of these types in the whole of Ireland.

Ossory, according to Butler (1949, p. 20),

was a region which corresponded roughly with the present county of Kilkenny, enlarged to the north by several baronies in Leix and Offaly. This region is not particularly strong in Nordic Alpines (Offaly-Leix-Kildare, 16.3 per cent, Tipperary-Kilkenny, 13.6 per cent). However, the latter county group is one of the strongest Dinaric regions in Ireland (24.2 per cent), while Offaly-Leix-Kildare has only 14.6 per cent of Dinarics. Some of the brachycephaly in the area which was once the Kingdom of Ossory may then be Danish.

However, to return to Antrim-Down, a considerable proportion of the Nordic types in these counties is probably referable to Scottish immigrants rather than to original Viking stock. We may defer a consideration of this problem until we have dealt with the other large Ulster block: N. Fermanagh-E. Donegal-Tyrone-Londonderry. This central group has 9.0 per cent of combined Nordic types, ranking third in all of the Irish county blocks. These two mainly Ulster groups contribute altogether 87 of 704 combined Nordics (12.3 per cent). The sources of Norse blood in this central block are Loch Foyle in Londonderry where the Norwegians had a fortress and where they were defeated by King Aedh in 866; the Lough Neagh settlement; the settlements in the neighborhood of Lough Erne, and possibly others.

Our morphological types have been sorted for religious affiliation, but not by county groups. The total of Presbyterians who are of Pure Nordic or Predominantly Nordic type is 41. Now, all of these Presbyterian Nordics come from the Ulster blocks we are discussing, and it may be assumed that they are mostly of Scottish origin. They constitute 47.1 per cent of the 87 Nordics from Ulster. There are also 46 combined Nordics who belong to the Church of Ireland. They might be of English or of Viking origin, but hardly Scottish. All of them are also of Ulster provenience. It thus appears that the Nordics of Scottish origin in Ulster probably constitute something like half of all the Nordics yielded by the Protestant counties. Of the 50 per cent remaining (only 46 individuals) perhaps more of them might be ascribed to the English than to the Norwegians. However, none of the Protestant Nordics seems to have originated outside of the two Ulster blocks, and it may then be doubted that many of the 87 per cent of Catholic Nordics can be ascribed either to recent English or to Scottish ancestry.

If we cut the percentages of Nordics in Antrim-Down and N. Fermanagh-E. Donegal-Tyrone-Londonderry to half of their present value, we should arrive at 4.25 per cent for the former block and 4.5 per cent for the latter as the proportion of the present population which might reasonably be attributed to Viking ancestry, dismissing the English as a source of the type. These figures would reduce the Nordics of Ulster, apart from those of presumably Scottish origin, to about the proportions found in Mayo and Clare, which are weak in these types, but it would still be almost twice as high as the proportions of Nordics in West Donegal (2.8 per cent).

If we subtract all of the possibly Scottish Nordic from the 7.4 per cent of the total Irish male population that the Nordics comprise, we still have nearly 6.5 per cent left. But these are only phenotypically Nordic and can represent merely the survival in observable recombination of a much larger proportion of Nordic blood which must have gone into the Irish amalgam. Assuming that light eyes are not recessive in Ireland, or alternatively that there have never been enough of dominant dark eyes in the population to reduce recessive light eyes to their expected proportions, much of the absorption of an originally long-headed, blond element may have gone into the reinforcement of the medium to dark-haired Keltic type. This is the more probable because dark hair is almost certainly dominant over light, and because most light hair darkens with age (whether as a mere age change, or because of the late assertion of dominance in more heavily pigmented hair).

But, if we still have some 6.5 per cent of phenotypical Nordics, even though blond hair is probably recessive, there must be concealed in the population as much as three times that proportion which has been assigned to other morphological types than the Pure Nordic and the Predominantly Nordic. However, any such amount as 26 per cent of Nordic blood could hardly have been due to the Vikings.

Their period of colonization and the numbers involved would surely have been insufficient to make them responsible for more than a quarter of the present population. Either there has been some other sizable immigration of Nordics or else some other blond, non-Nordic type, like the East Baltic or certain subtypes of the Dinarics, has reinforced the phenotypical Nordic proportions by producing a recombination of fair hair, blue eyes, and long heads through the crossing of brachycephalic blonds with dolichocephals of darker hair color. Another possibility of explanation is that certain subtypes within the Keltic morphological combination, which is blond save for hair, may be heterozygous in their brown hair color and may produce a certain proportion of Nordic phenotypes. The Keltic morphological type is, in any event, closely related to the Nordic and may well carry a high proportion of Nordic genes in its composition. If the Keltic type regularly spawns a minority of Nordics, we might expect to find high proportions of Nordics in those county groups which are characterized by Keltic excesses. No clear relationship of this kind obtains. Some county groups that are very high in Nordics are comparatively low in Keltics, and vice versa. Some are low in both and some high in both.

We seem to be unable to resolve this problem. At the moment it seems necessary to leave it with the statement that there seems to be too many Nordic phenotypes in the present Irish population to charge up solely to the Vikings, or even to the Vikings and the Scots together. Either the Normans and the English must have reinforced the blond, long-headed strain, or some of the pre-Norse invasions must have been of the Nordic type. Macalister (1949, p. 213) believes that the Iron Age invaders were of what he calls a long-headed, tall, blond Scandinavian type, but we are acquainted with no evidence in support of this opinion, except the tortuous argument we ourselves have just presented.

There is also a distributional problem in connection with the Nordic combined types. A glance at the map (fig. 29) shows that the Nordic concentration extends from Antrim-Down through the central Ulster blocks and then south through Sligo, Leitrim, Roscom-

mon and west through Galway. Apart from the Longford-Westmeath high concentration, the Nordics in the Midlands are massed west of the Shannon, and generally in Connaught except Mayo. Of course, the Vikings apparently colonized all up the Shannon, but the present Nordics seem to have pushed to the west bank, except in Longford and Westmeath. The eastern part of the Central Plain in which they are neither very sparse nor highly massed, is a region of very high Keltic concentration (Wicklow-Carlow; Meath-Louth-Dublin; E. Cavan-Monaghan-Armagh) and this is true also of Offaly-Leix-Kildare. The maps create the impression of a primary concentration of Keltics and a secondary massing of Nordic Mediterraneans that may have forced the Nordic type westward across the Shannon. Even the Ulster counties show a heavier Nordic concentration in the center than along the eastern coastal strip of Antrim-Down. If we omit from consideration all of the Ulster Nordic extension, because of the complicating Scottish reinforcement, we still have the picture of a more or less crescentic Nordic band, bulged east of the Shannon in Longford-Westmeath and wrapped around the non-Nordic county of Mayo in the west.

Since the Cromwellian displacement of the Irish across the Shannon is usually considered to have affected principally the gentry and land-owners with such of their dependents as they could induce to accompany them, we must consider this and earlier similar expulsions of the eastern coastal pre-Norman upper classes at the hands of the Irish themselves from the time of Brian Boru to the Anglo-Norman conquest, and thereafter. It is clear from the historical record that the Norsemen, in the period after they had ceased merely raiding and had begun to colonize and to conquer, established themselves as kings and overlords very extensively in many areas of Ireland and that they intermarried with the Irish and were absorbed largely into the land-owning and ruling classes of the Irish tribes. It therefore seems probable that any expulsion of Irish land-owners from the eastern part of the central plain would include unduly high proportions, not only of the Norse who had retained their ethnic identity, but also of those who had become, in one way or another, kings or chiefs of the mainly Irish tribes. This seems the most plausible explanation of the thinning out of Nordic types in the Midlands east of the Shannon. For, after the time of the Anglo-Norman conquest, Pales were established along the east coast, of variable extent, according to the strength of the English, and also outside of many of the Norman-held towns. The peasant Irish were left in the eastern Midlands, and these, judging from general distributions today, and also from the data on the Keltic invasions, movements, and settlements presented by O'Rahilly, may have been principally of the Keltic and Nordic Mediterranean types. It is our opinion that the Goidels were largely brachycephals, and since before the coming of the Norse they had established themselves pretty generally as the rulers of the Irish tribes, they would naturally share with the gentry of Norse origin, the fate of expulsion to the less desirable lands beyond the Shannon.

The single passage of the works of the mediæval chronicler, Giraldus Cambrensis (1881, p. 139), that deals with the physical appearance of the natives of Ireland tells of some sailors who were driven by a violent storm to take shelter under a small island in the Sea of Connaught. When the storm had abated, they saw a small skin boat rowing toward them from the mainland.

In it were two men, stark naked, except that they wore broad belts of the skin of some animal fastened round their waists. They had long yellow hair, like the Irish, falling below the shoulders and covering great part of their bodies. The sailors, finding that these men were from some port of Connaught, and spoke the Irish language, took them into the ship.

Beddoe (1885, p. 267), who calls attention to this passage, remarks that they might have been ancestors of the people whom he saw on the island of Inishmurray, which lies off the coast of Sligo. Says Beddoe of the Inishmurray people:

They were a decidedly fair race and not uncomely: a few had remarkably long faces, narrow, but with the usual projection of the malar bones, very pointed chins, and aquiline noses.

If the informants of Giraldus were accurate, the Sligo blondness antedates all Anglo-Norman and English settlements of the region, whether or not it is ascribable to the Norse. Another passage of that perspicacious anthropologist, Beddoe (p. 268), is also worth quoting in this connection.

Ancient Irish poetry indicates that there was always great variety of complexion and hair-colour among the people, but that blue eyes and yellow hair were most characteristic of the higher ranks, or ruling caste. Some heroes however are described as having blue eyes and *black* hair, . . . a combination very rare out of Ireland.

I think it probable that the military caste or stratum of the Irish at the time of the Anglo-Norman invasion, was fairer than the bulk of the population, and that it has been more reduced, in comparison, by slaughter and emigration, while at the same time the fairer races of Great Britain have largely supplied its place.

THE RELATIONSHIP OF THE ANGLO-NORMAN CONQUEST AND OF SUBSEQUENT HISTORICAL EVENTS IN IRELAND TO THE PRESENT DISTRIBUTION OF MORPHOLOGICAL TYPES

WE CAN be certain that the Norman conquest of Ireland introduced no sub-racial or morphological types that were not already represented in the population, and the same can be said of further colonization by the English and whoever else arrived subsequently in sufficient force of numbers to count in the present day population of Ireland.

The best appraisal of the racial composition of the Normans is still that to be found in the classic work of John Beddoe (1885, pp. 93–96). However, that writer concerns himself mainly with the Normans in Britain and gives but scanty information concerning their racial effect upon Ireland. Beddoe recognizes the following elements in the army of William the Conqueror: Gauls belonging to the Belgic confederation, probably dolichocephalic and of mixed pigmentation; short, round-headed, dark people, "the true Celts of Broca," chiefly from the left bank of the Seine; Saxons from Bayeux, probably of the Nordic type; Scandinavians from the region of the Seine, Danes from the Cotentin, thought to be generally long-headed and blond or rufous. Beddoe thinks that the Norman leaders were mainly of true Scandinavian blood, but that the rank and file resembled the Normans of today, whom he describes as of two leading types: Kymric—tall, long-faced, aquiline-nosed, "with square forehead and usually darkish hair"; another type resembling the north of England people—hair darker than that of most of the English, but lighter than that found in Wales and the West, mesocephalic. Bretons in large numbers were included. Beddoe describes the Bretons from personal observations as prevailingly short, sturdy, with brown or black hair, "but pretty often with blue or gray eyes." The heads are short and broad, the faces likewise, with coarse features.

The foregoing lists, which are somewhat speculative, would include our Nordic and Nordic Mediterranean types, some of our Nordic Alpines, and quite possibly some Di-narics and even Keltics. In short, this inventory would include nearly everything we recognize in Ireland today. It is our impression that Beddoe may have overemphasized the Nordic elements in the Normans, as so many writers on racial matters have often been prone to do.

The ethnic composition of the Normans who conquered England is possibly less important to Irish history than the fact that the Norman conquest of Ireland was conducted through Wales, and probably with troops drawn largely from that part of Great Britain. In 1156 a deposed Irish king of Leinster, with the help of a letter from Henry II, went to Bristol and sought the aid of Richard de Clare, Earl of Pembroke, for the recovery of his kingdom. This, Earl Richard agreed, on consideration of his being given the hand of the daughter of MacMurrough (the Leinster tyrant), and agreed with two other Normans in Wales to invade Ireland the ensuing spring. The first contingents landed at Wexford in 1169 and secured the submission of the Danes of Wexford. The next year de Clare himself, known as Strongbow, landed at Waterford. The Norman leaders were mostly near relations and descended from a Welsh princess. These Normans had been one hundred years in Britain before invading Ireland, and a body of them, principally Flemings, had settled in the southern part of Wales along the Bristol Channel, by St. David's Head, where they could see Ireland. Professor J. V. Kelleher is of the opinion that the rank-and-file of the invaders were Welsh. At any rate, whatever may have been the ethnic antecedents of Strongbow's army, it is stated that he settled down among the Irish, married an Irish woman and became to all intents and purposes Irish, as did his captains. Prendergast (1922, p. 25) is of the opinion that the early English conquerors everywhere were assimilated in this fashion, the Irish retaining the land and the English becoming overlords who quickly grew

223

to be Irish in language, customs, and sympathies.

In connection with the startling excess of blondness in Waterford-Wexford and its possible relationship to Norse and Anglo-Welsh settlements, it is interesting to reproduce the comment of that skilled observer, John Beddoe (1885, pp. 264–65).

The people of Forth and Bargy baronies, which form the southern peninsula of the county of Wexford, are said to be descendants of a colony from Pembrokeshire. Their character is said to be more English than Irish, and I should say the same of their appearance. It will be remembered that southern Pembrokeshire is more Anglo-Flemish than Welsh.

North and west of these baronies, in the county of Wexford, and in the city and neighborhood of Waterford, appears, as I have said elsewhere, a tall, fair race, which extends, with some modifications, up the northern bank of the Suir, across the Golden Vale of Tipperary, into the county of Limerick. The Wexford men, among whom countenances quite Norwegian in aspect are pretty numerous, have the reputation of being peaceable and industrious, but bold and fierce when roused: they were the backbone of the rebellion of '98.

When Henry II came to Ireland with an army, he fought no battles, but took hostages at Dublin, Waterford, and Cashel, and received the homage of Roderick O'Connell, the high king. The Norman overlords succeeded in occupying the open plains and fertile valleys and the east coast from Bray to Dundalk, but in the more defensible regions, centers of resistance were preserved—the O'Neills in Tyrone and Armagh, the O'Donnels in Donegal, and the Macarthies in Cork. The situation was very similar in the reign of King John, with Irish submissions but no displacements.

Generally speaking, it appears that the Irish absorbed small quantities of Norman or English blood in their ruling classes, but gradually these practically lost their English identity and the essentially English colony was restricted to a "Pale," which in the time of Henry VIII included only Dublin, Louth, Kildare, and a part of Meath. The principal cities were mostly not Irish but free cities. The house of Ormonde established a small Pale about Kilkenny and a part of Wexford was colonized by the English. Everywhere, except in the cities and walled towns, the English had become Irish in language and condition.

The complete conquest of Ireland took place under Elizabeth and was a disgraceful and bloody enterprise. Previously, in the reign of Mary, the territories of the O'Moores and the O'Connors, who had rebelled under Edward VI, were converted into King's and Queen's counties and the lands parcelled out to the English. Under Elizabeth, companies of planters out of Devonshire, Dorsetshire, Somersetshire, Lancashire, and Cheshire were sent out to take over the Earl of Desmond's territories in Munster, but exactly where these plantations were established and how much they contributed to the Irish population is unknown to the present writers. In the reign of James I there took place the Plantation of Ulster, in which Tyrone, Donegal, Armagh, Cavan, Fermanagh, and Derry were parcelled out to English and Scottish colonists, with portions reserved for the natives. The site of Derry was granted to citizens of London, who fortified it and made it a subsequent bulwark in two wars. At about the same time plantations were established also in Leitrim, Longford, King's County, and Wexford. The general principle involved in these plantations was to remove to waste places in Munster and Connaught all Irish who had been in arms, together with their families, followers, and cattle. Some who were allowed to remain had to be removed from the land allotted to the planters to such places as enabled them to be under the eyes of the "servitors," who were those planters who had shares given them in reward for their war services (Prendergast, 1922, p. 44). The Irish gentry whose lands were not forfeited retained only a portion of their estates under impossible conditions of tenure, such as that of immobilizing in villages their creaghts, or nomadic tribal retainers, and exacting from them fixed rents. The result of this imposition was that many of the Irish landlords found it impossible to live and fled to Spain or elsewhere. In the Wexford plantation of 1611, the lands to be planted consisted of some 66,800 acres, besides woods and mountains. Of 447 Irish claiming freeholds, only 21 were to be allowed to retain their habitations; 36 others were to be provided for elsewhere; and the rest of the

390 freeholders with the other inhabitants, estimated at 14,500, were removable at the will of the planters (Prendergast, 1922, p. 46). How far these iniquitous measures were carried out, we are unable to judge.

Some idea of the size of the British settlement in Ulster may be gained from a survey, ten years from the date of the articles of the Plantation. There were then something short of 2,000 families. In 1633 by a similar survey it was revealed that there were twice the number of men fit to bear arms as had been recorded in the previous survey, which listed 6,215. These planters were mostly Scotch, and there were some English settlers who had preceded them and some traders and families of broken-down soldiers in the towns. Antrim and Down were filled with Scots, who had first made a lodgement there in the time of Henry VIII. In the rebellion of 1641 doubtless the number of British colonists in Ireland was sharply reduced. Clarendon's stories of the massacre of the English (154,000 to 300,-000) are probably wildly exaggerated (Prendergast, 1922, p. 61). However, many English were certainly killed in the process of being driven out of the possessions they had taken from the Irish 30 years previously, but thousands escaped to other parts of Ireland and some made their way back to England. The reprisals of the English against these alleged massacres were savage and unconstrained.

Our reason for summarizing here these sordid happenings is simply that it is necessary to glean information about the various plantations, settlements, and dislodgements, if we are to have any clear idea of the proportions of the foreigners introduced into Ireland after the Anglo-Norman invasions, where they were, and what became of the Irish whom they expelled. In a country repeatedly overrun by invasions, wracked by war, and subjected to violent removals of large sections of the population from one area to another, it is absurd to suppose that the distribution of races, tribes, types, etc., can be assumed to be virtually that of the Early Iron Age, or of any other prehistoric period. It begins, in fact, to appear very naive for us to attempt to match up the present distribution of morphological types with the period of the Goidelic invasion. So we must go through the

Cromwellian settlement and attempt to find out what further displacements occurred. For it may be that our present distributions are explicable only in the light of these atrocious historical events.

Cromwell's campaign in Ireland ruined the country and reduced the population to about 850,000, of whom 150,000 were English and Scots (*Encyc. Brit.*, vol. 14, p. 778). Something like 40,000 Irishmen had been allowed to enlist in foreign armies and about 9,000 (mostly widows and orphans) were sent to virtual slavery in the West Indies. If the population figures are approximately correct (which is very doubtful), the English and Scotch at the end of the Cromwellian invasion were nearly 18 per cent of the total Irish population.

The scheme of the Plantation was to parcel out the best Irish lands between a group of "Adventurers" who had advanced money for the conquest, and the soldiers who had to be rewarded for their services in the campaign. The government reserved for itself the towns, the church lands, and the counties of Dublin, Kildare, Carlow, and Cork. Connaught was set apart for the habitation of the Irish themselves. But it was principally the land-owners who were transplanted. The ploughmen, laborers, and the lower classes in general were exempted. They were to serve the English, and it was hoped that they would be converted to Protestantism. On the other hand, the gentry, without servants, would be reduced in Connaught to peasant status.

Connaught was selected for the residence of the Irish because it was surrounded by the sea and the Shannon, except for 10 miles. The Irish area was to be further isolated by a four-mile belt around the coast and along the left bank of the Shannon to be given over to the soldiery to plant. None of the inhabitants of Kerry, Cork, or Limerick was allowed to be placed in Clare, from which he might behold his native plains, and none of the inhabitants of Cavan, Fermanagh, Tyrone, or Donegal was to be placed in Leitrim, as being too near Ulster. The inhabitants of any one county were to be dispersed through Connaught. The belt reserved for the soldiery was afterwards contracted from four miles to one mile in breadth. Ultimately the soldiery also took most of Sligo and some of the better part of Mayo. Leitrim was first occupied by the Ulster creaghts, but at length was taken also for the soldiery.

The following is a list of assignments of the displaced Irish (Prendergast, 1922, pp. 161–62):

Inhabitants of Ulster (except Antrim and Down): Baronies of Muckullen (now Moycullen), Rosses, Ballinihinsey (now Ballynahinch), in the territory of Ere Connaught, and County Galway (except the reservation on the sea line); baronies of Moyrisk (now Murrisk), Burryshoule (now Burrishoole), part of Tyrawley, Costello, and Tyaquin. (This amounts to all of the rugged coastal regions of Galway and Mayo and a couple of more easterly baronies.)

Inhabitants of Cork and Wexford: Baronies of Dunkellyn and Kiltartan in Galway; Athlone and half of Moycarnane in Roscommon. The first two baronies are on Galway Bay and the last two on the west bank of the Shannon.

Inhabitants of Kerry: Burren and Inchiquin in Clare; Artagh in Roscommon. The first mentioned is on the south shore of Galway Bay, the second in the center of Clare. Artagh is on the west bank of the Shannon in the extreme north of Roscommon.

Inhabitants of Kilkenny, Westmeath, Longford, Kings, Tipperary: Tulla, Bunratty, Islands, Corcomroe, Clonderalau, Moyfartagh (now Moyferta), Ibracan—all southern baronies of Clare, and half of the barony of Bellamo (now Ballymoe) in northeast Galway.

Inhabitants of Carlow, Waterford, and Limerick: Loughrea and Leitrim in southeastern Galway, Dunmore in north central Galway, Kilconnell in east central Galway and Longford in southeastern Galway bordering the Shannon.

Inhabitants of Meath, Kildare, Queens, and Dublin: Roscommon, Ballintober, Boyle in Roscommon and Bellamo in northeast Galway.

These locations may be summarized by saying that the central and western Ulster people were banished to the most westerly parts of Galway and Mayo, the Antrim-Down people to the southeastern counties of Mayo; the inhabitants of the southeasterly counties,

Cork and Wexford, to East Galway and east Roscommon; Kerry folk to north Clare and extreme northwest Roscommon; Tipperary, Kilkenny, Longford, Westmeath, and Offaly—south central counties—to south Clare and southeast Galway; Waterford, Carlow, and Limerick to East Galway; Meath, Kildare, Leix, and Dublin to northeast Galway and Roscommon.

We may now equate the present populations of counties whose land-owners were transplanted with the present populations of the Connaught counties to which they were sent.

In table XXI-1 unweighted averages of percentages of the three Ulster counties are compared with unweighted averages of the two Connaught counties which received the transplanted, and the differences are calculated. The comparison is very crude because it is unweighted, but its importance does not warrant the labor of a more accurate computation. It shows that the Connaught counties differ little from the Ulster counties in combined Nordic types, since weakness in West Donegal is balanced by weakness in Mayo. There is a net loss of 4.2 per cent of the Keltic type in Connaught, a net gain of 4.2 per cent in Nordic Alpine, a gain of 1.1 per cent in Dinaric, and a very small loss in Nordic Mediterranean.

Clare (Table XXI-2) has fewer Nordics, Keltics, and Nordic Mediterraneans than the average of counties which furnished transplantees to it. It is much stronger than the averages of such counties in Dinarics and Nordic Alpines, although not quite as strong as Kerry in the two brachycephalic types combined.

Table XXI-3 shows that East Galway-Roscommon differs from the average type composition of counties from which it received transplantees in being slightly stronger in Nordics, Keltics, and Nordic Mediterraneans and correspondingly weaker in the two main brachycephalic types.

We have now to consider the question whether the present type differences between the receiving counties—Clare, Galway, Roscommon, Mayo—and the counties which sent transplantees are in any way relevant to the Cromwellian settlements. In the first place, in order to make these differences relevant in this situation, we should have to suppose that before the Cromwellian settlements, all the counties of Ireland had approximately the same distribution of morphological types. Such a supposition seems highly improbable, since we know that in previous invasions and conquests, various defeated tribes were pushed into the wilds of Connaught, i.e., the Fir Bolg, at the hands of the Lagin. Secondly, we should have to postulate that the transplanted land-owners were mainly of the types which are in excess in Clare and Connaught as contrasted with the donor counties. Thirdly, we should have to assume that the transplanted came in sufficient numbers to change the type distribution of the recipient areas enough to produce a lasting effect over a period of nearly 300 years. But this is only one side of the problem. We have to take into account also the changes that took place in the donor counties, not only as a result of the removal of the land-owners, but also those consequent upon the settlement of soldiers, adventurers, and others in the counties vacated. The whole situation is pretty much of a "mare's nest." Add to the preceding the fact that the whole of Mayo was later assigned to the soldiers (whether or not they occupied it), also most of Sligo and Leitrim, also a band of variable width going all around the sea-coast of Connaught and along the west bank of the Shannon. These soldiers must have contributed a good many genes to the population of the transplanted area.

How many people were actually transplanted, how many of the transplanted settled down and left progeny in areas to which they went, how many seeped back across the Shannon, we are totally unable to say or even to estimate. But Prendergast (1922, app. II, pp. 363–76) gives in his Appendices some very intriguing descriptions of individuals certified for transplantation in "Transplanters' Certificates." Names, ages, hair colors, estimates of stature, status as fee-holder, tenant, servants, etc., as well as acreage and number and description of livestock. It has amused us to tabulate the hair color of males and females for the large following of John Hore and Matthew Hore of Shandon, Waterford (amounting to 124 persons whose hair color is described) and of some 10 certificates of

persons to be transplanted from various places in Limerick.

In table XXI-4 we have compared the hair colors of the persons who were to be transplanted from Waterford with our Waterford-Wexford sample, and the Limerick transplantees with our Limerick sample. We have also tabulated the female transplantees with no comparative data on modern hair color from these counties. Some liberties have had to be taken with our hair color classification to equate it approximately with the descriptions of the Cromwellian commissioner. We have ascertained "white" in the transplanted to mean what is commonly called ash blond, platinum, or tow, since all of the persons whose hair color is designated as "white" are either immature or young adults. As roughly comparable to the Cromwellian flaxen, yellow, and white, we have lumped together our golden brown, ash brown, golden, and ash.

It is first of all noticeable that the transplanted Waterford males are less dark-haired, more brown-haired, and very much more blond than the males of Waterford-Wexford today. The small female sample of the Waterford transplantees is overwhelmingly blond.

The same contrast is found between those who were to be transplanted from Limerick and the Limerick men of today, except that the transplanted show no excess in the browns over Limerick men of today but even stronger excesses of red and blond. The Limerick females of the transplanted sample had more red hair and less blond hair than the Waterford females.

We have also introduced into the comparison the hair color of men of E. Galway-Roscommon as observed in our survey, since it is this county combination which was supposed to receive the transplanted from Waterford and Limerick. E. Galway-Roscommon has much less black or dark brown hair than either Waterford-Wexford or Limerick, but only a trifle less than the transplanted males from Waterford and Limerick. Roscommon has a little more brown hair than the male transplantees from the two more easterly counties, but very much more than is found in either of them in the contemporary series. E. Galway-Roscommon also comes much closer to the transplantees in high frequency of red hair, but it is considerably lower than the transplantees in combined blond hair, in which it falls between the proportions now found in Limerick and those in Waterford-Wexford. It is of considerable interest that the transplantees of Waterford and of Limerick both resemble more closely in hair color the present population of E. Galway-Roscommon than the present populations of their respective counties of origin. Since the transplantees are more blond than the present population of the counties from which they came, it raises the possibility that more of the Nordic type may have been included in the transplantees than in the Irish who were allowed to remain behind. E. Galway-Roscommon is one of our more strongly Nordic blocks, but, for that matter, Waterford-Wexford today is even higher in that type.

The persons who were transplanted from Ulster, except those from West Donegal, are from areas that are now high in Nordics and other blonds. So is West Galway, which received a part of that transplantation, but Mayo is very low in Nordics and generally low in blondness, though somewhat high in rufosity. The Antrim-Down transplantees who were settled in southeastern Mayo were, according to Prendergast (1922, p. 161), of ancient Scottish and Hebridean descent and might be supposed to elevate Mayo blondness. We have no evidence that such is the case.

Clare at present has relatively fewer Nordics than any of the counties from which transplantees were sent to it, and is really rather closely similar to Kerry in its morphological type composition, although Kerry received no transplantees. Clare is the leading type in Dinarics, but very little higher than Kerry and Tipperary-Kilkenny, which sent it transplantees, although far higher than Longford-Westmeath and Offaly-Leix-Kildare, which also sent settlers into Clare. There is no particular reason for supposing that Clare's lead in Dinarics is attributable to the Cromwellian settlements.

We must now consider the possible effect of the settling of soldiers whose arrears were supposed to be satisfied by grants of land. The army consisted of about 35,000. The arrears of 22,000 English brought over by Cromwell were supposed to be settled in ten

counties which they were to share with the adventurers. These were Waterford, Limerick, Tipperary, Meath, Westmeath, Kings Co., Queens Co., Antrim, Down, Armagh. The next arrears were of those soldiers who had fought in England for the Parliament. These were called "English arrears."

This class was given the whole county of Mayo, which was to be taken from the transplanted Irish, but two-thirds had already been taken by the army. There is nothing particularly distinctive about the present morphological type composition of Mayo. It is perhaps most like Limerick, Kerry, and Cork.

The arrears of men who had served in Ireland before June 5, 1649 were called "Forty-nine arrears." The first body of Forty-niners were to receive land in Fermanagh, along the southern shore of Lough Erne; in a barony of Louth; and in five baronies in northern Cork, comprising a range of mountains running west to east from Fermoy to Kenturk with the River Blackwater along its southern base. Further they received the rugged baronies of Kinalea, Carberry, and Kilmore, southward and westward from Cork. The morphological type composition of Cork today is not at all peculiar. It closely resembles that of Limerick and Kerry.

Another group of Forty-niners, "the old Protestant army of Munster," was given Donegal, Longford, Wicklow, Leitrim, and whatever of the mile belt around Connaught that had not been disposed of previously.

Most of these arrears were temporarily satisfied by "debentures" which were not really deeds or certificates of possession of the land and were supposed to be exchanged for the latter. However, by the time of the Restoration only about one-third of the 33,419 debentures had been returned. It appears that the common soldiers sold most of them to officers or to others or were cheated out of them. Most of these soldiers were apparently unwilling to settle in Ireland. The officers who took possession of land usually were forced to keep the Irish as tenants, since they could induce no colonists to come. Very soon these officers were absorbed into the Irish population.

Prendergast lists 1,360 adventurers who had contributed funds for the conquest of Ireland, consisting of Englishmen of many sorts and conditions. These adventurers apparently fared worse than the Army in the colonization. It was even more difficult for them to evict the Irish owners than for the officers of the army who were trying to get possession. The officers were in the field first and often took sides against the adventurers. Many of the latter were killed by the Irish.

It seems very doubtful that any effect of the army plantation in the counties that were assigned to it, in part or wholly, is now traceable. There is, of course, the puzzling belt of blondness and comparatively heavy concentration of Nordic types that extends from Sligo Bay southward west of the Shannon, but including Longford-Westmeath and then taking in West Galway. It is in the southern part of this blond crescent (E. Galway-Roscommon) that the transplanted whose hair colors we tabulated were assigned. At the north of this crescent, Sligo, Leitrim, and South Fermanagh were assigned to the army, also Longford and whatever was left of the mile wide protective strip. All of these territories are in the blond belt, and it is tempting to suppose that the "Old Protestant army of Munster" may have included many blonds who settled in this area, but there is nothing whatsoever to substantiate such a speculation. This same Forty-niners group was also assigned Donegal and Wicklow, which are poor in Nordics. Also, as noted above, the county of Mayo, theoretically handed over to the army for plantation, is the poorest in all Ireland in Nordics, except only West Donegal. There is no evidence known to us that would point to a greater blondness among the English soldiery (except the Scottish) than in the Irish population in general.

On the whole, it seems much more probable that the blond belt in Ireland is related to earlier Norse colonization along the Shannon than to the Cromwellian settlements, although it is just possible that the transplanted from the eastern and southern counties were fairer in hair color than those who remained on the land and may have contributed a little to the relative rufosity and blondness of the belt west of the Shannon. The proportions of Nordic types in all of the Irish county groups except West Donegal, Mayo, Clare, and Cork are fairly stable, between 6 and 12.7 per cent.

An Act of Parliament of 1653 reserved all forfeited property in the cities and towns for the state. While Dublin, Waterford, Drogheda, Cork, and Limerick were built by the Danes or the Northmen, and Galway was a seat of traders of English and French origin, these urban populations, according to Prendergast (1922, pp. 272–73), were in 1653 and had been for centuries, occupied almost entirely by English. He states that the Irish were forbidden to inhabit the towns, but that just outside of the town walls there was usually an Irish settlement. This is somewhat contradictory to his further statement that the Irish preferred to live in the open country. In any case, by the Act of Parliament, these townsfolk of English or non-Irish origin were expelled and the towns reserved for new English settlement. Since the latter failed to eventuate, the towns and cities became ruinous and desolate and the army settlers and others tore down many buildings for firewood. The pre-Cromwellian English settlers in Ireland were, of course, mostly Loyalists and all Catholics. Consequently, they fared no better than the Irish in the process of confiscation and expulsion from their estates and abodes. When the Restoration came, the old English Loyalists expected to be restored to their original abodes, but this in general did not happen, since the English in possession were Parliamentarians and Protestants, and, in any event, had no inclination to give up what they had grabbed. Nor did the English monarchy intervene to any extent in support of the claims of the Loyalists. Thus the Cromwellian evictions and transplantations were almost as much the displacement of English land-owners and gentry, as of real Irish. They must also have included a great share of the Irish of Danish and Norwegian and Scottish descent.

The whole result of this tragic and evil policy must have been, in addition to the wholesale destruction of lives and property and the decimation of the population, a forced amalgamation of all the oppressed pre-Cromwellian inhabitants of Ireland—Irish, English, Scottish, Danish, and Norwegian. Whereas, at first glance the alignment of concentrations of certain morphological types of the present population west of the Shannon and in southwestern Munster makes one seize upon the

Cromwellian settlements as the probable explanation, the more carefully the situation is examined, the less probable it seems that the transplantations of 1653 had much of anything to do with the present alignment of types.

Ireland has a fertile central plain which is easily invaded from the east. Each group of invaders has attempted to seize this central plain and to drive the previous occupants westward into the barren lands of further Connaught, northwestward into the equally undesirable reaches of Donegal, or south into the highlands of Cork and Kerry. The Megalithic people probably carried out this operation on their Neolithic or Mesolithic precursors. The Bronze Age people may have served the builders of the great stone monuments in the same way. When we get to the semi-historical, semi-legendary period of the Keltic invasions, we have traditions and some detailed accounts. The Lagin drove in and thrust the Fir Bolg into Connaught. Later on the Goidels did the same thing to the Lagin. The Norse operated a little differently. They occupied the sea-ports, sailed up the Shannon, and overran the desirable Central Plain through that waterway. The process of landing on the east coast and in the Waterford region and penetrating the Central Plain from these areas was again repeated by the Anglo-Norman invaders. The Cromwellian plan of transplantation was only an attempt to put on paper, legalize, and formalize the same old scheme of pushing the defeated out into the undesirable corners of the island. The highlands of western Ulster, of Connaught, and of southwestern Munster are, so to speak, raised population beaches in which are to be found the remnants of earlier peoples who have been washed out of the central area and piled up on each other. But considerable layers of these populations are also superimposed upon the flat surface of the Central Plain. The tides of invasions swept away to the west and south the upper crust of each group of peoples that successively dominated Ireland, but left a good deal of the lower strata on the flat bottom, there to be more or less consolidated.

It seems quite probable that the Cromwellian transplantations were the latest and least effective of all of these floodings and washouts. It is to be doubted that they radically transformed the population landscape. Hence we do not believe that our admittedly speculative identifications of certain types of the population with earlier historic and prehistoric immigrants and settlers in various regions of Irish are rendered invalid by the Cromwellian settlements.

In connection with these Cromwellian settlements there remains to be considered one small and isolated area—the Aran Islands. These three barren limestone islands, lying across Galway Bay and having a total area of only 11,579 acres, are a part of Galway. Dupertuis separated the Aran anthropometric sample from that of any of the adjacent regions, because he rightly considered the population to be distinctive. The Arans today, judging by our sample, have the tallest statures, relatively the lowest heads and the flattest chests of any Irish subsample, and are different in other metric features. They are not especially distinctive in morphological type composition, although somewhat low in combined Nordic types, low in all of the brachycephalic types, and very high in Keltics and Nordic Mediterraneans. Men with black hair are rarer here than in any other Irish groups except West Galway and Longford-Westmeath. The Arans have the highest proportions of flat brown and red-brown hair in Ireland, are high in red hair, and have none of the blond shades. The traditional inhabitants were the Fir Bolg, who were supposed to have taken refuge there when defeated by the Lagin.

The islands suffered various vicissitudes and changes of government—a sack by the Danes in 1081, a conquest or plundering by the Lord Justice, Sir John D'Arcy in 1334, an expulsion of the O'Briens, who had been lords of the islands for a long time, in 1586 (Haddon and Browne, 1893, vol. III, p. 824). In 1586 Queen Elizabeth granted the islands to John Rawson of Athlone, on condition of his "retaining constantly on the islands, twenty foot soldiers of the English nation." In 1651 the islands were fortified by the Loyalists, then occupied by the Irish, and finally taken by the parliamentary forces. According to the Cromwellian plan, all of the islands off the coast of Connaught were to have been cleared of the Irish. It is doubtful that the Arans were so cleared.

Ultimately Richard Butler purchased the title from an adventurer and was created Earl of Aran in 1662. In 1691, after the surrender of Galway to King William's forces, Aran was garrisoned, a barrack built, and soldiers quartered there for many years.

In such an isolated and thinly populated area, there must inevitably have been a considerable admixture of the soldiers with the natives. Beddoe (1885, p. 267) remarks on this point:

We might be disposed, trusting to Irish traditions respecting the islands, to accept these people as representatives of the Firbolg, had not Cromwell, that upsetter of all things Hibernian, left in Aranmore a small English garrison, who subsequently apostatised to Catholicism, intermarried with the natives, and so vitiated the Firbolgian pedigree.

Formerly we were inclined to regard the distinctiveness of the Aran Islanders as probably referable to isolation and a more intensive inbreeding than characterizes our other subgroups, but it may well be that the Cromwellian and subsequent English garrisons have had something to do with the matter.

Summary

It may be advisable to summarize our rather unclear findings in this matter of the Cromwellian settlements. We first of all listed the inhabitants of counties who were to suffer transplantation and the parts of Clare or Connaught to which they were to be sent. We then took the per cent type compositions of the recipient counties, averaged them, took the corresponding type compositions of the donor counties and similarly averaged them, in order to see in what types the recipient counties showed excesses and deficiencies over the donor counties. This process was undertaken on the supposition that the excess types in the recipient counties might possibly be the result of the drainage from the donor counties of the land-owners and their followers. This exercise showed that Mayo and West Galway were higher in Nordic Alpines and Dinarics than the average of the counties from which they received transplantees. Clare was also found to have excesses of these brachycephalic types. But East Galway and Roscommon, which received transplantees

from a different set of counties, showed losses of the brachycephalic types and gains in the basic Nordic Mediterranean type and to some slight extent in the Nordic types. This result would show, if our assumption as to the significance of excess types were valid, that the land-owners coming from Ulster to Mayo and West Galway were of different morphological types than those from Munster and Leinster who were sent into E. Galway and Roscommon. At this point we abandoned as unprofitable the operation of equating recipient counties with donor counties. If all of the recipient counties had shown piling up of the same morphological types, we might have been able to make something of the argument, but this was not the case.

We then embarked upon a small digressional tabulation of the hair color and eye color of a couple of hundred of males and females listed in the transplantation certificates as due for expulsion from Waterford and Limerick to E. Galway and Roscommon. It turned out that the persons to be transplanted were much lighter in hair color than the residual population today of the counties from which they were expelled, and raised the intriguing possibility that some of the excess of rufosity and blondness in these recipient counties is due to the excess of the fairer haired persons whom they received. But it is merely an interesting possibility.

Next a consideration of the settlements of English soldiers and of the adventurers was embarked upon, but the evidence seemed to indicate that the realization of these army settlements was very small indeed, since most of the soldiers sold out their debentures. Further, there is nothing to suggest that the settling soldiery introduced any new morphological type into the population or any predominance of a single morphological type. We therefore reverted to our earlier opinion that the blondness of the area west of the Shannon, and to some extent just east of it, is more likely to have been due to Norse colonization along the Shannon than to any of the Cromwellian manipulations of land and population. It seemed to us that the western part of Connaught, the southwestern part of Munster, and to some extent West Donegal, were refuge areas of displaced elements in the population long before the Anglo-Norman invasions, and that the stratified population layers in these remote regions were the result of successive overrunning of the fertile Central Plain by various waves of invaders. About the only place where there is a substantial reason for supposing that the present type of the inhabitants has been altered by Cromwellian events is the Aran Islands, which for many years was the seat of an English garrison which was ultimately absorbed.

COMPARISON OF THE PRESENT DISTRIBUTION OF MORPHOLOGICAL TYPES IN IRELAND WITH SIMILAR TYPES IN WALES AND IN THE ISLE OF MAN

THERE is very little in the works of Giraldus Cambrensis, the Norman chronicler of the conquest of Ireland, that is of use to physical anthropologists. However, he makes it perfectly clear that the entire conquest was accomplished by a few Norman leaders from Wales with a very small number of troops raised from their own kinsmen and retainers. Thomas Wright, the editor and commentator on Giraldus, points out that the latter gives the exact number of men who participated in each of the several expeditions and that the total did not much exceed 2,000 (Giraldus Cambrensis, p. 312, note 1). This is exclusive of the army of King Henry, which is said to have numbered 500 men-at-arms, although no account is given of the rest of his forces. Henry's army did no fighting. The commentator on Giraldus is particularly interested in the paucity of numbers wherewith Ireland was conquered. Our interest is in the subsequent contribution of the Anglo-Norman-Welsh forces to the population of Ireland. Even if the conquering forces were small, it is probable that in the course of continued occupation a good deal of Norman-Welsh blood was poured into the Irish population. Although he remains silent about the details of physical appearance of the Irish, Giraldus describes a number of Norman leaders. Earl Richard or Strongbow is stated to have had a ruddy complexion and freckled skin, feminine features, a weak voice, and a short neck (p. 226). He was tall. Maurice Fitzgerald, the uncle of Giraldus, had a ruddy complexion and good features. He was of middle height (p. 246). Henry II, king of England "had a reddish complexion, rather dark, and a large round head. His eyes were grey, bloodshot, and flashed in anger. He had a fiery countenance, his voice was tremulous, and his neck a little bent forward; but his chest was broad and his arms were muscular. His body was fleshy, and he had an enormous paunch, rather by the fault of nature than

from gross feeding" (p. 250). (Evidently Henry was an endomorphic mesomorph.)

Raymond Fitzgerald "was very stout, and a little above the middle height; his hair was yellow and curly, and he had large, grey round eyes. His nose was rather prominent, his countenance high-coloured, cheerful, and pleasant; and although he was somewhat corpulent, he was so lively and active, that the incumbrance was not a blemish or inconvenience" (p. 265). Evidently Raymond was also an endo-mesomorph and probably brachycephalic (from the description of the eyes). Possibly, then, he was an East Baltic or a Dinaric. Meyler, another of the Norman leaders (of Welsh extraction), "was of a dark complexion, with black eyes, and a stern and piercing look. Below the middle height, for his size he was a man of great strength. Broad-chested and not corpulent, his arms and other limbs were bony and muscular, and not encumbered with fat" (p. 266).

Hervey "was a tall and handsome man, with grey and rather prominent eyes, a pleasant look, fine features, and a command of polished language. His neck was so long and slender that it seemed scarcely able to support his head; his shoulders were low, and both his arms and legs were somewhat long. He had a rather broad breast; but was small and genteel in the waist, which is generally apt to swell too much, and, lower down, his stomach was of the same moderate proportion. His thighs, legs, and feet, were well shaped for a soldier, and finely proportioned to the upper part of his body. In stature he was above the middle height" (p. 268). Seemingly, Hervey was a meso-ectomorph.

Hugh de Lacy: "If you wish to have a portrait of this great man, know that he had a dark complexion, with black, sunken eyes, and rather flat nostrils. . . His neck was short, his body hairy and very muscular. He was short in stature, and ill-proportioned in shape" (p. 289).

It has seemed worth while to quote these descriptions of Norman leaders by Giraldus because it shows how highly diversified in physical type they were. It can hardly be assumed that their followers were racially more homogeneous. These Norman Welsh contributed a not inconsiderable proportion to the composition of the southeastern Irish population. Professor J. V. Kelleher of Harvard University informs me that the mediæval cities of southeastern Ireland were typically Flemish in their manner of life. Flemings, of Franco-Frisian or Belgo-Frisian breed, and, according to Beddoe, on the whole Teutonic in blood and speech, came in large numbers under William Rufus and Henry I and settled in the southern half of Pembrokeshire, in Gower, in the low country of Glamorgan, where they helped consolidate the power of the Norman lords and adopted the English language (Beddoe, 1885, p. 96). These Flemings seem to have been of Nordic and Nordic Alpine types, judging from the population in this area today. They were an important element in the Norman-Welsh conquest of Ireland.

It is very fortunate indeed, because of the proximity of Wales to Ireland and the historical evidence of the invasion of the latter from the former, that there is available for comparison the admirable survey of the Welsh population carried on by Fleure and James (1916). A slight rearrangement of the data of these investigators makes possible an approximate comparison of the modern Welsh with the Irish of our survey. The principal incompatibility in the two sets of data is in the rating of "dark eyes." Fleure and James stated that they used the Martin Augenfarbentafel and they count as "dark" any shade up to (and apparently including 10) in the Martin scale. However, only numbers 1, 2, 3, 4, in that scale are really homogeneous dark eyes, varying from almost black to light brown. Numbers 5 to 12 are all mixed eyes, with varying amounts of superficial pigments and light backgrounds. Numbers 13 to 16 are the only pure "light eyes"—grays, gray-blue and blue. It is then clear that Fleure and James have counted as "dark" many eyes that in our survey are rated as gray-brown, green-brown, blue-brown mixed eyes with a no-

tation as to the proportions of superficial pigment to peripheral background pigment. The other difficulty is that the Fleure and James survey did not include measurements of the nose, so that we cannot use the nasal index for the subdivision of brachycephalic types.

Tables XXII-1 and XXII-2 are the data of Fleure and James for Wales, divided, as we have done in our survey, into those with cephalic indices under 80 and those with cephalic indices above 80. We may first take the males that correspond to our combined Pure and Predominantly Nordic types, which in Ireland constitute 7.4 per cent of the population. In Wales they would include "hair light, eye dark (darker than 10)" 2.38 per cent, "hair fair or light brown, eye light," 15.28 per cent, and about two-thirds of the long-headed men with red hair (5.24 per cent). (In the Harvard sortings we assigned long-headed, red-haired men to the Nordic type when their sutures were 170 or over; otherwise to the Keltic type.) The total figure for Welsh Nordics is slightly more than 21 per cent, which is nearly three times as high as in Ireland.

The next category of Fleure and James in the long-headed moiety is "hair dark, eye light (lighter than 10)"—22.25 per cent. This classification corresponds fairly closely to our Keltic type, which constitutes 25.3 per cent of the Irish males. But "lighter than 10" would include some very light mixed eyes and our Keltic type has no mixed eyes, however light. Thus it seems probable that the incidence of the Keltic type in Wales should be scaled down to no more than 20 per cent, if that.

"Hair dark (but not black), eye dark (10 or darker)," would correspond to our Nordic Mediterranean type in Ireland, except that the latter has some 4.7 per cent of black hair. The type as designated in the Wales sample constitutes 22.25 per cent of all the Welsh males, whereas our type, including the black hair, is 28.9 per cent of the Irish males, or without the black-haired men, 24.2 per cent. It is apparent then that the proportions of the long-headed, dark-haired, mixed-eyed Nordic Mediterraneans are about the same in both countries.

"Hair black, eye dark," which is a Purely

Mediterranean type, comprises 7.67 per cent of the Welsh but only 0.3 per cent of the Irish. It seems probable that the Welsh proportion would be scaled down somewhat, if only purely dark eyes were counted. Probably it includes some dark mixed eyes.

A notable difference between the Irish and the Welsh series is that the Irish males include 38.1 per cent of men with cephalic indices 80 or above, but the Welsh only 24.13 per cent. The excess of Welsh long-heads is mostly Nordic and Pure Mediterranean. It is not possible to equate our Irish types exactly with the data on the Welsh round-heads, because we have used the nasal index to differentiate between Nordic Alpines and Dinarics and East Baltics. No nasal measurements on the Welsh are available.

Of the Welsh brachycephals 8.20 per cent are light-haired or red haired; 15.93 per cent are dark-haired (these are percentages of the total Welsh male series). The Welsh series includes 2.70 per cent of brachycephals who have black hair and dark eyes. These would be real Alpines (if all of the eyes are purely dark). None such are found in the Irish series. Although the data are not wholly comparable, it can be judged by inspecting the hair color combinations found in our different brachycephalic types, that the Irish round-heads tend to be prevailingly more dark-haired than the Welsh and have lighter eyes. Red hair in the Welsh series totals 7.13 per cent, as against only 3.9 per cent among the Irish males.

Making some allowance for differences of technique in the two surveys, we find that the Welsh males include about 14 per cent less of brachycephals (or near-brachycephals) than the Irish, and nearly three times as many blonds of approximately "Nordic" types. The Welsh series has 7.57 per cent of long-heads described as "hair black, eye dark," whereas our Pure Mediterranean type includes only 0.3 per cent of the Irish. However, if we take away from our Nordic Mediterraneans and add to the Pure Mediterraneans all of those who have mixed eyes rated as "very pronouncedly dark" or "pronouncedly dark," we should be able to bring the total of our Mediterraneans up to 4.1 per cent and reduce our Nordic Mediterraneans to 24.8 per cent (as

against 23.1 per cent of the Welsh). By a similar method of shifting the darkest shades of mixed eyes in brachycephals, we could arrive at a total of about 2.4 per cent of more or less dark-haired, dark-eyed brachycephals in Ireland, as against 9.5 per cent in Wales. Even with this juggling there are about four times as many approximate "Alpines" in Wales as in Ireland, nearly twice as many approximate Pure Mediterraneans, and nearly three times as many approximate Nordics.

It is important to note, however, that in both Ireland and Wales the proportionately strongest morphological type is what we call Nordic Mediterraneans—long-heads with dark hair and mixed eyes. This seems to us to be the fundamental type of the British Isles. It probably incorporates in both countries the bulk of the descendants of Palaeolithic settlers (present in Britain only), of the Mesolithic inhabitants, of the Neolithic and Megalithic peoples, with some reinforcement from later comers.

The morphological type second in strength in both countries is what we have called the Keltic type—long-headed and with pure light eyes. It is probably somewhat stronger in Ireland than in Wales.

The long-headed, blond, light-eyed Nordic type is a good deal more numerous in Wales than in Ireland. Of course, the latter country escaped the Anglo-Saxon invasions and was much less intensively colonized than Britain by Norwegians and Danes. What there is of Nordic in Ireland is probably referable to the Norsemen and to later settlements of Scots and English.

The heavier quota of brachycephalic types in Ireland, as compared with Wales, can hardly be attributable to Bronze Age invaders alone. It is our supposition that brachycephalic types were very strongly represented in at least two of the Keltic invasions—that of the Bolgi or Fir Bolg, and that of the Goidels (if the latter came from southwestern France, as O'Rahilly believes).

However much allowance we make for the over-liberal classification of dark mixed eyes as "dark" in Wales, there seems little doubt that really dark, homogeneous, brown eyes are a good deal commoner in that country than in Ireland. It also appears from the excellent survey of Fleure and James that many of the classic "racial" or subracial types of Europe are represented in that country in a less mixed condition than in Ireland. For example, these authors (1916, pp. 113–17) recognize at least five varieties of the Mediterranean type. These types are not selected by specific sortings of combinations of metric and morphological features as in our survey, and are to some extent subjective, but we do not doubt their reality. One of these types of whom they found "only the slightest traces" is small, markedly dolichocephalic, with dark eyes, closely curled black hair, a rather broad nose and short stature (Fleure and James, 1916, p. 116). This is not like our Pure Mediterranean type, which has no curly hair. Markedly curved hair is extremely rare in Ireland. Hair form in Wales is not recorded by Fleure and James, although it is occasionally mentioned. We have the impression that curly hair is much commoner in Wales than in Ireland. Certainly, black hair is much more frequently seen in Wales. Its incidence among the males, according to our authors, is 10.37 per cent, as against 2.8 per cent in Ireland. Our criteria for black hair color may be a little more severe than those of the British anthropologists, since we do not accept as "black" any hair that shows brownish or reddish tints by transmitted light. There is also no tabulation of skin color in the Welsh survey, but here again the text of the work, describing various types, suggests that there are many more persons with dark or swarthy complexions in Wales than in Ireland.

Fleure and James mention two very dark, broad-headed types of men that are apparently Alpine, in addition to other round-heads of lighter complexion. A couple of these latter seem to correspond to our Dinaric type. It is a pity that they have not given the exact descriptions and incidence of the various types they describe. One of the round-headed types, described by Fleure and James (1916, pp. 117, 137–38) as "powerfully built, often intensely dark, broad-headed, broad-faced, strong and square-jawed men" is stated to occur on patches of the rural coast, usually cliff-coast, in Wales. These authors say they have encountered this type in considerable numbers on the east coast of Ireland round Wicklow, but they do not think it at all characteristic of the hill country behind the coast toward Glendalough. They believe that it is also characteristic of the Boyne. Their suggestion is that this type may be the remnant of a trading population that followed a coastal route in the Bronze Age or later.

Our survey shows 15.0 per cent of the Nordic Alpine type in Wicklow-Carlow and 13.6 per cent of Dinarics, and for Meath-Louth-Dublin 12.8 and 12.4 of these two types respectively. However none of these has pure dark eyes. A much stronger center of brachycephaly in this part of Ireland is Waterford-Wexford, which has 23.7 per cent of Nordic Alpines and 18.3 per cent of Dinarics. This is also the strongest county group in Ireland except Antrim-Down in pronouncedly dark and very pronouncedly dark mixed eyes, some of which no doubt, go with the two brachycephalic types mentioned. Our opinion is that in Waterford-Wexford the strength of the rather brunet brachycephals is more probably associated with the Black Danes who founded these towns, than with prehistoric traders. But they may well have come in some numbers with the Norman Welsh and subsequent invasions.

From Fleure and James, we gain the impression that Wales is a country rather more characterized by the preservation of local types through isolation and inbreeding than is Ireland—at least Ireland as a whole. However, if we were to concentrate upon local types in some of the more isolated regions, such as Mayo, West Donegal, and Kerry, attempting to relate them to geographical features such as islands, valleys, mountains, we should undoubtedly be able to find various peculiar breeds. Several admirable studies of such local types were made by A. C. Haddon and C. R. Browne in the nineties and have been considered in this report in the sections dealing with the counties concerned. Indeed, Dupertuis recognized a number of such local types in the west of Ireland, and some of their anthropometric and morphological characters have been tabulated, but are not published here. Initially Dupertuis was instructed to travel all over Ireland and try to get impressions of the morphological types prevalent in various parts of the country before he began his anthropometric survey. This he did, but he soon felt that the multiplicity of local types was so great that it was necessary to abandon this method of subjective visual impressions in the treatment of the whole country. There was substituted an objective selection of morphological types by sorting criteria, made in the process of the statistical analysis of the data and not in the field.

It may be that Ireland has been so repeatedly invaded and overrun and the population has been subjected to so many thrusts out from the center into the corners that there has been more admixture and breaking down of local types than is the case in Wales.

On the other hand, our rigorous distinction between dark and mixed eyes and between mixed and light eyes, tends to militate against facile recognition of multiple types based upon visual impression unsubstantiated by the tabulation of combinations of observed and measured characters. However, we do feel that there may be a sharper segregation of types in Wales than in most parts of Ireland except the isolated refuge areas of that island.

Other than Wales, there is no adequate survey of Great Britain that can be compared with our Irish series. It is particularly unfortunate that material of a satisfactory nature on Scotland is not available, since the latter country was the immediate source of most of the early immigrations into Ireland, as well as a good share of the later comers. However, a survey of the Isle of Man has been made by Elwyn Davies and Professor H. J. Fleure on lines similar to that of the Welsh study (Davies and Fleure, 1936, pp. 129–87), and we may consider briefly the results obtained there, as they bear upon the anthropology of Ireland.

The data in table XXII-3 show that the Manxmen with cephalic indices under 80 (on the long-headed side) consist of 25.42 per cent of Nordic types, or 27.57 per cent if we add the red-heads to the Nordic category. In any event, this is the leading type and it slightly exceeds the proportions found in Wales (if red hair is not counted) and is more than three times the proportion found in Ireland. This Nordic element is probably attributable to the Norwegians who held the island for several centuries, although the language spoken is Keltic.

The second type in frequency is the dark-haired, long-headed, mixed- or dark-eyed Nordic Mediterraneans who constitute 21.72 per cent, which is slightly weaker than the corresponding type in Wales and considerably less than the proportion of that type in Ireland. The type we call Keltic, with dark hair and light eyes, is found in only 8.83 per cent of Manxmen, as contrasted with 15.28 per cent of Welshmen and 25.3 per cent of Irishmen.

Brachycephals (index 80 or over) constitute 41.83 per cent of the Isle of Man males, as against 24.13 per cent in Wales and 34.4 per cent of the Irish. Although Davies measured the nose and tabulated the nasal index for his series of 1200, we cannot utilize his figures to divide the brachycephals into East Baltics, Dinarics, and Nordic Alpines or Alpines, because he measured nose length "from the most depressed part at the root of the nose" (Davies and Fleure, 1936, p. 176) and not from nasion, as in our survey. The most depressed part of the nasal root is commonly at least 2 mm. below nasion. Since a difference of one mm. in nose height at average European breadth affects the nasal index by approximately one unit, it is clear that the nasal indices calculated from Davies data will run higher than by our method. Taking the Davies and Fleure values of the nasal index, as we must, there are but 4.83 per cent of these Manx brachycephals (percentage of total series) whom we should classify as Dinarics and the residue of the brachycephals (37 per cent of the total series) would be either Nordic Alpine or East Baltic. If we were to add half of the brachycephals and high mesocephals (cephalic index 78.6 and over) who range between 64 and 69 in the nasal index, they would make another 12.5 per cent of Dinarics, bringing the total to a little more than 17 per cent and reducing the Nordic Alpines and East Baltics to something like 24 per cent. This would be our guess as to the distribution, if the nasal height were measured according to our method. In the round-heads of the Isle of Man with the higher nasal indices, there tend to be rather more blonds than darks and comparatively few intermediates (dark hair, light eyes). They are much fairer than the Irish brachycephals and without doubt include many more whom we should classify as East Baltics rather than as Nordic Alpines. Brachycephals with hair that could be called "fair" constitute a little less than 11 per cent in both our Irish Dinarics and our Irish Nordic Alpines if we are willing to call golden-brown a "fair" shade. Neither of these types includes men with really blond hair.

The composition of the Welsh population resembles that of Ireland far more closely than does that of the Isle of Man. Although the data from Man are not entirely comparable with those of the earlier Welsh survey, it appears that heavily brunet types are comparatively rare in the small island in the Irish Sea. In Wales they are certainly much more common than in Ireland. The Isle of Man population seems then to be heavily dominated by Nordics and by blond brachycephals, both of which are quite rare in Ireland. One gets the impression from the survey of the Isle of Man that the population has reached a virtual state of panmixia. On the other hand, in Wales there appears to have been the survival in isolated refuge areas of "nests" of local types, some of them perhaps descendants of early populations which have remained segregated. This condition probably obtains also in Ireland in the out-of-the-way regions, but again we must call attention to the fact that pure dark eyes in Ireland are only found in 43 of nearly 10,000 males, and there is reason for supposing that they are vastly more common in Wales. In the Isle of Man there are 142 persons with "even brown eyes" which seem to be pure darks, 11.91 per cent of the male series. 125 of those with "even brown" eyes have dark brown hair or medium brown hair (only 9 of the latter). Probably about 40 per cent of these dark eyes go with brachycephals, so that it seems clear there must be a fair number of persons whom we should classify as Pure Mediterraneans, purely brunet Alpines, and possibly purely brunet Dinarics.

CARLETON S. COON'S PREVIEW OF THE DATA OF THIS SURVEY

THE preliminary data of this survey were made available to Professor Carleton S. Coon for use in his work, "The Races of Europe" (Coon, 1939, pp. 376–84). Dr. Coon's summary of the material presented in detail here will be found, by anyone who takes the trouble to check his figures with ours, to differ insignificantly in some of the means and percentages quoted, because Coon used the results of our first statistical run which was superseded by a completely new statistical analysis when some of the data had been found incorrectly sorted in respect of the county groupings. However, the Coon preview is substantially correct and is, in our opinion, an excellent summary. It is Coon's interpretations that we wish to discuss here.

His conclusions are most conveniently embodied in the following quotations:

In stature and in sagittal dimensions of the head and face, the composite Irishman might well be considered a Nordic in the Iron Age sense, of the Hallstatt variety as represented by living inhabitants of eastern Norway, or even of the Keltic Iron Age variety as represented by abundant skeletal series from England. But in total bulk and in lateral diameters, he exceeds any known Nordic form, and in fact cannot be considered an unmixed descendant of the greater Mediterranean family of races. He is comparable in these respects to the western Norwegians, to the Livs, and to some of the Finns. In order to explain his metrical character, it is necessary to invoke the mass absorption by either Megalithic Atlanto-Mediterraneans, or Iron Age Nordics, or both, of an earlier Upper Palaeolithic strain, which entered Ireland in a Mesolithic cultural tradition. The living composite Irishman is not a pure Crô-Magnon or Brünn-Předmost man, but it would be no exaggeration to say that, from a metrical standpoint, at least half of his genetic ancestry is to be derived from such a source. Since the number of Mesolithic cultural survivors must have been quite small in proportion to that of the later invaders of Ireland, we are faced with a not uncommon situation, in which an older racial element has, by differential breeding rates, reëmerged (Coon, 1939, p. 378).

. . . the Irish people represent a blend between two principal racial groups, (a) the survivors of the unreduced Upper Palaeolithic people of northwestern Europe, in a mesocephalic or sub-brachycephalic form, and (b) a Keltic Iron Age Nordic. The other two factors, (c) the tall, long-headed Mediterranean form brought by the Megalithic invaders, and (d) the Dinaric introduced during the Bronze Age, have both been submerged by the earliest and latest population waves.

The Upper Palaeolithic people are concentrated in southwestern Ireland, especially in Kerry and Cork; just in the part of Ireland from which the Irish in America are mostly derived. The Iron Age Nordic element is concentrated in the eastern counties and in the fertile Great Plain region of central Ireland; what other Nordic elements brought by Danes and English are also centered here. The Megalithic and Bronze Age minority elements are found also in the east, and the latter is particularly common among members of the Protestant landlord class (Coon, 1939, p. 383).

The principal point at issue is Coon's hypothesis of the "survival" or "reëmergence of Upper Palaeolithic" types, which is his favorite theme and explanation of the occurrence of tall, rugged dolichocephals and brachycephals in northwestern Europe. There is, it seems to us, no *a priori* objection to identifying or designating certain contemporary crania as of "Upper Palaeolithic" type, providing that they do, in fact, more closely resemble Upper Palaeolithic skulls metrically and morphologically than they resemble other crania of later archæological provenience. It is a much more precarious business to select living individuals, whose crania are clothed with flesh and other soft parts, as representing Upper Palaeolithic types, since, without an X-ray eye, it is very difficult to discern many important morphological details of the cranium, to say nothing of the fact that comparatively little of the detail of eyes, nose, ears, lips can be deduced from a study of the skull and absolutely nothing at all relative to pigmentation and amount and character of hair. Hence, if we designate certain living types as "Upper Palaeolithic survivors" we are not on solid grounds as to their cranial features and have no ground at all to stand upon as respects their resemblance to men of the Palaeolithic in soft parts of the head and face. Nevertheless, in spite of these objections, it is by no means improbable that some rugged, primitive-looking contemporary men are replicas of their Upper

239

Palaeolithic ancestors and it is not wholly objectionable and indefensible to designate them tentatively by names suggesting such resemblance.

However, the implication that such contemporary "Upper Palaeolithic" types represent actual straight line descendants of genetically isolated Palaeolithic stocks is very difficult to accept anywhere, and especially in a region so thoroughly overrun by successive streams of invaders and colonizers as has been the case in Western Europe and even in Ireland, its jumping-off place.

Again, although there is considerable skeletal and other evidence that suggests that a certain process of slenderizing and refinement has commonly taken place in *Homo sapiens* since the close of the Ice Age, tending to produce human types with less massive skeletal structure and of generally more gracile form; it is hardly reasonable to designate all of the rugged, heavy-boned men as "Palaeolithic survivors" and to relegate all of the less sturdy to other categories which have putatively undergone "reduction." We cannot be sure that the entire recent trend of evolution of *Homo sapiens* has been consistently in the same direction. It is wholly possible that high-statured, heavy-boned massive types have emerged in certain areas as a result of diet and other environmental conditions, hybridization and heterosis, or other causes quite removed from having preserved unbroken the types of their Palaeolithic ancestors. Of course, all of us must have had Palaeolithic ancestors and probably some of them were runts and some giants.

In the case of the Irish, it seems to us unsafe to conclude that because they are tall and have big heads, they are necessarily derived in large measure from putative Mesolithic settlers of "Upper Palaeolithic" types. In the first place we have no skeletal remains that can be attributed with certainty to these Mesolithic settlers and consequently we do not know that they were of the "Brünn" and the "Borreby" types. In the second place there is no evidence of a Mesolithic culture in Kerry and Cork, or anywhere in western Ireland, where Dr. Coon identifies living types as particularly little modified "Palaeolithic survivors." To suppose that these massive and

physically superior western Irish types were necessarily the earliest in Ireland and were banished to the farthest and least desirable quarters of the island by physically inferior invaders who knew how to polish stone is a somewhat gratuitous assumption. Actually, we are far more certain that the Bronze Age or Beaker types of men who invaded Great Britain and Ireland, were tall, heavy-boned, and generally rugged, than we are of such characteristics of Upper Palaeolithic or Mesolithic inhabitants of the British Isles. Of course, we can argue that the Bronze Age invaders are themselves "Palaeolithic survivors," but that gets us nowhere.

One of the principal difficulties encountered by the student who attempts to use Coon's racial classification of whites is his failure to define clearly the pigmental characteristics of the racial or subracial types that he distinguishes. This is apparently a consequence of his attempt to base his classification primarily upon the cranial forms of archæological specimens of which the pigmental associations are naturally unknown. Coon recognizes "Large-headed Palaeolithic survivors"—the dolichocephalic Brünn and the brachycephalic Borreby; "Pure and Mixed Palaeolithic and Mesolithic Survivors of Moderate Head Size"—mostly brachycephals and including Alpines, "Ladogans" (divided into Neo-Danubian and East Baltic) and Lapps (Coon, 1939, pp. 291–92). This second group of "survivors" is supposed to be somewhat "reduced" in head size, and, in the case of the Alpines, "foetalized." His third group comprises "Pure and Mixed Unbrachycephalized Mediterranean Derivatives." Under this are included a general group, "Mediterraneans," with the following subtypes: (a) Mediterranean proper—defined merely as short-statured, dolichocephalic and mesocephalic, (b) Atlanto-Mediterraneans—described as tall, straight-nosed and markedly dolichocephalic, and (c) Irano-Afghans—long-faced, high-headed, hook-nosed, usually of tall stature. The second large group, Nordics, is divided into 4 living varieties: (a) Keltic Iron Age type, described as mesocephalic and low-vaulted with a prominent nose; (b) Anglo-Saxon type—"heavy-boned and rather high-headed"; (c) Trondelagen type—stated to be a hybrid type; (d) Osterdal type—"the original Hallstatt Nordic, smaller-headed and finer-boned" than the two previous Nordic types enumerated.

Finally Coon has a group of "Brachycephalized Mediterranean Derivatives, Probably Mixed." It includes (1) Dinarics—"a tall brachycephalic type of intermediate pigmentation, usually planoccipital, and showing the facial and nasal prominence of Near Eastern peoples"; (2) Armenoids—a similar type to the above, but with larger face and nose, usually brunet pigmentation and well developed pilous system; (3) Noric—"a blond, planoccipital brachycephal."

All of these types are described in greater detail in the sections of Coon's work on the various parts of Europe where they occur. Apparently, Coon's primary criteria of classification are absolute head size and the cranial index, together with massiveness of gracility of the cranial, facial, and postcranial skeleton. Of lesser importance in his scheme are stature and the form of the nose and face. The importance of hair color, eye color, and skin color is still less. It is implied that all of the varieties of Mediterranean are brunet, and of Nordic blond, but we are unable to deduce from his work whether a blue-eyed dark-haired dolichocephal should be classified as "Atlanto-Mediterranean" or "Keltic Iron Age." We think that Coon would include most of our "Keltic" type under his Atlanto-Mediterranean class, but those with medium brown hair under his Keltic Iron Age type, which is a subdivision of Nordic. Coon did not utilize our sorted types, since, of course, they do not conform to his scheme of classification. This difference in classification makes it very difficult for us to compare Coon's conclusions on Irish anthropology with ours, in spite of the fact that he has utilized our data. Our deductions with regard to historic and prehistoric sequences of types are based upon distributions of types established by sorting on the basis of objective criteria; his are based upon the general metric and morphological features of the entire Irish series of males, integrated subjectively into a sort of composite Irish type, and then subdivided in accordance with his ideas as to their relationships to Palaeolithic cranial types or cranial types of later origin, with some attention paid

to the geographical distribution of these types within Ireland. Our sorted types are definite and rigid to the extent of being, possibly, Procrustean. Coon's are indefinite, fluid, and almost Protean.

However, many of the differences are of a minor character. For example, there is probably no difference whatsoever between Coon's "Mediterranean Proper" and our "Pure Mediterranean," nor between his Dinaric type and ours, except that ours includes also some of Coon's blond "Nordics." Coon's "Atlanto-Mediterranean" type apparently includes most of our Keltic and Nordic Mediterranean types, but some with especially big heads he would assign to the Brünn Palaeolithic type. Our Nordic-Alpine type seems to conform generally with Coon's Alpine, because he does not insist upon dark eyes as a criterion of the type, although we gather that he considers the hair color to be medium brown or darker. But some of our large-headed Alpines would be assigned to the Borreby type by Coon. All of our Pure and Predominantly Nordic types would fall somewhere in Coon's Nordic group and our East Baltic type would be the same as his, with again the exception of those considered by him to have too massive heads.

Having cleared the ground for a comparison of Coon's results with ours, by attempting to equate his racial classification with ours, we may now proceed to a brief discussion of the differences and agreements in conclusions.

In the first place, we do not think that the big-headed, heavy-bodied men of western and especially southwestern Ireland are necessarily Upper Palaeolithic or Mesolithic "survivors" or descendants, because we have no evidence that the Mesolithic people in Ireland either possessed such physical characteristics or ever reached western and southwestern Ireland. We do not agree that size and ruggedness of the cranial vault and stature are sufficient criteria for the identification of Upper Palaeolithic or Mesolithic types. The evidence for the stature and general size of Mesolithic man in northwestern Europe is so scanty as to be almost infinitesimal. The chances of a direct genetic survival of a Mesolithic or Upper Palaeolithic type in western Ireland, either through isolation and inbreeding or selective survival, seem to us very small. On the other hand, there is nothing improbable about the idea of a "reëmergence" of Irish Mesolithic or Palaeolithic types in the more remote areas of Ireland or elsewhere in isolated regions of northwestern Europe. We think that such ancient types do recur in modern man by recombinations of ancestral characters. We do not know that the western Irish represent such a "reëmergence" of Irish Mesolithic types because we do not know what the latter were. We are perfectly willing to admit that these western Irish do appear to be similar in the flesh to those heavy-featured north-western Danes, Germans and Norwegians whom Coon refers to as the survival of Palaeolithic strains. It seems very unlikely to us, nevertheless, that "at least half of the genetic ancestry" of the composite modern Irishman is to be referred to the survival of strains from the original Mesolithic settlers.

Our second disagreement with Dr. Coon is in his conclusion that the second principal Irish stock (in addition to "survivors of the unreduced Upper Palaeolithic people") is Keltic Iron Age Nordic. All of the types that can, by any reasonable extension of the term, be called "Nordic" do not amount to much more than 7 per cent of Irish males and our evidence suggests that these more or less blond and long-headed types are more plausibly referable to the later colonizations of Nor-wegians, Danes, and Scots, and even Normans and English, than to Iron Age Keltics. We think that the earlier Keltic invasions (all of them Iron Age) were Nordic Mediterranean, the later probably Keltic (in our sense of long-headed, dark-haired and light-eyed), and the last, that of the Goidels, mainly Nordic Alpine and possibly Dinaric. The identifica-tions of our morphological types with dif-ferent waves of Keltic invaders are admittedly speculative, but it is pretty certain that the supposition that the Iron Age Keltics were of a Nordic type is wrong.

Coon thinks that the tall, long-headed Medi-terranean type was brought by the Megalithic invaders and it seems certain that some of our Nordic Mediterranean type must be refer-able to such a source, but it also seems neces-sary to suppose that many, if not most, of the preceding Neolithic and Mesolithic people belonged to this type, to say nothing of a con-siderable share of nearly every later invading people. This long-headed, dark-haired, tall type of mixed pigmentation is the basic and leading type in Ireland and in nearly every county group in the island. We think, also, on the basis of very tenuous evidence indeed, that a short, very dark Mediterranean type (our "Pure Mediterraneans") may be con-nected with the coming of some of the more elaborate types of passage-graves. We see no sign of the "submergence" of the Mediter-ranean type except in so far as purely dark eyes have nearly disappeared and short stature is generally uncommon.

Coon speaks of the Dinaric type as having been introduced during the Bronze Age, and, on the basis of the archæological evidence consisting of all too few skulls, he is perfectly correct, but he neglects the Alpine or our Nordic Alpine type, which on the same evi-dence also appeared during the Bronze Age and is today numerically nearly as strong as the Dinaric, and only partly coincident with the latter in distribution. Nor does Dr. Coon's statement in regard to the concentration of Nordic elements in the eastern counties of Ireland and in the fertile Great Plain region of central Ireland entirely fit the distributional facts, especially in respect of the "easterly counties." Moreover, the Bronze Age minor-ity, if it is to be identified with our Dinarics or even with our Nordic Alpines, is certainly not strong in the east but concentrated in the west and southwest.

We may conclude this discussion by the summarizing statement that Dr. Coon's very able analysis of Irish racial composition and history, based upon our data, seems to us to exaggerate the supposedly "Upper Palaeolithic" elements in the contemporary Irish population and also the "Nordic elements." The basic Irish strain today is, and probably always has been, a tall, long-headed, dark-haired mixed-eyed or dark-eyed type which we call Nordic Mediterranean and is surely not referable, for the most part, to Mesolithic inhabitants of Ireland, although they probably contributed to it. The second strain is also long-headed and dark-haired but light-eyed. We have called it "Keltic." Some of this type may have come in during the Megalithic period. We think that more may have been brought by the Laginian Keltic invasion.

So far as archæological evidence carries us, round-headed types first appeared in the Bronze Age. It is possible, of course, that some of the Mesolithic settlers with Coon's Upper Palaeolithic skull type may have been brachycephalic! But we are not aware of any brachycephals in Britain during the Upper Palaeolithic or Mesolithic periods. Dr. Coon neglects entirely to mention the lowly Alpine

type in Ireland, preferring, we suppose, to assign all brachycephals that are not Dinarics to the Upper Palaeolithic or Mesolithic Borreby type. However, a considerable proportion of our Nordic Alpines are brachycephals without great dimensions of the cranial vault and are also somewhat shorter and broader in the body than most Irish types. I am afraid that we must admit their Alpine affinity and bring them in, not only in the Bronze Age, but with the later invasions of Fir Bolg, Goidels, Danes, and even Normans!

SUMMARY OF MORPHOLOGICAL TYPE SEQUENCES AND CORRELATIONS IN IRELAND

THE PRE-KELTIC IRISH, THE KELTIC IRISH, AND THE POST-KELTIC IRISH

HISTORICAL, archæological, linguistic, and anthropological data should give us some idea of the sequences of peoples or sub-racial groups in association with the succession of Irish cultures. From a linguistic standpoint the inhabitants of Ireland may be divided into the pre-Keltic people, the Keltic tribes, and the post-Keltic invaders and settlers. Archæologically, the pre-Keltic period includes the Mesolithic, Neolithic, Megalithic, and Bronze Age cultures. We follow O'Rahilly and the other better, more recent students of the subject in rejecting the hypothesis that the Bronze Age peoples introduced the Keltic language into Ireland. These languages seem to have been introduced by at least four waves of Kelts, all coming in the Iron Age, beginning soon after 600 B.C., or, at any rate, in the fifth century. These were the Priteni or Cruthin, the Bolg or Bolgi, the Lagin, and the Goidels. The coming of the last wave, which brought the present Keltic speech and imposed it upon both Keltic and pre-Keltic predecessors, is placed by O'Rahilly between 150 B.C. and 50 B.C. All of these were then Iron Age peoples. After them we have to consider the Vikings (Danes and Norwegians, particularly the latter), the Anglo-Normans (including more Welsh than English), the English, and the Scots.

All of these successions of invaders have amalgamated to form the modern Irish peoples, who fall into several morphological types, most of which arise from the mixtures of two or more subraces of whites. In previous chapters we have discussed the possible identifications of these morphological types with historical events and archæological cultures, and here it is our purpose to recapitulate.

All of our morphological types are Irish and the individuals belonging to each of them look Irish. There is something about the process of breeding within the same geographical and social environment that imparts to types of diverse racial origins a common stamp of nationality. Thus Irish Nordics resemble Swedish Nordics, but the former are Irish in their general appearance and the latter Swedish, etc. Every morphological type in Ireland has its counterpart in other European countries. Perhaps it would be both unfair and incorrect to select one of these Irish types and identify it as the most distinctively and characteristically Irish. Yet we propose to do so (of course, in a very tentative and timorous way), simply because one of the great morphological types of Ireland is far commoner there than anywhere else in the world and exists in sizable groups principally, if not exclusively, only in the areas that are now, or recently have been, Keltic in speech. This is the dark-haired, blue-eyed, long-headed type that we have called "Keltic." It occurs, of course, also in Gaelic Scotland, in Wales, in the Isle of Man, to some extent in England, and in Brittany. Individuals and even small groups of this physical type are to be found sporadically elsewhere in European populations. Paradoxically enough, the Keltic type in Ireland is, of all the types, least Irish in speech at the present day. The reason for this contradiction is that it is most thickly concentrated in the areas of Ireland that have been taken over nearly completely by the English and the Scottish peoples. It is also probable that this Keltic type was introduced in large numbers by the third Keltic or Laginian invasion, and spoke a Keltic language of the p rather than the q type (if this distinction is not altogether discredited), that was not the Goidelic. The Goidels certainly imposed their language upon their Keltic predecessors, but in the eastern part of Ireland most of these readily abandoned Goidelic in favor of English after the Anglo-Norman invasions and subsequent English and Scottish settlements.

244

It could be argued that the most authentically Irish types are those that dwell in the parts of Western Ireland in which Irish is spoken today. However, all morphological types in Ireland are represented in this area and the closest one can come to a generalization that seems apposite to our discussion is that the round-headed types and the blond and rufous types are particularly concentrated in the west and in the south. There is, however, a strong probability, that the Goidelic language, which is present-day Irish, was introduced mainly by brachycephals, either Dinaric or Nordic Alpine, or both. So, in this sense, it might be claimed that one or other, or both of these types, has the best right to be called distinctively Irish. However, as stated above, the physical type combination that comes closest to being distinctively and characteristically Irish is the "Keltic."

Some of our morphological types, long domiciled in Ireland and completely Irish in appearance, customs, and even in speech are certainly exotic and of historically non-Irish origin. That is most clearly the case in the Pure and Predominantly Nordic types, which seem to have been mainly post-Keltic. The Pure Mediterranean, East Baltic, and Pure Alpine types, all numerically insignificant, seem to be remnants of both pre-Keltic and post-Keltic invasions. The great and widespread Nordic Mediterranean type is perhaps the oldest of all in Ireland, but it is just as much British and Scottish and Welsh and, generally speaking, fundamental, brunet, long-headed Northwestern European, as Irish. It is this type which is related by Coon, with some measure of plausibility, to the earlier Stone Age inhabitants of the region.

We shall now list once more, our morphological type correlations and sequences.

The Mesolithic Inhabitants of Ireland

The cultures of these peoples, known only in Antrim and Down, are dubiously represented by 8 skulls from the Raised Beaches. From the measurements they were mostly short-statured dolichocephals. Of the contemporaneous morphological types, the most probable to represent the Raised Beach people would be the long-headed, dark-haired, mixed-eyed, Nordic Mediterranean type, which is the most evenly distributed over Ireland, and rather strongly over-represented in Antrim-Down. However, there is no necessity of supposing that the few and remote Mesolithic colonizers would leave in the present population any type or even any individuals who would actually carry Mesolithic genes. All that we imply is that this brunet, long-headed type creates the impression of being very ancient, or at any rate, the most ancient in Ireland, and as such, its ancestral representatives are most likely to have been associated with the earliest human cultures.

The Neolithic and Megalithic Inhabitants of Ireland

The skeletal material from the Megalithic monuments is equally scanty and consists, with the exception of one brachycephal of uncertain date, of dolichocephals with lower heads than the skulls of the Raised Beaches, with long faces and rather narrow noses. The skulls could be duplicated in our Nordic Mediterranean, Keltic, and Predominantly Nordic types. The last is almost certainly of much later age in Ireland than the Neolithic or Megalithic. Again the Nordic Mediterranean is the most likely legatee of the Neolithic people, with the exception of the small Pure Mediterranean type, which has a Midland distribution that tempts one to identify it as the remnant of the people who brought the Passage Graves. Since we cannot reconstruct the hair color and the eye color from crania, all that we can be sure of is the vague identification of this later Stone Age group of immigrants with one of our basically long-headed types. We doubt that the blue-eyed Keltic type or either of the Nordic types goes back to this period.

The Bronze Age People

Here we are on somewhat surer ground. The very few Bronze Age crania reported from Ireland can be definitely associated with our Dinaric (round-headed, long-faced, long-nosed) type, and with our Nordic Alpine (round-headed, broad-faced, and somewhat broader-nosed type). They could also correspond to our fair or rufous round-headed, East Baltic type. There is little doubt that the first two of these types arrived in the Bronze Age. There was probably a strongly rufous strain in these peoples and it may be that the blond or rufous (generally the latter) East Baltic type merely represents the segregation of this element. At this point we may remind the reader that there have been too many invasions of different peoples into Ireland and that there exist today too few distinct morphological or subracial types in Ireland to permit the identification of each archæological culture, or each protohistoric and historic invasion, with one exclusive morphological type. In any event, history does not usually happen that way. Invading peoples are generally, and probably almost invariably, racially mixed. It would be gratifying to be able to assert with confidence that the Early Bronze Age invaders were Dinarics and the Middle to Late Bronze Age invaders Nordic Alpines and East Baltics. Any such assertion would be sheer nonsense.

THE PEOPLES OF THE IRON AGES

The extant skulls of Iron Age Irish are invariably those of dolichocephals and it is a temptation, on other grounds, to identify them as the ancestors of our dark-haired, light-eyed, long-headed Keltic type. However, there were several Iron Age invasions of Keltic-speaking peoples and they certainly were not always of one physical type. On the basis of correlating the present distribution of these types with O'Rahilly's accounts of the history and distribution of these various waves of Keltic invaders, we have made the following speculative identifications:

1) The Cruthin or Pretani with the long-headed, dark-haired, mixed-eyed Nordic Mediterranean type.

2) The Builg or Bolgi with rounder-headed types carrying the lighter shades of hair color —that is with Dinarics, in part, and East Baltics.

3) The Laginian tribes with the dark-haired, blue-eyed, long-headed Keltics.

4) The Goidels with the darker, broad-faced, broad-nosed Nordic Alpine and possibly also with the pure Alpine remnant.

THE VIKINGS

These were pretty certainly the main source of our Pure and Predominantly Nordic types. However, it is almost certain that the Danes,

at any rate, contributed to some of our brachycephalic types—perhaps to all of them.

THE ANGLO-NORMANS

By the time of the beginning of the Anglo-Norman conquest, presumably all of the morphological types now recognizable in Ireland were already there in force. Nothing new could then be added to the population. We think that the Norman invasions reinforced the brachycephalic types as well as the longheads (especially the more brunet brachycephals), and that the blond dolichocephals (Nordics) among them were probably relatively few. The Welsh origin of the Norman invasion of Ireland suggests the inclusion of a strong brunet element.

THE ENGLISH AND THE SCOTS

Our inadequate information about the modern anthropology of England, to say nothing of its historical anthropology, hardly permits us to identify any particular morphological type in Ireland today as possibly of English origin. It is probable, however, that the English contributed more to the long-headed types than to the round-heads, because the brachycephals of Britain are probably a small minority. We can also guess that the English would hardly have contributed much to the Keltic type, since that is rare in England. This leaves us with the Nordic Mediterranean type as probably the largest legatee of English blood, but also the two Nordic types. Certainly these last may have received increments from the English settlers, although hardly to the extent of the brunet Nordic Mediterraneans (probably the fundamental British type, whether Welsh, English or Scottish).

Perhaps some inkling of the contributions of English and Scottish settlers to our various morphological types may be drawn from scanning the contributions of those professing Church of Ireland and Presbyterian affiliation to the several types. Probably many of the Church of Ireland communicants are of at least partially English origin, or at any rate, adherents to the nobility of English descent. Certainly, it may be presumed that the bulk of the Presbyterians are of Scottish origin. Table XIV-6 gives the requisite data. Here we note that the Church of Ireland contributes considerably more than its proportionate quota to the Pure and Predominantly Nordic type, especially the former. This might suggest that a fair proportion of the Pure Nordics (9.4 per cent), and a smaller but still excess proportion of the Predominantly Nordics (6.4 per cent) may possibly be of English origin. However, the Church of Ireland contributes in excess of its numbers to all of the morphological types, with the clear exception of the Nordic Alpine and the Dinaric. But its excess of Keltics is so little as to be negligible. The excess of East Baltics and Pure Mediterraneans, as well as of Nordic Mediterraneans, in the Church of Ireland sample are also impressive. If all of these 485 men scattered throughout Ireland were of English descent, we should have to conclude that the English contributions were, in order of importance: (1) Pure Nordic, (2) East Baltic, (3) Predominantly Nordic and Pure Mediterranean, (4) Nordic Mediterranean, (5) Keltic, (6) Dinaric, (7) Nordic Alpine. In other words, the English would contribute particularly to the blond and rufous types, but also to the more brunet long-headed types, and least to the round-heads of darker pigmentation.

The Scottish contributions, as indicated by the regions of the morphological types, are of equal interest. Their most disproportionately large contribution is to the Pure Mediterraneans, followed by the Predominantly Nordics. There are insignificant excesses of Pure Nordics and Keltics. All of the other types are deficient (but not significantly so, in the case of the Nordic Mediterraneans).

Our Protestant samples constitute together only 8.5 per cent of the morphological types and the Presbyterians are all from Northern Ireland. However, it seems possible to deduce from the data discussed above that the English and Scottish settlers in the population may have reinforced the Nordic, Pure Mediterranean, and possibly East Baltic types to a greater extent than any other.

EFFECT OF THE CROMWELLIAN AND OTHER TRANSPLANTATIONS AND PLANTATIONS UPON THE DISTRIBUTION OF MORPHOLOGICAL (SUBRACIAL) TYPES

A lengthy, laborious, and not altogether profitable examination of the data pertaining to the expropriation of the more desirable lands in the Midlands and East of Ireland, first to make room for English and Scottish settlers, and subsequently, to reward the Cromwellian armies and to repay the "adventurers," yielded at any rate some interesting and anthropologically instructive material. The net result was to convince us that the land-owners, gentry, and their followers who were deprived of their lands and driven westward, mostly across the Shannon into Connaught, were by no means exclusively the Irish of Keltic and pre-Keltic times, but in large measure also the pre-Cromwellian Catholic English and the mixed descendants of the Vikings who had intermarried into the old Irish nobility. When we add to them the actual settlements in Western Ireland of scattered bands of the English Army (assuming that the majority of them did not take up their rights), we come to the conclusion that all of these ructions and removals may have added a little more to this or that preexisting morphological or subracial type, but probably had no great effect upon the composition of the population, either in the area from which the Irish and others were expelled, or in that to which they were sent.

We are of the opinion that the concentration of blondness west of the Shannon is more reasonably attributable to the Norwegian settlements, the incorporation of Viking blood in the land-owning class, and their subsequent sharing the fate of those transplanted, than to any other factor. There is reason for supposing, however, that whatever elements were added to the earlier Irish population by the settling of English and Scottish in various regions are more likely to have reinforced the blond, long-headed Nordic types, and the brunet long-headed Pure Mediterranean and mixed-eyed Nordic Mediterranean type, than any of the others.

PART IV

THE WEST COAST IRISH FEMALES

BY

HELEN DAWSON

SOCIOLOGICAL OBSERVATIONS

Marital State (Table XXV-1). Over 69 per cent of Dr. Dawson's female series from West Ireland were single women. This high proportion of celibacy is referable in part to the fact that nearly one-fourth of the subjects fell into the 15–19 year age group. But it is obviously due in far greater measure to the late age of marriage in Ireland. Kerry, which has the highest proportion of married women (38.8 per cent), is also highest in mean age (34.95 years). Clare and Leitrim, which are the two youngest county samples in mean age, have the highest proportions of single women (75.5 and 76.4 per cent respectively). Kerry also has the highest proportion of widows, but Leitrim, which is far younger in mean age, is second in widows.

The marital statistics for the Irish males were not tabulated, although the field blanks record these facts. Hence no comparison of male and female marital status can be made here.

Number of Siblings (Table XXV-2). In table XXV-2 the number of siblings does not include the subject or propositus. Therefore the number of children in families is one more than the number of siblings listed in the table. Our female subjects have a modal frequency of 5 siblings—i.e., the commonest number of children in the families from which they come is 6. The reader will be impressed with the large size of families. No less than 6.3 per cent of the women or girls had 12 brothers or sisters. Only 2.4 per cent of the females were "only children."

Comparison of the county differences in respect of number of siblings indicates that the Leitrim women come from the smallest families. The Galway families and those from Donegal seem particularly strong in the highest categories. These statistics on the number of siblings give a better idea of the size of West Irish families than the table on the number of children, since the latter includes more marriages of short duration and also is based upon the entire percentage of female subjects, about three-quarters of whom are unmarried.

Number of Children (Table XXV-3). Of 1771 females reporting, 76.7 per cent had no children. In the total females series only 25.9 per cent of 1865 were married and 5.04 per cent widowed—altogether 574 women qualified matrimonially for the bearing of offspring. Actually, our table indicates that of the 1771 females reporting, 412 had children. This would imply that not more than 162 women who were married were childless. The total number of offspring reported for these women who had borne children is 2751, an average of 6.7 children per mother. The modal number of offspring is 5, borne by 3.7 per cent of all females reporting, but by 15.8 per cent of those who had any children at all. Since we have no data on the duration of marriages, we cannot comment in much detail about this table, except to draw attention to the impressive numbers of mothers who have borne from 6 to 12 children.

Education (Table XXV-4). The percentage of illiterates among Dawson's West Coast Irish females is only 1.2, which is to be compared with 3.3 per cent for total males of the Catholic County series. Probably the reason for the difference is principally the low percentage of middle-aged and elderly women in the West Coast sample. Similarly, the females show 26.4 per cent who have attended secondary schools, as contrasted with only 11.6 per cent of the males. The difference is made up in the National School category which is much more heavily represented among the males. There is no real difference between the proportions of the sexes who have attended a university. It is hardly worth while to enter into any elaborate study of the county differences in education among the females. The Donegal women are least well educated with the highest percentage of illiteracy and the lowest percentage of secondary school attendants. The Kerry women, who are the oldest, include no university students and a deficiency of secondary school students. Clare, the youngest subgroup, has the highest proportion of secondary school attendants. The Galway women are, on the whole, well educated.

Language (Table XXV-5). Only 31.9 per cent of the West Coast females know no Irish and 26.7 per cent are native speakers. These proportions are to be contrasted with those of the total males who include 54.8 per cent who have no Irish and 14.8 per cent of Irish speakers. However, it must be remembered that the females are all derived from the counties in which Irish is commonly spoken, except Sligo and Leitrim. The Donegal females show nearly the same proportion of native speakers as is shown by the West Donegal males (females 47.0 per cent, males 46.2). In Mayo and Kerry the percentages of native speakers are approximately the same for both sexes also. Among the Galway females, native speakers total almost 20 per cent less than in the West Galway males, but the areas are not strictly comparable, since East Galway and Roscommon have been combined in the males and this group shows comparatively few Irish speakers (12.7 per cent). Sligo and Leitrim are almost devoid of Irish speakers in both sexes. Clare has a respectable number of males who speak Irish (15.6 per cent), but the small proportion in the female sample (5.0 per cent) is probably attributable to the very young mean age of the Clare female series.

Considerably more females than males have studied Irish at school (42.1 per cent as against 30.4 per cent). This difference is again referable, in all probability, to the overloading of the females series with the subadult and very young adult subjects. The lowest percentage of females who have studied Irish at school occurs in Galway. One would naturally attribute this fact to the high percentage of native speakers in that county. However, Donegal, which has the highest percentage of Irish speakers among the females, shows only a moderate deficiency of those who have studied the language at school.

On the whole, there is nothing about the distribution of the Irish language among the West Coast females that is incompatible with the male data from the same counties, taking into consideration the overloading of the females with young subjects who are very unlikely to be native speakers.

Religion (Table XXV-6). The West Coast female series includes 20 individuals (0.6 per cent) who are Protestant. Of course, all of our Irish Catholic county male series consists of Catholics. Of these female Protestants, 12 of the 20 come from Leitrim or Sligo.

Occupation (Table XXV-7). The female occupations are naturally somewhat restricted. By far the largest category is housekeeper (44.7 per cent), in spite of the fact that only 25.9 per cent of our females are married. The second most numerous occupation is household servant (12.1 per cent). The 4.3 per cent of females listed as "at home" are presumably too young to work, or of no occupation. Factory workers among the women number 10.7 per cent, which is vastly above the 1.4 per cent in the male total series. On the other hand, there are only 3.1 per cent of shop assistants among the females as contrasted with 10.2 per cent of the males. However, in the females we have an additional category "business," which accounts for another 2.8 per cent. The women fall only a little behind the men in clerking (1.1 per cent, as compared with 1.8 per cent). There are 9.5 per cent of school girls in the West Coast series, but only 1.6 per cent of males are students. Teachers include 2.3 per cent as against 2.4 per cent of the whole professional class, including clergy, among the men.

There are also in the female series 6.8 per cent of nurses and actually 37 individuals (2.0 per cent) who are assigned to the "medical profession." Only one of these was a qualified physician.

A few county variations in female occupations are worthy of remark. In the household servant category the Kerry series (highest in mean age) is definitely in excess and the Leitrim and Sligo subseries are deficient. On the other hand, Leitrim and Sligo are very high indeed in the "at home" category and have no factory workers at all. This last named occupation is particularly well represented in Donegal, Mayo, and Galway, is deficient in Clare, and altogether lacking in Kerry. The occupation of housekeeper is heavily overrepresented in Kerry and in Donegal, and apparently deficient in Leitrim. The Sligo and Leitrim subseries seem to be somewhat overloaded with nurses. The Clare series, which is unduly packed with young girls, naturally is overloaded in the "schoolgirl" category.

In general, the small subseries from Sligo and Leitrim are derived from an apparently different and superior economic level from that represented in most other counties, in that the women from these counties are rarely household servants, oftenest at home in a technically unemployed status, never factory workers, often nurses. The Leitrim and Sligo subseries are not, however, completely homogeneous in occupation. The former has an insignificant excess of clerks and is low in housekeepers. The latter has a normal quota of housekeepers, no clerks, and an overrepresentation in the "medical profession." This last probably accounts for the primacy among the Sligo women of individuals who have attended the university. The Sligo group is quite devoid of uneducated persons, and there is but one such individual in the Leitrim subseries.

The Donegal women are the leaders in factory workers, in "business," and are second in proportion of shopkeepers. They are, on the whole, the least well educated of the subseries.

Age (Table XXVI-1). The West Coast females studied by Dr. Dawson average 4.30 years younger than the Irish County series males of Dr. Dupertuis. The female age range is much more restricted, with an upper limit of 69. Our male series includes a sizeable group between 80 and 94 years. Moreover, the standard deviation of age of the females is 0.6 years higher than that of the males. An inspection of the seriation of age reveals the fact that the youngest group, 15–19 years, includes 425 subjects, and the next group, 20–24 years, with 442 subjects is the modal age group of the series. Thereafter the numbers drop off very rapidly. These data will be considered in more detail in connection with the sorting of characters by age groups.

The Donegal women are virtually equal numerically to the males measured in West Donegal by Dr. Dupertuis and average only 1.15 years lower in age. The greatest age discrepancy occurs in Clare, which has the modal subseries in both sexes. In this county the males average 8.80 years older than the females. Our oldest county group of females is Kerry, in which, however, the males still enjoy an average age superiority of 2.40 years.

Weight (Table XXVI-2). The West Coast women average 22.90 lbs. lighter than the total Catholic County series of males. How much of this weight difference is attributable to the lighter clothing worn by the women is problematical. In the United States today the weight of women's clothing is usually no more than half that of the males. If a man's clothing weighs 7 lbs., that of a woman dressed for the same season will hardly exceed half of that amount. Dr. Dawson thinks that the older Irish women wear clothing heavier than that of the men, except the shoes. Nearly all older women wore two to four heavy woolen underskirts. The women were depressed by their light weight. One of them commented to Dr. Dawson when told her weight, "Sure, now and it's a poor weight and most of that peelings." Most of the women were fully clothed, except for shoes. Dr. Dawson saw few fat women.

The Clare women, who are the youngest subseries, are considerably the lightest, because of an overloading with girls between 15 and 19 years. These young girls, according to Dr. Dawson, did wear fewer and lighter clothes. Conversely, the Kerry women are considerably the highest in mean weight, and, at the same time, are the oldest county subgroup. The Kerry men are the fourth heaviest county subgroup in all of Ireland. Our Mayo women average 1.20 lbs. over mean weight and rank third among the county subgroups. whereas the male Mayo series ranks second in mean weight in all of the Irish counties.

The standard deviations of weight do not differ markedly, being 22.90 lbs. in the females and 22.50 lbs. in the males.

Stature (Table XXVI-3). The Irish women cannot be accounted tall, with a general mean of 158.55 cm. Their average stature is 92.2 per cent of male average stature for all of the Catholic county series. The tallest women are in the small subseries from Leitrim, which in the males is combined with other counties and therefore incomparable. The Kerry women are second tallest and in the male series Kerry ranks third in stature. Our shortest females come from Mayo, but in the male series the Mayo subseries is somewhat above mean stature. The standard deviation of female stature for the combined series is 6.18, as contrasted with 6.84 cm. in the male series.

Span (Table XXVI-4). The rankings in span generally follow those in stature. The mean span of the West Coast females is only 90.1 per cent of that of the males, whereas their mean stature is 92.2 per cent of the corresponding male figure. Thus it would appear that the females are not characterized by as great length of arms as are the males. It is possible, of course, that the females did not attempt to outdo each other in arm stretching, as did the males, but Dr. Dawson got them to "reach out" as far as they normally would.

It will be recalled that Dupertuis' male subjects generally made a game out of the determination of maximum span. The standard deviation of the female series is again below that of the males, but only to the extent of 0.75 cm.

Relative Span (Table XXVI-5). The mean relative span of the females, 102.80, is actually 2.52 units below that of the males. One expects a sex difference in this direction. Hrdlička found relative span in Old American males to be 102.6 and in females 99.6. Thus the difference between the two sexes in the Old American is even greater than in the Irish (Hrdlička, 1925, p. 120). It would appear that the Irish females are just as long-armed for their sex as are the males. Consequently, the possibility of the lack of a desire to excel each other in the measurement of arm stretch, as suggested above, probably does not apply. As a matter of fact, the matching of the female and male data, with span measured by two separate observers, indicates that the Irish are both absolutely and relatively long-armed and that the high relative span recorded in both sexes is not referable, in all probability, to the technique of measurement.

The standard deviation of relative span is slightly higher in the females than in the males (0.46), contrary to the situation in the case of the absolute measures.

There is no great variation in relative span among the county subseries of females.

Biacromial Diameter (Table XXVI-6). The biacromial diameter of the West Coast female averages 1.98 cm. less than the mean of all Irish males of the Catholic county series. The female mean is 94.86 per cent of the male average. The standard deviations of the female series are somewhat higher on the average (0.21 cm.).

The young female subseries from County Clare is considerably the lowest in mean biacromial diameter, and the Kerry women have by far the broadest shoulders. It will be recalled that the latter are the oldest and heaviest subseries, and the former the youngest and lightest. The Kerry women have an uppermost limit of 48 cm., which is equalled in the male series only in that same county. However, in the males, both Clare and West Galway exceed the biacromial mean of Kerry.

The latter ranks third among the Irish counties in shoulder breadth.

Relative Shoulder Breadth (Table XXVI-7). The relative shoulder breadth of the females exceeds that of the males on the average by 0.40 index units. The standard deviation of the females is 0.12 units higher. The Kerry women have significantly broader shoulders than those of any other county subseries. The upper limit of the female range of relative shoulder breadth is 29, reached in both Kerry and Sligo. No male series ranges above 27.

It is thus apparent that the West Coast Irish women are consistently broader in the shoulders relative to their stature than are the males of any of the Irish counties. However, this difference may be due to a divergence in measuring techniques whereby Dr. Dawson got higher values for biacromial diameter than did Dr. Dupertuis.

Sitting Height (Table XXVI-8). The mean sitting height of the women is 8.10 cm. less than that of the men—91.1 per cent of the male mean. This is nearly the same percentage relationship that obtains between the female stature and the male stature. It is therefore apparent that there can be no disproportionate excess of length of the head and trunk and deficiency of leg length in Irish females as compared with males, although such a finding has frequently been made in other groups. The standard deviations of sitting height average 1.08 higher in the female series. There is no reason for supposing that Dr. Dawson's technique of measuring sitting height was different from that of Dr. Dupertuis.

The county subseries show considerable deviations from the total mean of sitting height. The lowest mean by far is that of Mayo, whereas the Leitrim women have an average that exceeds the total mean by 1.64 cm. The latter subseries, which is very small, has also considerably the highest mean of stature and of span.

Relative Sitting Height (Table XXVI-9). The relative sitting height (sitting height as a percentage of stature) has a total mean in the West Coast Irish series of 52.88. In the total Catholic county series of Irish males it is 53.22. This sex difference is in the opposite direction of what is usual, since females ordinarily are expected to have relatively longer trunks and relatively shorter legs than males. The upper limit of the range of this index is 63 in the females and only 59 in the males.

The standard deviations of relative sitting height are, on the average, 0.44 index units higher in the females than in the males. Relative sitting height averages highest in the Sligo women, with Leitrim and Kerry close behind. It is to be expected that the shorter groups in stature would have the higher relative sitting heights, but this expectation is not realized. On the contrary, in these West Coast Irish women the higher relative sitting heights seem to occur generally in the taller subseries.

Head Length (Table XXVI-10). The average head length of the females falls below that of the males by 8.46 mm. The female mean is 95.7 per cent of the male. The standard deviation of the female series is significantly lower—0.30 index units. The comparison of the ranges is of some interest. That of the females is from 161 mm. to 214 mm., a spread of 64 mm. In the case of the males the range is from 170 to 223 mm., a total of 54 mm. In every county subseries the upper limit of the female range exceeds 200 mm. and in every one of the male county series it is more than 210 mm. The Irish, whether males or females, tend to have great head lengths.

In our female series the Galway women have the highest mean of head length, and the somewhat immature Clare sample, definitely the lowest. In the male series the highest mean of head length is that of the Aran Islands, closely followed by West Galway and E. Galway-Roscommon. Since the female series includes Aran Islanders and women from other parts of Galway, it is clear that the primacy in head length of the Galway women is shared by the men of that county.

In the male series Clare is approximately at the total Irish mean of head length and we may suppose that the inferior head length of the Clare females is attributable to the inclusion in the sample of an unduly large number of girls between 15 and 19 years.

Head Breadth (Table XXVI-11). The mean of female head breadth falls 5.61 mm. below that of the males (all Catholic county series) and is 96.4 per cent of the male average. The widest heads among the females occur in Kerry, which has a mean 1.23 mm.

above the total female average. Kerry also leads the male series in head breadth. Head breadths run higher in the south and west of Ireland than in the east. Since all of our female series is West Coast, we expect consistently high head breadths, and get them. The lowest mean is that of the Sligo women. In the male series Sligo is included in a group of counties, and head breadth in this group is about at the Irish mean, but a little low for western Ireland.

The standard deviation of head breadth in the female series is 0.72 mm. below that of the males.

Cephalic Index (Tables XXVI-12; XXVI-13). The mean cephalic index of our Irish women is 0.60 units above that of the Catholic county males. The cephalic index of the females is then 100.8 per cent of the male mean. The standard deviations of the two sexes are about the same. In both series we have individual ranges from 61 to 94—as wide a spread as we could expect to find in any population.

The lowest mean of the index is found in the females of Galway and this accords well with our male data, since Aran Islanders have the lowest cephalic indices of western Ireland and W. Galway men rank next to them. The highest female mean occurs in Clare, followed by Kerry, and in the male series these rankings are reversed. Kerry is the only county in which mean value of this index is lower for females than for males, and this difference is trifling and insignificant. A consideration of the male values for the mean cephalic index in only the counties included in the female series would undoubtedly reduce the difference between the male and female means.

In comparison with the total male Catholic county series, the West Coast Irish women have 6.3 per cent fewer dolichocephals, 3.6 per cent more brachycephals, and, of course, an excess of 2.8 per cent of mesocephals. The expectation of a slightly higher cephalic index in females than in males is thus fulfilled.

In the male series the Aran Islands lead in dolichocephals with 35 per cent. Among the females, Galway, which includes the Aran Islands, is also first in long-heads with 26.2 per cent. Sligo is second, with 6.9 per cent fewer. Again, in the males, Kerry has considerably the lowest percentage of dolicho-cephals (11.7 per cent) and this ranking is duplicated in the West Coast females (11.3 per cent). However, in our female series Clare ranks first in brachycephals, and Kerry second. These rankings are reversed in the males.

Head Height (Table XXVI-14). The head height of the females is 5.24 mm. less, on the average, than that of the Irish males. The female mean is 95.8 per cent of the male average. The standard deviation of head height for females averages 1.32 mm. higher for females than for males. There is no male county subseries that does not exceed in mean height that of every county subseries of the West Coast females, with the sole exception of the Aran Islands, in which small series Dupertuis has recorded the minimum average head height for all Irish males — 120.18 mm. It is interesting to note that our minimum female mean for head height occurs in Galway, which in our female series includes the Aran Islands. The highest mean head height in the female series occurs in Donegal. In the male series, West Donegal has the highest mean found in any western county group and the adjacent county group, N. Fermanagh, E. Donegal, Tyrone, and Londonderry, has the maximum average head height in Ireland.

Length-Height Index (Table XXVI-15). The female mean of this index exceeds the all-Ireland mean of the males by only 0.15 index units, but the females have a mean standard deviation 0.75 index units higher than that of the males.

The highest mean of the length-height index is found in Donegal. In the male series the group N. Fermanagh-E. Donegal-Tyrone-Londonderry ranks first in length-height index, closely followed by West Donegal. Our female series accords well with the males. Again, in the males the lowest mean of the length-height index occurs in the Arans and this is matched in the female series by the minimum value of this index in Galway.

Breadth-Height Index (Table XXVI-16). The West Coast females fall below the Irish males in the mean of this index by 0.30 index units (i.e., the women have lower heads relative to head breadth than have the men). The standard deviation is 0.81 index units higher

in the total female series.

Among the females the mean of this index is highest in Donegal. In general, the same situation obtains in the males, as respects West Donegal among the western counties and E. Donegal-N. Fermanagh-Tyrone-Londonderry for the whole of Ireland.

However, the lowest mean value of this index is found in the female subseries from Clare and not, as in the males, in the group that includes the Arans.

Minimum Frontal Diameter (Table XXVI-17). The West Coast women fall below the mean of the Irish males by 4.80 mm. The female average is 95.6 per cent of the male figure. The standard deviation is 0.32 index units lower in the females. The lowest West Coast value of this measurement occurs in the male series of the Aran Islands, with other county subgroups that include Galway men falling at the all-Irish mean or slightly above it. In the females the Galway women have significantly narrower foreheads, possibly because of the inclusion of a large number of Aran females. The other groups in the female series do not vary widely. Among the males, Cork, Clare, and Mayo are outstandingly high in the means of the minimum frontal diameter.

Fronto-Parietal Index (Table XXVI-18). The females average 0.69 index units lower than all Irish males in this index and the standard deviations are virtually identical. The highest mean occurs in the Sligo women and the lowest in Kerry. Kerry is also somewhat low in the male series, but there is no close correspondence in male and female rankings, even for the Western Coast counties.

Bizygomatic Diameter (Table XXVI-19). The total West Coast female mean falls below that of all Irish males of the Catholic county series by 8.20 mm. and is 94.2 per cent of the male mean. However, the standard deviation of the females averages 0.65 mm. less than that of the males.

The Kerry women have the broadest faces, followed by the women of Mayo. In the males the rankings are the same for these two counties (omitting County Cork, from which we have no female sample).

Cephalo-Facial Index (Table XXVI-20). The females have a mean cephalo-facial index 1.88 index units below the average of all males. Their mean is 97.9 per cent of the male average. The implication of the difference is that faces in the females are narrower relative to head breath than in the other sex, and this is an ordinary sex difference. The standard deviation of the total female series is 0.24 index units below the corresponding figure for the males.

The highest mean value of the index for the females falls in the Galway subseries. In the male series the first ranking is held by E. Galway-Roscommon, and the second by West Galway. The female subseries from Galway includes one individual with a cephalo-facial index of 111, which is certainly suspect. Among the male county groups the lowest ranking in this index is West Donegal. However, in the females, the Donegal subseries has a mean slightly above average. Again, in our female series the minimum of this index occurs in Clare, probably because the Clare subseries is overloaded with immature subjects. The value of this index in the Clare males is a mere trifle below the mean of the total male Catholic county series.

Zygo-Frontal Index (Table XXVI-21). The mean of the female index is 101.2 per cent of the male, 0.92 index units higher. This is a consequence of a greater difference in favor of the males in bizygomatic diameter than in minimum frontal diameter. Such a sex difference is quite ordinary. The standard deviations for the two sexes are practically identical. In spite of a fairly wide range of individual variation in this index, the spread of the means of subseries is not great. In the females the lowest mean occurs in Kerry, whereas in the other sex Kerry has to yield to the Arans in the low value of the mean of this index. In the males, again, West Donegal, with an average of 78.38, ranks second only to Tipperary Kilkenny. In the female series, Donegal is only insignificantly high. The top value is reached in the small Sligo subseries. However, the combined county group of males that includes Sligo falls below the all-Irish mean.

Bigonial Diameter (Table XXVI-22). The bigonial diameter of the females averages 7.64 mm. less than that of the males. The female mean is 93.0 per cent of the male. The standard deviations in females are substantially lower—0.80 mm. on the average. In the females the broadest jaws occur in Mayo and Kerry—counties in the male series that also rank high—presumably because of their large proportions of broad-faced brachycephals. Our lowest female value is found in Sligo, which in the males is included in a subseries that has a low mean of bigonial diameter.

Fronto-Gonial Index (Table XXVI-23). In the Irish males this index is usually near to parity—i.e., the breadth of the forehead and the breadth of the jaws are approximately equal. In the females, however, the breadth of the jaws is ordinarily less than that of the forehead. Females average 2.60 index units less than males but have only insignificantly lower standard deviations. In the male series by far the highest value of this index is found in the Arans (101.90) in which inbred group the jaws seem fairly consistently wider than the foreheads. Our Galway sample of females reflects this situation in having the highest mean of the series. The lowest value of this index in the males occurs in West Donegal. The Donegal subseries of females is also low, but both Sligo and Clare are still lower.

Zygo-Gonial Index (Table XXVI-24). This index is bigonial diameter expressed as a percentage of bizygomatic diameter. The females have narrower jaws relative to facial breadth than have the males. The difference amounts to 0.99 index units, on the average. The males are slightly more variable. Among the females this index runs highest in Galway, a situation which is paralleled by the primacy of the Aran Islands and West Galway in the male series (although Offaly-Leix-Kildare ties West Galway for third place). A low value in the Sligo women is faintly reflected in the minimum of the index among males which occurs in the combined group, Sligo-Leitrim-S. Fermanagh-W. Cavan, and also in E. Galway-Roscommon.

Total Face Height (Table XXVI-25). The West Coast females show a mean total face height that falls below the average of all Irish males by no less than 11.7 mm. The female mean is 90.8 per cent of the male average. Both sexes of the Irish have, nevertheless, very long faces. The standard deviation of the female series is 0.60 mm. less than that of the male series. Male total face heights are by far the greatest in the Aran Islands and in West Galway, but our female series shows both the Donegal and the Mayo women exceeding those of Galway in the mean of this measurement. The Clare women have the shortest faces, probably in part because of the immaturity of this subseries. However, the Clare males rank among the shorter-faced in the Irish Catholic county series. Similarly, in Dr. Dawson's West Coast females the Kerry subseries falls below the total mean (although not significantly), but this is not true in the case of the Irish males.

Facial Index (Table XXVI-26). The West Coast women have relatively wider and shorter faces than the Irish males. The latter exceed the mean of the total facial index of the women by 3.25 units. There is no male county group that does not exceed the mean of every West Coast female subseries. Among the males mean values of the total facial index fall slightly below 90 in Mayo, Clare, Kerry, Cork, E. Galway-Roscommon, and Limerick. Thus most of our female subseries originate in areas where faces are less leptoprosopic than in the generality of Irish counties. The highest value of this index among the females occurs in the Sligo subseries, which in the males is included in a county group that is only slightly above mean value of this index. Actually, the most leptoprosopic mean of all the Irish males is found in the Aran Islands. Our female Galway subseries (which includes the Arans) exceeds the total mean but falls considerably short of the value found in the Sligo women.

The facial index mean is lowest among the females in Kerry, which ranks among the lowest values of this index in the males, but is slightly higher than Clare, Cork, and Limerick.

Upper Face Height (Table XXVI-27). The females average 5.45 mm. less than the males and their mean is 92.5 per cent of the male average. In total face height the females are only 90.8 per cent of the males and their mean deficiency in this measurement is 11.7 mm. Thus the females are particularly inferior to the males in the depth of the mandible, an unusual sex difference.

The standard deviation of upper face height is insignificantly less in the males than in the females.

The Donegal women have the longest upper

faces among the females. In the male series West Donegal is well above average and the county group that includes E. Donegal is even higher. However, among the men the Kerry subseries ranks first in all Ireland for upper face height, whereas among the women it is only a little high. The minimum average of this facial measurement is found in the women of Clare, undoubtedly partly because of the large number of young girls in the Clare subseries. However, in the great male series the Clare mean is somewhat below average.

Upper Facial Index (Table XXVI-28). The upper facial index in the females is 0.99 units below that of the males and is 98.1 per cent of the male value. Thus the women diverge from the men in proportions of the upper face less widely than in the total face. The usual sex difference obtains in that the women have relatively shorter and wider upper faces.

The lowest mean value of the index is found in the Clare subseries, probably because of the number of immature subjects included in that series. Among the males the upper facial index in Clare is also below the all Irish mean, but several other counties show slightly lower values. In our female series the Sligo women have the highest mean index, whereas in the male series Sligo is included in a county group which is next to the lowest of all Ireland.

Nose Height (Table XXVI-29). The Irish have long noses, but the West Coast females fall behind the males in the mean value of this measurement to the extent of 4.92 mm. Their noses average only 91.3 per cent of the male mean. Here again is a sex difference in the usual direction. Nose heights are to some extent a function of age, since the nose increases in length (height) in middle years and thereafter. Consequently, the longest noses are likely to be found in the group of highest mean age. This principle does not hold in our West Coast Irish females, since the Kerry women are considerably the oldest, but have a nose height slightly below the mean. The longest noses of the male series are found in the Aran Islands, a fairly young group. The shortest noses in our females are found in Leitrim and in Clare, and these are the youngest in mean age. Our Sligo women have considerably the longest noses, but their primacy in this measurement does not accord with any such situation in the male group of which Sligo is a part.

Nose Breadth (Table XXVI-30). Female nose breadth is, on the average, 3.78 mm. less than that of the males. The female is 89.5 per cent of the male mean. The females have a standard deviation lower by 0.45 mm.

On the whole, the means of the subseries differ very little, in every instance by less than one mm. The Kerry women have slightly the broadest noses and the Sligo women the narrowest.

Nasal Index (Table XXVI-31). The mean female index is 0.96 index units below that of the Irish males and is 98.5 per cent of the latter. The standard deviation is 0.20 index units higher in the females. The difference, with the females more leptorrhine, is commonly but not consistently observed in anthropometric series. Among the women the Galway subseries has considerably the lowest mean of the nasal index, but no similar distinction is enjoyed by any of the male county groups that include men from various parts of Galway. However, in the males the Arans and West Donegal are somewhat below mean value of the nasal index, but West Galway is very high. Again, in the females the Kerry women have the highest mean index while the Kerry men are below the all-Irish average. There seems, then, to be no particular relationship in rankings between the West Coast Irish men and the women from the same regions. Of course, all of these Irish are markedly leptorrhine in their average.

Conclusions on Sex Differences (Tables XXVI-32 and XXVI-33). The age differences between West Coast Irish females and total Irish males must not be interpreted as implying anything else than that the female series includes some 48.1 per cent of subjects under 25 years of age, whereas the Catholic county series of males has only 30.4 per cent in these age categories (15–19 years, 20–24 years). Furthermore, in the 15–19 year age group are 23.6 per cent of the females, but only 9.8 per cent of the males. It is particularly in this youngest age group that size deficiencies, connected with the immaturity of the subjects, are greatest. Therefore, it follows that all of the sex differences in size, here to be summarized, may be somewhat exaggerated on account of age disparity in the two series.

The weight deficiency of the females, amounting to 22.9 pounds, makes their average weight only 85.40 per cent of that of the males. Most of this weight deficiency is probably real although some allowance has to be made for the overloading of the female series with young girls and young adult women. Those have not attained the full weight of middle years, and, besides, are likely to wear less clothing than the older women, a fact which would bring their mean weight even lower.

In body measurements it is interesting to find the females approaching the male means closest (94.9 per cent) in biacromial diameter or shoulder breadth. The figures suggest that the average Irish female is broader in the torso, shorter in the arms and trunk, than the average Irish male. There is a possibility which must be faced that the technique of taking this measurement employed by Dr. Dawson, diverged from that of Dr. Dupertuis and yielded somewhat higher means.

The notably higher variability of the females in sitting height and their failure to achieve as high a percentage ratio to male sitting height as in the case of stature is puzzling and a little disturbing. Females usually have relatively longer trunks and shorter legs than males of the same stock, but these females have the opposite. It is very difficult to get some persons to sit up straight enough to insure that their sitting height attains its full quota of their standing height. However, this difficulty is likely to be enhanced in older subjects rather than in the immature and in young adults. And our Irish female series is overloaded with the immature! Moreover, Dr. Dawson was especially careful to get her subjects to sit erect, but without enhancing their height by contracting their gluteal muscles.

The tabulation of differences in measurements of the head and face has several interesting features. In the first place it is notable that the females approximate the male measurements far more closely in diameters of the cranial vault than in facial dimensions. They are closest to the males in head breadth—and this is probably quite usual as a sex difference.

Of the facial measurements, the females do best in competition with the males in the bizygomatic diameter or face breadth. This fact is explicable on the basis of the close connection of bizygomatic diameter with head breadth, and, in general, with the size of the cranial vault. The great discrepancy between female total face height and the corresponding average in the male and the percentile relationships of female to male means throughout the face show that the males have very much deeper lower jaws and the females smaller noses.

The summary of indicial differences adds little that cannot be deduced from the study of the differences in raw measurements. The most impressive postcephalic difference is in the vastly smaller relative span of the females.

In the facial and cephalic indices the most outstanding sex difference is that between the means of the total facial. The Irish female has usually a relatively much shorter and broader face than the male, with the difference its maximum in the lower part of the face.

The comparative variabilities of the females and males, as based upon the values of the standard deviations, do not suggest that one sex is either metrically or indicially more or less variable than the other. Marked elevations of the female standard deviations seem to occur notably in sitting height and head height and the derivative indices. These are both measurements involving technical difficulties and a fairly wide margin of error. Hence we cannot be sure that the higher female variability is anthropological rather than a result of observational equation.

Skin Color, Inner Arm (Table XXVII-1). The West Coast Irish women have pale skins in 3.8 per cent, as against only 0.3 per cent of skins so classified among the males. However, women are less exposed to sunlight than men in most countries. There is not much sex difference in proportions of pink skins. The women have 3.1 per cent less than the men and almost the same proportions of dark-skinned persons are found in the two sexes. Clare is our most dark-skinned female subseries, but the Clare males are less than average in brunetness. The Clare female series also shows the highest percentage of pale skins.

All that can be concluded from the sex comparison is that there are a few more females who have pale skins, and a few less who have pink skins.

Vascularity (Table XXVII-2). There is an interesting sex difference in vascularity between the West Coast females and the Irish males in general. The females show about 5.8 per cent more of subjects with submedium vascularity and 6.6 per cent less of pronounced vascularity. This corresponds roughly to the excess of pale skins among the females. An inspection of vascularity in the males of the counties from which the female series are derived suggests that the differences are not the result of observational equations between the two observers. For, Sligo and Leitrim among the females are especially low in subjects of pronounced vascularity and the group that includes these counties is similarly low in the males. Mayo, Galway and Clare are especially strong among the females in pronounced vascularity, and the last two are also very high in this category in the male series.

It is quite likely that outdoor life with exposure to the elements is to some extent accountable for the greater vascularity of the Irish males.

Freckles (Table XXVII-3). Forty-eight per cent of our females are more or less freckled, as compared with 39.6 per cent of the males in the Catholic county series. However, our females are all West Coast, which is

the heaviest area for freckling in Ireland. Our Donegal women have far less freckling than West Donegal males, and a little less than the central block of counties that includes E. Donegal. The women from Mayo are also markedly less freckled than are the men. In Kerry, the most heavily freckled county in the females, the proportions of freckled as compared with non-freckled do not differ markedly between the sexes. The Clare subseries of females, heavily loaded with young girls, has 21 per cent more of freckled subjects than is found in the male series from that county. Our Leitrim females are the least freckled, but a comparison with males is difficult. The Sligo females have about the same proportion of freckles as has the combined male group which includes Sligo-Leitrim-S. Fermanagh-W. Cavan. Certainly one gets the impression that very pronounced and massed freckles are fewer among the females than among the males from the same counties. However, this is not true of Clare, which has more freckling and heavier freckling in the female series than in the male. Of course, freckles are likely to occur oftener in young people and Clare is our youngest subseries.

It seems impossible to conclude from these data that the women are oftener freckled or more heavily freckled than the men, particularly in view of the juvenility of the female series, which ought to be enough to give them more freckling than the older male series.

Moles (Table XXVII-4). About 10 per cent of our female subjects are recorded to have few or many moles visible on hands, arms, face, or necks. This proportion exceeds that observed in the males which is 6.1 per cent. Every one of our 7 counties in which females were observed shows a higher percentage of moles in that sex. It is possible that the females expose more skin area for observation of moles on neck and arms than do the males, but it is hardly likely that this is the differentiating factor. We expect more moles in darker skinned persons but the females do not exceed the males in brunet and swarthy skins, but only in "pale" skins. It may be that persons with very white or pale skins have a tendency toward mole production similar to that of dark-skinned individuals.

Hair Form (Table XXVII-5). The Irish women have 17.4 per cent more of straight hair than the total males and fall below the latter in every category of curved hair. This statement also applies to the county comparisons where these are possible. It is unlikely that the sex difference is referable to observational equation. The only categories of hair form that are difficult to distinguish in short-haired males are straight and low waved. But the females fall below the males by 8.5 per cent in the deep-waved category and by 1.3 per cent in the curly class. Again, in the males the principal difficulty of discrimination is between straight and low waved owing to the fact that low waves are not always discernible in short hair. An error of classification due to this cause would tend to heap up the males in the straight category and diminish their number of low waves. Exactly the opposite occurs, in that the males relative to females are high in low waves and low in straight hair.

Hair Texture (Table XXVII-6). The females have one per cent less of coarse hair than the males, but 24.7 per cent more of fine hair. Dupertuis classified the male hair as of medium texture in 92.5 per cent of all cases. While we might reasonably expect that females would show more fine hair than males, the difference here is so great that one suspects it may be due in large measure to the variation in the standards of Dupertuis and Dawson. It is the experience of the authors that judgments of hair texture are often quite difficult and liable to a strong personal equation. Many observers are prone to regard their own hair texture as "medium" whether it is "coarse" in reality or "fine." Such observers are likely to get skewed distribution in their samples. The senior author has no reason for supposing that the present difference is due to this particular factor, but is inclined to conclude that a real difference in favor of finer hair among the females may have been enhanced to some extent by varying standards of judgment as to what constitutes "medium" as contrasted with "fine."

Hair Quantity, Head (Table XXVII-7). In 12 per cent of cases the Irish females have pronounced hair quantity or thickness, as compared with only 2.6 per cent of males. Further, submedium hair quantity occurs in only 1.5 per cent of females, but in 2.3 per cent of males. Males, of course, are much more subject to thinning of the hair and balding than are females. Consequently, this sex difference is to be expected. Yet this observation is difficult and tricky, since it is supposed to be based upon the thickness of the hair (i.e., upon the closeness of the implantation of hairs), rather than upon length and mass as determined by length. It is interesting in this connection to note that the counties in which "pronounced" hair quantity is least frequent in the females, Sligo and Donegal, both fall into county groups which in the males are below par in pronounced hair quantity. However, the Leitrim females are only a little below average in this category of hair quantity, but in the males Leitrim is grouped with Sligo and other counties that show a slight deficiency of pronounced head hair quantity. In the females the highest percentage of thick or pronounced quantity of head hair occurs in Clare, which is a very young group. The male Clare series, which is not below mean age, is not so distinguished. Therefore it seems probable that the mean age of the sample has an effect upon this type of observation in so far as older females and older males alike tend to have thinner hair. Yet it must be noted that our oldest female group, Kerry, is by no means deficient in pronounced head hair thickness, whereas the second youngest group (Leitrim) is a little below female par in this category.

Hair Quantity, Body (Table XXVII-8). No Irish female is recorded to have "pronounced" body hair and only 2.6 per cent of the total Irish males. The Irish, on these data, cannot be considered a hairy nation. The women have only 3.6 per cent of medium body hair, as against 91.1 per cent of males and there is, of course, a compensation in the submedium category which contains the vast bulk of the females. On the other hand, only 0.6 per cent of females are recorded as devoid of body hair, which is not much more than the significant percentage of this category (0.4) found in the males. One curious fact is recorded in the table. The small Leitrim sample includes 14 females (20.5 per cent) who have "medium" body hair. This is vastly more than in any other county subseries.

Grayness, Head (Table XXVII-9). The Irish females have 12.4 per cent less graying of the hair than is found among the males. This difference may be due in large measure to the fact that the mean age of the females is 4.3 years less than that of the total males. In the females, absence of grayness is at a maximum in the Clare series which is youngest in mean age, and at a minimum in the Kerry series which is the oldest. On the whole, graying seems to be related fairly closely to mean age.

Hair Color, Head (Table XXVII-10). The Western Irish females tend to have darker hair color than the males, either in West Ireland or in the whole country. The percentage of black hair in our total female series exceeds that in the male total series by 1.3 per cent. The women have 11.8 per cent more of dark brown hair, but 12.8 per cent less of flat brown hair. The males have 2.1 per cent less of red-brown hair and 3.2 per cent more of golden brown. In the lighter shades of hair, which are rare in both sexes, the differences are small.

The women of Leitrim have considerably the darkest hair shades of the counties in which the females were observed. Sligo is second darkest, but both of these counties are represented by lamentably small subseries. Both of these small samples are virtually devoid of blondes. In all the female subseries the modal hair color is dark brown. This shade totals 65.8 per cent in Sligo. Sligo and Leitrim are also lowest in red hair. The two counties with the lightest hair shades are Clare and Galway. These are strong in flat brown, golden brown, and, to some degree, in most of the lighter hair shades. The Clare sample leads in red hair and it is possible that the inclusion of large numbers of subadults in this series has had the effect of increasing the frequency of light hair shades.

In the male series, Mayo and Kerry are outstanding among the western counties because of high frequency of dark brown hair, but West Donegal has most black hair. The darkness of hair color found in the females of Sligo and Leitrim is not paralleled in the male subseries that includes these counties. There is no parallelism of county trends between males and females, even if we take into consideration the generally lighter distribution of male hair shades.

Eye Color (Table XXVII-11). In line with the darker shades of hair encountered among the Irish females as compared with the males, is their darker eye color. Whereas the huge male Catholic county series, numbering 8909 subjects for the recording of eye color, yielded only 41 pure dark eyes or 0.5 per cent, among the 1855 West Coast females there are 108 with dark eyes, a total of 5.8 per cent. The largest category of these dark eyes is dark brown; the others mostly dark-light brown, but a few light brown. It should be noted that a dark-light brown eye has a dark brown pigmented zone surrounding the pupillary zone, with a light brown zone outside of that and bordering the peripheral zone or outside ring of the iris. Another difference between the males and the females lies in the high frequency of gray-brown eyes in the latter, exceeding the male proportion by 22.3 per cent. On the other hand, the males have exactly 20 per cent more of blue-brown eyes than have the females. Again, the females have 20.6 per cent of combined gray and gray-blue eyes, while the males have only 4.4 per cent of these shades. Finally pure blue eyes in the males exceed the proportion found in the females by 28.8 per cent.

It is thus evident that the West Irish females differ profoundly from total Irish males in eye color, not only in darkness but in the nature of the light eye shades found. Even in the mixed eyes the women run to gray-browns and the men to blue-browns, while in the pure lights we again have the predominance of gray and gray-blue in the females and pure blue in the males.

The distribution of the interesting small minority of pure dark eyes is not particularly uneven. With 5.8 per cent of combined dark eyes in all of the female subseries the range is only from 4.0 per cent in Clare to 10.2 per cent in Leitrim. Sligo has 6.9 per cent, Galway 6.8 per cent, Donegal 6.6 per cent, Mayo and Kerry 5.4 per cent. In the male Catholic county series, the group Sligo-Leitrim-S. Fermanagh-W. Cavan has 1.0 of pure dark eyes (7 individuals). Other county groups with more than 2 dark eyed men are Longford-Westmeath (1.2 per cent), Offaly-Leix-Kildare (1.1 per cent), and Meath-Louth-Dublin (1.3 per cent). It is then of some interest to note that our darkest eyed female subseries falls in a county group which in males is high in the excessively rare dark eyes. In the female series Sligo and Leitrim are also remarkable for their leading proportions of gray-brown eyes, although Mayo presses them closely. However, the male group that includes Sligo and Leitrim is one of the lowest in gray-brown eyes. Green-brown shades are notably deficient among the Sligo and Leitrim females, but enormously in excess in the Clare subseries. Here again there is no parallel in the male series. Clare, Galway, and Kerry females are rather high in the mixed blue-brown eyes that are so much more common in the males than in the females, while in the male series this eye shade is notably above par in the Arans, Kerry, West Donegal and Mayo, but only slightly high in West Galway and Clare. So here, again, there is no close matching of male and female trends in the western counties.

There is nothing that seems instructive in the distribution of the various shades of light eyes among the females. Their low frequency in Clare seems to compensate for an extraordinarily high proportion of green-brown eyes in that county and may be related to the juvenility of the Clare subseries. Kerry has grossly the highest percentage of blue eyes in the female series, but Kerry in the male series is one of the lowest counties in blue eyes. However, we have evidence that blue eyes increase in frequency in the males in the older age groups, apparently as a result of some obscure selectional process. Our Kerry sample of females is our oldest subseries. It is possible that the low frequency of blue eyes in Clare and the high frequency in Kerry (both among females) may be connected with the phenomenon observed in the Irish males, whereby mixed eyes diminish and blue eyes increase with age after maturity.

We cannot disregard the possibility that the wide variation between the sexes (gray-brown versus blue-brown; gray and gray-blue versus blue) may have been increased to some extent by an observational equation. However, it seems very doubtful that Dupertuis consistently judged to be "blue" an iridial color classified by Dawson as "gray." Dr. Dawson's comment upon this point is that she never had any difficulty in matching shades of color or identifying them and that she does not think that she was inclined to "slight" blue, her favorite eye shade.

Pigment, Mixed Eyes (Table XXVII-12). This set of observations was designed to make some gradation of the amount of melanotic pigment in mixed eyes by estimating the area of the more heavily pigmented zone around the pupil and the medial part of the ciliary zone in relation to the area of the lighter zone toward the periphery of the iris, where background rather than superficial pigment shows through from the deeper layers of the iris. Whether male or female, Irish mixed eyes are predominantly *very pronouncedly light* mixed. Both observers agree on this point to a fractional per cent (59.3 per cent of males, 59.2 per cent of females). However, in the category *pronouncedly light* there are 12.3 per cent less of males than females; in the *even* category, there are 7.6 per cent more of males; in the *pronouncedly dark* category 2.7 per cent more of males, and in the *very pronouncedly dark* an excess of 1.9 per cent of males. The data then suggest that mixed eyes tend to be somewhat lighter in the Irish females than in total Irish males.

In this observation some consideration of county differences among the females and a search for similarity in county trends in both sexes seems worthwhile. The highest percentage of very pronouncedly light mixed eyes occurs in Donegal along with an absence of very pronouncedly dark eyes. Perhaps it may be stated that this county shows the greatest prevalence of very light mixed eyes in the females. The Sligo subseries is also very high in the lightest mixed eyes and is probably second only to Donegal in general lightness of the mixed eyes. The Clare series is notable for a piling up of an excess in the *pronouncedly light* as contrasted with the *very pronouncedly light* category, and one is tempted to relate this irregularity to the very low mean age of the County Clare group.

Nothing is revealed by a comparison of the females of the western counties with the males from the same county groups, except the consistency of the sex differences stated above, whether or not they are complicated by an observational equation.

Iris (Table XXVII-13). There is little agreement in the recording of iris pattern between males and females. In the *clear* category the males have an excess of 13.5 per cent, in the *rayed* a deficiency of 13 per cent, in the *zoned* category a deficiency of 14.7 per cent, in the *spotted* category a deficiency of 6.3 per cent, in the *diffuse* an excess of 22.6 per cent, and in the *scalloped* a deficiency of only 1.9 per cent. One suspects that these differences may be enhanced by observational equations of the two observers and also by variations in source and degree of flight in the different places where the observations were made. The classification of iris here followed is very unsatisfactory and has been abandoned since the Irish survey. This old classification is ambiguous in some places and the categories are not mutually exclusive. In particular, a "clear" eye was supposed to be an eye more or less homogeneous in iris color and without specific pattern. The term "diffuse" was originally intended for use in eyes that showed an irregular pigment staining of yellow or brown, looking like an ink blot that has run. However, some of our Harvard observers have interpreted it again as roughly equivalent to "unpatterned." A "rayed" eye and a "zoned" eye are usually distinguishable, but a "spotted" eye may be rayed or zoned also, and the term "scalloped" is usually applied to the border of the pupillary zone of the eye and scallops may occur in spotted eyes, rayed eyes, or zoned eyes.

In view of the poor classification of iris variations there is every excuse for a difference of standards to arise between the observers, and there is comparatively little that can be salvaged from the methodological mess.

Probably it can be deduced correctly that the eyes of the Irish males are less likely to show distinct patterning than are those of the females (i.e., the male eye is oftener clear or diffuse, much less commonly clearly rayed, zoned or spotted). Rays, zones, and spots are much commoner in mixed eyes than in pure light eyes and they also occur oftener in pure dark eyes than in pure light eyes.

A discussion of county differences in iris pattern among the females seems unprofitable.

Eyefolds, External (Table XXVII-14). External eyefolds in some degree of development occur in nearly 9 per cent more of males than females and this is an ordinary sex difference. It is probably connected with larger brow ridge overhang in the males, deeper set eyes, and a consequently greater tendency for the external part of the upper eyelid to sag in middle and old age. It is also a phenomenon of old and middle age, and the large number of young subjects in our female series might make a difference in the occurrence of this feature in favor of the males.

The small subseries from Sligo and Leitrim are notably poor in external folds, but this is not true of the county group of males that includes these areas.

Eyefolds, Median (Table XXVII-15). In median eyefolds the situation is reversed. The males show this feature in 3 per cent only and the females have an excess of 10.1 per cent.

In the female series, Leitrim is notable for a marked deficiency of median folds and Sligo for an excess. The Clare series is also somewhat low in median folds. It is to be noted that these folds tend to develop with advancing age, and these are our two youngest subseries. However, the excess in Sligo, which is a trifle below mean age, and the lack of a marked excess in Kerry, which is considerably the oldest subseries, indicate that this feature is by no means altogether age determined. It shows very little age regression in Irish males. There are no important differences between the West Coast counties in the male series.

Eyefolds, Internal (Table XXVII-16). Internal eyefolds are very rare in Ireland in either sex. The males have 1 per cent and the females 1.1 per cent.

Eye Obliquity (Table XXVII-17). Some obliquity of the eye openings occurs in 90.4 per cent of the West Coast females, but in only 35.6 per cent of the males. It seems possible that this sex difference has been increased by a divergence of standards between our two observers, particularly because in the male series the counties from which we have comparative data for the other sex are conspicuously low in eye-slant. Dr. Dupertuis thinks that Dr. Dawson may have been more aware of eye obliquity than he was. Both judged it by holding a horizontal on the level of the internal canthus and evaluating the slope to the external canthus. They, therefore, differ more from the female distribution of eye-slant than do many of the eastern counties. A good reason for the more frequent obliquity of eye openings in the females is the lesser development laterally and anteriorly of the malars and of the lower orbital border in the females. However, the differences here recorded seem rather excessive.

In our female series, Kerry and Clare are notable for their great excesses of eye-slant (almost always upward), and the high frequency of a medium degree of upward slant in the Clare sample raises the question of an age factor in the degree of apparent upward obliquity. However, our Leitrim subseries is, relative to other female groups, low in eye obliquity and this subseries is only a little higher in mean age than the Clare subseries.

Males show 5.8 per cent of downward obliquity of the eye openings as contrasted with our 2.2 per cent of females who exhibit this feature. This is an ordinary sex difference.

Eye Opening, Height (Table XXVII-18). The males have low or submedium eye openings in 3.6 per cent more of cases than have the females and they also exceed the females in openings of pronounced height by a trifling 0.5 per cent. There is no indication, then, of a marked sex difference in this feature.

Eyebrow Thickness (Table XXVII-19). Females have pronounced or very pronounced eyebrow thickness in 42.9 per cent of cases as contrasted with only 3.6 per cent in the males. The females fall below the males insignificantly in proportions of submedium or thin eyebrows. It is difficult to account for the vast sex difference on any other theory than that of a divergence of standards between the two observers. It seems very doubtful that thicker eyebrows in women than in men is a valid sex difference. Of course, eyebrows thin in old age, and this thinning would probably affect females less than males. Further,

our female series falls below the male series in mean age. Nevertheless and notwithstanding, it seems probable that Dupertuis was more conservative in judging eyebrow thickness and therefore graded many eyebrows as *medium* which Dawson would have graded as *pronounced* in thickness.

Among the females, the Leitrim and Sligo subseries are outstanding for relative deficiency in pronounced and very pronounced eyebrow thickness. The thickest eyebrows occur in Galway, followed at some distance by Kerry.

Eyebrow Concurrency (Table XXVII-20). Eyebrow concurrency is absent in 15.3 per cent of females, as against 1.8 per cent of males. At the other end of the distribution the females have but one per cent of pronounced concurrency, whereas the males exhibit 10.3 per cent. The sex difference is usual and expected. The majority of males have medium concurrency (64.7 per cent) whereas the overwhelming preponderance in females is submedium. In the females Clare leads in medium and pronounced concurrency, in spite of the tender mean age of the Clare sample. Galway also seems to be high in medium concurrency. These rankings are not duplicated in the male series.

Brow Ridges (Table XXVII-21). The highest proportion of absence of brow ridges is found in the Clare subseries, which has the lowest mean age. Apart from this one instance, the differences in mean ages of the female subseries seem to bear little relationship, if any, to size of brow ridges. Males naturally exceed the females vastly in size of brow ridges. For example, the male series shows 20.8 per cent of pronounced or very pronounced brow ridges, and the female series only 2.4 per cent. At the other end of the range, brow ridges are recorded as absent in 28.6 per cent of females, but in only 2.2 per cent of males. In the female series, Sligo and Donegal appear to run to somewhat better developed brow ridges than in other counties, but no such phenomenon is discernible in the male series.

Forehead Height (XXVII-22). The West Coast Irish females have foreheads of medium height in the vast majority of cases. Only 9.8 per cent are recorded as having foreheads of pronounced height, whereas, in the male series, Dupertuis records 53.7 per cent of such foreheads. According to our experience, the males usually do have higher foreheads than the females, and this impression is often enhanced by recession of the hair line in the males. Nevertheless and notwithstanding, it would seem probable that some difference in the standards of the observers may have militated in favor of a larger sex difference than in fact exists. It is to be noted that Dr. Dawson records foreheads of submedium height in 6.4 per cent of females, while Dupertuis has only 3.7 per cent of males in this category. Dupertuis now feels that he may have been over-impressed with the height of the male Irish forehead. Dawson is sure of her own accuracy.

In the female series high foreheads seem commonest in Leitrim, followed by Clare. Sligo is a little above the average in height of foreheads. In the males, however, the county group that includes both Sligo and Leitrim is somewhat lower than average in forehead height, and Clare is very deficient in high foreheads. In the females Galway seems to be distinguished by the trend toward foreheads of lower height than is characteristic of the generality of the female series. An apparently similar trend shows up in the male series, notably in the Arans, but also in W. Galway and E. Galway-Roscommon.

Actually, a reference to figure 22 (which plots the distribution of the excess of foreheads of pronounced height over medium and submedium) shows that all of our West Coast Irish females are in the zone which in males shows lower foreheads.

Forehead Slope (Table XXVII-23). Females are well known to have more bulging and vertical foreheads and fewer pronouncedly sloping foreheads than males. This sex difference is strikingly manifested in Ireland. Absence of forehead slope (vertical foreheads) is 23.7 per cent fewer in the males. Submedium slopes, medium, pronounced, and very pronounced forehead slopes are all more frequent in the males. In pronounced plus very pronounced the male excess is 5.2 per cent.

Among the females the Kerry subseries is notable for a trend toward more than ordinary forehead slope, revealed by a marked deficiency in the absent category and a marked excess in the medium category. Nothing of the sort shows up in the Kerry males. The Kerry females are Dr. Dawson's oldest subgroup. The youngest subgroup, Clare, shows a trend in the opposite direction from Kerry in that absence of forehead slope (vertical foreheads) are in considerable excess. The small Leitrim series, which is second youngest, seems also to show a trend toward diminished forehead slope, but there is clearly no close correlation between forehead slope and mean age. In the females there appears to be a piling up of excesses of submedium forehead slopes in Sligo, Mayo, and Galway. In the male series the groups that include Sligo and the county of Mayo are also characterized by excesses of submedium forehead slope, but the subgroups that may be compared with the Galway women are rather high in medium forehead slope. In the males the groups that include Donegal are high in submedium forehead slopes and in absence of forehead slope. The Donegal women show an excess in the absent category and deficiencies in medium and submedium. There is thus a suggestion of agreement between males and females in diminished slope in this county.

A reference to figure 23, which plots the excess of foreheads of comparatively little slope over those of medium and pronounced slope, shows that Mayo and Sligo are both in zones of excess of small forehead slope. Donegal is in the area of greatest excess of little forehead slope. Galway, Clare, and Kerry on the other hand, belong in zones where excess of foreheads of little or no slope is either absent or very small. The female data fit for Kerry but not very well for Clare, where an excess of forehead slope "absent" suggests that foreheads are a little less than usually sloping, possibly because of the juvenility of the group.

Nasion Depression (Table XXVII-24). We expect the nasion depression to be absent or slight in a far larger proportion of females than males and this expectation is realized. The modal category in the females is "very small" with 60.4 per cent, whereas in males it is 2 grades higher (medium) with 60.8 per cent. This sex difference is found in most stocks and is particularly marked in such races or ethnic groups as exhibit a strong development of brow ridges and glabella in the males.

In our female series, absence of a nasion depression is by far most frequent in Clare, which, as we recall, is a subseries overloaded with young girls. This immaturity probably accounts for the phenomenon. Nasion depressions do not occur until the frontal sinus and brow ridges have reached their full development. In the female series there is no clear county trend with respect to development of the nasion depression.

Nasal Root Height (Table XXVII-25). Because females are more infantile than males, we expect lower nasal roots in the former. This sex difference is typified by the finding that the height of the nasal root is very small or submedium in only 3.0 per cent of males, but in 14.2 per cent of females, and that the nasal root height is classified as pronounced in 18.9 per cent of males, but in only 14.3 per cent of females. Boths sexes, however, have their mode at "medium."

In the female series the data suggest that nasal roots of pronounced height are commonest in the small series from Leitrim, and that Clare has the highest proportion of roots of submedium height. The male group that includes the Leitrim and Sligo counties is hardly distinguished by high nasal roots. The Arans and West Donegal are the subseries in this part of Ireland characterized by excesses of nasal roots of pronounced height. Similarly, Kerry in our female series has an excess percentage of high nasal roots, but Kerry in the male series is quite ordinary. There seems then to be little relation if any between male and female trends in the same counties.

Nasal Root Breadth (Table XXVII-26). The women show an excess of 1.3 per cent in combined small and submedium nasal root breadth, and a deficiency of 4.2 per cent in the pronounced category. They thus appear more conservative than the males.

Nasal roots of pronounced breadths are seemingly most common in Kerry. None of these counties stands out in the male series. The sex differences are not large.

Nasal Bridge Height (Table XXVII-27). We expect many more low nasal bridges and

fewer of pronounced height in females than in males of the same stock. The Western Irish females show 12.1 per cent of submedium height nasal bridges and the total Irish males only 3.1 per cent. In the pronounced category are 19.3 per cent of males, but only 11.1 per cent of females.

On the face value of the figures the Leitrim women have the highest nasal bridges and the Mayo women the lowest. Neither of these counties is distinguished for high nasal bridges in the male series. Kerry is the only West Coast county which in the male series has any considerable excess of pronounced nasal bridge height. In the females it has but an insignificant excess of high nasal bridges.

Nasal Bridge Breadth (Table XXVII-28). Females show 7.5 per cent less of pronounced or very broad nasal bridges and 2.3 per cent more of submedium or narrow bridges than do total Irish males. The female data indicate that broad nasal bridges are commoner in Clare, Mayo and Galway than in the other western counties, but the differences are not really reliable. Sligo and Leitrim seem to run to narrower nasal bridges as suggested by their insignificant excesses of *submedium* and their equally equivocal deficiencies of *pronounced* and *very pronounced*. However, the female trends do not agree very well with the male data. In the latter, all of the western counties except Kerry fall into a group in which wide nasal bridges are markedly deficient. Galway is the only county in which females surpass the males in pronounced and very pronounced nasal bridge breadths. Kerry is the one county in which the male excesses of broad bridges are really great (13.4 per cent).

Nasal Septum (Table XXVII-29). The majority of the Irish females (77.4 per cent) have straight or concave nasal septa, whereas in Dupertuis' male series the majority (61.7 per cent) have convex septa. Only 4 of 18 male subseries have more than 50 per cent of straight or concave septa, but the lowest percentage of such septa among the females (63.4) is in Clare. The great sex difference may be complicated by an observational equation, but the grading of this trait does not seem to present great difficulty. Yet it must be admitted that this sex difference of so great a magnitude is new to us and we are inclined to regard it as possibly exaggerated. Among the women Clare has by far the highest percentage of convex septa. In the male series, Clare is also very high in convex septa, but West Donegal is still higher. There seems to be no close agreement between males and females in county trends.

Nasal Tip, Thickness (Table XXVII-30). The Irish female nose tip is of medium thickness in an overwhelming majority of cases. The women exceed total Irish males in submedium or thin tips by 2.3 per cent, but have about 8 per cent fewer of thick tips. We expect the male nasal tip to be thicker than that of the female.

Our female data suggest that thick nasal tips are commonest in Mayo, but this county subseries among the males is about average in tip thickness.

Nasal Tip, Inclination (Table XXVII-31). Irish nasal tips are inclined upward in the majority of cases, but the West Irish women surpass the men by 10 per cent in nasal tips that are horizontal and by 1.5 per cent in tips directed downwards. Among the women horizontal tips are in excess in Galway and Clare, and there is a slight corresponding excess in the male series from those counties. It is rather surprising to find that the males have a stronger upward tilt of the nasal tip than the females, because the snubbed tip is an infantile feature and the horizontal and downward directed tips are adultiform.

Nasal Wings (Table XXVII-32). The flare of the alae is nearly always medium in the females. Total Irish males have 1.4 per cent more of compressed alae and 4.8 per cent more of flaring nostril wings. Differences among the county subseries seem not to be very important in either sex.

Nostril Visibility, Frontal (Table XXVII-33). There is ordinarily a submedium frontal visibility of the nostrils in both sexes of the Irish. The absence of such visibility is 1.7 per cent commoner in males than in females. Differences between counties seem unimportant in both sexes.

Nasal Profile (Table XXVII-34). Straight noses are the commonest nasal profile among the West Irish women, but convex profiles are strong seconds. A similar distribution is found in the Irish males, in whom, however, convex noses are proportionately more numerous. They exceed the women in this type of nasal profile by 5.6 per cent. The sex difference is according to expectation. Concave noses are virtually equally represented in both sexes.

Convex noses are slightly the least common and concave noses the most common in the Donegal females. Kerry leads in convex noses, but also has a strong representation of concave profiles. In the male series Kerry is one of the strongest counties in nasal convexity, but has to yield to West Donegal. Our Donegal females do not accord with the male data in excesses of nasal convexity.

Lips, Integumental Thickness (Table XXVII-35). Integumental lips of submedium thickness are found in 4.2 per cent less of males than of females. Otherwise the sex difference is negligible. Regional differences are unimportant in both sexes.

Upper Lip, Membranous Thickness (Table XXVII-36). The females fall below the males in very small and submedium thickness of the upper membranous lips by 9.9 per cent and exceed the latter in pronounced thickness of the upper lips by 5.0 per cent. This is an ordinary sex difference, probably increased a little by the overloading of our female series with young subjects. In youth, the membranous lips are fuller than in middle and old age.

In our females pronounced thickness of the upper membranous tip is commonest in Donegal and Leitrim, followed by Mayo and Sligo. Upper lips seem to be thinner in Clare and Kerry. There is no correspondence in the male series.

Lips, Eversion (Table XXVII-37). Submedium eversion of the lips is 9.2 per cent commoner in the males than the females and the males also show a slight excess of pronounced eversion. The sex difference in the former case is to be expected, especially in view of the larger number of middle-aged and old adults among the males.

Regional differences in the females are not marked. Least eversion occurs in Kerry, probably because the subseries is considerably the oldest.

Lip Seam (Table XXVII-38). Some development of the lip seam is recorded in 17.5 per cent of West Irish females but in only

2.1 per cent of the males. The males do indeed have thinner lips than the females, and the thinner the lips the less conspicuous and the more frequently absent the lip seam.

The highest frequency of lip seam development among the females is found in the very young Clare sample. It seems probable that lip seams tend to be less conspicuous and to decrease with age. Probably because of their rarity, the age changes in lip seam development have not been tabulated for the Irish males.

Lip seams are most frequently absent in the Donegal females and these data are supported by the very great rarity of lip seams in the male groups that include County Donegal. However, this feature is so scarce in the males all over Ireland, that a sex comparison by counties is useless. Considerably the highest frequency of lip seams occurs in the Clare sample, perhaps in connection with its low mean age.

Alveolar Prognathism (Table XXVII-39). The Irish of either sex show very little alveolar prognathism. Dupertuis reports some degree of it in 2.3 per cent of males and Dawson in 2.6 per cent of females. In the male series alveolar prognathism is rarest in general in the western counties, but the Sligo-Leitrim-S. Fermanagh-W. Cavan group has its normal quota. Among the females, what little alveolar prognathism there is shows no great inequality of distribution. It happens to be commonest in the very small Leitrim subseries.

Mid-facial Prognathism (Table XXVII-40). This type of prognathism is somewhat commoner in both sexes, but the male series records only 8 per cent, as against 14.8 per cent in the female series from Western Ireland. In mid-facial prognathism, again, there seems to be a tendency for this feature to manifest itself in the east of Ireland to a greater extent than in the west. Some of the eastern county groups of males exhibit this characteristic in proportions closely similar to those of the Western Irish females. In Wicklow-Carlow there is more male mid-facial prognathism than in any of the counties from which we have female subseries. Figure 25 plots the distribution of mid-facial prognathism in males and shows clearly the position of the female series in the zone of little

to least prognathism. In our female series Kerry has least mid-facial prognathism and this accords well enough with the male distribution in that county. However, the Clare females have considerably the most mid-facial prognathism, although Clare among the males is again one of the lowest in the feature. Since our male series indicates that this character diminishes with age (probably because of dental loss and alveolar recession), it seems probable that the position of Clare may be due to its very low mean age.

Chin Prominence (Table XXVII-41). In anterior projection of the chin the females show a higher proportion of subjects in the predominant "medium" class, 4.3 per cent less who show "submedium" prominence, and one per cent less with "pronounced" prominence. Such small variations might easily be the result of slight differences of standards between the two observers. In the male series, three western county groups are notable for submedium chin prominence: West Donegal, Sligo-Leitrim-S. Fermanagh-W. Cavan, West Galway. There is no indication of such a position in regard to this character among the females. The most submedium prominence and the most pronounced prominence are found alike in the rather juvenile Clare sample. In the male series submedium chin prominence is commonest in the age groups up to 30 and pronounced prominence in the groups between 45 and 70 years.

Chin Type (Table XXVII-42). Median chins are found in only 3.4 per cent of males, as against 97.6 per cent of females. This is a well established sex difference. Very few women indeed have square chins with a cleft in the middle. The percentage of median chins recorded for the Irish males is probably unusually low, since a fair number of males in most ethnic and racial groups have the pointed or median chins. It is of interest, though probably of no importance, to note that no bilateral chins whatsoever have been reported from the small female subseries representing counties Leitrim and Sligo, and only one lone female from the larger Donegal series has such a chin. In the male series the group that includes Sligo and Leitrim is one of the very lowest of Ireland (in fact second lowest) in proportion of median chins among males and West Galway shows the highest incidence in Ireland of median chins in males. The county differences in this feature between the female series do not then accord well with those found in the males. Nor is there any particular reason why an anatomical character that shows such a wide sex difference should exhibit similar county gradations in opposite sexes.

Bite (Table XXVII-43). In classification of the bite, there is little difference between West Coast Irish females and total Irish males. The females exhibit 2.7 per cent more of pronounced overbites, 0.6 per cent more of edge-to-edge bite, and exactly the same proportion (0.6 per cent) of underbites.

Teeth, Wear (Table XXVII-44). In the male series tooth wear is recorded as absent or submedium in 11.8 per cent more of males than of females. The females show an excess of 3.5 per cent of medium wear and an excess of 8.2 per cent of pronounced and very pronounced wear. This seems to be consistent with their record of more severe tooth loss.

Wear is most marked in the Kerry subseries which is considerably the oldest. However, the Clare series, which is the youngest in mean age, ranks second only to Kerry in lowness of percentage of subjects showing wear absent or submedium. Factors other than age obviously affect the wear of the teeth. Leitrim, which is our second youngest county, shows, on the whole, the least teeth wear, but is hard pressed for this honor by Donegal, a subseries which is more than one year over mean age. Sligo also occupies a favorable position in respect to tooth wear.

The female data from Donegal approximate very closely the distribution of grades of tooth wear in West Donegal in the male series. The Mayo females show an excess wear over Mayo males amounting to roughly 6 per cent. The Leitrim and Sligo female subseries do not depart markedly from the distribution of tooth wear in the combined male series that includes these two counties. However, in Clare and in Galway, recorded amount of tooth wear seems considerably more in the females than in the males. Kerry in the male series has the greatest amount of tooth wear to be found in any Irish county group. The female series accords well with the male in

its general ranking, but shows an excess of wear among the females amounting to 7.4 per cent in the pronounced and very pronounced categories, and a deficiency of 13.9 per cent in the absent and submedium class.

The comparison of the records of the two observers does not suggest that any very great personal equation between them has operated in this feature.

Teeth, Loss (Table XXVII-45). The West Coast Irish females show 5.9 per cent more of individuals who have suffered no tooth loss, as compared with the total Catholic county series of males. In the *very small* category, the females have 7.8 per cent fewer than the males, in the *submedium* category 9.3 per cent fewer, in the *medium* category 0.8 per cent more, and in the *pronounced* category 10.5 per cent more. Thus, as compared with total males, the females show substantial excesses of those who have lost no teeth and, at the other end, of those who have lost many teeth (17+). Perhaps the excess of females who have lost no teeth is attributable to the larger proportion of subadults and young adults in the female series. The high percentage of females with pronounced loss seemingly represents the real sex difference, uncomplicated by age.

The greatest proportion of pronounced tooth loss (an excess of 14.6 per cent over the figure for the total female series), occurs in the Kerry subseries which is the oldest subgroup (3.5 years over mean age). But the proportion in the Kerry group showing no tooth loss is insignificantly higher than that of the small Sligo subseries, which is virtually at mean age. The Sligo series, incidentally, ranks second to Kerry in proportions of women with pronounced loss, and, in view of its mean age, may be taken as the county subseries in which tooth loss has been most severe. The Mayo and Galway series are notable for excess percentages of women or girls who have lost no teeth, although in the matter of pronounced loss they do not deviate strongly from the proportions found in the total group. It may be said, therefore, that tooth loss seems to have been least in these counties. The very young subseries from Clare is hardly notable in the matter of tooth loss.

If we compare the women of the various

counties with the men of the same provenience, the following conclusion can be derived. The women of Donegal have suffered much more severe tooth loss than the males either of West Donegal or of the central north group that includes the eastern half of County Donegal.

The Mayo women have a much higher percentage of individuals who have lost no teeth (probably from the overloaded first two age groups), but, as compared with the males, an excess of 13.4 per cent of pronounced tooth loss. Sligo and Leitrim differ from the male subseries that includes these counties largely in their substantial excess of persons who show pronounced loss, but Sligo tooth loss is considerably more severe than that of Leitrim. The Galway female series differs from the male series that include various parts of Galway, again in showing many more subjects who have suffered no dental loss, and many more who have incurred pronounced dental loss. Our young subseries of females from Clare is superior to the male series in suffering less dental loss, but here again age may be a factor. The Kerry series of females greatly exceeds the male series in dental loss.

Generally speaking, the West Coast counties, with the exception of Clare and Kerry, are in a favorable position with respect to most of the rest of Ireland in this matter of dental loss. The reader should consult figure 26. Dental loss in the males is in general most severe in the south of Ireland, but the situation is complicated by age composition of the various county subseries. It so happens that some of the subseries of highest mean age are southern.

Teeth, Caries (Table XXVII-46). Of 1856 female subjects, 1411 were observed for dental caries. This is about 76 per cent. In the male county series observations of dental caries were made on 6857 of 8908 individuals, which is nearly 77 per cent. Therefore the proportion of persons who had enough of their own teeth left to make it worthwhile to observe them for caries seems to have been about the same in each sex. Here, however, the resemblance ceases. We find only 0.8 per cent of males who are recorded as having no caries, against 18.5 per cent of females. Again, the proportion of males with "very small"

caries falls below that of the females by 30.2 per cent. "Submedium" caries is 29.3 per cent more frequent in the males; medium caries 13.9 per cent in excess, and pronounced caries 4.1 per cent commoner in the men. Thus it would appear that the women are far less severely afflicted by dental caries than the men, although more of them have suffered pronounced dental loss. The situation seems paradoxical. It can be explained in part, however, by the overloading of the female series with adolescents and very young adults.

However, Dupertuis found only 4.1 per cent of males free from caries, even in the 15-19 year age group, and only 75 males of 7618, or 1.0 per cent caries immune. On the other hand, Dawson, in her total females, finds 18.5 per cent devoid of caries, taking all ages together. Now the females may indeed be superior to the males in their condition with regard to this dental disease, but it is almost inconceivable that the difference should be so great. One can hardly avoid the conclusion that an observational equation between the observers has enhanced the sex difference. If we take the age group data for the males, we find that Dupertuis lists only 58 males in the first two age groups (15-19 and 20-24) free of caries, from a total of 1971 subjects. This latter number is more than 100 larger than the total female series. But Dawson finds 104 of 425 females between the ages of 15 and 19 free of caries (26.8 per cent). It would seem that Dupertuis was more rigorous and thorough in his dental examinations than Dawson. The latter appears to have recorded as caries only the more obvious dental lesions. Neither observer counted lost teeth as carious.

Face Shortening (Table XXVII-47). Shortening of the face as a result of wear of the teeth, loss of teeth, and resorption of the alveolar processes is recorded in the female series as considerably greater than in the males. In the *absent* category, the males exceed the females by 10.8 per cent, in *submedium* the females have an excess of 1.6 per cent; in *medium* the females have 5.3 per cent more, and in *pronounced* an excess of 3.8 per cent.

Face shortening as a result of wear is by far the most marked in the relatively elderly Kerry group and is considerably the lowest in

Leitrim. The Leitrim female subseries agrees very well in this observation with the combined county group of males that includes it and Sligo, but the females of Sligo show more tooth wear. Among the males the amount of face shortening as a result of wear is more marked in Clare than in any other county. Hence the distribution of categories of face shortening in Clare among the females fits the male distribution pretty well. However, our Clare female subseries is overloaded with 34.3 per cent of girls 15–19 years and with 20.6 per cent of young women in the age group 20–24. Consequently the agreement is somewhat specious, since the female group is much lower than the male in mean age. Yet the female group agrees in showing a great deal of wear considering low mean age.

Teeth, Crowding (Table XXVII-48). The sex difference in this observation is extraordinary in that the males show 57.4 per cent of some degree of crowding and the females only 13.6 per cent. It is difficult to accept such a wide divergence as uncomplicated by observational equation. It would seem probable that Dupertuis observed this condition rather more rigorously than Dawson. The latter states that she reported crowding as present only if it resulted in torsion or in staggering of the teeth in the jaws. Yet it does not seem to be an observation which in the "present" or "absent" categories should present great difficulty. In view of the wide disagreement, it is not worthwhile to discuss sex trends by counties.

Malars, Frontal Projection (Table XXVII-49). The frontal projection of malars is recorded as *pronounced* by Dr. Dawson in 35.2 per cent of cases as against only 16.5 per cent of cases among the males so graded by Dupertuis. Under the "absent and submedium" combined category the females exceed the males by 3.9 per cent. There can be little doubt of a difference in standards of observation between the two field workers in this feature. Each observer is consistent with himself in his various subseries but departs rather strongly from the other.

In the male series, in general, pronounced frontal projection of the malars seems to be at its highest in the West Coast counties. The female types of these counties may well surpass the males in this frontal jut of the malars but here, as in some other observations, we are forced to conclude that Dupertuis was probably more conservative, and tended to assign his borderline cases to the medium class, where Dawson, more liberal, was inclined to put them in one or other of the more extreme categories. This sort of a difference between observers, in grading features that must be marked by an ideal and subjective system, is possibly related to their individual psychologies and personalities. The senior author has almost always encountered differences of such a character, sometimes great and sometimes small, when he has tried to combine the observations of two field workers, even though both of them have received the same training. Furthermore, such differences manifest themselves more markedly in certain observations that are difficult to grade, than in others in which the categories are clearer or the differences more obvious.

Malars, Lateral Projection (Table XXVII-50). Whereas both sexes have a majority of instances in which the malar projection is rated as *medium*, the males exceed the females in this category by 12.6 per cent. The excess of females in the *pronounced* category is 7.8 per cent and in the *absent, submedium* category, 5.3 per cent. It would thus appear that the females tend to give the appearance of a wide flare of the malars considerably oftener than do the males. Of course, it is a fact that in mixed groups derived from two or several contrasting racial or subracial types, the females are likely to incline toward the parental extremes and the males to show intermediate characters. This is apparently the case in Ireland, but the variant tendencies of the two sexes may well be exaggerated by the similar psychological differences in our two field observers, male and female.

However, if we compare the female gradations of this feature with the male county groups from which the females come, it becomes evident that the western and southwestern Irish counties, as a whole, are high in lateral projection of malars, when compared to other parts of the island. Our Donegal females show nearly the same amounts of lateral projection in the *medium* and *pronounced* category as do the West Donegal males. The Mayo women show only a small excess of *pronounced* and *very pronounced* lateral malar juts when compared with males of the same county provenience. The Galway women show a little less lateral projection of the malars than do the West Galway males, but considerably more than the E. Galway-Roscommon male group and the male series from the Arans. Leitrim is not far from the figures for the combined county male series that includes it, but Sligo shows much more pronounced lateral projection, and both of these counties are very high in proportions of females who show absent and submedium lateral projection of the malars. Malar projection (lateral) in the Clare females is very close to that found in Clare males (in spite of a considerable difference in age composition). Finally the Kerry women show only a 3 per cent excess over the males from that county.

It may be concluded that the Western Irish counties are remarkable for pronounced lateral malar projection and that males and females alike display this feature. The excess of pronounced lateral juts in the females is hardly enough to arouse the suspicion of a difference in observational standards that would vitiate the sex comparison.

Gonial Angles (Table XXVII-51). We expect *pronounced* and *very pronounced* gonial angles to occur much more commonly in males than in females of the same ethnic group. Males have larger and stronger mandibles with the gonia far more often everted. The expectation is realized among the Irish. The males of the total series have an excess of 23 per cent in the combined *pronounced* and *very pronounced* categories. It is a little surprising to find that the males also show an excess of 1.5 per cent in the submedium category, but very few Irish of either sex are assigned to this grade.

Among the female subseries, Clare and Galway are distinguished by somewhat high frequency of pronounced gonial angles and rarity of submedium angles. Neither of these counties is notable in the male series. E. Galway-Roscommon is by no means one of the leaders in flaring gonia; the Arans are very low in this feature; and West Galway is quite ordinary. In the male series Kerry has the most pronounced lateral projection or prominence of the gonial angles. The females from Kerry do not show much of this gonial prominence. It is very rare in the Leitrim women and comparatively low in the county series of males that includes Leitrim. The Sligo women concur, and are to be compared with the same combined male group.

Ear Helix (Table XXVII-52). A pronounced roll or breadth of roll of the helix is found in 6.7 per cent more of females than of males. In *very small* and *submedium* helices the females exceed the males by 12.7 per cent. Probably these differences again express to some degree the divergence in standards of judgment in our two field workers. However, they may well exist in actuality, though perhaps to a less degree than the crude figures indicate.

The female figures for the different county subseries are fairly consistent. The Donegal women are poorest in pronounced roll of the helix and rather high in the *very small* category. Among the males West Donegal is lowest of all the county groups in pronounced roll of the helix.

Ear Antihelix (Table XXVII-53). The comparative data show a marked sex difference in that the males exceed the females in the pronounced category by 8.2 per cent, but show 18 per cent less of antihelices that are absent or submedium. This may well be a real sex difference, although again there is displayed the tendency of our male observer to pile up frequencies in the middle class and of our female observer to be more liberal in the extreme ratings. The female ratings are quite consistent within themselves. *Pronounced* antihelices are commonest in Kerry and Clare, least frequent in Galway and Donegal. In the male series the greatest fluctuations of the pronounced category seem to occur in the west. The Arans have by far the highest frequency of this variation in the whole of Ireland, but West Galway is lowest in Ireland and Clare, Mayo, and the combined group that includes Sligo and Leitrim is also very low.

Darwin's Point (Table XXVII-54). This nodule on the rim of the helix is very rare in the Irish females (4.4 per cent) but occurs in some degree of development in 25.7 per cent of the Irish males. The sex difference is usual in kind but rather extreme in degree. In the male series it is least often found in the Aran Islands of all the separate and combined county groups, with Kerry next in respect of rarity.

Ear Lobe (Table XXVII-55). The sexes differ in ear lobe attachment in that the majority of females have *attached* lobes (54.2 per cent) and the majority of males have *free* lobes (58.2 per cent). Females show an excess of 3.5 per cent of *soldered* lobes. Although this feature is quite simple to grade, it seems improbable that the sex differences are not in part referable to observational equation.

The Clare females show the lowest proportions of free lobes and the highest of attached lobes. This is in conformity with their position as the most youthful group and the known fact that attached and soldered ear lobes decrease and free lobes increase with age in the males. (Hooton and Dupertuis, 1951, table XCIV, p. 98.) However, Sligo has the highest proportion of free lobes although it is slightly below mean age. The group that includes Sligo and Leitrim in the male series is also very high in free ear lobes and is exceeded in this respect only by the Arans and by E. Galway-Roscommon.

Ear Lobe, Size (Table XXVII-56). There is again a wide difference between West Coast females and all males, of whatever provenience, from the records of the two observers. Dupertuis finds 45.2 per cent of lobes of pronounced size (large), but Dawson only 2.6 per cent. It is evident that different scales of size were employed by the two observers. We should expect the males to show larger proportions of ear lobes of pronounced size than the females, because ear lobe size increases with age and most of our male subseries are older than the female series. But the discrepancy is too great to be explained away by age difference.

It is necessary to study the data on females without reference to the information on the males. Dr. Dawson's observations on this feature are internally consistent. The female series that is youngest, Clare, has the largest proportions of ear lobes of submedium size and absent. Kerry, the oldest group, together with Donegal, which is almost a year above

mean age, seem to be lowest in submedium and absent ear lobes, and especially high in those of medium size. But Sligo, which is slightly below mean age, is well up in size of ear lobes, and Galway, our second oldest group, is somewhat deficient in ear lobe size. Mayo, also, although practically at mean age, has a slight excess of submedium ear lobes. Mayo and Galway are both overloaded in the young adult (20–24 year) age group.

Ear Protrusion (Table XXVII-57). In the total male Catholic county series, Dupertuis finds 21.9 per cent of *pronounced* ear protrusion, which is more than twice that recorded for the females by Dawson. It is of course easier to observe ear protrusion in males than in females. Dawson also has 5.4 per cent of ears of submedium protrusion, whereas Dupertuis records only 0.7 per cent for males. Several of the western counties from which we have series of females show, in the array of male county subseries, percentages of pronounced ear protrusion that are well below the total Irish average. Mayo, Sligo-Leitrim-S. Fermanagh-W. Cavan, West Donegal, and E. Galway-Roscommon are such county groups. Only Clare and Kerry show slight excesses in the male series of ears that are pronouncedly protruding. In general, this West Coast trend tends to reduce the difference between the proportions of *pronounced* recorded by our two observers. Thus the excess of Mayo males over Mayo females in this category is only 5.3 per cent; in West Donegal (taken to represent all of Donegal) the male excess is 4.4 per cent, etc. However, every female subseries shows marked excesses of submedium protrusion when compared with the male series from the same county.

We incline to the conclusion that male ear protrusion is in fact more marked than female protrusion, but that differing standards of the two observers make the data on the sexes nearly, if not quite, incomparable.

Temporal Fullness (Table XXVII-58). The male series shows 6.6 per cent more of submedium temporal fullness and 16.9 per cent more of pronounced temporal fullness. This is an instance in which the male series shows heavier proportions at the extremes of the variation than does the female. We have hypothesized a possible tendency on the part of our male observer (C. W. D.) to be more conservative than our female observer (H. D.), with the result of the former piling up observations in the middle or medium categories and the latter tending to assign the borderline cases to the extremes. Here, however, the situation is reversed. The apparent sex difference, when both records are taken as comparable, is in a strong tendency for the females to fall in the medium category of temporal fullness. This may be a real sex difference. It may be an illusion due to observational equation.

The Donegal females are highest in pronounced temporal fullness. The largest proportions of submedium fullness are in Clare and Galway. But Clare is also high in pronounced fullness. Sligo and Leitrim are notably piled up in the middle category. In the male series, the Aran Islanders stand apart in this observation, with a huge excess of medium temporal fullness and marked deficiencies at both ends. In our female series the Aran women are thrown into the Galway subseries, so that they cannot be checked against the males.

This observation on temporal fullness, according to the experience of the senior author, is more than ordinarily difficult to take accurately and consistently on the living. It even presents difficulties when made on dried skulls.

Occipital Protrusion (Table XXVII-59). The amount of occipital projection is easier to observe in males than in females because of closely cropped hair. Our female data differ from the male in showing an excess of 2.3 per cent of absent and submedium occipital protrusions and a deficiency of 11.2 per cent in the pronounced category. The sex difference in favor of the males with respect to occipital projection of more marked character seems reasonable in view of the fact that the females are somewhat more brachycephalic. In our male series all of the western counties are very low in pronounced occipital protrusion except West Donegal. That county, coincidentally, is highest in pronounced occipital protrusion among our female subseries. By far the lowest in all Ireland in the male series are West Galway and Arans, where occipital projection "pronounced"

amounts to 9.2 per cent in the former and 4.3 per cent in the latter, as against 8.7 per cent for all Galway females. Clare is our lowest female subseries in pronounced occipital projection and highest in submedium projection. Clare is also one of the highest counties of the males series in occipital projection absent or submedium. In the male series West Donegal and Kerry, in addition to West Galway and Clare, have excesses of individuals in whom occipital projection is absent and submedium. Similar excesses in the female series occur only in Mayo and in Clare. There is thus some sort of rough fit between the male and female data on occipital projection. If there was a personal equation between our two observers in respect to this observation, it was probably not big enough completely to vitiate the sex comparison.

Lambdoid Flattening (Table XXVII-60). The West Coast females show only 15 per cent of lambdoid flattening of various grades, as against 80.9 per cent of the males of the total Irish county series. Since there is no particular reason to suppose that this is a sex limited character, we must suspect that there was a marked divergence in standards of observation between the field workers.

Generally speaking, lambdoid flattening in the male series is high in the western counties, reaching its maximum in the Arans, closely followed by E. Galway-Roscommon. It is relatively low only in the Sligo group.

In our female series it is commonest by far in Clare, with 26.8 per cent of various grades of the feature; next most common in Galway with 17.6 per cent; least common in Donegal with only 3.2 per cent.

Occipital Flattening (Table XXVII-61). In general, there is a fairly close agreement between the observers in the matter of occipital flattening. It is recorded in 5 per cent more of the males than of the females and, particularly, the males show pronounced flattening in 4.3 per cent more than do the females.

In the male series, the West Coast counties are relatively very low in occipital flattening. By far the highest percentages are recorded in Antrim-Down and the neighboring northern counties. Thus we find that in some counties our Western Irish women actually tend to exceed the males of that part of the country in this feature. In Clare this occipital flattening is recorded in 19.9 per cent of females as against 12.7 per cent of males; in Mayo the women have 14.0 per cent and the men 10.7 per cent. County Galway in the males is split into several different combination groups, all of which show less occipital flattening than the Galway females. However, in the other western counties from which we have female subseries, the males slightly exceed the females in this feature.

Facial Asymmetry (Table XXVII-62). Dupertuis found 26 per cent of the facial asymmetry in this male series, but Dawson records it in only 7.3 per cent of her West Coast females. It is probable that a sex difference does exist, but it seems likely that one observer recorded minor amounts of facial asymmetry which the other did not. In the male series a bulging right side of the face (arbitrarily recorded as a *right* asymmetry) is more than twice as frequent as *left* asymmetry. Just the opposite is true of the females.

In the female series, Clare is considerably the highest in facial asymmetry. Clare is notable for this feature in the male series also, but the males of every subseries except the Aran Islands vastly exceed the females in this feature.

THE distribution of morphological (sub-racial) types among the females presents an interesting comparison with the male series. In the West Coast counties, the females are slightly below total Irish males in the Pure Nordic type (deficiency of 0.3 per cent), but exceed them in the Predominantly Nordic types (excess of 1.4 per cent). The latter difference is hardly significant (critical ratio 2.97 per cent). In the very important Keltic types the females fall below the total males by exactly 10 per cent, and make up for this deficiency, in large part, by exceeding the males in Dinarics by 8 per cent. The pro-portion of the ash blond, or golden or red-haired and blue-eyed brachycephals of the East Baltic type is substantially the same in both series. The women also are deficient, by 3 per cent, in the Nordic Mediterranean type, which is the most numerous in the males. In Nordic Alpines there is virtually no difference, but the women have 3.1 per cent of pure dark-eyed, dark-haired, long-headed Pure Mediterranean, whereas the men have the merest handful of this type (0.3 per cent). The women also include a type which is not represented in the male series—the Pure Alpine type with dark eyes and dark hair (0.7 per cent).

In summary, the most marked difference between the males and females is that the latter have substantially fewer Keltics and more Dinarics. Less important are the small excess of the Predominantly Nordic type in the females, the small deficiency in Nordic Mediterraneans. Of considerably more inter-est is the much more substantial representation of Pure Mediterraneans in the females, and the appearance of a handful of Pure Alpines.

These differences are referable, for the most part, to the following sex divergences in metric and morphological features: higher cephalic indices and lower nasal indices in the females; far greater frequency of pure dark eyes in the females. The higher cephalic and lower nasal indices in combination build up the Dinaric type among the females, prob-ably at the expense of the Nordic Mediter-raneans. The female excesses of Pure Medi-terraneans and of Pure Alpines are due to the relatively great frequency of dark eyes in that sex.

These comparisons are not as important as they would be if the female series were drawn from the entire county instead of from west-ern counties only. It is more pertinent to com-pare the distribution of female morphological types with the male subseries from the same counties. This we shall now proceed to do, as far as possible.

Donegal (Table XXVIII-1). We have to compare the females of Donegal with Du-pertuis' West Donegal series and also with his combined N. Fermanagh-E. Donegal-Ty-rone-Londonderry group. In the male series, West Donegal is entirely devoid of Pure Nordics and notably deficient in Predomi-nantly Nordics. However, both of these types are adequately represented in the combined group that includes E. Donegal. In the fe-male series, Donegal has about its quota of both the Pure and the Predominantly Nordic type, both more numerous than in the males. In the male series, West Donegal has about its normal quota of Keltics, and the adjacent group that includes E. Donegal is over-repre-sented in this type. Total Irish representation of the Keltic type is 25.3 per cent. In the female series, Donegal has 18.8 per cent of the Keltic type, which is 3.5 per cent over its female total for Ireland, but substantially below that of the males of this type. The East Baltic type in males is deficient in West Donegal but in excess in the group that in-cludes E. Donegal. Among the females it seems to be deficient, but insignificantly so, in County Donegal. Among the males the Di-naric type is in strong excess in West Donegal, but deficient in the combined group to the east. In the female series the Dinaric type is proportionately under-represented in Donegal (deficiency of 5.9 per cent). In the males the Nordic Mediterranean type is in strong excess in West Donegal, but slightly deficient in the

279

county block to the east. In the females this type is strongly over-represented (although it actually occurs in a somewhat smaller proportion than in West Donegal males). The Pure Mediterranean type is wholly lacking among West Donegal males and occurs in but one lone individual in the county block to the east. The female series from Donegal includes 7 Pure Mediterraneans, which is about par for the western county females.

Nordic Alpines are deficient in West Donegal males and somewhat in excess in the combined group to the east. In the Donegal females they are deficient to the extent of 2.2 per cent. This county has 1.8 per cent of Pure Alpine females, a type not found in the males.

In summary, County Donegal has more Pure Nordics and Predominantly Nordics among the females than the West Donegal male series and fewer Keltics, although it is strong in Keltics as compared with other female subseries. Donegal is deficient in Dinarics in comparison with the male series of the same provenience. It agrees with the male series in strong over-representation of the Nordic Mediterranean type and slight deficiency of Nordic Alpines.

Sligo and Leitrim (Table XXVIII-1). The male group that includes Sligo and Leitrim is slightly under-represented in Pure Nordics and over-represented in Predominantly Nordics. In the female series, neither of these counties has yielded a Pure Nordic; Leitrim has no Predominantly Nordics and Sligo is under-represented. It is thus apparent that any way one looks at them, these counties are deficient in Nordic females. The Keltic type has its normal representation in the male group that includes Sligo and Leitrim, and is a little stronger than normal (although numerically inferior to the male representation) in the females. East Baltics are strong in the male group but totally lacking among the females of these two counties. Dinarics are definitely deficient in this series of males. In the female series they are deficient in Sligo but have their maximum Irish female representation in Leitrim. The Nordic Mediterranean type has its usual par representation in this county group in the men, and is strongly over-represented in both female subseries. Leitrim has exactly

the same percentage of Nordic Mediterraneans as has the combined male group, and Sligo has 4.5 per cent more. Pure Mediterraneans are most strongly represented in this combined male group of any Irish area, and the same applies to the females. Nordic Alpines are about at par in the male group, but strongly deficient in both female county subseries. Sligo has the highest percentage of Pure Alpines; Leitrim has none.

The most striking feature of this comparison is the agreement of Sligo and Leitrim with the combined male group in their piling up of pure brunet Mediterraneans. Confirmatory is the over-representation of Nordic Mediterraneans among the females and the deficiency of Nordic Alpines. Blonds are very rare, and hence deficiencies of the Nordic and East Baltic types occur.

Mayo (Table XXVIII-1). In the male series Mayo has an over-representation of Pure Nordics but is somewhat deficient in Predominantly Nordics. In the female series Mayo has no Pure Nordics but is normal with 8.1 per cent of Predominantly Nordics. Note that this absolute percentage of Predominantly Nordics exceeds that in the male series by 5 per cent. In Mayo the Keltic type is deficient in males, but still numbers 10.7 per cent of the county subseries. In the female subseries Keltics account for 19.1 per cent of the county sample, which is an excess of 3.8 per cent and the highest proportion of Keltics to be found in any county subseries. East Baltics are in excess in both male and female series from Mayo, but this is always a numerically negligible type. Dinarics are markedly in excess in the Mayo male subseries, but slightly below average among the females with 26.0 per cent. Yet in the males they account for only 22.5 per cent, because this type is the third in numerical strength in Irish males, but first in females. In Nordic Mediterraneans Mayo is about at par for males but 4.8 per cent deficient in females. The Pure Mediterranean type has its normal quota in females but is deficient in the males. Nordic Alpines are slightly in excess among the males of this county and also in the females.

Galway (Table XXVIII-1). The Galway comparison is complicated by the partition of that county in the male series into West Galway, the Arans, and E. Galway-Roscommon. However, both Nordic types are in excess in West Galway and the whole county in the female series leads in Predominantly Nordics and is at par for Pure Nordics. The Arans are deficient in both Nordic types. East Galway and Roscommon are slightly deficient in Pure Nordics but have an excess of Predominantly Nordics. The Keltic type is in moderate excess in all of the Galway groups of males except the Arans, in which sample it is in marked excess. In the female subseries from Galway, Keltics are at their average strength which is considerably less than in males. East Baltics are deficient in both sexes in County Galway. Dinarics are also slightly deficient in the females and in every Galway subseries of males. Nordic Mediterraneans, on the contrary, are in excess strength in every Galway series, but notably in the Aran Island males and in the county as a whole among the females. The Pure Mediterranean type is strong in the Galway females, but almost unrepresented in the three Galway male subseries. Nordic Alpines are slightly in excess in West Galway males, extremely deficient in the Arans, and slightly deficient in E. Galway-Roscommon. In the female series they are enormously deficient—weaker than in any other county from which we have female samples. Nor has the Galway series of females any Pure Alpines. In Galway the type distributions in the sexes agree well.

Clare (Table XXVIII-1). Clare is deficient in both types of Nordics in the males but about at par for females (who are usually stronger in this type). It is slightly deficient in Keltics in the male series but very weak indeed in this type among females—by far the poorest representation of all female subseries. In this county the East Baltic type is normal in males and very markedly in excess in females. It should be recalled here that the Clare female subseries is very young, and that East Baltic and Nordic types that specify ash blond or golden or even red hair are likely to be over-represented in young groups. Among the males the strongest Dinaric representation is that of County Clare. In the females this type is also in great excess, but has to yield primacy to the very small Leitrim subseries. Nordic Mediterraneans are at slightly less than normal

strength in both sexes in this county. The same holds for Pure Mediterraneans. On the other hand, Nordic Alpines are in slight excess in both sexes.

Kerry (Table XXVIII-1). This county is deficient to a slight degree in both Nordic types in both sexes. It is very weak in the Keltic type in males, but slightly in excess of its quota for females. East Baltics are in comparatively great strength in Kerry males, but insignificantly deficient among the females. In the male series Kerry ranks second in Dinarics (yielding only to Clare), but the female series from this county shows a 2.8 per cent deficiency. Nordic Mediterraneans are deficient in both sexes. So are Pure Mediterraneans, but of course, most strikingly in the male sex in which Kerry has no representative of the type. Nordic Alpines are in great excess in both sexes.

Summary by Counties. The very rare Pure Nordic type of blond, blue-eyed long-heads is slightly less common in females than in males. It occurs in only 5 of 1792 persons, yet the part of Ireland covered by our female series is in general the half of the country in which Pure Nordics are commoner. The Predominantly Nordic type is slightly stronger in West Coast females than in total Irish males. The small female subseries from Sligo and Leitrim are unduly poor in Nordic types, of either sort, in comparison with the male series. The strength of the Nordic types in the Galway women is paralleled in the various male series from this county with the exception of the Arans. Clare is weak in this type among the males, but normal in females. Both Nordic types are slightly deficient in Kerry.

The Keltic type is in general much weaker in the females than in the males. This sex deficiency tends to be regular in the western counties, but in one instance, where the males are very strong in the Keltic type, the females show, within their own range, similar excesses. The deficiency of this type in Clare is greatly exaggerated in females, but in Kerry, where there is also a male deficiency, the females slightly exceed their quota. Mayo is very strongly over-represented in this type among females, but deficient in the males.

The East Baltic type is too rare, and its occurrence too much influenced by age, for the comparison between males and females in the western counties to be important.

The great strength of the Dinaric type in the West Coast females does not always agree with strength or deficiency in this type in the males. Donegal seems to be relatively deficient in this type in the females, although West Donegal has an over-representation among the males. In the Sligo group of males, Dinarics are very deficient, as they are in the female subseries from Sligo. But the very small subseries of Leitrim females is tremendously overloaded with Dinarics. The Mayo females do not match the males of that county in Dinaric strength, but the Galway series agree in Dinaric weakness of both sexes. Again, Clare is the leading Dinaric county for males and is matched in the female by a great excess of the type. However, Kerry, which is second strongest in male Dinarics, is slightly deficient in this type of female.

The basic Nordic Mediterranean type is about 3 per cent less common in females than in males (compensated perhaps in the former by the 3 per cent Pure Mediterraneans). Its

great strength in Donegal is manifest in both sexes. In Sligo and Leitrim, its female representation is stronger than among the males. In Galway, Nordic Mediterranean is an excessive type in both sexes. In Mayo it is somewhat deficient in the females. In Clare and Kerry, slight deficiencies of the type occur in men and women alike.

The very rare Pure Mediterranean type cannot be profitably compared in its county distributions, but there is a very important agreement in the piling up of this type in Sligo and Leitrim females and in the male subseries that includes these two counties.

Nordic Alpines have almost the same strength in both sexes when West Coast females are compared with total Irish males. This type is in great excess in Kerry in both sexes, slightly in excess in Clare and Mayo, enormously deficient in Galway females, and perhaps deficient in males. The type is definitely deficient in Sligo and Leitrim females, but not in males.

The Pure Alpine group has no male representatives. Of its 13 members among the females, none are found in Leitrim and Galway.

DISCUSSION OF MORPHOLOGICAL TYPES

We must, however reluctantly, come to grips with the problem of the significance of the difference of occurrence and distribution of these morphological or subracial types in the males and in the females. There are a number of obvious explanatory possibilities: (1) the type differences between the sexes are due to the fact that all of the females come from the West Irish counties, whereas they have been compared mainly with the total distribution of males all over Ireland; (2) the differences are merely the expression of normal sex differences and have no ethnic, racial, or other genetic significance; (3) the differences are mainly referable to variations in standards of observations and in techniques of measurements between our two field anthropometrists; (4) the differences arise from the fact that females tend to preserve certain ancestral types in a purer form than do the males and consequently may represent better the original,

unmixed racial types that have contributed to the modern Irish population.

The first possibility that the type differences between Irish males and West Coast females may be due in large part to the localized character of the female sample has already been discounted by the comparison of Dawson's West Coast females with the separate county groups of males of the same provenience within Ireland. It transpires from these comparisons that when Mayo females are compared with Mayo males, Clare females with Clare males, etc., there are, in a substantial number of cases, reductions of the sex differences. However these diminished differences almost always are of degree and not of kind. The basic or radical sex differences generally persist even when the county of birth is the same for both.

We must now discuss the possibility that the morphological type differences are purely sex differences and have no other genetic connotation. The bulk of the sex differences ascertained, whether metrical or morphological, do not affect the combination of indices and attributes by which the morphological types have been sorted. There are, however, some exceptions. The length-breadth index of the head (the cephalic index) has been generally used in the determination of types, with a simple bipartite division (below 80, and 80 and above) utilized to separate the round-headed sheep from the long-headed goats. Now it is fairly well known that within the same population females usually, although not always, are somewhat higher in the cephalic index than males. This arises partly from the fact that the length of the brain case is rather more highly correlated with stature than is the breadth, and males are taller than females of the same stock. Again, the development of bony brow ridges and often of nuchal crests in the males is likely to give them a purely osseous advantage in head length. The actual mean of the female cephalic index is only 0.60 units higher than that of the total Irish males and the excess of women put into the round-headed racial types, as contrasted with males, is something about 5 to 6 per cent. Thus Nordic Alpines, Dinarics, East Baltics, and Pure Alpines would have a putative 5 to 6 per cent increment due to sex difference. The long-headed morphological types would suffer to the same degree. Actually, the excess of males, added type by type in the long-headed morphological types, amounts to 8.1 per cent, and the excess of females over males in the brachycephalic types, type by type, adds up to 9.2 per cent. However, most of the deficiency of dolichocephals among the female morphological types is concentrated in the Keltic type (10 per cent) and, similarly, the excess of brachycephals among the females is mostly in the single Dinaric type (8 per cent). The sex difference in head form is not distributed randomly among the types, and in two of the minor dolichocephalic type the females actually exceed the males proportionately (predominantly Nordic, female excess 1.4 per cent; Pure Mediterranean, female excess 2.8 per cent). It therefore appears that the sex differences in morphological type distributions are influenced to a very minor degree only by sex differences in the cephalic index.

Another differentia that might affect the female allotment of type is the nasal index. Sortings based upon the nasal index were used solely to differentiate the Dinaric brachycephalic type, on the one hand, from the East Baltic and Nordic Alpine on the other, on the basis of individual nasal index below 63 for the Dinarics and above for the other round-headed types. Now, the mean nasal index of West Irish women is 0.96 index units below that of the males and, consequently, we might expect some Dinaric increment (possibly about 5 to 6 per cent) in the female series as a result of this difference. Actually, the principal difference between the sexes in brachycephals is in reality the 8 per cent excess of this type that the females enjoy. The concentration of the sex difference in brachycephalic types in the Dinaric class does appear to indicate that the lower mean nasal index of the Irish women may have had some effect in this type distribution. However, lower nasal indices in the female sex cannot be stated to be a regular and standard sex difference. A consultation of the literature indicates that on the living the sex differences is about as likely to be in one direction as the other. The implication is that, although the Irish women may have more Dinarics amongst them than the Irish males, this may not be a consequence of a real sex difference, but possibly rather the preservation in the West Irish females of generally more leptorrhine noses because of a closer adherence in the sex to an ancestral racial type. There are virtually as many male Nordic Alpines and male East Baltics as females, but the females have in addition about 8 per cent more of the long-nosed brachycephals whom we call Dinarics.

The other sex differences that affect the sorting of the females into different subracial types or different proportions of subracial types than are shown in the males are hair color and eye color. Let us deal first with the former. The West Irish females have more black hair and more dark brown hair than have the males, but this would hardly tend to confuse the racial sortings because any kind of dark hair can go into either round-headed or long-headed morphological types—the Dinaric, Nordic Alpine, and Pure Alpine in the former case, the Keltic, Nordic Mediterranean, and Pure Mediterranean in the latter. Only the Pure and Predominantly Nordic and the East Baltic types are restricted to the lighter hair shades, and in these types, indeed, the sex differences are quite small. In any event there is very little difference in the sex distribution of the lighter shades of hair. It hardly seems, then, that the crude sex differences in hair color can be called to account for the sex difference in type distribution.

The matter of eye color is somewhat different. The excess of females who are classified as Pure Mediterranean (2.8 per cent) and the very existence of the Pure Alpine type (not found in the males) depends upon Dr. Dawson's finding in the females of a respectable percentage of pure dark eyes (5.8 per cent), which are nearly absent in males (0.3 per cent). It seems improbable that we can regard dark eyes in the female, and a virtual absence of them in the male, as a standard sex difference. However it certainly occurs in mixed strains—at any rate, in the form of an excess of pure dark eyes among the females. Hrdlička (1925, p. 39) recorded in his Old Americans 16.5 per cent of pure brown eyes in the males and 20 per cent in the females. In the islands of Garumna and Lettermullen in Galway, Browne (1899, p. 229) found 1.08 per cent of dark eyes in males and 9.74 per cent in adult females. In the Arans, Haddon and Browne (1893, p. 785) found 2.51 per cent of dark eyes in adult males and 3.55 per cent in adult females. In Carna and Mweenish, Galway, Browne (1901, p. 507) found 6.05 per cent of dark-eyed males and 74.80 per cent (!) of dark-eyed females. Finally, in Clare Island, and Inishturk, County Mayo, the same redoubtable anthropometrist (1898, p. 44) records no dark eyes at all in adult males, but 3.12 per cent in females. While there can be no doubt that Browne and Haddon classified as "dark eyes" a considerable number of eyes that in our survey would be graded "dark mixed," we may be assured that the sex difference in favor of the women in the matter of darker eyes was a correctly observed fact.

Our contention is that the darker eyes of the women, as well as the darker hair, are not a real sex difference but due to the principle well expressed by Hrdlička (1925, p. 29) long ago in his statement that "the women evidently, . . . preserve better the different ancestral conditions from which the mixture represented now by the Old Americans arose, while the men show more fusion, more blend." In the same passage that great anthropologist cites the evidence that the women of England, Scotland, and Wales have more dark hair than the men—a fact so well known that it hardly requires reiteration here.

Our conclusion on this matter of sex difference as affecting the division into subracial or morphological types is that such differences are not, properly speaking, sex differences, except in so far as they represent the ancestral conservatism in type of the female and the blending, more hybridized, and variant tendency of the male.

We have also to discuss the possibility that the morphological type differences between the sexes are largely referable to differences in techniques and standards of morphological observations in our two field workers. We reject that explanation in toto after careful scrutiny of the evidence in the various measurements and indices, and attribute gradations previously discussed under their separate headings.

If we accept, as we are inclined to do, the explanation that the difference in the morphological type composition between males and females is largely referable to the tendency of the women to preserve better the ancestral racial types, and of the males to vary away from these types in the direction of blended, composite, or hybridized types, we have to consider the implications of the female type distribution for the racial history of Ireland.

The only new subracial or morphological type found in the women is the Pure Alpine type, with dark hair, pure dark eyes, cephalic index over 80, and nasal index 63 or above. Certainly, the existence of this Pure Alpine type as an antecedent racial strain of the present Irish population is clearly implied by the strength of the Nordic Alpine mixed stock in the males. The only surprising fact is that no Pure Alpines were found in that sex, and it is within the bounds of possibility that Dupertuis' criteria for "pure darks" in eyes were slightly more severe than those of Dawson (i.e., that the former might have called "dark mixed" some few eyes that the latter would classify as "dark"). We are convinced, however, that this matter does not seriously enter into the comparison of the males and females within our two great Irish series, although it crops up unmistakably when we consider the data of other anthropometrists who have worked in Ireland. The Pure Alpine type, exemplified by the West Irish females in 13 of 1792 individuals, may never have entered Ireland in an unmixed form in any very considerable number of persons. It would certainly be rash to pick out one of the putatively prehistoric, legendary protohistoric, or historic invasions or migrations into Ireland and say of it, "This was the stock that brought in the Pure Alpine type."

The reinforcement of our exiguous and almost dubious Pure Mediterranean type in males by its occurrence in 55 of 1792 females, or a substantial 3.1 per cent, is particularly gratifying, especially since this type in the females is distributed in general accord with the glimpse we have of it in the males from the same counties. The residue of "Pure Mediterraneans," being much larger than that of the "Pure Alpines," suggests that these long-headed, dark-haired, dark-eyed people may have been much more numerous in that color combination in Ireland in ancient and prehistoric times than were ever the Alpines. Such Pure Mediterranean types are apparently far more common today in Wales, Scotland, and in England than in Ireland.

SUMMARY AND CONCLUSIONS

When two observers use the same scheme of subjective morphological rating on the same subjects, there is inevitably some difference of result, even if the observers have been trained together in the same institution by the same instructor. When two observers apply the putatively identical rating method to different series of individuals, their divergences cannot be referred with confidence to observational equation (i.e., difference of the standards of judging employed). For two random samples or selected samples from the same population will probably, in fact, differ from each other rather markedly in many morphological minutiae. When one observer's subjects are males and the other's females, we may reasonably expect many marked sex differences, and we cannot lightly attribute marked morphological differences in the records of the two sexes to observational equation.

In the present case, one observer (C. W. Dupertuis) obtained all of his anthropological training at Harvard. The other (Helen Dawson) was trained in anatomy by Professor Robert J. Terry of the Anatomy Department of Washington University and in anthropometry by Professor Harry L. Shapiro. Dr. Dawson, at the time of the Irish field work, was a National Research Council Fellow. She and Dr. Dupertuis consulted on method and

technique only once in Ireland, but she on one occasion watched Dupertuis measure and observe, and she also received some instructions from the senior author prior to going into the field.

In the comparison of the West Irish females with the Irish males, the senior author has frequently been disturbed by differences of such a magnitude that they raise the suspicion of observational equation, and he has not hesitated to discuss these doubts frankly with the reader and with the two original observers, both of whom he regards as extremely careful and competent. Following a method long ago employed by him in a large anthropometric investigation of criminals, in which three observers participated, the senior author has classified morphological observations made upon the Irish into three categories. The first of these consists of those observations in which the agreements are so close, or the divergences so plausibly referable to real sex difference, that no serious fear of the intrusion of observational equation is aroused. Fortunately this category includes the majority. The second category includes observations in which it is suspected that there may have been slight to moderate exaggeration of the real sex difference by the existence of an observational equation. The third category consists of observations in which the sex difference from the records is so great as to create a virtual certainty that it must be in great measure the result of radically different grading on the part of the two observers.

The first category requires no further discussion beyond the statement that even these observations, relatively unimpeachable on the grounds under examination, can never be completely free from suspicion of differences attributable to personal equation. Even a single experienced and highly skilled observer may and must differ from time to time in his own judgments in subjective rating of morphological variations.

The second category of observations, judged to have been influenced to some extent by observational equation but not to a point where the sex comparison is entirely invalidated, consists of the following: hair texture, eye color, amount of pigment in mixed eyes, median eyefolds, nasion depression, nasal bridge breadth, lip seam, chin prominence, chin type, occipital protrusion.

The third category, in which there is almost certainly a pronounced observational equation with which we must reckon, includes the following: iris pattern, eye obliquity, forehead height, nasal septum, nasal tip inclination, teeth crowding, teeth caries, malars—frontal projection, ear helix, ear antihelix, Darwin's point, ear lobe attachment, ear lobe size, ear protrusion, temporal fullness, lambdoid flattening, facial asymmetry.

Class I (Probably no observational equation)

Skin color: females have more pale skins and fewer pink skins.

Vascularity: females less vascular.

Freckling: no clear sex difference.

Hair form: women have more straight hair and less curved hair.

Hair quantity, head: women have thicker head hair.

Hair quantity, body: women have much less body hair.

Grayness, head: women have less grayness but difference may be due to lower mean age.

Eyefolds, external: 9 per cent less common in females.

Eyebrow concurrency: less marked and more frequently absent in females.

Brow ridges: much smaller and more frequently absent in females.

Forehead slope: less marked and more frequently absent in females.

Nasion depression: more frequently absent and less in females.

Nasal root height: less in females.

Nasal bridge height: lower in females.

Nasal tip, thickness: less in females.

Lips, integumental thickness: less often thin in males.

Upper lip, membranous thickness: thicker in females.

Lips, eversion: oftener submedium in males.

Mid-facial prognathism: commoner in females.

Teeth, wear: much more severe in females.

Teeth, loss: much greater in females.

Face shortening: much greater in females.

Gonial angles: less pronounced in females.

Occipital protrusion: less in females.

Class II (Probably a moderate observational equation)

Hair texture: much finer in females.

Eye color: darker in females; more gray-browns and less blue-browns, more gray and gray-blue, less blue.

Pigment, mixed eyes: lighter in females.

Eyefolds, median: commoner in females.

Chin type: bilateral type very rare in females.

Occipital flattening: less in females.

Class III (Probably a serious observational equation)

Iris: less often distinctly patterned in males; more often spotted in females.

Eye obliquity: much more marked upward slant in females.

Forehead height: less often high in females.

Nasal septum: less often convex in females.

Teeth, caries: less recorded in females (probably not a valid difference).

Teeth, crowding: less in females.

Malars, frontal projection: far more often pronounced in females, somewhat oftener absent or submedium in females.

Malars, lateral projection: excesses of females in pronounced and submedium or absent categories.

Ear helix: excesses of females in both pronounced and very small or submedium categories.

Ear antihelix: less often pronounced in females, but also less often submedium or absent.

Ear, Darwin's Point: very rare in females, common in males.

Ear lobe, attachment: majority of females have attached lobes; majority of males free lobes.

Ear lobe, size: tremendous excess of large ear lobes in males.

Ear protrusion: pronounced ear protrusion far commoner in males.

Temporal fullness: less often submedium and less often pronounced in females.

Lambdoid flattening: far less common in females.

Facial asymmetry: far less common in females.

Most of the sex differences listed above are not unexpected and many of them are quite in line with previous anthropological experience. In spite of the probable intervention of some amount of observational equation, we are confident of the validity of most of these sex differences. There are a few, however, in which our confidence is limited. For example, the piling up of female mixed eyes in gray-browns and of male eyes in blue-browns depends upon a judgment that is often very difficult—the distinction between a grayish and a bluish background. A similar situation obtains in distinguishing between blue and gray-blue.

In the Class II observations, most of the sex differences seem probably exaggerated rather than wrong. An especial mention should be made, however, of caries, which is recorded in a far smaller percentage of women than of men, in spite of much more severe wear and tooth loss in the former. Part of the explanation of this seeming contradiction certainly lies in the fact that the women have many more teeth missing and that these teeth were probably lost through caries (although not counted) and they had left only a few of their own teeth in which caries could be counted. There is probably an observational difference in the recording of caries also which we have not yet specifically determined—something in the nature of looking for very small cavities or merely recording as carious obviously decayed teeth.

The sex differences on almost every detail of ear morphology are so large that they arouse suspicion. Yet all of them are in the direction which is in accordance with expectation.

These differences, whenever it seemed probable that they were referable to divergence in observational standards, have been the subject of correspondence and discussion between the authors of this work. In no case has this honest and frank exchange of opinions resulted in a resolution of any of the difficulties. None seems to be due to carelessness on the part of either observer nor to any basic misunderstanding of any morphological features. In the opinion of the senior author, these variations are probably referable to unavoidable differences in the subjective rating scales of two individual observers enhanced by the fact that one was dealing with one sex, the other with the other. The theoretical scale of reference also is supposed to be that of the modal Northwestern European male in all matters of size judgment. This ideal scale is also theoretically to be used for the females. Unfortunately, in any large series of observations on a race or on any ethnic group, it is very difficult for the observer to keep his standards from regressing toward the mode of that group. For example, he is likely to judge brow ridges to be small "for an Irish male" rather than small with reference to the modal Northwestern European male. As long as we have to deal with such features as attributes, graded by size only on a subjective verbal scale, as long as we have to depend upon judgments of texture, color, etc., rather than measurements, such personal equations will continue to rear their Hydra heads. Even if we use only measurements, we do not get away from this difficulty. Two equally skilled anthropometrists may take the same measurement differently. The techniques of the measurement of man are usually rough and the technicians are individuals not machines. And even machines differ.

AGE CHANGES IN WEST COAST IRISH FEMALES

SOCIOLOGICAL OBSERVATIONS

Marital State (Table XXIX-1). The figures on marital status reveal the rather astounding fact that marriage is not very late but almost "rare" in these West Coast Irish females. Surely it is remarkable to find a group of 425 females between the ages of 15 and 19 years, not one of whom is married. It is even more surprising to find one-third of the women between 35 and 54 years still single. Of course, these facts have long been known about Irish marital status, but they continue to impress.

Number of Siblings (Table XXIX-2). The tabulation of the number of siblings by age groups clearly shows that the females of the two younger age groups come from smaller families, but it must be assumed that in the 15–19 year age group are many girls who belong to families not yet completed. This may even apply to some members of the 20–34 year age group. Considering the lateness and rarity of marriage the numbers of siblings tabulated are appallingly large.

Number of Children (Table XXIX-3). Several facts of interest may be extracted from this table. Of the 104 married women in the 20–34 year age group, 16.3 per cent have no children and the largest number of children born to any mother is 7 (3 cases). The modal number of offspring of wives in this age group is one. In the 35–54 year age group 17.3 per cent of married women have no children and the modal number of offspring is 5 (13.4 per cent). Of the 166 wives 55 years and upward, only 8.4 per cent have no offspring and the mod-

al number is found to be 10 (11.4 per cent).

If we compare the number of children born to the women 55 years and over, with the number of siblings in the families of the women of this age group, it becomes apparent that our female subjects of this age range have produced far fewer children than their mothers. The same holds for the comparison of the offspring of mothers in the 35-54 year age group with the number of siblings in the families from which they have sprung.

Education (Table XXIX-4). Education tabulated by age groups shows the expected superiority in the advantages enjoyed by the two younger age groups. University attendance is naturally the largest in the group between 20 and 34 years of age. This female series is, in general, far better educated than the total male series, and shows it in every educational status except *university*.

Language (Table XXIX-5). The interesting feature of education by age groups is the fact that the lowest age group has fewest proportionately who knew no Irish. This is, of course, the effect of the comparative recency of the general teaching of Irish in schools. It is rather astounding that the 3 individuals who speak nothing but Irish are in the first two age groups and consequently below 35 years of age. A comparison with the age grouping of language in males cannot be made very closely because all of the females come from the parts of Ireland where Irish is still spoken commonly.

MEASUREMENTS AND INDICES

The data on the Irish females have been classified into 4 age groups only: an immature group (15–19 years), young adults (20–34 years), middle-aged adults (35–54 years), old adults (55–69 years). These data can be compared with the material on age change in the Irish males (Hooton and Dupertuis, 1951). A somewhat complicating factor in these com-

parisons is the subdivision of the much larger male series into 14 age groups instead of only 4. The male groupings are by 5 year intervals, except the last, which is a residual group of males aged 80–94 years. However, our females series includes no women over 69 years, so that the last 3 male groups are out of the range of Dr. Dawson's West Coast

Irish females. It is not worth while to regroup the male series to correspond to the female age groups, or vice versa, since, in any event, only differences between age trends in the males and females are to be sought. Actual metric differences between males and females at each successive age group, or percentage differences in the distribution of morphological features would be of little or no interest.

Weight (Table XXX-1). The great weight increment in the females occurs between the 20–34 year and the 35–54 year age groups. It amounts to an average of 13.27 pounds. Maximum average weight, which is only 1.3 pounds higher, is found in the oldest age group. In the male series the weight increment between the 15–19 year age group and even the next 5-year age group is vastly larger than the female increment (in the males from 15–19 to 20-24 years, 10.80 pounds). Roughly, it may be said that the middle-age weight increment in the males begins to manifest itself before the 30th year, but, in the females, after the 34th year. The actual maximum of weight in the males falls between the 45th and 59th years, which corresponds to the maximum in females. The last occurs in the age group 55 and upwards.

Stature (Table XXX-2). In raw means, the females show a steady decline in stature from the earliest to the oldest age group, but the differences are not significant until the interval between the middle-aged and the old group is reached. In the Irish males, on the contrary, stature does not reach its maximum until the ages 30–39 are attained, and it begins to diminish immediately thereafter.

There is an intriguing suggestion that the Irish females, in showing their absolute maximum of stature in the 15–19 year age groups, have been affected by the phenomenon that we sometimes call "modernization." This is the increase in stature manifested progressively by recent generations, whereby the children are taller than their parents and, often, the younger children in a family are taller than their older brothers and sisters. The classic study of such changes is that of Bowles (1932), relating to body size in Harvard sons, fathers, and grandfathers and to changes in body size between mothers and daughters in several eastern United States women's colleges. How-

ever, if our Irish female data were to be interpreted in this way, we ought also to have found that the 15–19 year Irish males are taller than the succeeding age groups, and this is not the case. It therefore seems more reasonable to suppose that the stature maximum attained by the Irish females in the 15–19 year age group reflects their sex precocity in growth and maturation rather than any secular change.

Span (Table XXX-3). Span is insignificantly higher in the second age group than in the first, and thereafter diminishes. Yet it is of interest that maximum stature should have been attained by the females in the first (15–19) age group, but maximum span possibly not until the second age group. In males, span and stature achieve their maxima at roughly the same period (30–39 years). The difference displayed by the females again recalls the possibility that the lowest age group has been affected by a secular change in body form, so that the females of this group are different from those of the next age group.

Relative Span (Table XXX-4). There is a possibly significant increase in relative span between the first and second age groups which corresponds to an apparently similar rise of relative span in males at this time. In males, however, the maximum relative span is not reached until 50-54 years, whereas in females the apparent maximum is attained in the 20–34 year period.

Biacromial Diameter (Table XXX-5). This measurement in the females increases and reaches its maximum in the 35–54 year age group. In the males, the maximum is reached at 30–34 years and held for a decade. It begins to decline perceptibly in the 55–59 year age group. There is also a decline in the females in the terminal age group, but it is not statistically significant, although it is possibly real.

Relative Shoulder Breadth (Table XXX-6). Shoulder breadth relative to stature increases through the four age groups. A similar increase, but not as marked, is discernible in the male series. However, the females throughout are relatively broader shouldered than the males.

Sitting Height (Table XXX-7). Sitting height increases 0.56 cm. from the earliest to the second age group and thereafter diminishes, with the principal drop between the middle-aged and the old group. In the males a much sharper rise occurs in the period after the youngest age group and sitting height begins to diminish slowly from 40 years onward.

Relative Sitting Height (Table XXX-8). This increases through the first three age groups and declines in the terminal group. A similar decline is to be noted among the males. It is probably due to a more rapid shrinkage in sitting height than in stature.

Head Length (Table XXX-9). Strangely, there is no increase of head length in the females between the first two age groups, but thereafter successive increases. In the males this dimension does not reach its maximum until the 50–54 year age group and the decline thereafter is very slight. The males, however, show a sharp increase between the first two age groups. It seems improbable that Irish heads should increase in length by growing after the age of 34 years. We have to accept this improbability or resort to the explanation of a selective force eliminating the shorter-headed and preserving those with the longer crania.

Head Breadth (Table XXX-10). Head breadth rises a little between the first two age groups, remains the same until the 55–on group and then drops off a little, in a possibly insignificant amount. The male age changes are similar.

Cephalic Index (Table XXX-11). The cephalic index declines slightly in the last two age groups and the same trend is observed in the males, but to a more marked degree. The data suggest some factor operating in favor of the survival in the older age groups of the more dolichocephalic.

Head Height (Table XXX-12). In the females, this measurement changes little (on the basis of the means) until the middle age group when it rises a little and reaches its maximum in the oldest group. However, the spread of the means is only 0.63 mm., so that it can be said that there is virtually no change in the age groups. In the males, on the contrary, head height declines slowly but steadily from the age of 25 years.

Length-Height Index (Table XXX-13). Apparently this index in the females remains the same until 35 years, and then drops nearly

an unit. In the males, there is a gradual drop from first to last.

Breadth-Height Index (Table XXX-14). This index remains the same up to 34, and then rises and keeps on rising. In males it declines irregularly from first to last groups. The sex difference in the trends is marked, but not easily explicable.

It is quite apparent that the drop in the female length-height index after 35 years is due to the greater head lengths of the females in the two older age groups. Similarly, the rise in the breadth-height index among the females in the last two age groups is due to a slight increase in height and a slight diminution of breadth, both most easily discernible in the last age groups. However, this is merely pointing out the shifts in the pairs of variables from which the indices are calculated. It is no explanation.

Minimum Frontal Diameter (Table XXX-15). This measurement diminishes through every age group, although the difference between the means of the various age groups are not statistically significant. Nevertheless, the consistency of the decrease seems to suggest that we are dealing here with a real trend and not merely with chance variations. In the males, minimum frontal diameter initially rises sharply from the immature to the young adult group, then stays about constant until the 60–64 year age group, and finally begins to diminish and continues to do so until the minimum is reached in the last two age groups (75–79 years, 80–94 years). In the male series, this last phenomenon of old age distribution was tentatively interpreted as the result of selection for survival of individuals with narrow foreheads, rather than as an age change. It seems probable that the same explanation may be valid in case of the females. There is no good reason for a senile decrease in this measurement.

Fronto-Parietal Index (Table XXX-16). In the Irish females the means of this index fluctuate, with the highest value found in the youngest age group. In the males, this index also fluctuates through the age groups, with a tendency for the higher values to occur in the earlier groups. There is, however, no regular regression upon age.

Bizygomatic Diameter (Table XXX-17). This measurement of facial breadth rises a millimeter between the immature and young adult age groups, but then keeps on rising until it attains its maximum in the last age group. It is hardly conceivable that there should be any age change which would augment this measurement after the age of 54 years. The same phenomenon occurs in the male series, in which the maximum bizygomatic diameter is reached and maintained between 50 and 64 years, after which there is some senile diminution. The long continued increase of this measurement is more likely to be a selective result than an age change.

Cephalo-Facial Index (Table XXX-18). The data on the 20–34 year age group pertaining to the distribution of this index have been lost and the importance of the mean for this age group does not justify the labor of sorting and calculation which a new determination of the mean would necessitate. In the three age groups for which we have the information, there is a steady rise in the cephalo-facial index. The same phenomenon occurs in the male series with the maximum of the index attained in the 65–69 year age group, followed by a diminution in the terminal small group of octogenarians. Thus the old women and the old men both have wider faces relative to head breadth than those in the younger age groups. The explanation is probably to be sought in selective factors making for the survival into old age of the broader-faced individuals.

Zygo-Frontal Index (Table XXX-19). This index follows the pattern observed in the males in its consistent diminution from the earliest group onwards. In the females the difference between the immature and young adult groups is, however, statistically insignificant. Again it seems probable that the regression is due to the selection of individuals with narrower foreheads and wider faces for survival into old age. It is hardly conceivable that any real age change is involved.

Bigonial Diameter (Table XXX-20). This hinder breadth of jaws stays about the same for the first two age groups, then increases more than one millimeter and stays the same in the last two age groups. In the males it rises with fair regularity up to the 55–59 year age group, and then fluctuates. The higher value in the upper age groups may be an actual change due to continued accumulation of fatty or muscular tissue. In the far more numerous and more finely divided subgroups of the males, the consistent increases up and through middle age seemed to indicate an actual age change rather than a selective process.

Fronto-Gonial Index (Table XXX-21). As in the males, the means of this index appear to increase consistently with age. It seems necessary to invoke the same factors for both sexes: long continued increase in the bigonial diameter and a rather strange falling off of the value of the minimum frontal diameter in the older individuals.

Zygo-Gonial Index (Table XXX-22). As in the males, so in the females, the means of this index seem to hold fairly constant through the 4 age groups. Both diameters involved show either long continued growth through middle age or have been influenced similarly by selective factors tending to operate for the survival of persons with the larger dimensions. It is interesting that the index remains about the same, and it suggests that the late increases in these diameters are closely correlated, if they are age changes.

Total Face Height (Table XXX-23). In the females, the means of the age groups of total face height appear to follow the pattern observed in the males. Between the immature and the young adult groups there is a substantial increase which can certainly be attributed to growth. Then the facial height mean diminishes, probably, in part, because of loss of teeth and alveolar resorption.

Facial Index (Table XXX-24). The index rises one unit between the immature and young adult groups, certainly because the vertical growth of the jaws in the subadult period is greater than the increase of the bizygomatic diameter. In the middle-aged and old groups, the mean of the index keeps decreasing, perhaps entirely because of face shortening. However, the long increase in the bizygomatic diameter, which is hardly an age change, is also involved in this diminution of the facial index. The trend in the male series is identical, but not so marked.

Upper Face Height (Table XXX-25). This diameter exhibits in the females the same astonishingly long increase of the means that was observed in the males. The maximum in the female series is reached in the 35–54 year age group. In the males, this maximum occurs in the 50–54 year age group. The diminution in the terminal female age group amounts only to 0.17 mm. which is statistically insignificant, but is probably real, nevertheless. A similar dropping off in the oldest age groups is found in the males.

It would take a very credulous person to believe that nasion-prosthion height actually increases in individuals beyond the 34th year. Selective factors have to be invoked.

Upper Facial Index (Table XXX-26). As in the males, the upper facial index in females is moderately stable. However, in the females there is a perceptible rise between the first two groups—attributable, no doubt, to continued vertical growth of the maxilla. The means of the two middle age groups (spanning the 20th to 54th year) are virtually identical, and then there is a slight (statistically insignificant, but probably real) dropping off in the terminal group. The same trend, spread over more age groups, is discernible in the males.

Nose Height (Table XXX-27). It is well known that the nose grows in middle age. In our Irish females the maximum height does not occur until the age group that comprises the years 35–54. In the Irish males the maximum value of this measurement is still later—about 55–59 years. In both sexes, the final old age diminution is so slight as to be negligible.

Nose Breadth (Table XXX-28). In the Irish females the breadth of the nose shows no increase between the immature and the young adult groups, but rises in the middle-aged group and continues and accentuates this elevation in the old group. Of course, most of the differences are not statistically significant, but we are convinced that they would be, if only the age group samples were larger. In the males also, the age groups above 54 exhibit the highest means of nose breadth. It seems certain that this diameter, as well as nose height, increases through middle age, and even into old age. There is always, of course, the possibility of some mysterious selective factor operating in the dark.

Nasal Index (Table XXX-29). The age regression of this index is substantially the same for both sexes of Irish. The mean diminishes from the immature to the young adults, because the height of the nose increases with the height of the upper face, both of which are still growing fairly rapidly in the late adolescent and subadult periods. At this time nose breadth is increasing very little, if at all. After the 20–34 year age group, the nasal index keeps on increasing reaching its maximum after the age of 55. This is true of males also.

CONCLUSIONS ON METRIC AND INDICIAL AGE CHANGES

Our treatment of "age changes" in the female series has been much less detailed and thorough than in the case of the males, because the female series is far smaller and does not permit fine subdivision into age groups of 5 years duration. In comparison with the male age group changes, there are some interesting divergences on the part of the females, and some very striking agreements.

We may deal with the divergences first. As far as can be judged from our West Coast Irish females, they attain their middle-age increment of weight later than do the males, although their stature maximum is reached at least 10 years earlier. Again, the females do not achieve their maximum span until the age group period subsequent to that in which they have attained maximum stature, whereas in the males both stature and span maxima are reached at about the same time.

Another curious difference lies in the failure of the females to show any increase in head length between the immature and the young adult age groups, at a time when head length is almost certainly still growing, and in the interval when the Irish males show their greatest increment of that diameter. The measurements create the impression that the females have mostly finished their growth in the 15–19 year age period, and stay about the same in the next 20–34 year period, whereas the males in the 15–19 year group and several subsequent 5 year age groups are still immature and growing. This lack of increment between the 15–19 and 20–34 year age group holds in many of the female measurements: head length, head breadth, head height, minimum frontal, bigonial, nose breadth; and, in bodily measurements, in stature. However, in most of the other measurements here dealt with, the females show an increment from the youngest to the next group that is substantially similar to that displayed by the males: span, biacromial diameter, sitting height; and, in the head and face, bizygomatic diameter, total face height, upper face height, nose height.

Among the apparent agreements in age changes, whether phenomena of bodily growth, shrinkage, or selection, are: decrease in stature in the terminal age groups; fairly protracted increase in biacromial diameter and relative shoulder breadth; decrease in sitting height in the older age groups, decline in relative sitting height in old age; increases of head length into old age; terminal age group decrease in head breadth; terminal age group decrease in cephalic index; decrease in minimum frontal diameter through the middle-aged and old-aged groups; increase of bizygomatic diameter into middle-aged and old groups; increase of cephalo-facial index into old age, consistent diminution of the zygo-frontal index, increase of the fronto-gonial index, constancy of the zygo-gonial index; growth in total face height between immature and young adult groups followed by diminution, accompanied by similar rise and fall of the total facial index; long increase of the upper facial height with slight terminal diminution; slight terminal diminution of the upper facial index; late increases in nose height and nose breadth; initial diminution and subsequent rise of the nasal index.

MORPHOLOGICAL OBSERVATIONS

Skin Color, Inner Arm (Table XXXI-1). The females show an entirely different age regression from the males. In the latter, pink skins increase and brunet and swarthy skins decrease in successive age groups. In the females, the regression is quite regular but in the opposite direction. Yet the total percentages of different skin colors are very similar.

Vascularity (Table XXXI-2). Here, again, the West Coast females show a perfectly consistent regression in the direction opposite from that displayed by the males. Vascularity diminishes with age in the females; increases in the males.

Freckles (Table XXX-3). Here the two sexes agree in that freckling diminishes sharply with age.

Moles (Table XXXI-4). In the males, moles diminish and practically disappear with age. In the females, there is no apparent age regression.

Hair Form (Table XXXI-5). The age regressions of hair form among the females are nearly the same as among the males. Deep-waved and curly hair are sharply decreased in the last two large age groups; straight hair is increased and low-waved hair, after slight fluctuations in the first three age groups, increases sharply in the last group.

Hair Texture (Table XXXI-6). In the male series, there was no regression of hair texture upon age. Among the females there is a small but regular increase of coarse hair, accompanied by a marked diminution of fine hair, and an irregular increase in the medium category. This is an age change that seems reasonable. We suspect that Dr. Dawson was especially skillful in the recording of this difficult observation.

Hair Quantity, Head (Table XXXI-7). Pronounced thickness of hair decreases; medium and submedium thicknesses increase with age. The changes are not great, nor were they in the male series.

Hair Quantity, Body (Table XXXI-8). There is no consistent regression of amount of body hair upon age. The same is true in the male series.

Grayness, Head (Table XXXI-9). There is, of course, the expected increase of grayness with age. However, it is interesting to note that it seems to proceed more slowly in the West Coast Irish females than in total Irish males. For instance, the 20–34 year age group of women still shows 90.6 per cent without grayness. The figures for males are split into smaller age groups and are not exactly comparable. Yet it is clear that the males in this year span have more gray hair (20–34 years, 96.6 per cent absent; 25–29 years, 84.6 per cent absent; and 30–34 years, 61.6 per cent absent).

Hair Color, Head (Table XXXI-10). Black hair increases and reaches its maximum in the 35–54 year age group. In the males, the maximum of black hair is reached at 40–44 years. Dark brown hair in the females reaches its maximum in the third age group, and declines only insignificantly in the fourth. The diminution of this shade in the male is regular and marked after 54 years. Flat brown declines steadily from the first, as in the males. Red-brown hardly changes. Golden brown, which is less common in the females, diminishes sharply after the first age group. Ash brown, on the whole, increases with age in the females, reaching its maximum in the 35–54 year age group. This shade is much rarer in males and gradually disappears with age. Golden hair diminishes and disappears in the last age group. Red hair is commonest in the 15–19 year age group, but does not diminish regularly after the second age group. It does so diminish in the males, but in the male series we have much better representation of the advanced age groups.

On the whole, the age regressions of hair color in the two sexes are very similar.

Eye Color (Table XXXI-11). As in the males, the percentage of dark eyes in the females fluctuates in the various age groups, but shows no real regression. Gray-brown eyes, which are far commoner in the females, increase slightly with age, as they do also in the males. Similarly, in accordance with the male age change, the few green-brown eyes diminish a little. Blue-brown eyes in the females do not change regularly with age. In the males this eye shade, which is far commoner, declines with age. The light eyes—gray, gray-blue and blue, show very little age change. If anything, they decrease a little. This is completely contrary to the male regression in which these light eyes increase steadily with age.

Pigment, Mixed Eyes (Table XXXI-12). As in the males, the amount of pigment in mixed eyes does not show any clear and simple regression upon age. In both series the very pronouncedly light eyes seem to increase in the older age groups. In the females the pronouncedly light eyes seem to decline a little. Perhaps the same can be said of the males.

Iris (Table XXXI-13). Comment upon the somewhat confused scheme of reporting iris pattern used in this survey has already been made. The categories are often overlapping. The data on this feature show no clear age regression in the Irish females. In the total Irish males, there was some suggestion of an increase of spotted eyes of various patterns with age. This apparent increase of spots, whether in clear eyes, diffuse eyes, rayed, or zoned eyes, seems to occur also in the females. Thus, in the first age group, the percentage of eyes with spots is 5.3; in the second, 7.7; in the third, 12.0; and in the fourth, 13.7.

Eyefolds, External (Table XXXI-14). These folds, always rare in the females, increase more or less regularly with age, as in the males.

Eyefolds, Median (Table XXXI-15). The median folds, recorded by Dawson in about four times as many females as in total Irish males, also increase fairly regularly with age. There are indications of an increase of this type of fold in the males, but Dupertuis records only 3 per cent in the total series. Consequently, little age regression can be discerned.

Eyefolds, Internal (Table XXXI-16). The number of these internal folds is negligible, and it is very strange that of the few that are recorded with more should appear in the two upper age groups. The internal fold is most likely to be manifest in infancy and childhood. In the males, the few internal folds diminish with age.

Eye Obliquity (Table XXXI-17). Medium obliquity upward, or upward slant of the eye openings, diminishes markedly with age in the Irish females. Submedium obliquity increases from the first to the second age group and then remains constant, or nearly so. The absence of obliquity increases. Obliquity downward seems to increase slightly after the first age group. The regression in the male series is very different. There absence of obliquity diminishes through the age groups; submedium, medium, and pronounced upward obliquities all increase, and so do downward obliquities.

Eye Opening Height (Table XXXI-18). Low eye openings increase with age in the females, as in the males. The female age diminution in pronounced height of eye opening is clearer than the male.

Eyebrow Thickness (Table XXXI-19). Eyebrows tend to become thinner with advancing age in the females, but this phenomenon is much more definite and marked in the males.

Eyebrow Concurrency (Table XXXI-20). The females agree with the males in showing definite diminution of eyebrow concurrency with advancing age.

Brow Ridges (Table XXXI-21). In the West Coast females, there is a regular increase in size of brow ridges age group by age group, shown in every category except submedium. It is interesting to find this regression in the females, because in the Irish males maximum brow ridge size seems to be attained about 30–34 years and then fluctuates through the older age groups without any clear regression. (Hooton and Dupertuis, 1951, table LXIII, p. 67). Of course, the brow ridges in females are consistently smaller than in the males, with their mode in the submedium category instead of the medium.

Forehead Height (Table XXXI-22). While the proportion of foreheads of submedium height shows no particular change from age group to age group, there can be no doubt that forehead height increases with age in these females, or perhaps that some selectional process operates to favor the old age survival of more women with high foreheads. This is precisely the opposite phenomenon to that observed in the male series. Their forehead heights strikingly decrease in the older age groups. In neither sex does this seem to be a real age change. In the females it might be possible to attribute apparently increased forehead height in the older age groups to recession of the frontal hairline. However, the only type of frontal recession that would tend to give a specious impression of added forehead height is rare in men and perhaps nonexistent in women. This is "a region of midfrontal sparseness, or denudation of such depth that it extends as a band of uniform width along the entire anterior border of the scalp" (Hamilton, 1951, p. 713). Hamilton found this so rare a type in men that he did not include it in routine classification. The same author states that the most advanced type of denudation that is usually observed among women is his Type II, in which there are

triangular areas of recession at the temples. Such recession would hardly increase the apparent height of the forehead. On the whole it seems very doubtful that frontal hairline recession can be invoked to explain the greater number of females with pronounced forehead height in the old age groups of the Irish.

If this increased forehead height in the elderly is not due to an age change, it must be referred to a selectional factor. If that is the case, it must operate in one direction in one sex, and in another in the other. These are mysterious phenomena.

Forehead Slope (Table XXXI-23). There is an expected and very clear age regression in the direction of fewer forward slopes, fewer vertical foreheads (slope *absent*), fewer foreheads of steep or submedium slope, and more of medium and pronounced slope as one goes from age group to age group. The same phenomenon is manifest in the male series (Hooton and Dupertuis, 1951, table LXV, p. 69). It is difficult to regard this regression as an age change. It is in accordance with the increased number of women with large brow ridges in the older age groups. Of course, the slope of the forehead tends to be quite consistently less in the females than in the males, but within their own range the females show the same age regression as does the other sex.

Nasion Depression (Table XXXI-24). The females again agree with the males in showing an increase in the depth of the nasion depression from age group to age group. This is within the female range of variation, in which nasion depths are consistently less than in males. The mode in males is a medium depression with 77.3 per cent, whereas in females is at *very small*. In the males, *very small* and *submedium* have had to be combined, and total together only 3.0 per cent. There are no males in whom the nasion depression is recorded as absent.

It strikes us as very interesting that in a feature in which there is such a wide difference between the sexes, identical and undisputable age regression of the same nature should be found.

Nasal Root Height (Table XXXI-25). There is no clear regression of nasal root height upon age in either sex of the Irish.

Nasal Root Breadth (Table XXXI-26). This feature shows no clear age regression. In the males the broadest nasal roots occur in the youngest age group, but thereafter there is no regression.

Nasal Bridge Height (Table XXXI-27). This feature shows no regular age regression in the females. If anything, bridges seem to be lowest in the oldest age group. In males pronounced height of the nasal bridge seems to rise with age.

Nasal Bridge Breadth (Table XXXI-28). The women of the oldest age group certainly have the broadest nasal bridges, but otherwise the age regression is not clear. In the males broad nasal bridges very definitely increase in the age groups from 55 years upward.

Nasal Septum (Table XXXI-29). There is no clear regression on age in the females. In the males there is a definite increase of straight and concave septa at the expense of convex through the age groups.

Nasal Tip, Thickness (Table XXXI-30). The highest percentage of thick nasal tips is found in the oldest age group, but otherwise there is no clear regression. In the males pronounced thickness of the nasal tip certainly rises with age.

Nasal Tip, Inclination (Table XXXI-31). With age, upward inclinations of the nasal tip decrease, horizontal and downward inclinations increase. The same regression obtains in the males.

Nasal Wings (Table XXXI-32). Flare of the nasal wings definitely increases in the third and fourth groups, whereas thin or compressed tips fluctuate and tend to decrease. In the males, flaring nasal wings increase steadily in the age groups above 45 years, but there is also a less regular increase of compressed tips.

Nostril Visibility, Frontal (Table XXXI-33). Frontal visibility of the nostrils decreases with age in the females as in the males. This phenomenon is due to the downward growth of the nasal tip in middle and old age.

Nasal Profile (Table XXXI-34). There is no certain age regression of nasal profile in the West Coast Irish females. In the males convex noses increase, straight noses diminish, concave profiles decrease.

Lips, Integumental Thickness (Table XXXI-35). Integumental lips of submedium thickness tend to increase markedly with age in the Irish females, and integumental lips of pronounced thickness (quite rare) appear to diminish. The regression is clearer in the females than in the males, but in the same direction.

Upper and Lower Lip, Membranous Thickness (Tables XXXI-36 and XXXI-37). The regression in the females, as in the males, is a steady decrease of thickness of the membranous lips with age. Throughout the age groups the females tend to show fewer lips of submedium thickness and more of medium and pronounced thickness than do total Irish males. The regression is the same in the lower lips, which were observed separately by Dawson. Usually the lower lip in an individual is thicker than the upper and this difference is maintained throughout the age groups, but with the same regressional direction as in the upper.

Lips, Eversion (Table XXXI-38). Lip eversion also decreases with age in both sexes, with the females tending throughout to show higher proportions of medium eversion and less of the extreme categories than the males.

Mid-facial Prognathism (Table XXXI-39). Alveolar prognathism is so rare in this female series that no age regression is shown and the tabulation is not reproduced here. Mid-facial prognathism, which is apparently much more common in the females than in the total Irish males, diminishes sharply in the successive age groups. The males also show a decrease with age, but less spectacular. The age change is probably due to dental loss and alveolar resorption.

Chin Prominence (Table XXXI-40). Apparent chin prominence increases with age, probably because alveolar resorption consequent upon dental loss throws the mental eminence into greater prominence. However, the mandible is likely to be displaced forward to some extent, as a consequence of the same dental loss and readjustment of the bite.

Bite (Table XXXI-41). The bite classification in the West Coast females shows several slight age regressions not discernible in the male series. There is an unreliable increase in underbites and in pronounced overbites with age and a diminution of submedium (normal) overbites. The classification of bite in this survey was too simple and crude to be of much use, in any event.

Teeth, Wear (Table XXXI-42). Tooth wear shows the expected regression upon age in both sexes. Wear in the female series is greater throughout the age groups, but we cannot be absolutely certain that the sex difference is uncomplicated by observational equation.

Teeth, Loss (Table XXXI-43). In comparison with the males, the females tend to show more severe tooth loss in the successive age group. The difference manifests itself even in the 15–19 year age group. Here the males enjoy a 4.9 per cent advantage in subadults who have lost no teeth.

Teeth, Caries (Table XXXI-44). The females show a natural increase of caries in successive age groups. Unfortunately, the data are not exactly comparable with those of the male series, partly because caries are recorded as in teeth still in the mouth, and by our system of recording, take no account of teeth lost through caries. Thus the West Coast females appear to have less caries than the males, largely because they have fewer teeth left on which to make the caries count. A better way of handling this problem would be to use the D.M.F. index, in which number of decayed teeth, number of filled teeth and number of missing teeth are added together and related to the number of individuals in the population. This index can still be calculated from our raw data blanks, but cannot be undertaken for this monograph.

Malars, Frontal Projection (Table XXXI-45). Apparent anterior projection of the malars seems to increase somewhat through the age groups. The regression is the same in males, but less clear.

Malars, Lateral Projection (Table XXXI-46). There is a definite indication in the females of less pronounced lateral projection of malars in the youngest age group, and some increase in degree of projection between the second and the last two age groups. Such a regression is not discernible in males.

Gonial Angles (Table XXXI-47). Pronounced gonial angles decrease in the successive age groups. In the males, this diminution is not apparent until 55–59 years and thereafter.

Ear Helix (Table XXXI-48). Degree of roll of the helix shows no regression upon age in either sex.

Ear Antihelix (Table XXXI-49). There is no clear regression of this feature upon age in either sex.

Darwin's Point (Table XXXI-50). This feature is certainly a little commoner in the earlier age groups of females than in the last two. However, it is present in only 4.3 per cent of females, and consequently the age regression is unreliable. In the males it is much commoner, and shows no age regression.

Ear Lobe Attachment (Table XXXI-51). Ear lobes of the attached variety diminish with age and free ear lobes increase in females, as in males. Throughout, however, the females exhibit more of the former and fewer of the latter. There is no clear regression of soldered ear lobes upon age in either sex. Ear lobes attached in youth and early maturity almost certainly grow downward in middle and old age and may quite probably be converted into lobes classified as "free" by the observer.

Ear Lobe, Size (Table XXXI-52). There is a fairly consistent increase of size of ear lobes in the successive age groups of females, as is also the case in the males. However, throughout, there is clearly a pronounced sex difference in the vastly inferior proportion of ear lobes of pronounced size in the females. This is compensated by the higher proportions of women in which the ear lobe is recorded as absent or submedium in size.

Ear Protrusion (Table XXXI-53). In the female series submedium protrusion, never very common, seems to increase through the age groups. Pronounced protrusion increases from the first through the second age group, and then declines. Medium protrusion merely fluctuates. The increase of pronounced ear protrusion through the second age group (20–34 years) is paralleled in males, in whom, however, the maximum of this feature occurs somewhat later, between 40 and 44 years. Submedium ear protrusion increases with age in the men also, although it is so rarely recorded in comparison with that found in the women that the regression through 15 age groups is necessarily somewhat irregular. In general, then, the same age regressions are found in both sexes, with the difference that pronounced and aural protrusion is consistently rarer in the females and submedium protrusion somewhat commoner.

Temporal Fullness (Table XXXI-54). Here again the regression upon age are identical for both sexes. Submedium temporal fullness increases with age; pronounced fullness declines. However, in all age groups the females are recorded as having much less pronounced and submedium fullness and much more medium fullness. This is a very interesting exemplification of the fact that identical age regressions may be manifest even in two series in which the observers quite probably differed fairly strongly in their judgments as to the boundary between the ends of the middle category and the beginnings of the two extreme categories. It may well be that females in this observation (temporal fullness) are less inclined to the extreme variations than are the males. We do not impugn the judging abilities of our two observers. However, the important fact is that the same age regression occurs. It can hardly be attributed to anything else than some selectional advantage possessed by those persons with less pronounced temporal fullness. It is, of course, quite in line with the decrease in the number of brachycephalics in the higher age groups.

Occipital Protrusion (Table XXXI-55). The regression is clearer in females than in males, in that in the former there is a decrease of submedium and increase of pronounced occipital protrusion through the age groups. In the males pronounced occipital protrusion increases in the early age groups and then declines with senility, whereas submedium protrusion seems to increase in the latest senile age groups. Our female series is not long enough in the matter of representation, of the advanced ages to show this eventual terminal decline in occipital protrusion, even if it were present. As contrasted with the males, the females show a consistent piling up in the medium category.

Lambdoid Flattening (Table XXXI-56). In the females only 15 per cent of lambdoid flattening is recorded, as against almost 77 per cent in males. In the females, however, it is clear that lambdoid flattening increases through the age groups (but only to the extent of about 5 per cent).

In the males, lambdoid flattening appears to increase up to 59 years and then to decline. Our female series does not include enough of the really old females to show this old age decline, if it occurs. The difference in the female age groups, if real, must be due to selection rather than to age change.

Occipital Flattening (Table XXXI-57). This feature is recorded in only 14.1 per cent of females as against 20.6 per cent of males. The regressions are in exactly the opposite directions. In the females, medium occipital flattening decreases sharply with age. In the males it increases about 5 per cent, as does also pronounced flattening (but about 8 to 9 per cent). These unusual contradictions in age regressions of the two sexes are in neither case so clear, and so great as to inspire unlimited confidence. Yet in the female series they look genuine and amount to a decrease of more than 15 per cent in occipital flattening between the youngest and the oldest group.

Facial Asymmetry (Table XXXI-58). Facial asymmetry is recorded in only 7.3 per cent of females as against 25.7 per cent of males. Both sexes agree in the decrease of this feature through the age groups.

CONCLUSIONS ON MORPHOLOGICAL AGE CHANGES

As in the preceding sections, we may first deal with the features in which males and females appear to show age regressions in the opposite direction; then with the features in which one sex shows a specific age regression that the other fails to exhibit; finally with the morphological features in which the sexes agree in the age regression.

The first radical disagreement in age regression is in skin color and vascularity; females show an increase of darker skins with age and decreased vascularity, males precisely the opposite. Eye obliquity upward diminishes with age in females, but increases in males. High foreheads become increasingly common in females in the older age groups; the reverse in the males. Occipital flattening decreases with age in females and increases in males.

Age regressions found in one sex but not in the other include: diminution of moles in males; increase of coarse hair in females; increase of blue eyes in males; increase in height of nasal bridge in males; increase of convex noses in males; increase in lateral projection of malars in females.

Regressions in the same direction in both sexes are: decrease of freckling; decrease of deep-waved and curly hair; decrease of head hair quantity; increase of grayness; increase of black hair up to middle age, decrease of flat brown hair; slight increase of gray-brown eyes and diminution of green-brown; increase of spots in the iris; increase of external eye folds; increase of low eye openings; thinning of eyebrows; increased forehead slope; decrease in upward inclination of nasal tip; decrease of frontal visibility of nostrils; decrease in thickness of integumental lips; decrease of lip eversion; decrease of mid-facial prognathism; increases of tooth wear, tooth loss, and caries; increase in anterior projection of malars; decrease in prominence of gonial angles; decrease in attached ear lobes and increase in free ear lobes; increase in size of ear lobes; decrease of ear protrusion; decrease of facial asymmetry.

No clear regressions upon age are shown by either sex in the following features: quantity of body hair; amount of pigment in mixed eyes; iris pattern (apart from spots); nasal root height, nasal root breadth, roll of the helix, development of the antihelix, Darwin's Point.

The causes of age regressions of morphological or metric features are not easily determinable in a cross-sectional study in which the different ages are represented by different individuals. The ordinary possibilities are, obviously, straightforward age change involving those from the subadult to the mature stage, thence to middle age and senility. Many regressions such as thinning of the hair, graying, increase of dental pathology are referable to such causes. The more puzzling age regressions are those that do not pertain to features well known to alter with the deterioration of the human organism. Some of these are probably attributable to selection which picks out for survival individuals with certain attributes and metric features that are not obviously closely related to health or pathology, or to the ageing of the organism. Many of these have been discussed in great detail for the Irish males, and there can be no utility of repeating such discussions here (Hooton and Dupertuis, 1951).

The following age regressions in females are possibly the result of selective survival: decrease of deep-waved and curly hair, increase of forehead slope, increase in lateral projection of malars, increase in anterior projection of malars, increase of high foreheads, decrease of eye obliquity, decrease of occipital flattening, decrease of temporal fullness, decrease of facial asymmetry. These attributions are merely guesses.

Another possibility remains to be considered. The younger generation of our female subjects may exhibit certain bodily changes that are often called secular or cyclic. That is to say that they show differences from their parental stocks that are not facilely attributable to genetic factors, nor even plausibly to environmental factors. Such changes have been discovered in size and proportions in recent American generations. They have not been recorded for most morphological features (attributes not easily measurable and of necessity graded subjectively or put into qualitative categories). There is no particular evidence of metric or indicial variation in the younger age groups of women from West Ireland that would support the hypotheses of secular change, although we have considered it. Nor are there any morphological age regressions that seem more reasonably attributable to secular change than to selective survival. Nevertheless, the possibility remains that some of the features that disappear in the later age groups, and others that increase are merely the result of the appearance in the young of variations that their parents for unknown reasons did not exhibit, even in their youth.

REFERENCES

REFERENCES

ARENSBERG, CONRAD M.
1937. The Irish countryman; an anthropological study. New York.

ARENSBERG, C. M. AND KIMBALL, SOLON T.
1940. Family and community in Ireland. Cambridge.

BEDDOE, JOHN
1885. The races of Britain. London.

BOWLES, GORDON T.
1932. New types of old Americans at Harvard and at eastern women's colleges. Cambridge.

BROWNE, CHARLES R.
1894. The ethnography of Inishbofin and Inishshark, County Galway. *Royal Irish Academy, Proceedings,* series 3, vol. 3, no. 2.
1895. The ethnography of the Mullet, Inishkea Islands, and Portacloy, County Mayo. *Royal Irish Academy, Proceedings,* series 3, vol. 3, no. 4.
1896. The ethnography of Ballycroy, County Mayo. *Royal Irish Academy, Proceedings,* series 3, vol. 4, no. 1.
1898. The ethnography of Clare Island and Inishturk, County Mayo. *Royal Irish Academy, Proceedings,* series 3, vol. 5, no. 1.
1899. The ethnography of Garumna and Lettermullen, in the County Galway. *Royal Irish Academy, Proceedings,* series 3, vol. 5, no. 2.
1901. The ethnography of Carna and Mweenish, Parish of Moyruss, Connemara. *Royal Irish Academy, Proceedings,* series 3, vol. 6, no. 3.

BUTLER, HUBERT
1949. The dumb and the stammerers in early Irish history. *Antiquity,* vol. 23, pp. 20–31.

COON, CARLETON S.
1939. The races of Europe. New York.

DAVENPORT, CHARLES B. AND LOVE, ALBERT G.
1919. Physical examination of the first million draft recruits; methods and results. Washington.

DAVIES, ELWYN AND FLEURE, H. J.
1936. A report of the anthropometric survey of the Isle of Man. *Journal of the Royal Anthropological Institute of Great Britain and Ireland,* vol. 66, n.s., vol. xxxix.

DUPERTUIS, C. W. AND HADDEN, J. A., JR.
1951. On the reconstruction of stature from long bones. *American Journal of Physical Anthropology,* n.s., vol. 9, pp. 15–54.

ENCYCLOPÆDIA BRITANNICA
1910. Eleventh edition. "Ireland," vol. 14.

FLEURE, H. J. AND JAMES, T. C.
1916. Geographical distribution of anthropological types in Wales. *Journal of the Royal Anthropological Institute of Great Britain and Ireland,* vol. 46.

GAMBLE, D. P., WALMSLEY, T. AND MOGEY, J. M.
1946. The peoples of Northern Ireland; an anthropometric survey. *Ulster Journal of Archaeology,* series 3, vol. 9.

GIRALDUS CAMBRENSIS
1881. The historical works of Giraldus Cambrensis, containing the topography of Ireland, and the history of the conquest of Ireland. Translated by Thos. Forester. Revised and edited by Thomas Wright.

HADDON, A. C. AND BROWNE, C. R.
1893. The ethnography of the Aran Islands, County Galway. *Royal Irish Academy, Proceedings,* series 3, vol. 2, no. 5, pp. 768–830.

HAMILTON, JAMES B.
1951. Patterned loss of hair in man: types and incidence. In: "The growth, replacement, and types of hair." Edited by J. B. Hamilton. *Annals of the New York Academy of Sciences,* vol. 53, article 3.

HOOTON, E. A.
1939. The American criminal. Vol. 1. Cambridge.
1946. Up from the ape. Revised edition. New York.

HOOTON, E. A. AND DUPERTUIS, C. W.
1951. Age changes and selective survival in Irish males. *American Journal of Physical Anthropology, Studies in Physical Anthropology,* no. 2.

HOWELLS, W. W.
1941. The early Christian Irish: the skeletons at Gallen Priory. *Royal Irish Academy, Proceedings,* vol. 46, sect. C, no. 3.

HRDLIČKA, ALEŠ
1925. The old Americans. Baltimore.

KEITH, SIR ARTHUR
1925. The antiquity of man. 2 volumes. 2nd edition. Philadelphia.

KROGMAN, WILLIAM M.
1939. A guide to the identification of human skeletal material. *F.B.I. Law Enforcement Bulletin* 8 (8), August: 3–31.

MACALISTER, R. A. S.
1949. The archaeology of Ireland. 2nd edition. London.

MARTIN, CECIL P.
1935. Prehistoric man in Ireland. London.
MARTIN, RUDOLF
1928. Lehrbuch der Anthropologie in systematischer Darstellung. Vols. 1–3. Jena.
O'RAHILLY, THOMAS F.
1946. Early Irish history and mythology. Dublin.
PIGGOTT, STUART
1949. British prehistory. Home University Library of Modern Knowledge. Oxford University Press.
PRENDERGAST, JOHN P.
1922. The Cromwellian settlement of Ireland. 3rd edition. Dublin.
RAFTERY, JOSEPH
1951. Prehistoric Ireland. London.
SHETELIG, HAAKON
1940. Viking antiquities in Great Britain and Ireland. Part I: An introduction to the Viking history of western Europe. Oslo.

TROTTER, MILDRED AND GLESER, GOLDINE C.
1952. Estimation of stature from long bones of American whites and negroes. *American Journal of Physical Anthropology*, n.s., vol. 10, no. 4, pp. 463–514.
WARNER, W. LLOYD AND LOW, J. O.
1947. The social system of the modern factory. Yankee City series, vol. 4. New Haven and London.
WARNER, W. LLOYD AND LUNT, PAUL S.
1941. The social life of a modern community. Yankee City series, vol. 1. New Haven and London.
1942. The status system of a modern community. Yankee City series, vol. 2. New Haven and London.
WARNER, W. LLOYD AND SROLE, LEO
1945. The social systems of American ethnic groups. Yankee City series, vol. 3. New Haven and London.

THE PHYSICAL ANTHROPOLOGY OF IRELAND

NO. 2
TABLES AND HALF-TONES

PAPERS

OF THE

PEABODY MUSEUM OF ARCHÆOLOGY
AND ETHNOLOGY, HARVARD UNIVERSITY
VOL. XXX, NOS. 1–2

THE PHYSICAL ANTHROPOLOGY
OF IRELAND

BY

EARNEST A. HOOTON

AND

C. WESLEY DUPERTUIS

WITH A SECTION ON

THE WEST COAST IRISH FEMALES

BY

HELEN DAWSON

No. 2
TABLES AND HALF-TONES

CAMBRIDGE, MASSACHUSETTS, U.S.A.
PUBLISHED BY THE MUSEUM
1955

PRINTED BY THE CRIMSON PRINTING COMPANY
CAMBRIDGE, MASSACHUSETTS, U.S.A.

STATISTICAL TABLES

TABLE I-1. LIST OF COUNTIES AND TOWNS WITH NUMBER OF SUBJECTS MEASURED IN EACH

NORTH IRELAND

Antrim

1. Armoy	12
2. Ballycastle	15
3. Ballyclare	13
4. Ballymoney	18
5. Broughshane	22
6. Bushmills	24
7. Clogh Mills	12
8. Crumlin	15
9. Cushendall	13
10. Kells	16
11. Portglenone	12
12. Randalstown	13
13. Toomebridge	12
Total	**197**

Armagh

1. Bessbrook	11
2. Blackwatertown	10
3. Camlough	8
4. Crossmaglen	14
5. Keady	28
6. Loughgall	8
7. Markethill	22
8. Middletown	16
9. Millford	10
10. Newtown Hamilton	24
11. Poyntzpass	12
12. Richhill	9
13. Tanderagee	20
14. Tynan	8
Total	**200**

Down

1. Annalong	16
2. Ballynahinch	24
3. Crossgar	12
4. Dromara	8
5. Dromore	17
6. Hillsborough	17
7. Hilltown	14
8. Kilkeel	10
9. Killyleagh	13
10. Newcastle	14
11. Rathfriland	16
Total	**161**

Fermanagh

1. Ballinamallard	16
2. Belcoo	23
3. Belleek	14
4. Derrygonnelly	18
5. Derrylin	10
6. Garrison	5
7. Irvinestown	14
8. Kesh	18
9. Kinawley	9
10. Lisbellaw	22
11. Lisnaskea	14
12. Newtownbutler	11
13. Pettigoe	7
Total	**181**

Londonderry

1. Castlerock	16
2. Claudy	11
3. Draperstown	15
4. Dungiven	21
5. Feeny	10
6. Garvagh	18
7. Gulladuff	7
8. Kilrea	18
9. Magherafelt	26
10. Moneymore	15
11. Portstewart	25
12. Swatragh	9
Total	**191**

Tyrone

1. Ballygawley	21
2. Carrickmore	14
3. Castlederg	21
4. Clogher	10
5. Coagh	12
6. Coalisland	15
7. Drumquin	15
8. Fintona	20
9. Fivemiletown	15
10. Gortin	22
11. Mountfield	12
12. Plum Bridge	10
13. Pomeroy	7
14. Stewartstown	18
Total	**212**

TOTAL FOR NORTH IRELAND 1142

IRISH FREE STATE

Carlow

1. Bagenalstown	2
2. Borris	14
3. Leighlinbridge	8
4. Tullow	22
Total	**46**

Cavan

1. Arvagh	8
2. Baillieborough	20
3. Ballinagh	15
4. Ballyconnell	16
5. Ballyhaise	16
6. Ballyjamesduff	21
7. Blacklion	13
8. Bownboy	17
9. Cootehill	23
10. Glangavlen	31
11. Killeshandra	12
12. Kingscourt	23
13. Shercock	14
14. Stradone	10
15. Virginia	26
Total	**265**

Clare

1. Ballyvaughan	29
2. Carrigaholt	22
3. Clarecastle	58
4. Corofin	32
5. Ennis	398
6. Ennistymon	16
7. Feakle	54
8. Inagh	25
9. Kilbaha	10
10. Kilfenora	10
11. Kilkee	27
12. Killadysert	18
13. Killaloe	27
14. Kilmihil	21
15. Kilnamona	12
16. Kilrush	32
17. Knock	10
18. Lahinch	29
19. Lisdoonvarna	37
20. Lissycasey	29
21. Milltown Malbay	30
22. Mountshannon	25
23. Newmarket-on-Fergus	7
24. Quilty	29
25. Quin	35
26. Scarriff	11
27. Sixmilebridge	30
28. Spanish Point	7
29. Tulla	44
Total	**1114**

Cork

1. Ballinspittle	16
2. Ballycotton	19
3. Ballydehob	19
4. Ballyneen	18
5. Bandon	17
6. Buttevant	16
7. Carrigaline	17
8. Carrigtohill	7
9. Castlemartyr	19
10. Castletownbere	10
11. Cloynes	17
12. Cobh	16
13. Crosshaven	14
14. Doneraile	13
15. Dunmanway	21
16. Glengarriff	14
17. Inishannon	10
18. Kilbrittain	11
19. Killeagh	20
20. Kilworth	16
21. Kinsale	14
22. Leap	43
23. Michelstown	17
24. Millstreet	16
25. Newmarket	14
26. Rathcormack	3
27. Rosscarbery	13
28. Schull	16
29. Skibbereen	27
30. Timoleague	21
31. Whitegate	18
Total	**512**

Donegal

1. Ardara	19
2. Ballybofey	8
3. Buncrana	15
4. Carndonagh	15
5. Carrick	8
6. Creeslough	23
7. Doochary	15
8. Dunfanaghy	17
9. Dungloe	32
10. Glenties	18
11. Killybegs	9
12. Kilmacrenan	11
13. Malinmore	10
14. Meenaveen	4
15. Moville	16
16. Pettigoe	8
17. Ramelton	9
18. Raphoe	11
19. Rathmullan	32
20. Teelin	16
Total	**296**

TABLE I-1. LIST OF COUNTIES AND TOWNS: SUBJECTS MEASURED (Cont.)

Dublin

1. Dublin
   - Civic Guards 114
   - Gov't Officials 17
   - Guinness Workers 65
2. Lucan 12

   Total 208

Galway

1. Aran Islands
   - Innishmaan 42
   - Innishmore 95
2. Athenry 38
3. Ballinasloe 56
4. Bohoona 16
5. Carna 28
6. Carraroe 39
7. Claddagh 17
8. Clifden 3
9. Clonbur 20
10. Dunmore 11
11. Eyrecourt 17
12. Galway
    - Civic Guards 14
    - Monks 15
    - Soldiers 72
    - Students 63
13. Gort 25
14. Headford 37
15. Leenane 10
16. Lettercalloe 4
17. Letterfrack 12
18. Lettermore 34
19. Lettermullen 20
20. Loughrea 30
21. Maum 32
22. Maummeen 8
23. Mount Bellow Bridge.... 11
24. Oughterard 43
25. Portumna 13
26. Roundstone 23
27. Spiddal 61
28. Teeranea 11
29. Tully Cross 15

    Total 935

Kerry

1. Ballinskelligs 15
2. Ballybunion 17
3. Ballyduff 13
4. Ballyferriter 48
5. Ballyheige 18
6. Barraduff 10
7. Blasket Island 32
8. Brandon 10
9. Cahirciveen 28
10. Castlegregory 21
11. Castle Island 21
12. Castlemaine 13
13. Causeway 4
14. Cloghane 9
15. Dingle 27
16. Glenbeigh 10
17. Headford 11
18. Kenmare 26
19. Kilgarvan 31
20. Killorglin 23
21. Lixnaw 3
22. Portmagee 24
23. Rathmore 16
24. Sneem 17
25. Tarbert 18
26. Valentia Island 30
27. Waterville 39

    Total 534

Kildare

1. Athy 25
2. Ballymore Eustace 10
3. Clane 18
4. Kilcullen 20
5. Maynooth 16
6. Newbridge 20
7. Rathangan 16
8. Robertstown 40

   Total 165

Kilkenny

1. Ballyhale 17
2. Ballyragget 20
3. Bennettsbridge 18
4. Callan 31
5. Castlecomer 30
6. Freshford 22
7. Glenmore 8
8. Goresbridge 19
9. Graiguenamanagh 23
10. Johnstown 13
11. Kilmacow 10
12. Kilmaganny 12
13. Mooncoin 17
14. Mullinavat 8
15. Newmarket 10
16. Thomastown 20
17. Urlingford 18

    Total 296

Leitrim

1. Annaduff 17
2. Aghavas 12
3. Ballinamore 58
4. Borne Coola 14
5. Carrick-on-Shannon 135
6. Cloone 8
7. Derrycarne 14
8. Dromahair 25
9. Dromod 72
10. Drumshambo 60
11. Drumsna 14
12. Glenfarn 16
13. Kinlough 16
14. Leitrim 28
15. Manorhamilton 18
16. Mohill 95
17. Rassoun 14

    Total 616

Leix

1. Abbeyleix 22
2. Borris-in-Ossary 12
3. Durrow 19
4. Mountmellick 20
5. Mountrath 16
6. Stradbally 17
7. Timahoe 12

   Total 118

Limerick

1. Abbeyfeale 19
2. Adare 23
3. Ardagh 17
4. Askeaton 19
5. Athea 14
6. Ballingarry 10
7. Bruff 20
8. Bruree 17
9. Cappamore 20
10. Castleconnell 23
11. Croom 17
12. Doon 17
13. Glin 18

Kildare (cont.)

14. Hospital 1
15. Newcastle ....
16. Rathkeale 2
17. Shanagolden 1
18. Tournafulla ....

    Total 30

Longford

1. Ardagh 1
2. Ballinalee 1
3. Ballymahon 6
4. Drumlish 2
5. Edgeworthstown 6
6. Granard 8
7. Leanamore 2
8. Longford 10

   Total 37

Louth

1. Ardee 25
2. Carlingford 17
3. Castlebellingham 16
4. Clogher 16
5. Dunleer 22
6. Omeath 21

   Total 117

Mayo

1. Achill Sound 25
2. Ballina 53
3. Ballinrobe 31
4. Ballycastle 19
5. Ballyhaunis 35
6. Belmullet 37
7. Claremorris 28
8. Cong 20
9. Crossmolina 37
10. Dooagh 24
11. Dooega 31
12. Foxford 30
13. Keel 9
14. Kiltimagh 27
15. Louisburgh 22
16. Mallaranny 23
17. Murrisk 21
18. Newport 42
19. Rathlacken 16
20. Swinford 20

    Total 550

Meath

1. Ashbourne 14
2. Athboy 12
3. Crossakeel 28
4. Duleek 22
5. Dunshaughlin 17
6. Kells 27
7. Longwood 19
8. Navan 23
9. Oldcastle 22
10. Slane 14
11. Trim 19

    Total 217

TABLE I-1.   LIST OF COUNTIES AND TOWNS: SUBJECTS MEASURED (Cont.)

Monaghan

1. Ballybay	24
2. Carrickmacross	28
3. Castleblayney	30
4. Clones	18
5. Emyvale	19
6. Inniskeen	8
7. Newbliss	23
8. Scotstown	18
9. Smithborough	22
Total	190

Offaly

1. Banagher	25
2. Birr	18
3. Clara	58
4. Cloghan	23
5. Edenderry	19
6. Ferbane	20
7. Frankford	18
8. Moneygall	10
9. Philipstown	24
10. Rahan	20
11. Shinrone	3
12. Tober	36
Total	274

Roscommon

1. Athleague	12
2. Ballaghaderreen	9
3. Ballyfarnan	29
4. Boyle	43
5. Castlereagh	6
6. Elphin	24
7. Kilmore	35
8. Roscommon	15
Total	173

Sligo

1. Ballymote	23
2. Collooney	11
3. Easkey	15
4. Grange	13
Total	62

Tipperary

1. Ardfinnan	15
2. Ballingarry	11
3. Bansha	16
4. Borrisokane	18
5. Borrisoleigh	18
6. Cahir	17
7. Cappaghwhite	17
8. Carrick-on-Suir	2
9. Clogheen	16
10. Cloughjordan	20
11. Fethard	19
12. Hollyford	18
13. Killenaule	15
14. Kilsheelan	17
15. Laragh	12
16. Littleton	20
17. Mullinahone	14
18. Newport	24
19. Portroe	35
20. Roscrea	20
21. Templemore	16
22. Thurles	6
23. Toomevara	18
Total	384

Waterford

1. Ardmore	15
2. Cappoquin	21
3. Dunmore	13
4. Kilmcathomas	21
5. Lismore	18
6. Passage	19
7. Portlaw	20
8. Ring	15
9. Stradbally	18
10. Villierstown	13
Total	173

Westmeath

1. Ballymore	50
2. Coolatore	8
3. Kilbeggan	84
4. Moate	159
5. Mounttemple	45
6. Mullingar	108
7. Rathowen	9
Total	463

Wexford

1. Blackwater	18
2. Camolin	17
3. Castlebridge	22
4. Clonevin	12
5. Clonroche	13
6. Coolgreaney	12
7. Courtown Harbor	11
8. Duncannon	19
9. Duncormick	16
10. Enniscorthy	28
11. Ferns	8
12. Fethard	13
13. Gorey	29
14. Kilmore Quay	18
15. New Ross	26
16. Newtownbarry	25
17. Taghmon	22
Total	309

Wicklow

1. Arklow	25
2. Ashford	8
3. Aughrim	22
4. Baltinglass	22
5. Blessington	22
6. Carnew	15
7. Dunlavin	18
8. Greystones	16
9. Hollywood	41
10. Newtown Mt. Kennedy	16
11. Rathdrum	12
12. Shillelagh	12
13. Tinahely	21
14. Wicklow	23
Total	273

TOTAL FOR
IRISH FREE STATE 8976

GRAND TOTAL . . . . .

Number of Towns . . . .

TABLE I-2. LIST OF COUNTIES AND TOWNS IN WHICH FEMALES WERE MEASURED

Galway

Ballyconnealy	4
Carraroe	18
Cleggan	10
Clifden	43
Claddagh	15
Cranmore	18
Galway	196
Kilcolgan	8
Kylemore	7
Leenane	16
Loughrea	19
Letterfrack	8
Moycullen	14
Rosadilisk	6
Roundstone	15
Spiddal	20
Total	417

Mayo

Ballycastle	15
Ballyhaunes	32
Claremorris	39

Mayo (Cont.)

Castlebar	86
Crossmolina	16
Foxford	20
Killala	17
Kiltamagh	20
Westport	24
Total	269

Sligo

Ballingtoghen	13
Riverstown	15
Sligo	40
Tubbercurry	25
Total	93

Leitrim

Dromahair	9
Drumkerrin	13

Leitrim (Cont.)

Manorhamilton	43
Killycloghen	9
Total	64

Clare

Ballynacully	8
Ballycella	3
Clarecastle	6
Cooraclare	1
Corofin	22
Crastreen	5
Ennis	233
Ennistymon	16
Feakle	9
Inagh	10
Kilbaha	6
Killadysert	17
Kilrush	14
Labasheeda	11
Lascannor	11
Lisdoonvaena	26
Lohinch	13

TABLE I-2.   LIST OF COUNTIES AND TOWNS: FEMALES MEASURED (Cont.)

Clare (Cont.)

Doonbeg	8
Milltown Mubay	9
Mullagh	8
Newmarket	25
Quin	23
Scariff	14
Tulla	22
Tuilty	16
Whitegate	8
Total	544

Donegal

Ardara	31
Bunberg	12
Burtonport	15

Donegal (Cont.)

Carrick	13
Doochary	11
Dungloe	21
Dunkineely	33
Glencolumbkille	8
Glenties	30
Killybegs	33
Narin	13
Total	220

Kerry

Ballinskelligs	15
Ballyferriter	8
Ballynagall	18
Brandon	17

Kerry (Cont.)

Cahirciveen	28
Castlegregory	24
Cloghane	15
Dingle	19
Dunquin	5
Killarney	51
Knightstown	6
Protmagle	10
Sneem	22
Stradbally	13
Ventry	8
Waterville	24
Total	283
GRAND TOTAL	1,890
Number of Towns	86

SOCIOLOGICAL OBSERVATIONS

TABLE II-1. EDUCATION BY COUNTY SUBGROUPS

	Illiterate		Read and write		National school		Secondary school		University		Total
	No.	%	No.	%	No.	%	No.	%	No.	%	No.
W. Donegal	8	3.8	8	3.8	169	80.1	23	10.9	3	1.4	211
Mayo	21	3.6	12	2.1	477	82.4	50	8.6	19	3.3	579
Sligo, Leitrim, S. Fermanagh, W. Cavan	6	.8	6	.8	670	93.6	28	3.9	6	.8	716
W. Galway	47	10.9	19	4.4	334	77.7	19	4.4	11	2.6	430
Aran Islands	-	-	-	-	138	99.3	1	.7	-	-	139
Clare	9	1.0	-	-	769	81.5	147	15.6	19	2.0	944
Kerry	28	5.2	7	1.3	404	75.1	85	15.8	14	2.6	538
Cork	11	1.9	2	.3	414	72.1	126	22.0	21	3.6	574
Limerick	6	1.8	1	.3	272	80.0	50	14.7	10	2.9	339
E. Galway, Roscommon	11	2.1	5	1.0	421	82.1	39	7.6	37	7.2	513
Longford, Westmeath	1	.2	-	-	595	89.5	61	9.2	8	1.2	665
Offaly, Leix, Kildare	29	5.5	20	3.8	420	79.2	56	10.6	5	.9	530
Tipperary, Kilkenny	18	2.8	6	.9	518	79.7	99	15.2	9	1.4	650
Waterford, Wexford	37	8.0	9	1.9	357	77.3	50	10.8	9	1.9	462
Wicklow, Carlow	19	6.8	3	1.1	219	78.8	36	12.9	1	.4	278
Meath, Louth, Dublin	13	2.8	3	.6	373	81.6	58	12.7	10	2.2	457
E. Cavan, Monaghan, Armagh	21	5.4	2	.5	326	84.0	35	9.0	4	1.0	388
Antrim, Down	1	.6	-	-	122	80.3	23	15.1	6	3.9	152
N. Fermanagh, E. Donegal, Tyrone, Londonderry	8	2.5	1	.3	262	82.6	40	12.6	6	1.9	317
Total	294	3.3	104	1.2	7260	81.7	1026	11.6	198	2.2	8882

TABLE II-2. EDUCATIONAL RANKING OF COUNTY SUBGROUPS

	A (Illiterate + Read and write) %	B (Secondary school + University) %	B/A
1. Aran Islands	0.0	.7	-
2. Longford, Westmeath	.2	10.4	52.0
3. Antrim, Down	.6	19.1	31.8
4. Clare	1.0	17.6	17.6
5. Cork	2.3	25.6	11.1
6. Limerick	2.1	17.7	8.4
7. N. Fermanagh, E. Donegal, Tyrone, Londonderry	2.8	14.5	5.2
8. E. Galway, Roscommon	3.1	14.8	4.8
9. Tipperary, Kilkenny	3.7	16.6	4.5
10. Meath, Louth, Dublin	3.5	14.9	4.3
11. Kerry	6.5	18.4	2.8
12. Sligo, Leitrim, S. Fermanagh, W. Cavan	1.7	4.7	2.8
13. Mayo	5.7	11.9	2.1
14. E. Cavan, Monaghan, Armagh	5.9	10.0	1.7
15. Wicklow, Carlow	7.9	13.3	1.7
16. W. Donegal	7.6	12.3	1.6
17. Waterford, Wexford	10.0	12.8	1.3
18. Offaly, Leix, Kildare	9.2	11.5	1.2
19. W. Galway	15.3	7.0	.5
Total	4.5	13.8	3.07

TABLE II-3. LANGUAGE BY COUNTY SUBGROUPS

	No Irish No.	%	Native speaker No.	%	Irish only No.	%	School Irish No.	%	Total No.
W. Donegal	88	41.5	98	46.2	-	-	26	12.3	212
Mayo	230	39.6	140	24.1	-	-	210	36.2	580
Sligo, Leitrim, S. Fermanagh, W. Cavan.	565	79.0	3	.4	-	-	147	20.6	715
W. Galway	44	10.2	269	62.3	69	16.0	50	11.6	432
Aran Islands	5	3.6	132	95.0	1	.7	1	.7	139
Clare	486	51.4	147	15.6	-	-	312	.33.0	945
Kerry	130	24.2	238	44.2	13	2.4	157	29.2	538
Cork	269	46.8	73	12.7	2	.3	231	40.2	575
Limerick	209	61.6	11	3.2	-	-	119	35.1	339
E. Galway, Roscommon	289	56.3	65	12.7	-	-	159	31.0	513
Longford, Westmeath	433	64.1	4	.6	-	-	238	35.2	675
Offaly, Leix, Kildare	342	64.6	1	.2	-	-	186	35.2	529
Tipperary, Kilkenny	415	63.8	5	.8	-	-	230	35.4	650
Waterford, Wexford	291	62.8	27	5.8	-	-	145	31.3	463
Wicklow, Carlow	170	61.2	1	.4	-	-	107	38.5	278
Meath, Louth, Dublin	284	62.0	7	1.5	-	-	167	36.5	458
E. Cavan, Monaghan, Armagh	257	66.1	2	.5	-	-	130	33.4	389
Antrim, Down	130	85.5	1	.6	-	-	21	13.8	152
N. Fermanagh, E. Donegal, Tyrone, Londonderry	244	76.7	6	1.9	-	-	68	21.4	318
Total	4881	54.8	1230	13.8	85	1.0	2704	30.4	8900

TABLE II-4. OCCUPATION OF INDIVIDUAL BY COUNTY SUBGROUPS

	Hired laborer, tinker No.	%	Herdsman, farmer, farm steward, gardener No.	%	Farm dependent No.	%	Fisherman No.	%
W. Donegal	19	9.3	28	13.6	30	14.6	11	5.4
Mayo	48	8.5	104	18.5	91	16.2	4	.7
Sligo, Leitrim, S. Fermanagh, W. Cavan.	30	4.3	278	40.2	44	6.4	-	-
W. Galway	28	6.6	105	24.9	118	28.0	11	2.6
Aran Islands	-	-	94	67.6	29	20.9	8	5.8
Clare	35	3.8	95	10.3	62	6.7	7	.8
Kerry	43	8.2	51	9.8	28	5.4	70	13.4
Cork	23	4.1	30	5.4	13	2.3	22	4.0
Limerick	34	10.7	20	6.3	11	3.5	3	.9
E. Galway, Roscommon	9	1.8	116	22.9	23	4.5	3	.6
Longford, Westmeath	18	2.8	59	9.2	89	13.9	-	-
Offaly, Leix, Kildare	84	16.5	42	8.2	34	6.7	-	-
Tipperary, Kilkenny	33	5.3	58	9.3	28	4.5	5	.8
Waterford, Wexford	40	8.9	34	7.6	7	1.6	57	12.7
Wicklow, Carlow	62	22.8	31	11.4	13	4.8	-	-
Meath, Louth, Dublin	63	14.6	33	7.7	9	2.1	9	2.1
E. Cavan, Monaghan, Armagh	65	17.3	33	8.8	17	4.5	1	.3
Antrim, Down	13	9.0	12	8.3	4	2.8	13	9.0
N. Fermanagh, E. Donegal, Tyrone, Londonderry	19	6.4	29	9.8	13	4.4	2	.7
Total	666	7.8	1252	14.6	663	7.7	226	2.6

TABLE II-4, OCCUPATION OF INDIVIDUAL BY COUNTY SUBGROUPS (Cont.)

	Navvy No.	%	Semi-skilled trades No.	%	Transportation No.	%	Factory No.	%
W. Donegal	30	14.6	9	4.4	14	6.8	3	1.5
Mayo	79	14.0	31	5.5	14	2.5	9	1.6
Sligo, Leitrim, S. Fermanagh, W. Cavan.	102	14.7	41	5.9	27	3.9	2	.3
W. Galway	58	13.7	5	1.2	7	1.6	1	.2
Aran Islands	-	-	-	-	-	-	-	-
Clare	320	34.7	99	10.7	39	4.2	17	1.8
Kerry	102	19.5	40	7.6	26	5.0	5	1.0
Cork	119	21.4	62	11.2	42	7.6	9	1.6
Limerick	100	31.5	28	8.8	15	4.7	5	1.6
E. Galway, Roscommon	94	18.5	18	3.6	9	1.8	2	.4
Longford, Westmeath	226	35.3	50	7.8	16	2.5	-	-
Offaly, Leix, Kildare	141	27.7	43	8.4	22	4.3	3	.6
Tipperary, Kilkenny	184	29.4	74	11.8	28	4.5	19	3.0
Waterford, Wexford	97	21.6	43	9.6	35	7.8	12	2.7
Wicklow, Carlow	64	23.5	16	5.9	16	5.9	-	-
Meath, Louth, Dublin	127	29.5	38	8.8	17	4.0	3	.7
E. Cavan, Monaghan, Armagh	85	22.7	29	7.7	25	6.7	10	2.7
Antrim, Down	25	17.4	22	15.3	8	5.6	6	4.2
N. Fermanagh, E. Donegal, Tyrone, Londonderry	36	12.1	41	13.8	22	7.4	12	4.0
Total	1989	23.2	689	8.0	382	4.4	118	1.4

TABLE II-4. OCCUPATION OF INDIVIDUAL BY COUNTY SUBGROUPS (Cont.)

	Skilled trades		Shop assistants, small shopkeepers, merchants		Clerks		Professional, teachers, clergy	
	No.	%	No.	%	No.	%	No.	%
W. Donegal	4	2.0	14	6.8	4	2.0	9	4.4
Mayo	14	2.5	49	8.7	4	.7	9	1.6
Sligo, Leitrim, S. Fermanagh, W. Cavan.	17	2.4	69	10.0	7	1.0	5	.7
W. Galway	4	.9	25	5.9	3	.7	12	2.8
Aran Islands	-	-	1	.7	-	-	1	.7
Clare	30	3.2	75	8.1	41	4.4	29	3.1
Kerry	11	2.1	45	8.6	5	1.0	15	2.9
Cork	18	3.2	67	12.1	11	2.0	30	5.4
Limerick	7	2.2	39	12.3	9	2.8	8	2.5
E. Galway, Roscommon	17	3.4	40	7.9	1	.2	10	2.0
Longford, Westmeath	18	2.8	67	10.5	15	2.3	9	1.4
Offaly, Leix, Kildare	15	2.9	43	8.4	8	1.6	8	1.6
Tipperary, Kilkenny	17	2.7	83	13.3	12	1.9	17	2.7
Waterford, Wexford	14	3.1	61	13.6	3	.7	10	2.2
Wicklow, Carlow	9	3.3	33	12.1	3	1.1	2	.7
Meath, Louth, Dublin	13	3.0	47	10.9	10	2.3	10	2.3
E. Cavan, Monaghan, Armagh	6	1.6	52	13.9	7	1.9	8	2.1
Antrim, Down	3	2.1	10	6.9	4	2.8	7	4.9
N. Fermanagh, E. Donegal, Tyrone, Londonderry	10	3.4	54	18.2	7	2.4	8	2.7
Total	227	2.6	874	10.2	154	1.8	207	2.4

TABLE II-4. OCCUPATION OF INDIVIDUAL BY COUNTY SUBGROUPS (Cont.)

	Soldiers		Students		Total
	No.	%	No.	%	No.
W. Donegal	30	14.6	-	-	205
Mayo	91	16.2	16	2.8	563
Sligo, Leitrim, S. Fermanagh, W. Cavan.	68	9.8	2	.3	692
W. Galway	44	10.4	1	.2	422
Aran Islands	6	4.3	-	-	139
Clare	53	5.7	20	2.2	922
Kerry	67	12.8	15	2.9	523
Cork	96	17.3	13	2.3	555
Limerick	34	10.7	4	1.3	317
E. Galway, Roscommon	132	26.0	33	6.5	507
Longford, Westmeath	66	10.3	7	1.1	640
Offaly, Leix, Kildare	62	12.2	4	.8	509
Tipperary, Kilkenny	61	9.8	6	1.0	625
Waterford, Wexford	35	7.8	1	.2	449
Wicklow, Carlow	21	7.7	2	.7	272
Meath, Louth, Dublin	44	10.2	7	1.6	430
E. Cavan, Monaghan, Armagh	36	9.6	1	.3	375
Antrim, Down	15	10.4	2	1.4	144
N. Fermanagh, E. Donegal, Tyrone, Londonderry	40	13.5	4	1.3	297
Total	1001	11.6	138	1.6	8586

TABLE II-5. OCCUPATION OF INDIVIDUAL, RURAL OR URBAN, BY COUNTY SUBGROUPS

	Rural		Urban		Total
	No.	%	No.	%	No.
W. Donegal	88	42.9	117	57.1	205
Mayo	247	43.9	316	56.1	563
Sligo, Leitrim, S. Fermanagh, W. Cavan.	352	50.9	340	49.1	692
W. Galway	262	62.1	160	37.9	422
Aran Islands	131	94.2	8	5.8	139
Clare	199	21.6	723	78.4	922
Kerry	192	36.7	331	63.3	523
Cork	88	15.8	467	84.1	555
Limerick	68	21.4	249	78.5	317
E. Galway, Roscommon	151	29.8	356	70.2	507
Longford, Westmeath	166	25.9	474	74.1	640
Offaly, Leix, Kildare	160	31.4	349	68.6	509
Tipperary, Kilkenny	124	19.8	501	80.2	625
Waterford, Wexford	138	30.7	311	69.3	449
Wicklow, Carlow	106	39.0	166	61.0	272
Meath, Louth, Dublin	114	26.5	316	73.5	430
E. Cavan, Monaghan, Armagh	116	30.9	259	69.1	375
Antrim, Down	42	29.2	102	70.8	144
N. Fermanagh, E. Donegal, Tyrone, Londonderry	63	21.2	234	78.8	297
Total	2807	32.7	5779	67.3	8586

TABLE III-1. AGE BY COUNTY SUBGROUPS

	No.	Range	Mean	S. D.
W. Donegal	212	15-89	33.60 + 0.70	15.15
Mayo	580	15-89	35.25 ∓ 0.42	15.00
Sligo, Leitrim, S. Fermanagh, W. Cavan.	716	15-89	34.90 ∓ 0.39	15.35
W. Galway.	432	15-89	36.35 ∓ 0.53	16.45
Aran Islands	139	15-84	34.50 ∓ 1.00	17.55
Clare.	946	15-89	37.30 ∓ 0.33	15.15
Kerry.	539	15-94	37.35 ∓ 0.47	16.25
Cork	575	15-89	37.25 ∓ 0.45	16.00
Limerick	340	15-74	35.80 ∓ 0.52	14.30
E. Galway, Roscommon	515	15-84	34.40 ∓ 0.42	14.25
Longford, Westmeath	676	15-89	30.25 ∓ 0.29	11.20
Offaly, Leix, Kildare.	531	15-84	35.00 ∓ 0.43	14.75
Tipperary, Kilkenny	650	15-84	36.95 ∓ 0.40	15.30
Waterford, Wexford	463	15-94	40.90 ∓ 0.55	17.60
Wicklow, Carlow	278	15-84	38.30 ∓ 0.63	15.60
Meath, Louth, Dublin.	458	15-84	33.75 ∓ 0.47	14.90
E. Cavan, Monaghan, Armagh.	389	15-84	36.50 ∓ 0.52	15.20
Antrim, Down	152	15-84	33.60 ∓ 0.78	14.20
N. Fermanagh, E. Donegal, Tyrone Londonderry .	318	15-89	33.90 + 0.57	15.10
Total	8909	15-94	35.70 + 0.11	15.40

TABLE III-2. AGE GROUPS BY COUNTY SUBGROUPS

	15-19 No.	15-19 %	20-24 No.	20-24 %	25-29 No.	25-29 %	30-34 No.	30-34 %	35-39 No.	35-39 %	40-44 No.	40-44 %
W. Donegal	24	11.3	51	24.0	36	17.0	26	12.3	18	8.5	16	7.5
Mayo	55	9.5	137	23.6	68	11.7	69	11.9	57	9.8	50	8.6
Sligo, Leitrim, S. Fermanagh, W. Cavan.	76	10.6	173	24.2	91	12.7	85	11.9	61	8.5	47	6.6
W. Galway.	44	10.2	95	22.0	61	14.1	50	11.6	32	7.4	29	6.7
Aran Islands	30	21.6	33	23.7	12	8.6	6	4.3	13	9.4	7	5.0
Clare.	61	6.4	174	18.4	133	14.0	106	11.2	112	11.8	93	9.8
Kerry.	42	7.8	113	21.0	70	13.0	63	11.7	49	9.1	39	7.2
Cork	58	10.1	94	16.3	67	11.6	87	15.1	62	10.8	36	6.3
Limerick	32	9.4	62	18.2	46	13.5	46	13.5	31	9.1	32	9.4
E. Galway, Roscommon	47	9.1	119	23.1	66	12.8	66	12.8	65	12.6	44	8.5
Longford, Westmeath	106	15.7	180	26.6	115	17.0	100	14.8	52	7.7	40	5.9
Offaly, Leix, Kildare.	42	7.9	134	25.2	73	13.7	65	12.2	45	8.5	32	6.0
Tipperary, Kilkenny	58	8.9	118	18.2	83	12.8	70	10.8	77	11.8	54	8.3
Waterford, Wexford	42	9.1	60	13.0	58	12.5	39	8.4	45	9.7	42	9.1
Wicklow, Carlow.	21	7.6	45	16.2	37	13.3	32	11.5	25	9.0	26	9.4
Meath, Louth, Dublin.	42	9.2	78	17.0	81	17.7	60	13.1	46	10.0	31	6.8
E. Cavan, Monaghan, Armagh.	32	8.2	73	18.8	62	15.9	41	10.5	38	9.8	28	7.2
Antrim, Down	19	12.5	33	21.7	20	13.2	20	13.2	18	11.8	13	8.6
N. Fermanagh, E. Donegal, Tyrone, Londonderry.	43	13.5	63	19.8	49	15.4	39	12.3	42	13.2	19	6.0
Total	874	9.8	1835	20.6	1228	13.8	1070	12.0	888	10.0	678	7.6

TABLE III-2. AGE GROUPS BY COUNTY SUBGROUPS (Cont.)

	45-49 No.	45-49 %	50-54 No.	50-54 %	55-59 No.	55-59 %	60-64 No.	60-64 %	65-69 No.	65-69 %
W. Donegal	7	3.3	7	3.3	6	2.8	8	3.8	7	3.3
Mayo	30	5.2	31	5.3	35	6.0	19	3.3	17	2.9
Sligo, Leitrim, S. Fermanagh, W. Cavan.	41	5.7	46	6.4	27	3.8	36	5.0	16	2.2
W. Galway.	10	2.3	27	6.2	26	6.0	30	6.9	15	3.5
Aran Islands	7	5.0	4	2.9	6	4.3	11	7.9	6	4.3
Clare.	59	6.2	57	6.0	43	4.5	53	5.6	25	2.6
Kerry.	27	5.0	33	6.1	32	5.9	28	5.2	24	4.4
Cork	37	6.4	34	5.9	31	5.4	22	3.8	27	4.7
Limerick	22	6.5	26	7.6	15	4.4	14	4.1	10	2.9
E. Galway, Roscommon	30	5.8	28	5.4	15	2.9	9	1.7	10	1.9
Longford, Westmeath	21	3.1	19	2.8	10	1.5	16	2.4	9	1.3
Offaly, Leix, Kildare.	36	6.8	32	6.0	32	6.0	18	3.4	10	1.9
Tipperary, Kilkenny	43	6.6	41	6.3	42	6.5	27	4.2	12	1.8
Waterford, Wexford	35	7.6	19	4.1	30	6.5	38	8.2	27	5.8
Wicklow, Carlow	22	7.9	19	6.8	17	6.1	13	4.7	14	5.0
Meath, Louth, Dublin.	35	7.6	18	3.9	24	5.2	20	4.4	11	2.4
E. Cavan, Monaghan, Armagh.	34	8.7	31	8.0	12	3.1	13	3.3	11	2.8
Antrim, Down	7	4.6	6	3.9	7	4.6	2	1.3	3	2.0
N. Fermanagh, E. Donegal, Tyrone Londonderry.	13	4.1	10	3.1	14	4.4	5	1.6	11	3.4
Total	516	5.8	488	5.5	424	4.8	382	4.3	265	3.0

TABLE III-2. AGE GROUPS BY COUNTY SUBGROUPS (Cont.)

	70-74 No.	70-74 %	75-79 No.	75-79 %	80-94 No.	80-94 %	Total No.
W. Donegal	4	1.9	-	-	2	.9	212
Mayo	6	1.0	3	.5	3	.5	580
Sligo, Leitrim, S. Fermanagh, W. Cavan.	7	1.0	4	.6	6	.8	716
W. Galway.	5	1.2	6	1.4	2	.5	432
Aran Islands	1	.7	2	1.4	1	.7	139
Clare	18	1.9	9	1.0	3	.3	946
Kerry.	11	2.0	6	1.1	2	.4	539
Cork	10	1.7	5	.9	5	.9	575
Limerick	4	1.2	-	-	-	-	340
E. Galway, Roscommon	10	1.9	3	.6	3	.6	515
Longford, Westmeath	3	.4	2	.3	3	.4	676
Offaly, Leix, Kildare.	7	1.3	3	.6	2	.4	531
Tipperary, Kilkenny	21	3.2	3	.5	1	.2	650
Waterford, Wexford	8	1.7	16	3.4	4	.9	463
Wicklow, Carlow	3	1.1	3	1.1	1	.4	278
Meath, Louth, Dublin.	7	1.5	2	.4	3	.6	458
E. Cavan, Monaghan, Armagh.	9	2.3	3	.8	2	.5	389
Antrim, Down	3	2.0	-	-	1	.6	152
N. Fermanagh, E. Donegal, Tyrone, Londonderry.	5	1.6	2	.6	3	.9	318
Total	142	1.6	72	.8	47	.5	8909

TABLE III-3. WEIGHT BY COUNTY SUBGROUPS

	No.	Range	Mean	S.D.
W. Donegal	212	101-230	155.30 + 1.03	22.20
Mayo	579	101-250	160.80 ∓ 0.62	22.20
Sligo, Leitrim, S. Fermanagh, W. Cavan	716	101-270	158.50 ∓ 0.55	21.80
W. Galway.	432	101-250	160.60 + 0.69	21.30
Aran Islands	139	111-210	156.30 + 1.01	17.70
Clare	946	101-290	159.10 ∓ 0.47	21.30
Kerry	539	111-250	160.50 ± 0.65	22.40
Cork	575	101-270	159.60 + 0.69	24.70
Limerick	340	111-230	157.90 ∓ 0.83	22.60
E. Galway, Roscommon	515	101-280	161.00 ∓ 0.67	22.70
Longford, Westmeath	676	101-250	151.00 ∓ 0.51	19.60
Offaly, Leix, Kildare	530	101-270	154.20 ∓ 0.70	24.00
Tipperary, Kilkenny	650	91-250	157.70 ∓ 0.62	23.30
Waterford, Wexford	463	91-280	156.50 + 0.79	25.20
Wicklow, Carlow	278	101-240	154.80 ∓ 0.88	21.90
Meath, Louth, Dublin	458	101-250	153.00 + 0.71	22.40
E. Cavan, Monaghan, Armagh.	388	101-260	154.30 ∓ 0.72	21.20
Antrim, Down	152	91-230	154.50 ± 1.25	22.90
N. Fermanagh, E. Donegal, Tyrone, Londonderry.	318	91-240	155.60 ± 0.82	21.60
Total	8906	91-290	157.30 ± 0.16	22.50

TABLE III-4. STATURE BY COUNTY SUBGROUPS

	No.	Range	Mean	S.D.
W. Donegal	212	146-193	171.48 + 0.34	7.35
Mayo	578	149-196	172.17 ∓ 0.20	7.14
Sligo, Leitrim, S.Fermanagh, W. Cavan.	716	146-202	171.84 ∓ 0.17	6.84
W. Galway	432	155-196	172.98 ∓ 0.21	6.39
Aran Islands	139	158-193	174.48 ∓ 0.40	7.05
Clare	946	146-196	172.20 ∓ 0.14	6.60
Kerry	539	152-199	173.04 ∓ 0.20	6.90
Cork	575	152-193	172.47 ∓ 0.19	6.81
Limerick	340	152-193	171.96 ∓ 0.25	6.84
E. Galway, Roscommon	514	149-196	173.16 ∓ 0.21	7.08
Longford, Westmeath	674	152-187	171.36 ∓ 0.17	6.39
Offaly, Leix, Kildare	530	152-193	171.42 ∓ 0.20	6.81
Tipperary, Kilkenny	650	149-196	171.81 ∓ 0.18	6.87
Waterford, Wexford	463	149-190	171.00 + 0.22	6.96
Wicklow, Carlow	278	149-202	170.79 ∓ 0.28	6.96
Meath, Louth, Dublin	458	155-193	170.52 ∓ 0.20	6.45
E. Cavan, Monaghan, Armagh.	388	155-190	170.79 ∓ 0.22	6.54
Antrim, Down	152	149-187	171.51 ± 0.40	7.23
N. Fermanagh, E.Donegal, Tyrone, Londonderry	318	152-187	171.78 + 0.25	6.60
Total	8902	146-202	171.90 + 0.05	6.84

TABLE III-5. SPAN BY COUNTY SUBGROUPS

	No.	Range	Mean	S.D.
W. Donegal	208	152-205	180.60 + 0.40	8.61
Mayo	574	155-205	182.22 ∓ 0.23	8.22
Sligo, Leitrim, S.Fermanagh, W. Cavan	707	146-208	181.59 ∓ 0.20	7.86
W. Galway	420	161-211	182.04 + 0.24	7.23
Aran Islands	137	158-208	181.98 ∓ 0.46	7.92
Clare	900	152-208	181.20 ∓ 0.18	8.04
Kerry	534	158-208	182.70 ∓ 0.22	7.71
Cork	561	158-205	181.56 ∓ 0.22	7.77
Limerick	335	158-205	181.20 ∓ 0.29	7.83
E. Galway, Roscommon	484	155-211	182.70 ∓ 0.25	8.25
Longford, Westmeath	672	158-205	179.67 ∓ 0.20	7.53
Offaly, Leix, Kildare	514	158-205	180.60 ∓ 0.25	8.40
Tipperary, Kilkenny	628	146-208	181.29 ∓ 0.21	7.89
Waterford, Wexford	443	149-202	180.12 ∓ 0.26	8.13
Wicklow, Carlow	269	158-208	179.85 ∓ 0.32	7.83
Meath, Louth, Dublin	448	158-202	179.22 ∓ 0.24	7.56
E. Cavan, Monaghan, Armagh	380	161-205	180.33 ∓ 0.26	7.44
Antrim, Down	151	155-199	180.09 ∓ 0.44	7.98
N. Fermanagh, E.Donegal, Tyrone, Londonderry	310	152-202	181.02 + 0.30	7.77
Total	8675	146-211	181.14 + 0.06	7.92

TABLE III-6. RELATIVE SPAN BY COUNTY SUBGROUPS

	No.	Range	Mean	S.D.
W. Donegal	208	98-113	105.44 + 0.12	2.50
Mayo	572	98-115	105.88 ∓ 0.06	2.30
Sligo, Leitrim, S.Fermanagh, W.Cavan	707	96-115	105.68 ∓ 0.06	2.56
W. Galway	420	96-113	105.14 ∓ 0.08	2.56
Aran Islands	137	98-111	104.06 ∓ 0.14	2.52
Clare	900	98-113	105.20 ∓ 0.06	2.52
Kerry	534	98-113	105.58 ∓ 0.07	2.44
Cork	561	98-113	105.22 ∓ 0.07	2.44
Limerick	335	98-115	105.32 ∓ 0.10	2.66
E. Galway, Roscommon	484	98-113	105.28 ∓ 0.08	2.54
Longford, Westmeath	670	96-113	104.94 ∓ 0.07	2.64
Offaly, Leix, Kildare	514	98-113	105.30 ∓ 0.08	2.56
Tipperary, Kilkenny	628	98-115	105.40 ∓ 0.07	2.58
Waterford, Wexford	443	94-113	105.30 ∓ 0.08	2.66
Wicklow, Carlow	269	96-111	105.28 ∓ 0.09	2.30
Meath, Louth, Dublin	448	98-113	105.18 ∓ 0.08	2.50
E. Cavan, Monaghan, Armagh	380	98-113	105.60 ∓ 0.08	2.38
Antrim, Down	151	96-113	105.16 ∓ 0.13	2.30
N. Fermanagh, E.Donegal, Tyrone, Londonderry	310	96-113	105.26 + 0.10	2.48
Total	8671	94-115	105.32 + 0.02	2.52

TABLE III-7. BIACROMIAL DIAMETER BY COUNTY SUBGROUPS

	No.	Range	Mean	S.D.
W.Donegal	211	34-45	38.42 + 0.09	1.98
Mayo	579	31-45	38.51 ∓ 0.06	2.04
Sligo, Leitrim, S.Fermanagh, W.Cavan	711	31-45	38.51 ∓ 0.05	1.98
W. Galway	427	31-45	38.84 ∓ 0.07	2.13
Aran Islands	138	31-45	38.33 ∓ 0.14	2.37
Clare	944	31-45	38.99 ∓ 0.04	1.95
Kerry	536	34-48	38.81 ∓ 0.06	1.95
Cork	575	31-45	38.57 ∓ 0.06	2.13
Limerick	339	31-45	38.45 ∓ 0.07	2.01
E. Galway, Roscommon	513	31-45	38.78 ∓ 0.06	2.19
Longford, Westmeath	675	28-45	38.09 ∓ 0.05	2.07
Offaly, Leix, Kildare	529	31-45	38.54 ∓ 0.06	2.13
Tipperary, Kilkenny	650	31-45	38.57 ∓ 0.06	2.13
Waterford, Wexford	463	31-45	38.48 ∓ 0.06	2.04
Wicklow, Carlow	277	31-45	38.63 ∓ 0.09	2.16
Meath, Louth, Dublin	457	31-45	38.42 ∓ 0.06	1.98
E.Cavan, Monaghan, Armagh	388	28-45	38.36 ∓ 0.07	2.10
Antrim, Down	151	34-45	38.66 ∓ 0.11	2.04
N. Fermanagh, E. Donegal, Tyrone, Londonderry	317	31-45	38.48 + 0.08	2.04
Total	8880	28-48	38.57 + 0.01	2.07

TABLE III-8. RELATIVE SHOULDER BREADTH BY COUNTY SUBGROUPS

	No.	Range	Mean	S.D.
W. Donegal	211	20-25	22.36 + 0.04	0.94
Mayo	577	18-25	22.36 ∓ 0.03	1.06
Sligo, Leitrim, S. Fermanagh, W. Cavan.	711	18-25	22.46 ∓ 0.03	1.12
W. Galway	427	18-25	22.32 ∓ 0.04	1.12
Aran Islands	138	18-25	21.92 ∓ 0.06	1.12
Clare	944	18-25	22.60 ∓ 0.02	1.16
Kerry	536	18-25	22.40 ∓ 0.03	1.06
Cork	575	18-25	22.44 ∓ 0.03	1.12
Limerick	339	18-25	22.32 ∓ 0.04	1.12
E. Galway, Roscommon	512	18-25	22.42 ∓ 0.03	1.10
Longford, Westmeath	673	18-25	22.26 ∓ 0.03	1.14
Offaly, Leix, Kildare	529	18-25	22.50 ∓ 0.03	1.10
Tipperary, Kilkenny	650	18-27	22.50 ∓ 0.03	1.18
Waterford, Wexford	463	18-27	22.52 ∓ 0.04	1.16
Wicklow, Carlow	277	18-27	22.68 ∓ 0.05	1.18
Meath, Louth, Dublin	457	20-25	22.56 ∓ 0.03	1.06
E. Cavan, Monaghan, Armagh	388	18-27	22.46 ∓ 0.04	1.10
Antrim, Down	151	20-25	22.38 ∓ 0.06	1.04
N. Fermanagh, E. Donegal, Tyrone, Londonderry	317	20-25	22.36 + 0.04	1.04
Total	8875	18-27	22.44 + 0.01	1.12

TABLE III-9. CHEST BREADTH BY COUNTY SUBGROUPS

	No.	Range	Mean	S.D.
W.Donegal	211	20-40	28.77 + 0.11	2.37
Mayo	577	23-40	29.46 ∓ 0.07	2.43
Sligo, Leitrim, S.Fermanagh, W.Cavan.	712	20-40	28.80 ∓ 0.06	2.52
W. Galway	427	23-40	29.40 ∓ 0.08	2.46
Aran Islands	138	23-37	28.98 ∓ 0.13	2.22
Clare	944	23-40	29.43 ∓ 0.05	2.28
Kerry	537	23-37	29.01 ∓ 0.06	2.25
Cork	574	23-40	29.01 ∓ 0.07	2.52
Limerick	340	20-40	28.98 ∓ 0.09	2.40
E. Galway, Roscommon	512	20-40	29.25 ∓ 0.07	2.49
Longford, Westmeath	671	23-40	28.47 ∓ 0.06	2.19
Offaly, Leix, Kildare	529	23-40	28.44 ∓ 0.07	2.49
Tipperary, Kilkenny	649	20-40	28.47 ∓ 0.06	2.46
Waterford, Wexford	456	23-40	28.65 ∓ 0.08	2.43
Wicklow, Carlow	275	23-40	28.26 ∓ 0.09	2.19
Meath, Louth, Dublin	456	23-37	28.26 ∓ 0.07	2.31
E. Cavan, Monaghan, Armagh	382	23-40	28.44 ∓ 0.08	2.31
Antrim, Down	152	23-40	28.80 ∓ 0.14	2.61
N. Fermanagh, E. Donegal, Tyrone, Londonderry	312	20-37	28.77 + 0.09	2.34
Total	8854	20-40	28.86 + 0.02	2.43

TABLE III-10. CHEST DEPTH BY COUNTY SUBGROUPS

	No.	Range	Mean	S.D.
W.Donegal	210	18-31	23.22 + 0.09	2.02
Mayo	576	18-29	23.52 ∓ 0.06	1.96
Sligo, Leitrim, S.Fermanagh, W.Cavan.	711	18-31	23.00 ∓ 0.05	2.06
W.Galway	427	18-31	23.14 ∓ 0.06	1.94
Aran Islands	138	18-27	22.20 ∓ 0.11	1.90
Clare	944	18-31	23.48 ∓ 0.04	1.96
Kerry	537	18-29	23.36 ∓ 0.06	1.90
Cork	574	18-31	23.40 ∓ 0.06	2.14
Limerick	340	18-29	23.20 ∓ 0.07	2.04
E. Galway, Roscommon	512	18-31	23.22 ∓ 0.06	1.98
Longford, Westmeath	671	18-33	22.34 ∓ 0.05	2.02
Offaly, Leix, Kildare	528	18-31	23.06 ∓ 0.06	1.96
Tipperary, Kilkenny	648	18-31	23.24 ∓ 0.06	1.98
Waterford, Wexford	456	18-31	23.66 ∓ 0.06	2.04
Wicklow, Carlow	275	18-31	23.44 ∓ 0.07	1.82
Meath, Louth, Dublin	456	18-33	23.14 ∓ 0.06	2.00
E. Cavan, Monaghan, Armagh	381	18-29	23.26 ∓ 0.06	1.82
Antrim, Down	152	18-29	23.12 ∓ 0.11	1.96
N. Fermanagh, E.Donegal, Tyrone, Londonderry	313	18-31	23.16 + 0.07	1.96
Total	8849	18-33	23.20 + 0.01	2.02

TABLE III-11. THORACIC INDEX BY COUNTY SUBGROUPS

	No.	Range	Mean	S.D.
W. Donegal	210	61-100	80.50 + 0.28	6.04
Mayo	576	61-100	80.02 ∓ 0.19	6.76
Sligo, Leitrim, S. Fermanagh, W. Cavan.	710	61-104	80.06 ∓ 0.17	6.84
W. Galway	427	57-104	78.74 ∓ 0.20	6.24
Aran Islands	138	61- 92	76.78 ∓ 0.33	5.72
Clare	944	57-104	79.94 ∓ 0.15	6.80
Kerry	537	61-104	80.34 ∓ 0.19	6.56
Cork	574	61-104	80.94 ∓ 0.18	6.56
Limerick	340	57-104	79.94 ∓ 0.23	6.28
E. Galway, Roscommon	511	57-100	79.54 ∓ 0.20	6.64
Longford, Westmeath	670	57-104	78.74 ∓ 0.18	6.80
Offaly, Leix, Kildare	528	57-100	81.14 ∓ 0.19	6.60
Tipperary, Kilkenny	648	53-108	81.90 ∓ 0.18	6.76
Waterford, Wexford	456	57-108	82.94 ∓ 0.21	6.56
Wicklow, Carlow	275	61-104	83.18 ∓ 0.28	6.80
Meath, Louth, Dublin	456	61-104	81.78 ∓ 0.20	6.32
E. Cavan, Monaghan, Armagh	381	57-104	81.94 ∓ 0.22	6.52
Antrim, Down	152	57-108	80.74 ∓ 0.38	6.92
N. Fermanagh, E.Donegal, Tyrone, Londonderry	312	65- 96	80.86 + 0.22	5.84
Total	8845	53-108	80.54 + 0.05	6.72

TABLE III-12. SITTING HEIGHT BY COUNTY SUBGROUPS

	No.	Range	Mean	S.D.
W. Donegal	212	75-104	91.27 + 0.18	3.81
Mayo	579	75-101	91.54 ∓ 0.10	3.66
Sligo, Leitrim, S. Fermanagh, W. Cavan.	714	75-107	91.21 ∓ 0.09	3.51
W. Galway	429	81-104	91.48 ∓ 0.11	3.45
Aran Islands	138	81-101	91.21 ∓ 0.22	3.84
Clare	944	78-104	91.72 ∓ 0.07	3.33
Kerry	536	78-104	92.41 ∓ 0.10	3.54
Cork	575	81-104	91.90 ∓ 0.10	3.48
Limerick	340	81-104	91.81 ∓ 0.13	3.69
E. Galway, Roscommon	514	78-101	92.08 ∓ 0.11	3.69
Longford, Westmeath	674	78-104	90.88 ∓ 0.10	3.69
Offaly, Leix, Kildare	528	78-101	91.27 ∓ 0.11	3.63
Tipperary, Kilkenny	649	75-104	91.63 ∓ 0.10	3.66
Waterford, Wexford	462	75-101	90.91 ∓ 0.12	3.75
Wicklow, Carlow	275	84-107	91.42 ∓ 0.14	3.54
Meath, Louth, Dublin	458	81-101	91.12 ∓ 0.11	3.42
E. Cavan, Monaghan, Armagh	387	81-101	90.88 ∓ 0.12	3.39
Antrim, Down	152	78-101	90.94 + 0.20	3.57
N. Fermanagh, E.Donegal, Tyrone, Londonderry	318	78-101	91.45 + 0.14	3.66
Total	8884	75-107	91.48 + 0.02.	3.60

TABLE III-13. RELATIVE SITTING HEIGHT BY COUNTY SUBGROUPS

	No.	Range	Mean	S.D.
W. Donegal	212	50-57	53.30 + 0.07	1.52
Mayo	578	48-59	53.22 ∓ 0.04	1.50
Sligo, Leitrim, S. Fermanagh, W. Cavan.	714	48-59	53.10 ∓ 0.04	1.46
W. Galway	429	48-59	52.88 ∓ 0.05	1.50
Aran Islands	138	46-57	52.28 ∓ 0.09	1.50
Clare	944	48-59	53.30 ∓ 0.03	1.50
Kerry	536	48-59	53.36 ∓ 0.04	1.44
Cork	575	48-57	53.28 ∓ 0.04	1.42
Limerick	340	50-57	53.44 ∓ 0.05	1.46
E. Galway, Roscommon	514	48-59	53.14 ∓ 0.04	1.50
Longford, Westmeath	672	48-59	53.04 ∓ 0.04	1.50
Offaly, Leix, Kildare	528	48-57	53.22 ∓ 0.04	1.40
Tipperary, Kilkenny	649	48-57	53.34 ∓ 0.04	1.52
Waterford, Wexford	462	48-59	53.18 ∓ 0.05	1.58
Wicklow, Carlow	275	50-59	53.54 ∓ 0.06	1.38
Meath, Louth, Dublin	458	48-59	53.48 ∓ 0.05	1.46
E. Cavan, Monaghan, Armagh	387	50-59	53.28 ∓ 0.05	1.42
Antrim, Down	152	48-57	52.92 ∓ 0.07	1.32
N. Fermanagh, E. Donegal, Tyrone, Londonderry	318	50-57	53.22 + 0.05	1.32
Total	8881	46-59	53.22 + 0.01	1.48

TABLE III-14. HEAD LENGTH BY COUNTY SUBGROUPS

	No.	Range	Mean	S.D.
W. Donegal	212	173-217	194.94 + 0.29	6.18
Mayo	580	173-217	195.48 ∓ 0.19	6.69
Sligo, Leitrim, S.Fermanagh, W.Cavan	714	176-214	196.11 ∓ 0.16	6.18
W. Galway	432	176-214	196.62 ∓ 0.21	6.45
Aran Islands	138	182-220	198.36 ∓ 0.40	6.90
Clare	945	173-214	195.66 ∓ 0.14	6.33
Kerry	539	170-214	195.12 ∓ 0.19	6.42
Cork	575	176-217	195.90 ∓ 0.18	6.33
Limerick	339	173-220	195.54 ∓ 0.25	6.75
E. Galway, Roscommon	514	173-220	196.59 ∓ 0.19	6.33
Longford, Westmeath	675	176-217	195.69 ∓ 0.17	6.45
Offaly, Leix, Kildare	530	173-217	194.94 ∓ 0.19	6.63
Tipperary, Kilkenny	650	173-223	195.15 ∓ 0.18	6.69
Waterford, Wexford	463	173-220	194.76 ∓ 0.22	6.93
Wicklow, Carlow	278	176-214	195.00 ∓ 0.27	6.60
Meath, Louth, Dublin	457	176-214	195.66 ∓ 0.20	6.21
E. Cavan, Monaghan, Armagh	389	176-214	195.75 ∓ 0.23	6.63
Antrim, Down	152	179-217	194.97 ∓ 0.35	6.45
N. Fermanagh, E.Donegal, Tyrone, Londonderry	318	179-214	195.42 + 0.24	6.24
Total	8900	170-223	195.63 + 0.05	6.51

TABLE III-15. HEAD BREADTH BY COUNTY SUBGROUPS

	No.	Range	Mean	S.D.
W. Donegal	212	141-170	154.42 + 0.24	5.25
Mayo	580	138-170	155.14 ∓ 0.15	5.49
Sligo, Leitrim, S.Fermanagh, W.Cavan	712	132-173	154.18 ∓ 0.14	5.64
W. Galway	432	138-173	154.27 ∓ 0.17	5.34
Aran Islands	137	138-173	154.27 ∓ 0.31	5.40
Clare	945	135-173	155.65 ∓ 0.12	5.70
Kerry	538	141-173	155.92 ∓ 0.16	5.52
Cork	575	138-179	155.56 ∓ 0.16	5.88
Limerick	340	141-173	155.50 ∓ 0.21	5.67
E. Galway, Roscommon	513	132-179	154.36 ∓ 0.17	5.76
Longford, Westmeath	674	126-170	152.41 ∓ 0.14	5.37
Offaly, Leix, Kildare	530	138-173	152.44 ∓ 0.17	5.70
Tipperary, Kilkenny	650	132-173	154.12 ∓ 0.15	5.76
Waterford, Wexford	463	138-185	153.16 ∓ 0.17	5.55
Wicklow, Carlow	278	138-173	152.47 ∓ 0.22	5.55
Meath, Louth, Dublin	457	132-173	152.14 ∓ 0.17	5.43
E. Cavan, Monaghan, Armagh	389	141-176	152.44 ∓ 0.19	5.55
Antrim, Down	152	135-170	153.46 ∓ 0.30	5.52
N. Fermanagh, E.Donegal, Tyrone, Londonderry	318	138-176	153.94 + 0.21	5.52
Total	8895	126-185	154.12 + 0.04	5.73

TABLE III-16. CEPHALIC INDEX BY COUNTY SUBGROUPS

	No.	Range	Mean	S.D.
W. Donegal	212	71-91	79.11 + 0.15	3.21
Mayo	580	71-91	79.41 ∓ 0.09	3.39
Sligo, Leitrim, S.Fermanagh, W.Cavan	711	68-91	78.66 ∓ 0.08	3.15
W.Galway	432	68-91	78.45 ∓ 0.10	3.12
Aran Islands	137	68-88	77.79 ∓ 0.19	3.30
Clare	945	65-91	79.62 ∓ 0.07	3.36
Kerry	538	68-91	80.01 ∓ 0.10	3.33
Cork	575	68-94	79.50 ∓ 0.09	3.36
Limerick	339	71-91	79.47 ∓ 0.12	3.21
E.Galway, Roscommon	513	68-91	78.51 + 0.10	3.24
Longford, Westmeath	673	65-88	77.91 ∓ 0.08	3.27
Offaly, Leix, Kildare	530	65-91	78.24 ∓ 0.10	3.27
Tipperary Kilkenny	650	68-91	78.99 ∓ 0.09	3.33
Waterford, Wexford	463	71-91	78.75 ∓ 0.10	3.24
Wicklow, Carlow	278	68-88	78.24 ∓ 0.12	2.97
Meath, Louth, Dublin	457	71-88	77.79 ∓ 0.09	2.91
E. Cavan, Monaghan, Armagh	389	68-88	78.00 ∓ 0.11	3.15
Antrim, Down	152	65-91	78.96 ∓ 0.19	3.42
N. Fermangh, E.Donegal, Tyrone, Londonderry	318	65-91	78.72 + 0.12	3.27
Total	8892	65-94	78.84 + 0.02	3.30

TABLE III-17. CEPHALIC INDEX BY COUNTY SUBGROUPS

	(59-76) Dolichocephalic		(77-82) Mesocephalic		(83-94) Brachycephalic		
	No.	%	No.	%	No.	%	Total
W. Donegal	42	19.8	138	65.1	32	15.1	212
Mayo	103	17.8	379	65.3	98	16.9	580
Sligo, Leitrim, S. Fermanagh, W. Cavan	169	23.8	464	65.3	78	11.0	711
W. Galway	111	25.7	285	66.0	36	8.3	432
Aran Islands	48	35.0	78	56.9	11	8.0	137
Clare	153	16.2	620	65.6	172	18.2	945
Kerry	63	11.7	360	66.9	115	21.4	538
Cork	99	17.2	386	67.1	90	15.6	575
Limerick	49	14.4	240	70.8	50	14.7	339
E. Galway, Roscommon	125	24.4	335	65.3	53	10.3	513
Longford, Westmeath	232	34.5	389	57.8	52	7.7	673
Offaly, Leix, Kildare	158	29.8	323	60.9	49	9.2	530
Tipperary, Kilkenny	150	23.1	409	62.9	91	14.0	650
Waterford, Wexford	113	24.4	297	64.1	53	11.4	463
Wicklow, Carlow	71	25.5	187	67.3	20	7.2	278
Meath, Louth, Dublin	153	33.5	281	61.5	23	5.0	457
E. Cavan, Monaghan, Armagh	127	32.6	229	58.9	33	8.5	389
Antrim, Down	30	19.7	103	67.8	19	12.5	152
N. Fermanagh, E. Donegal, Tyrone, Londonderry	78	24.5	201	63.2	39	12.3	318
Total	2074	23.3	5704	64.1	1114	12.5	8892

TABLE III-18. HEAD CIRCUMFERENCE BY COUNTY SUBGROUPS

	No.	Range	Mean	S.D.
W. Donegal	211	535-624	570.05 + 0.77	16.50
Mayo	348	520-624	572.90 + 0.61	16.80
Sligo, Leitrim, S. Fermanagh, W. Cavan	647	505-654	573.95 + 0.46	17.55
W. Galway	397	520-624	573.80 + 0.54	16.05
Aran Islands	139	535-624	577.10 + 0.94	16.50
Clare	919	505-624	573.05 + 0.36	16.35
Kerry	532	520-624	572.00 + 0.46	15.60
Cork	561	520-654	573.05 + 0.47	16.50
Limerick	312	520-624	571.25 + 0.63	16.50
E. Galway, Roscommon	508	505-639	574.40 + 0.50	16.80
Longford, Westmeath	672	505-624	571.55 + 0.41	15.90
Offaly, Leix, Kildare	526	520-624	569.60 + 0.49	16.80
Tipperary, Kilkenny	640	520-639	572.30 + 0.45	16.95
Waterford, Wexford	436	520-639	570.50 + 0.57	17.55
Wicklow, Carlow	275	520-624	569.60 + 0.65	15.90
Meath, Louth, Dublin	436	520-624	569.60 + 0.53	16.35
E. Cavan, Monaghan, Armagh	225	520-639	572.00 + 0.74	16.50
Antrim, Down	148	520-624	569.45 + 0.87	15.75
N. Fermanagh, E. Donegal, Tyrone, Londonderry	312	535-624	571.40 + 0.57	15.00
Total	8244	505-654	572.15 + 0.12	16.50

TABLE III-19. HEAD HEIGHT BY COUNTY SUBGROUPS

	No.	Range	Mean	S.D.
W. Donegal	212	110-141	125.58 + 0.25	5.48
Mayo	578	110-145	124.90 + 0.17	6.00
Sligo, Leitrim, S. Fermanagh, W. Cavan	715	102-145	124.10 + 0.15	6.04
W. Galway	432	106-141	124.66 + 0.19	5.80
Aran Islands	138	106-137	120.18 + 0.31	5.48
Clare	945	106-145	125.10 + 0.13	6.00
Kerry	538	110-141	124.86 + 0.16	5.64
Cork	574	106-149	125.34 + 0.17	6.20
Limerick	338	106-145	125.74 + 0.22	5.88
E. Galway, Roscommon	514	106-145	124.86 + 0.19	6.44
Longford, Westmeath	676	106-141	123.14 + 0.16	6.08
Offaly, Leix, Kildare	531	106-145	125.50 + 0.18	6.12
Tipperary, Kilkenny	650	106-145	125.70 + 0.16	6.08
Waterford, Wexford	463	106-145	125.34 + 0.19	6.16
Wicklow, Carlow	278	106-145	125.74 + 0.25	6.24
Meath, Louth, Dublin	457	106-141	125.38 + 0.18	5.56
E. Cavan, Monaghan, Armagh	389	110-145	125.02 + 0.18	5.40
Antrim, Down	152	106-149	125.62 + 0.34	6.16
N. Fermanagh, E. Donegal, Tyrone, Londonderry	318	106-145	126.74 + 0.22	5.76
Total	8898	102-149	124.98 + 0.04	6.04

TABLE III-20. LENGTH-HEIGHT INDEX BY COUNTY SUBGROUPS

	No.	Range	Mean	S.D.
W. Donegal	212	55-72	64.52 + 0.15	3.18
Mayo	578	55-75	63.92 ∓ 0.09	3.24
Sligo, Leitrim, S. Fermanagh, W. Cavan	713	52-75	63.32 ∓ 0.08	3.30
W. Galway	432	52-75	63.53 ∓ 0.10	3.12
Aran Islands	137	52-69	60.50 ∓ 0.18	3.09
Clare	944	55-75	63.98 ∓ 0.07	3.21
Kerry	538	55-75	63.92 ∓ 0.10	3.27
Cork	574	55-75	64.07 ∓ 0.10	3.42
Limerick	337	55-75	64.28 ∓ 0.12	3.30
E. Galway, Roscommon	514	52-72	63.47 ∓ 0.10	3.45
Longford, Westmeath	675	52-75	62.87 ∓ 0.09	3.45
Offaly, Leix, Kildare	530	55-75	64.46 ∓ 0.10	3.27
Tipperary, Kilkenny	650	55-75	64.43 ∓ 0.09	3.30
Waterford, Wexford	463	55-78	64.34 ∓ 0.10	3.33
Wicklow, Carlow	278	55-75	64.43 ∓ 0.13	3.30
Meath, Louth, Dublin	457	55-75	63.98 ∓ 0.10	3.15
E. Cavan, Monaghan, Armagh	389	55-75	63.86 ∓ 0.11	3.12
Antrim, Down	152	55-75	64.40 ∓ 0.18	3.36
N. Fermanagh, E. Donegal, Tyrone, Londonderry	318	55-75	64.85 + 0.12	3.30
Total	8891	52-78	63.89 + 0.02	3.33

TABLE III-21. BREADTH-HEIGHT INDEX BY COUNTY SUBGROUPS

	No.	Range	Mean	S.D.
W. Donegal	212	70- 93	81.20 + 0.18	3.87
Mayo	578	67- 96	80.54 ∓ 0.12	4.35
Sligo, Leitrim, S.Fermanagh, W.Cavan	711	67- 93	80.51 ∓ 0.10	4.14
W. Galway	432	67- 96	80.84 ∓ 0.13	4.14
Aran Islands	137	67- 93	77.99 ∓ 0.24	4.20
Clare	944	67- 96	80.36 ∓ 0.09	4.14
Kerry	537	67- 93	80.03 ∓ 0.11	3.84
Cork	574	70-102	80.57 ∓ 0.12	4.29
Limerick	338	67- 93	80.84 ∓ 0.15	4.14
E. Galway, Roscommon	513	67- 99	80.81 ∓ 0.13	4.44
Longford, Westmeath	674	67- 96	80.66 ∓ 0.11	4.29
Offaly, Leix, Kildare	530	70- 96	82.22 ∓ 0.13	4.32
Tipperary, Kilkenny	650	70- 99	81.44 ∓ 0.11	4.23
Waterford, Wexford	463	70- 96	81.86 ∓ 0.13	4.11
Wicklow, Carlow	278	70- 96	82.25 ∓ 0.18	4.53
Meath, Louth, Dublin	457	70- 96	82.34 ∓ 0.12	3.93
E. Cavan, Monaghan, Armagh	389	70- 93	81.92 ∓ 0.14	4.02
Antrim, Down	152	67- 90	81.68 ∓ 0.22	4.08
N. Fermanagh, E. Donegal, Tyrone, Londonderry	318	70- 96	82.46 + 0.16	4.17
Total	8887	67-102	81.05 + 0.03	4.26

TABLE III-22. BIZYGOMATIC DIAMETER BY COUNTY SUBGROUPS

	No.	Range	Mean	S. D.
W. Donegal	212	125-164	140.40 + 0.29	6.30
Mayo	580	120-159	151.75 ∓ 0.16	5.80
Sligo, Leitrim, S.Fermanagh, W.Cavan	710	120-164	140.95 ∓ 0.15	5.95
W. Galway	432	125-164	141.40 ∓ 0.19	5.95
Aran Islands	139	120-154	141.05 ∓ 0.31	5.40
Clare	943	120-159	142.00 ∓ 0.13	5.90
Kerry	538	120-164	142.30 ∓ 0.17	5.80
Cork	575	125-169	142.00 ∓ 0.17	5.95
Limerick	340	120-164	141.40 ∓ 0.22	6.00
E. Galway, Roscommon	515	125-164	141.65 ∓ 0.17	5.75
Longford, Westmeath	673	120-159	139.20 ∓ 0.15	5.75
Offaly, Leix, Kildare	529	110-159	139.10 ∓ 0.18	6.05
Tipperary, Kilkenny	648	120-159	140.50 ∓ 0.15	5.80
Waterford, Wexford	463	120-164	140.00 ∓ 0.19	6.00
Wicklow, Carlow	278	125-159	139.65 ∓ 0.24	5.85
Meath, Louth, Dublin	457	120-159	139.25 ∓ 0.17	5.45
E. Cavan, Monaghan, Armagh	389	120-159	139.60 ∓ 0.19	5.55
Antrim, Down	152	120-154	139.95 ∓ 0.32	5.80
N. Fermanagh, E. Donegal, Tyrone, Londonderry	318	125-159	140.25 + 0.23	6.10
Total	8891	110-169	140.80 + 0.04	5.95

TABLE III-23. CEPHALO-FACIAL INDEX BY COUNTY SUBGROUPS

	No.	Range	Mean	S.D.
W.Donegal	212	82-102	91.04 + 0.15	3.30
Mayo	580	76-105	91.46 ∓ 0.09	3.33
Sligo, Leitrim, S.Fermanagh, W.Cavan	707	76-105	91.49 ∓ 0.08	3.15
W. Galway	432	79-105	91.70 ∓ 0.10	3.09
Aran Islands	137	76-102	91.49 ∓ 0.20	3.57
Clare	943	76-108	91.31 ∓ 0.07	3.30
Kerry	537	79-102	91.34 ∓ 0.10	3.30
Cork	575	79-105	91.31 ∓ 0.09	3.12
Limerick	340	82-105	91.10 ∓ 0.11	3.09
E. Galway, Roscommon	513	79-105	91.79 ∓ 0.10	3.42
Longford, Westmeath	671	76-105	91.25 ∓ 0.09	3.48
Offaly, Leix, Kildare	528	76-102	91.37 ∓ 0.10	3.24
Tipperary, Kilkenny	648	79-105	91.19 ∓ 0.08	3.21
Waterford, Wexford	463	79-102	91.52 ∓ 0.10	3.27
Wicklow, Carlow	278	82-102	91.55 ∓ 0.14	3.48
Meath, Louth, Dublin	457	82- 99	91.52 ∓ 0.10	3.06
E. Cavan, Monaghan, Armagh	389	79-108	91.64 ∓ 0.11	3.36
Antrim, Down	152	76-102	91.25 ∓ 0.19	3.48
N. Fermanagh, E. Donegal, Tyrone, Londonderry	318	79-108	91.22 + 0.13	3.36
Total	8880	76-108	91.40 + 0.02	3.30

TABLE III-24. TOTAL FACE HEIGHT BY COUNTY SUBGROUPS

	No.	Range	Mean	S.D.
W. Donegal	212	110-149	127.10 + 0.30	6.60
Mayo	579	100-154	127.25 ∓ 0.20	7.25
Sligo, Leitrim, S.Fermanagh, W. Cavan	715	100-154	127.20 ∓ 0.17	6.85
W. Galway	432	100-154	128.60 ∓ 0.21	6.50
Aran Islands	139	115-149	129.85 ∓ 0.39	6.80
Clare	945	105-149	126.55 ∓ 0.15	7.05
Kerry	538	100-149	127.45 + 0.20	6.90
Cork	575	95-149	127.10 ∓ 0.19	6.75
Limerick	340	105-144	126.70 ∓ 0.24	6.65
E. Galway, Roscommon	514	100-149	127.15 ∓ 0.20	6.90
Longford, Westmeath	670	100-154	126.35 ∓ 0.18	6.90
Offaly, Leix, Kildare	531	95-149	126.90 ∓ 0.21	7.30
Tipperary, Kilkenny	650	105-154	127.20 ∓ 0.18	6.90
Waterford, Wexford	463	105-149	126.85 ∓ 0.22	6.90
Wicklow, Carlow	278	100-149	127.35 ∓ 0.30	7.45
Meath, Louth, Dublin	457	105-149	126.50 ∓ 0.21	6.75
E. Cavan, Monaghan, Armagh	389	105-149	127.90 ∓ 0.25	7.30
Antrim, Down	152	110-149	126.50 ∓ 0.38	6.95
N. Fermanagh, E.Donegal, Tyrone, Londonderry	318	105-149	126.45 + 0.23	6.10
Total	8897	95-154	127.10 + 0.05	6.95

TABLE III-25. UPPER FACE HEIGHT BY COUNTY SUBGROUPS

	No.	Range	Mean	S.D.
W. Donegal	212	60-84	73.30 + 0.18	3.95
Mayo	580	55-89	73.00 ∓ 0.12	4.40
Sligo, Leitrim, S. Fermanagh, W. Cavan.	712	50-89	71.90 ∓ 0.12	4.85
W. Galway	432	60-89	72.80 ∓ 0.14	4.25
Aran Islands	139	60-84	72.50 ∓ 0.23	4.10
Clare	945	55-89	72.65 ∓ 0.09	4.30
Kerry	538	60-89	73.85 ∓ 0.12	4.30
Cork	575	55-89	73.70 ∓ 0.12	4.25
Limerick	340	60-89	72.80 ∓ 0.16	4.35
E. Galway, Roscommon	510	55-84	71.80 ∓ 0.13	4.45
Longford, Westmeath	673	50-89	70.60 ∓ 0.12	4.55
Offaly, Leix, Kildare	530	60-89	73.05 ∓ 0.12	4.25
Tipperary, Kilkenny	650	60-89	73.70 ∓ 0.12	4.65
Waterford, Wexford	463	60-84	73.25 ∓ 0.13	4.20
Wicklow, Carlow	278	60-89	73.60 ∓ 0.19	4.60
Meath, Louth, Dublin	458	55-84	72.45 ∓ 0.14	4.40
E. Cavan, Monaghan, Armagh	389	60-89	73.65 ∓ 0.16	4.60
Antrim, Down	152	60-89	73.60 ∓ 0.24	4.30
N. Fermanagh, E. Donegal, Tyrone, Londonderry	318	60-89	73.50 + 0.16	4.10
Total	8894	50-89	72.80 + 0.03	4.50

TABLE III-26. FACIAL INDEX BY COUNTY SUBGROUPS

	No.	Range	Mean	S.D.
W. Donegal	212	75-109	90.40 + 0.26	5.55
Mayo	579	70-109	89.60 ∓ 0.15	5.45
Sligo, Leitrim, S. Fermanagh, W.Cavan	709	70-109	90.30 ∓ 0.14	5.55
W. Galway	432	75-114	90.90 ∓ 0.18	5.50
Aran Islands	139	70-109	91.70 ∓ 0.33	5.70
Clare	942	70-109	89.25 ∓ 0.12	5.65
Kerry	537	70-109	89.50 ∓ 0.16	5.35
Cork	575	70-109	89.35 ∓ 0.15	5.20
Limerick	340	70-109	89.45 ∓ 0.19	5.10
E. Galway, Roscommon	514	75-109	89.70 ∓ 0.16	5.45
Longford, Westmeath	667	70-109	90.65 ∓ 0.14	5.50
Offaly, Leix, Kildare	529	75-109	91.10 ∓ 0.16	5.50
Tipperary, Kilkenny	648	70-109	90.40 ∓ 0.14	5.45
Waterford, Wexford	463	75-109	90.45 ∓ 0.17	5.40
Wicklow, Carlow	278	75-114	91.00 ∓ 0.23	5.80
Meath, Louth, Dublin	456	75-114	90.70 ∓ 0.17	5.50
E.Cavan, Monaghan, Armagh	389	75-109	91.40 ∓ 0.20	5.85
Antrim Down	152	75-104	90.20 ∓ 0.28	5.15
N. Fermanagh,E.Donegal, Tyrone, Londonderry	318	75-104	90.05 + 0.20	5.20
Total	8879	70-114	90.20 + 0.04	5.50

TABLE III-27. UPPER FACIAL INDEX BY COUNTY SUBGROUPS

	No.	Range	Mean	S.D.
W. Donegal	212	43-63	52.07 + 0.16	3.39
Mayo	580	37-63	51.35 ∓ 0.09	3.33
Sligo, Leitrim, S. Fermanagh, W. Cavan.	706	37-66	50.96 ∓ 0.09	3.60
W. Galway	432	40-66	51.41 ∓ 0.11	3.39
Aran Islands	139	40-66	51.08 ∓ 0.19	3.36
Clare	942	40-69	51.08 ∓ 0.08	3.42
Kerry	537	43-63	51.77 ∓ 0.09	3.21
Cork	575	43-63	51.74 ∓ 0.09	3.36
Limerick	340	40-66	51.32 ∓ 0.12	3.21
E. Galway, Roscommon	510	40-63	50.72 ∓ 0.10	3.24
Longford, Westmeath	670	37-63	50.60 ∓ 0.09	3.51
Offaly, Leix, Kildare	528	43-69	52.37 ∓ 0.10	3.48
Tipperary, Kilkenny	648	40-66	52.34 ∓ 0.09	3.48
Waterford, Wexford	463	43-63	52.25 ∓ 0.10	3.27
Wicklow, Carlow	278	43-66	52.58 ∓ 0.14	3.60
Meath, Louth, Dublin	457	40-63	51.98 ∓ 0.10	3.30
E. Cavan, Monaghan, Armagh	389	43-63	52.76 ∓ 0.12	3.51
Antrim, Down	152	40-60	52.25 ∓ 0.18	3.33
N. Fermanagh, E.Donegal, Tyrone, Londonderry	318	43-66	52.37 + 0.13	3.36
Total	8876	37-69	51.62 + 0.02	3.45

TABLE III-28. NOSE HEIGHT BY COUNTY SUBGROUPS

	No.	Range	Mean	S.D.
W. Donegal	212	44-67	56.14 + 0.19	4.08
Mayo	579	44-71	56.30 ∓ 0.11	4.04
Sligo, Leitrim, S.Fermanagh, W. Cavan	713	40-71	55.70 ∓ 0.10	4.12
W. Galway	432	44-71	56.74 ∓ 0.13	3.92
Aran Islands	139	48-67	57.10 ∓ 0.21	3.72
Clare	946	40-71	56.86 ∓ 0.09	4.12
Kerry	539	44-67	56.94 ∓ 0.12	4.08
Cork	574	48-67	56.90 ∓ 0.11	3.80
Limerick	340	44-71	56.10 ∓ 0.15	4.12
E. Galway, Roscommon	515	44-71	56.06 ∓ 0.12	4.08
Longford, Westmeath	673	40-67	55.30 ∓ 0.10	4.04
Offaly, Leix, Kildare	531	40-67	55.98 ∓ 0.12	4.08
Tipperary, Kilkenny	649	44-71	56.82 ∓ 0.11	4.24
Waterford, Wexford	462	40-67	56.58 ∓ 0.12	3.96
Wicklow, Carlow	278	44-67	56.54 ∓ 0.17	4.32
Meath, Louth, Dublin	457	44-71	55.78 ∓ 0.13	4.16
E. Cavan, Monaghan, Armagh	389	44-67	56.18 ∓ 0.13	3.72
Antrim, Down	152	44-71	56.02 ∓ 0.22	4.04
N. Fermanagh, E.Donegal, Tyrone, Londonderry	318	44-67	55.74 + 0.14	3.80
Total	8898	40-71	56.30 + 0.03	4.08

TABLE III-29. NOSE BREADTH BY COUNTY SUBGROUPS

	No.	Range	Mean	S.D.
W. Donegal	212	28-48	35.39 + 0.14	2.97
Mayo	580	28-45	36.11 ∓ 0.08	2.97
Sligo, Leitrim, S. Fermanagh, W. Cavan	715	28-57	35.90 ∓ 0.08	3.09
W. Galway	432	28-48	36.59 ∓ 0.10	3.12
Aran Islands	139	31-45	36.35 ∓ 0.16	2.82
Clare	945	28-48	36.05 ∓ 0.07	3.12
Kerry	539	28-48	36.20 ∓ 0.09	3.09
Cork	575	28-51	36.47 ∓ 0.09	3.21
Limerick	340	28-45	35.60 ∓ 0.11	2.94
E. Galway, Roscommon	515	28-48	35.90 ∓ 0.08	2.76
Longford, Westmeath	674	28-57	35.24 ∓ 0.08	2.94
Offaly, Leix, Kildare	530	25-45	36.26 ∓ 0.09	3.00
Tipperary, Kilkenny	650	28-45	35.90 ∓ 0.08	2.97
Waterford, Wexford	463	28-54	35.96 ∓ 0.10	3.33
Wicklow, Carlow	278	28-48	36.20 ∓ 0.13	3.18
Meath, Louth, Dublin	458	28-45	35.99 ∓ 0.10	3.15
E. Cavan, Monaghan, Armagh	389	25-45	36.20 ∓ 0.11	3.30
Antrim, Down	152	28-45	35.78 ∓ 0.17	3.15
N. Fermanagh, E. Donegal, Tyrone, Londonderry	318	28-45	36.23 + 0.13	3.36
Total	8904	25-57	36.02 + 0.02	3.09

TABLE III-30. NASAL INDEX BY COUNTY SUBGROUPS

	No.	Range	Mean	S.D.
W. Donegal	212	48-87	63.78 + 0.30	6.44
Mayo	579	44-91	64.66 ∓ 0.18	6.52
Sligo, Leitrim, S.Fermanagh, W. Cavan	712	44-95	64.94 ∓ 0.17	6.72
W. Galway	432	44-99	65.10 ∓ 0.22	6.84
Aran Islands	139	52-83	63.90 ∓ 0.36	6.24
Clare	945	44-95	63.98 ∓ 0.15	6.68
Kerry	539	44-83	63.98 ∓ 0.18	6.12
Cork	575	48-87	64.42 ∓ 0.17	6.00
Limerick	340	48-79	63.70 ∓ 0.21	5.84
E. Galway, Roscommon	515	48-91	64.46 ∓ 0.19	6.36
Longford, Westmeath	673	44-99	64.30 ∓ 0.18	6.88
Offaly, Leix, Kildare	530	48-87	64.86 ∓ 0.17	5.96
Tipperary, Kilkenny	649	44-87	63.66 ∓ 0.16	6.24
Waterford, Wexford	462	48-91	63.98 ∓ 0.20	6.40
Wicklow, Carlow	278	44-91	64.18 ∓ 0.27	6.72
Meath, Louth, Dublin	457	48-87	64.98 ∓ 0.22	7.12
E. Cavan, Monaghan, Armagh	389	48-95	64.82 ∓ 0.23	6.60
Antrim, Down	152	48-83	64.10 + 0.32	5.92
N. Fermanagh, E. Donegal, Tyrone, Londonderry	318	48-83	65.14 + 0.24	6.48
Total	8896	44-99	64.38 + 0.05	6.48

TABLE III-31. MINIMUM FRONTAL DIAMETER BY COUNTY SUBGROUPS

	No.	Range	Mean	S.D.
W. Donegal	212	89-128	109.74 + 0.22	4.84
Mayo	580	97-124	110.30 ∓ 0.14	4.92
Sligo, Leitrim, S. Fermanagh, W. Cavan	712	93-124	108.66 ∓ 0.12	4.88
W. Galway	432	93-128	109.78 ∓ 0.16	5.04
Aran Islands	139	97-120	108.46 ∓ 0.24	4.20
Clare	944	97-128	110.42 ∓ 0.10	4.68
Kerry	539	93-124	109.38 ∓ 0.14	4.68
Cork	574	93-124	110.02 ∓ 0.13	4.68
Limerick	340	93-124	109.38 ∓ 0.18	4.92
E. Galway, Roscommon	514	89-124	109.10 ∓ 0.15	5.12
Longford, Westmeath	675	93-124	107.18 ∓ 0.12	4.72
Offaly, Leix, Kildare	531	93-128	108.42 ∓ 0.13	4.60
Tipperary, Kilkenny	650	93-124	109.94 ∓ 0.12	4.48
Waterford, Wexford	462	89-124	109.26 ∓ 0.15	4.84
Wicklow, Carlow	278	97-124	108.62 ∓ 0.18	4.56
Meath, Louth, Dublin	457	89-124	108.50 ∓ 0.14	4.32
E. Cavan, Monaghan, Armagh	389	97-124	108.98 ∓ 0.16	4.68
Antrim, Down	152	97-124	108.06 ∓ 0.26	4.76
N. Fermanagh, E. Donegal, Tyrone, Londonderry	318	97-124	109.22 + 0.18	4.68
Total	8898	89-128	109.22 + 0.03	4.84

TABLE III-32. FRONTO-PARIETAL INDEX BY COUNTY SUBGROUPS

	No.	Range	Mean	S.D.
W. Donegal	212	63-83	71.38 ± 0.14	3.12
Mayo	580	63-83	71.26 ± 0.08	3.00
Sligo, Leitrim, S.Fermanagh, W. Cavan	709	60-86	70.66 ± 0.08	3.27
W. Galway	432	63-80	71.35 ± 0.10	3.21
Aran Islands	137	63-80	70.36 ± 0.17	3.00
Clare	943	60-83	71.08 ± 0.07	3.24
Kerry	538	60-80	70.39 ± 0.08	2.94
Cork	574	63-86	71.05 ± 0.08	2.94
Limerick	340	60-80	70.63 ± 0.10	2.82
E. Galway, Roscommon	512	60-83	70.90 ± 0.09	3.09
Longford, Westmeath	673	63-86	70.54 ± 0.08	3.21
Offaly, Leix, Kildare	530	63-80	71.29 ± 0.09	2.97
Tipperary, Kilkenny	650	63-80	71.41 ± 0.08	2.85
Waterford, Wexford	462	60-80	71.50 ± 0.10	3.03
Wicklow, Carlow	278	63-80	71.26 ± 0.12	2.97
Meath, Louth, Dublin	457	63-80	71.44 ± 0.09	2.85
E. Cavan, Monaghan, Armagh	389	63-83	71.62 ± 0.10	3.09
Antrim, Down	152	60-80	70.54 ± 0.18	3.30
N. Fermanagh, E. Donegal, Tyrone, Londonderry	318	63-86	71.02 ± 0.11	3.00
Total	8886	60-86	71.05 ± 0.02	3.09

TABLE III-33. ZYGO-FRONTAL INDEX BY COUNTY SUBGROUPS

	No.	Range	Mean	S.D.
W. Donegal	212	68-91	78.38 ± 0.15	3.32
Mayo	580	68-95	77.86 ± 0.09	3.28
Sligo, Leitrim, S. Fermanagh, W. Cavan	707	64-95	77.34 ± 0.08	3.36
W. Galway	432	68-91	77.90 ± 0.11	3.48
Aran Islands	139	68-91	76.94 ± 0.19	3.36
Clare	941	64-95	77.90 ± 0.07	3.16
Kerry	538	64-91	77.02 ± 0.10	3.28
Cork	574	68-95	77.70 ± 0.09	3.12
Limerick	340	68-91	77.54 ± 0.11	3.04
E. Galway, Roscommon	514	64-95	77.22 ± 0.10	3.44
Longford, Westmeath	672	64-95	77.30 ± 0.09	3.48
Offaly, Leix, Kildare	529	64-95	78.14 ± 0.10	3.52
Tipperary, Kilkenny	648	68-91	78.46 ± 0.08	3.08
Waterford, Wexford	462	68-91	78.14 ± 0.10	3.28
Wicklow, Carlow	278	68-87	78.10 ± 0.12	3.08
Meath, Louth, Dublin	457	68-91	78.06 ± 0.10	3.24
E. Cavan, Monaghan, Armagh	389	68-91	78.22 ± 0.10	3.04
Antrim, Down	152	68-87	77.46 ± 0.18	3.24
N. Fermanagh, E. Donegal, Tyrone, Londonderry	318	68-95	78.02 ± 0.13	3.40
Total	8882	64-95	77.78 ± 0.02	3.32

TABLE III-34. BIGONIAL DIAMETER BY COUNTY SUBGROUPS

	No.	Range	Mean	S.D.
W. Donegal	212	94-129	108.66 ± 0.26	5.60
Mayo	580	90-129	110.06 ± 0.15	5.32
Sligo, Leitrim, S. Fermanagh, W. Cavan	716	90-129	108.70 ± 0.13	5.32
W. Galway	431	94-133	110.34 ± 0.17	5.36
Aran Islands	139	94-125	110.78 ± 0.37	6.52
Clare	946	90-133	110.14 ± 0.12	5.60
Kerry	537	94-129	110.34 ± 0.16	5.44
Cork	574	94-133	110.06 ± 0.17	6.04
Limerick	339	90-129	109.14 ± 0.21	5.76
E. Galway, Roscommon	515	94-125	109.10 ± 0.16	5.32
Longford, Westmeath	674	90-129	107.62 ± 0.14	5.52
Offaly, Leix, Kildare	530	90-129	108.62 ± 0.16	5.32
Tipperary, Kilkenny	650	94-129	109.50 ± 0.14	5.44
Waterford, Wexford	462	94-133	109.50 ± 0.19	5.96
Wicklow, Carlow	277	90-125	108.90 ± 0.22	5.52
Meath, Louth, Dublin	456	90-125	108.58 ± 0.18	5.56
E. Cavan, Monaghan, Armagh	389	90-125	108.38 ± 0.20	5.84
Antrim, Down	152	86-125	108.18 ± 0.31	5.60
N. Fermanagh, E. Donegal, Tyrone, Londonderry	318	90-129	108.74 ± 0.22	5.92
Total	8897	86-133	109.26 ± 0.04	5.64

TABLE III-35. ZYGO-GONIAL INDEX BY COUNTY SUBGROUPS

	No.	Range	Mean	S. D.
W. Donegal	212	69-89	77.44 + 0.15	3.30
Mayo	580	66-89	77.65 ∓ 0.09	3.30
Sligo, Leitrim, S. Fermanagh, W. Cavan.	710	66-89	77.02 ∓ 0.08	3.24
W. Galway	431	69-89	78.04 ∓ 0.11	3.51
Aran Islands	139	69-92	78.28 ∓ 0.24	4.23
Clare	943	63-92	77.44 ∓ 0.08	3.60
Kerry	536	66-92	77.53 ∓ 0.10	3.33
Cork	574	66-89	77.47 ∓ 0.10	3.42
Limerick	339	66-89	77.32 ∓ 0.13	3.63
E. Galway, Roscommon	515	66-86	77.02 ∓ 0.10	3.27
Longford, Westmeath	671	66-92	77.26 ∓ 0.09	3.63
Offaly, Leix, Kildare	528	69-92	78.04 ∓ 0.10	3.60
Tipperary, Kilkenny	648	66-92	77.89 ∓ 0.09	3.36
Waterford, Wexford	462	66-86	78.13 ∓ 0.10	3.21
Wicklow, Carlow	277	66-86	77.92 ∓ 0.14	3.42
Meath, Louth, Dublin	456	66-86	77.83 ∓ 0.11	3.39
E. Cavan, Monaghan, Armagh	389	66-89	77.56 ∓ 0.12	3.54
Antrim, Down	152	69-86	77.14 ∓ 0.18	3.30
N. Fermanagh, E. Donegal, Tyrone, Londonderry	318	66-89	77.32 + 0.14	3.57
Total	8880	63-92	77.56 + 0.02	3.48

TABLE III-36. FRONTO-GONIAL INDEX BY COUNTY SUBGROUPS

	No.	Range	Mean	S.D.
W. Donegal	212	85-119	98.90 + 0.26	5.65
Mayo	580	85-124	99.70 ∓ 0.15	5.45
Sligo, Leitrim, S. Fermanagh, W. Cavan.	712	85-124	100.00 ∓ 0.14	5.40
W. Galway	431	85-119	100.30 ∓ 0.18	5.45
Aran Islands	139	80-124	101.90 ∓ 0.41	7.25
Clare	944	80-124	99.70 ∓ 0.12	5.45
Kerry	537	85-124	100.55 ∓ 0.16	5.35
Cork	573	80-119	99.80 ∓ 0.16	5.65
Limerick	339	80-114	99.75 ∓ 0.19	5.25
E. Galway, Roscommon	514	85-124	100.00 ∓ 0.16	5.45
Longford, Westmeath	673	80-124	100.10 ∓ 0.15	5.65
Offaly, Leix, Kildare	530	85-119	99.85 ∓ 0.16	5.55
Tipperary, Kilkenny	650	80-119	99.55 ∓ 0.13	5.10
Waterford, Wexford	462	85-124	100.00 ∓ 0.18	5.75
Wicklow, Carlow	277	85-119	100.20 ∓ 0.22	5.50
Meath, Louth, Dublin	456	85-119	99.75 ∓ 0.17	5.45
E. Cavan, Monaghan, Armagh	389	85-119	99.35 ∓ 0.18	5.15
Antrim, Down	152	85-119	100.00 ∓ 0.31	5.60
N. Fermanagh, E. Donegal, Tyrone, Londonderry	318	85-119	99.35 + 0.22	5.85
Total	8888	80-124	99.90 + 0.04	5.50

TABLE IV-1. SKIN COLOR, INNER ARM, BY COUNTY SUBGROUPS

	Pale No.	Pale %	Pink No.	Pink %	Brunet No.	Brunet %	Swarthy No.	Swarthy %	Total No.
W. Donegal	1	.5	195	92.0	12	5.7	4	1.9	212
Mayo	2	.3	554	95.5	22	3.8	2	.3	580
Sligo, Leitrim, S. Fermanagh, W. Cavan.	1	.1	663	92.6	50	7.0	2	.3	716
W. Galway	2	.5	395	91.4	33	7.6	2	.5	432
Aran Islands	-	-	119	85.6	20	14.4	-	-	139
Clare	3	.3	884	93.4	57	6.0	2	.2	946
Kerry	-	-	499	92.6	38	7.0	2	.4	539
Cork	1	.2	536	93.2	34	5.9	4	.7	575
Limerick	-	-	318	93.5	19	5.6	3	.9	340
E. Galway, Roscommon	1	.2	471	91.4	42	8.2	1	.2	515
Longford, Westmeath	7	1.0	543	80.3	126	18.6	-	-	676
Offaly, Leix, Kildare	2	.4	478	90.0	51	9.6	-	-	531
Tipperary, Kilkenny	3	.5	602	92.8	44	6.8	-	-	649
Waterford, Wexford	2	.4	426	92.0	31	6.7	4	.9	463
Wicklow, Carlow	-	-	256	92.1	21	7.6	1	.4	278
Meath, Louth, Dublin	-	-	411	89.7	46	10.0	1	.2	458
E. Cavan, Monaghan, Armagh	1	.2	365	93.8	23	5.9	-	-	389
Antrim, Down	-	-	144	94.7	8	5.3	-	-	152
N. Fermanagh, E. Donegal, Tyrone, Londonderry	-	-	301	94.6	17	5.3	-	-	318
Total	26	.3	8160	91.6	694	7.8	28	.3	8908

TABLE IV-2. VASCULARITY BY COUNTY SUBGROUPS

	Absent, submedium No.	Absent, submedium %	Medium No.	Medium %	Pronounced No.	Pronounced %	Total No.
W. Donegal	2	.9	165	77.8	45	21.2	212
Mayo	5	.9	420	72.4	155	26.7	580
Sligo, Leitrim, S. Fermanagh, W. Cavan	1	.1	585	81.7	130	18.2	716
W. Galway	8	1.8	283	65.5	141	32.6	432
Aran Islands	-	-	101	73.2	37	26.8	138
Clare	9	1.0	612	64.7	325	34.4	946
Kerry	2	.4	411	76.2	126	23.4	539
Cork	-	-	443	77.0	132	23.0	575
Limerick	3	.9	228	67.0	109	32.0	340
E. Galway, Roscommon	5	1.0	393	76.4	116	22.6	514
Longford, Westmeath	7	1.0	554	82.0	115	17.0	676
Offaly, Leix, Kildare	8	1.5	435	81.9	88	16.6	531
Tipperary, Kilkenny	3	.5	506	77.8	141	21.7	650
Waterford, Wexford	2	.4	360	77.8	101	21.8	463
Wicklow, Carlow	2	.7	205	73.7	71	25.5	278
Meath, Louth, Dublin	3	.6	346	75.5	109	23.8	458
E. Cavan, Monaghan, Armagh	3	.8	306	78.7	80	20.6	389
Antrim, Down	-	-	102	67.1	50	32.9	152
N. Fermanagh, E. Donegal, Tyrone, Londonderry	-	-	231	72.6	87	27.4	318
Total	63	.7	6686	75.1	2158	24.2	8907

TABLE IV-3. FRECKLES BY COUNTY SUBGROUPS

	Absent No.	Absent %	Submedium No.	Submedium %	Medium No.	Medium %	Pronounced massed No.	Pronounced massed %	Total No.
W. Donegal	80	37.7	65	30.7	51	24.0	16	7.5	212
Mayo	276	47.7	172	29.7	99	17.1	32	5.5	579
Sligo, Leitrim, S. Fermanagh, W.Cavan	416	58.2	193	27.0	80	11.2	26	3.6	715
W. Galway	274	63.4	97	22.4	43	10.0	18	4.2	432
Aran Islands	74	53.2	29	20.9	17	12.2	19	13.7	139
Clare	647	68.5	172	18.2	93	9.8	33	3.5	945
Kerry	227	42.1	191	35.4	105	19.5	16	3.0	539
Cork	325	56.5	156	27.1	83	14.4	11	1.9	575
Limerick	196	57.6	83	24.4	49	14.4	12	3.5	340
E. Galway, Roscommon	305	59.2	150	29.1	48	9.3	12	2.3	515
Longford, Westmeath	443	65.6	135	20.0	66	9.8	31	4.6	675
Offaly, Leix, Kildare	355	66.8	125	23.5	48	9.0	3	6	531
Tipperary, Kilkenny	441	67.8	158	24.3	42	6.5	9	1.4	650
Waterford, Wexford	331	71.6	98	21.2	31	6.7	2	4	462
Wicklow, Carlow	196	70.5	68	24.5	12	4.3	2	.7	278
Meath, Louth, Dublin	312	68.1	110	24.0	28	6.1	8	1.7	458
E.Cavan, Monaghan, Armagh	237	60.9	129	33.2	18	4.6	5	1.3	389
Antrim, Down	79	52.0	51	33.6	20	13.2	2	1.3	152
N. Fermanagh, E. Donegal, Tyrone, Londonderry	157	49.4	118	37.1	40	12.6	3	.9	318
Total	5371	60.3	2300	25.8	973	10.9	260	2.9	8904

TABLE IV-4. MOLES BY COUNTY SUBGROUPS

	Absent No.	%	Few No.	%	Many No.	%	Total No.
W. Donegal	204	96.2	8	3.8	-	-	212
Mayo	551	95.0	29	5.0	-	-	580
Sligo, Leitrim, S. Fermanagh, W. Cavan	670	93.6	41	5.7	5	.7	716
W. Galway	403	93.7	27	6.3	-	-	430
Aran Islands	135	97.1	3	2.2	1	.7	139
Clare	878	93.1	60	6.4	5	.5	943
Kerry	524	97.2	14	2.6	1	.2	539
Cork	542	94.3	27	4.7	6	1.0	575
Limerick	324	95.3	14	4.1	2	.6	340
E. Galway, Roscommon	477	93.0	34	6.6	2	.4	513
Longford, Westmeath	606	89.8	60	8.9	9	1.3	675
Offaly, Leix, Kildare	483	91.0	41	7.7	7	1.3	531
Tipperary, Kilkenny	616	94.8	31	4.8	3	.5	650
Waterford, Wexford	445	96.1	16	3.4	2	.4	463
Wicklow, Carlow	263	94.6	14	5.0	1	.4	278
Meath, Louth, Dublin	419	91.5	36	7.9	3	.6	458
E. Cavan, Monaghan, Armagh	368	94.6	21	5.4	-	-	389
Antrim, Down	143	94.1	9	5.9	-	-	152
N. Fermanagh, E. Donegal, Tyrone, Londonderry	308	96.8	10	3.1	-	-	318
Total	8359	93.9	495	5.6	47	.5	8901

TABLE IV-5. HAIR FORM BY COUNTY SUBGROUPS

	Straight No.	%	Low waves No.	%	Deep waves No.	%	Curly No.	%	Frizzly, Woolly No.	%	Total No.
W. Donegal	70	33.0	93	43.9	42	19.8	7	3.3	-	-	212
Mayo	126	21.7	316	54.5	98	16.9	37	6.4	3	.5	580
Sligo, Leitrim, S. Fermanagh, W. Cavan	157	21.9	415	58.0	116	16.2	25	3.5	3	.4	716
W. Galway	116	26.8	235	54.4	69	16.0	11	2.5	1	.2	432
Aran Islands	52	37.4	62	44.6	21	15.1	4	2.9	-	-	139
Clare	242	25.6	501	53.0	180	19.0	19	2.0	4	.4	946
Kerry	175	32.5	256	47.6	91	16.9	15	2.8	1	.2	538
Cork	190	33.2	238	41.5	124	21.6	21	3.7	-	-	573
Limerick	100	29.5	176	51.9	55	16.2	8	2.4	-	-	339
E. Galway, Roscommon	110	21.4	286	55.5	106	20.6	12	2.3	1	.2	515
Longford, Westmeath	96	14.2	393	58.1	153	22.6	34	5.0	-	-	676
Offaly, Leix, Kildare	147	27.7	249	46.9	113	21.3	21	4.0	1	.2	531
Tipperary, Kilkenny	236	36.3	283	43.5	114	17.5	16	2.5	1	.2	650
Waterford, Wexford	172	37.1	217	46.9	60	13.0	14	3.0	-	-	463
Wicklow, Carlow	113	40.6	119	42.8	38	13.7	8	2.9	-	-	278
Meath, Louth, Dublin	145	31.6	207	45.2	94	20.5	12	2.6	-	-	458
E. Cavan, Monaghan, Armagh	144	37.0	182	46.8	53	13.6	10	2.6	-	-	389
Antrim, Down	40	26.3	74	48.7	28	18.4	10	6.6	-	-	152
N. Fermanagh, E. Donegal, Tyrone, Londonderry	124	39.0	135	42.4	51	16.0	8	2.5	-	-	318
Total	2555	28.7	4437	49.8	1606	18.0	292	3.3	15	.2	8905

TABLE IV-6. HAIR TEXTURE BY COUNTY SUBGROUPS

	Coarse No.	%	Medium No.	%	Fine No.	%	Total No.
W. Donegal	4	1.9	205	96.7	3	1.4	212
Mayo	24	4.1	547	94.3	9	1.6	580
Sligo, Leitrim, S.Fermanagh, W.Cavan	43	6.0	660	92.2	13	1.8	716
W. Galway	24	5.6	395	91.4	13	3.0	432
Aran Islands	3	2.2	135	97.1	1	.7	139
Clare	48	5.1	876	92.6	22	2.3	946
Kerry	31	5.8	495	91.8	13	2.4	539
Cork	27	4.7	523	91.0	25	4.3	575
Limerick	22	6.5	306	90.3	11	3.2	339
E. Galway, Roscommon	32	6.2	468	90.9	15	2.9	515
Longford, Westmeath	31	4.6	614	91.0	30	4.4	675
Offaly, Leix, Kildare	19	3.6	497	93.8	14	2.6	530
Tipperary, Kilkenny	34	5.2	590	90.8	26	4.0	650
Waterford, Wexford	22	4.8	428	92.4	13	2.8	463
Wicklow, Carlow	4	1.4	258	92.8	16	5.8	278
Meath, Louth, Dublin	18	3.9	424	92.6	16	3.5	458
E. Cavan Monaghan, Armagh	9	2.3	375	96.4	5	1.3	389
Antrim, Down	9	5.9	142	93.4	1	.6	152
N. Fermanagh, E. Donegal, Tyrone, Londonderry	11	3.4	304	95.6	3	.9	318
Total	415	4.6	8242	92.5	249	2.8	8906

TABLE IV-7. HAIR QUANTITY, HEAD BY COUNTY SUBGROUPS

	Submedium No.	%	Medium No.	%	Pronounced No.	%	Total No.
W. Donegal	4	1.9	206	97.2	2	.9	212
Mayo	11	1.9	556	95.9	13	2.2	580
Sligo, Leitrim, S.Fermanagh, W.Cavan	20	2.8	684	95.5	12	1.7	716
W. Galway	12	2.8	412	95.4	8	1.8	432
Aran Islands	1	.7	138	99.3	-	-	139
Clare	26	2.8	900	95.2	19	2.0	945
Kerry	18	3.3	517	95.9	4	.7	539
Cork	12	2.1	554	96.3	9	1.6	575
Limerick	18	5.3	308	90.8	13	3.8	339
E. Galway, Roscommon	18	3.5	481	93.4	16	3.1	515
Longford, Westmeath	9	1.3	630	93.5	35	5.2	674
Offaly, Leix, Kildare	5	.9	513	96.6	13	2.4	531
Tipperary, Kilkenny	22	3.4	617	94.9	11	1.7	650
Waterford, Wexford	9	1.9	447	96.5	7	1.5	463
Wicklow, Carlow	2	.7	264	95.0	12	4.3	278
Meath, Louth, Dublin	11	2.4	430	93.9	17	3.7	458
E. Cavan, Monaghan, Armagh	6	1.5	367	94.3	16	4.1	389
Antrim, Down	2	1.3	142	93.4	8	5.3	152
N. Fermanagh, E. Donegal, Tyrone, Londonderry	2	.6	302	95.0	14	4.4	318
Total	208	2.3	8468	95.1	229	2.6	8905

TABLE IV-8. HAIR QUANTITY, BEARD, BY COUNTY SUBGROUPS

	Very Small, submedium No	%	Medium No.	%	Pronounced, very pro. No.	%	Total No.
W. Donegal	7	3.3	205	96.7	-	-	212
Mayo	9	1.6	570	98.3	1	.2	580
Sligo, Leitrim, S.Fermanagh, W. Cavan	29	4.0	676	94.4	11	1.5	716
W. Galway	27	6.2	396	91.7	9	2.1	432
Aran Islands	23	16.5	114	82.0	2	1.4	139
Clare	25	2.6	903	95.4	18	1.9	946
Kerry	32	5.9	479	88.9	28	5.2	539
Cork	45	7.8	491	85.4	39	6.8	575
Limerick	19	5.6	305	90.0	15	4.4	339
E. Galway, Roscommon	15	2.9	493	95.7	7	1.4	515
Longford, Westmeath	82	12.1	585	86.5	9	1.3	676
Offaly, Leix, Kildare	44	8.3	468	88.1	19	3.6	531
Tipperary, Kilkenny	51	7.8	562	86.5	37	5.7	650
Waterford, Wexford	27	5.8	400	86.4	36	7.8	463
Wicklow, Carlow	13	4.7	257	92.4	8	2.9	278
Meath, Louth, Dublin	29	6.3	403	88.0	26	5.7	458
E. Cavan, Monaghan, Armagh	20	5.1	356	91.5	13	3.3	389
Antrim, Down	10	6.6	126	82.9	16	10.5	152
N. Fermanagh, E. Donegal, Tyrone, Londonderry	15	4.7	285	89.6	18	5.7	318
Total	522	5.8	8074	90.6	312	3.5	8908

TABLE IV-9. HAIR QUANTITY, BODY, BY COUNTY SUBGROUPS

	Absent No.	%	Submedium No.	%	Medium No.	%	Pronounced No.	%	Total No.
W. Donegal	-	-	6	2.8	206	97.2	-	-	212
Mayo	1	.2	9	1.6	569	98.1	1	.2	580
Sligo, Leitrim, S. Fermanagh, W. Cavan	4	.6	28	3.9	675	94.3	9	1.2	716
W. Galway	2	.5	28	6.5	395	91.4	7	1.6	432
Aran Islands	1	.7	22	15.8	113	81.3	3	2.2	139
Clare	1	.1	27	2.8	911	96.3	7	.7	946
Kerry	1	.2	32	5.9	481	89.2	25	4.6	539
Cork	-	-	41	7.1	503	87.5	31	5.4	575
Limerick	-	-	18	5.3	318	93.8	3	.9	339
E. Galway, Roscommon	2	.4	14	2.7	493	95.7	6	1.2	515
Longford, Westmeath	20	3.0	86	12.7	567	84.0	2	.3	675
Offaly, Leix, Kildare	1	.2	47	8.8	465	87.6	18	3.4	531
Tipperary, Kilkenny	-	-	52	8.0	570	87.7	28	4.3	650
Waterford, Wexford	-	-	27	5.8	408	88.1	28	6.0	463
Wicklow, Carlow	-	-	16	5.8	254	91.4	8	2.9	278
Meath, Louth, Dublin	-	-	29	6.3	405	88.4	24	5.2	458
E. Cavan, Monaghan, Armagh	-	-	21	5.4	356	91.5	12	3.1	389
Antrim, Down	-	-	10	6.6	130	85.5	12	7.9	152
N. Fermanagh, E. Donegal, Tyrone, Londonderry	-	-	15	4.7	293	92.1	10	3.1	318
Total	33	4	528	5.9	8112	91.1	234	2.6	8907

TABLE IV-10. BALDNESS BY COUNTY SUBGROUPS

	Absent No.	Absent %	Submedium No.	Submedium %	Medium No.	Medium %	Prounced No.	Prounced %	Total No.
W. Donegal	126	59.4	49	23.1	22	10.4	15	7.1	212
Mayo	336	58.0	134	23.1	69	11.9	40	6.9	579
Sligo, Leitrim, S. Fermanagh, W. Cavan	443	62.0	166	23.2	64	9.0	42	5.9	715
W. Galway	272	63.0	93	21.5	48	11.1	19	4.4	432
Aran Islands	83	59.7	25	18.0	28	20.1	3	2.2	139
Clare	519	54.9	256	27.1	99	10.5	72	7.6	946
Kerry	305	56.6	107	19.8	83	15.4	44	8.2	539
Cork	338	58.8	120	20.9	66	11.5	51	8.9	575
Limerick	196	58.0	81	24.0	44	13.0	17	5.0	338
E. Galway, Roscommon	321	62.3	131	25.4	40	7.8	23	4.5	515
Longford, Westmeath	464	68.6	132	19.5	62	9.2	18	2.7	676
Offaly, Leix, Kildare	341	64.2	120	22.6	37	7.0	33	6.2	531
Tipperary, Kilkenny	354	54.5	162	24.9	69	10.6	65	10.0	650
Waterford, Wexford	235	50.8	113	24.4	59	12.7	56	12.1	463
Wicklow, Carlow	150	54.0	52	18.7	39	14.0	37	13.3	278
Meath, Louth, Dublin	273	59.6	95	20.7	49	10.7	41	9.0	458
E. Cavan, Monaghan, Armagh	230	59.1	89	22.9	43	11.0	27	6.9	389
Antrim, Down	85	55.9	40	26.3	14	9.2	13	8.6	152
N. Fermanagh, E. Donegal, Tyrone, Londonderry	196	61.8	65	20.5	33	10.4	23	7.2	317
Total	5267	59.2	2030	22.8	968	10.9	639	7.2	8904

TABLE IV-11. GRAYNESS, HEAD, BY COUNTY SUBGROUPS

	Absent No.	Absent %	Submedium No.	Submedium %	Medium No.	Medium %	Pronounced No.	Pronounced %	Total No.
W. Donegal	124	58.5	47	22.2	14	6.6	27	12.7	212
Mayo	309	53.3	149	25.7	63	10.9	59	10.2	580
Sligo, Leitrim, S.Fermanagh, W.Cavan	412	57.5	127	17.7	99	13.8	78	10.9	716
W. Galway	231	53.5	103	23.8	61	14.1	37	8.6	432
Aran Islands	87	62.6	33	23.7	13	9.4	6	4.3	139
Clare	453	47.9	226	23.9	142	15.0	124	13.1	945
Kerry	269	49.9	115	21.3	86	16.0	69	12.8	539
Cork	286	49.8	127	22.1	92	16.0	69	12.0	574
Limerick	170	50.1	78	23.0	54	15.9	37	10.9	339
E. Galway, Roscommon	304	59.0	116	22.5	61	11.8	34	6.6	515
Longford, Westmeath	482	71.3	117	17.3	55	8.1	22	3.2	676
Offaly, Leix, Kildare	309	58.2	97	18.3	68	12.8	57	10.7	531
Tipperary, Kilkenny	330	50.8	145	22.3	89	13.7	86	13.2	650
Waterford, Wexford	198	42.8	98	21.2	74	16.0	93	20.1	463
Wicklow, Carlow	126	45.3	63	22.7	53	19.1	36	12.9	278
Meath, Louth, Dublin	247	53.9	98	21.4	60	13.1	53	11.6	458
E.Cavan, Monaghan, Armagh	201	51.7	83	21.3	68	17.5	37	9.5	389
Antrim, Down	92	60.5	33	21.7	17	11.2	10	6.6	152
N.Fermanagh, E. Donegal, Tyrone, Londonderry	183	57.5	79	24.8	31	9.7	25	7.9	318
Total	4813	54.0	1934	21.7	1200	13.5	959	10.8	8906

TABLE IV-12. GRAYNESS, BEARD, BY COUNTY SUBGROUPS

	Absent No.	Absent %	Submedium No.	Submedium %	Medium No.	Medium %	Pronounced No.	Pronounced %	Total No.
W. Donegal	158	74.5	10	4.7	25	11.8	19	9.0	212
Mayo	392	67.6	46	7.9	104	17.9	38	6.6	580
Sligo, Leitrim, S. Fermanagh, W. Cavan	480	67.1	70	9.8	99	13.8	66	9.2	715
W. Galway	292	67.6	38	8.8	69	16.0	33	7.6	432
Aran Islands	97	69.8	21	15.1	16	11.5	5	3.6	139
Clare	617	65.2	59	6.2	158	16.7	112	11.8	946
Kerry	323	59.9	48	8.9	96	17.8	72	13.4	539
Cork	356	61.9	54	9.4	96	16.7	69	12.0	575
Limerick	214	63.1	28	8.2	61	18.0	36	10.6	339
E. Galway, Roscommon	367	71.3	57	11.1	59	11.4	32	6.2	515
Longford, Westmeath	567	83.9	59	8.7	35	5.2	15	2.2	676
Offaly, Leix, Kildare	343	64.7	58	10.9	83	15.7	46	8.7	530
Tipperary, Kilkenny	396	60.9	79	12.2	118	18.2	57	8.8	650
Waterford, Wexford	245	52.9	45	9.7	84	18.1	89	19.2	463
Wicklow, Carlow	136	48.9	50	18.0	60	21.6	32	11.5	278
Meath, Louth, Dublin	282	61.6	61	13.3	70	15.3	45	9.8	458
E.Cavan, Monaghan, Armagh	228	58.8	54	13.9	75	19.3	31	8.0	388
Antrim, Down	102	67.1	22	14.5	20	13.2	8	5.3	152
N. Fermanagh, E.Donegal, Tyrone, Londonderry	218	68.6	41	12.9	33	10.4	26	8.2	318
Total	5813	65.3	900	10.1	1361	15.3	831	9.3	8905

TABLE IV-13. HAIR COLOR, HEAD, BY COUNTY SUBGROUPS

	Black No.	%	Dark brown No.	%	Brown No.	%	Red brown No.	%	Golden brown No.	%
W. Donegal	16	7.5	83	39.2	73	34.4	11	5.2	9	4.2
Mayo	20	3.4	261	45.0	184	31.7	34	5.9	30	5.2
Sligo, Leitrim, S. Fermanagh, W. Cavan	11	1.5	247	34.6	240	33.6	51	7.1	66	9.2
W. Galway	4	.9	168	38.9	145	33.6	35	8.1	46	10.6
Aran Islands	1	.7	31	23.0	66	48.9	15	11.1	10	7.4
Clare	40	4.2	367	38.8	322	34.1	69	7.3	64	6.8
Kerry	26	4.8	227	42.1	177	32.8	20	3.7	43	8.0
Cork	15	2.6	220	38.3	196	34.1	28	4.9	69	12.0
Limerick	8	2.4	139	41.0	115	33.9	22	6.5	28	8.2
E. Galway, Roscommon	6	1.2	167	32.4	203	39.4	35	6.8	53	10.3
Longford, Westmeath	2	.3	183	27.5	291	43.8	36	5.4	88	13.2
Offaly, Leix, Kildare	10	1.9	236	44.5	172	32.4	33	6.2	43	8.1
Tipperary, Kilkenny	15	2.3	285	43.8	200	30.8	31	4.8	64	9.8
Waterford, Wexford	16	3.4	216	46.6	118	25.5	16	3.4	59	12.7
Wicklow, Carlow	15	5.4	117	42.1	98	35.2	9	3.2	19	6.8
Meath, Louth, Dublin	16	3.5	207	45.2	163	35.6	7	1.5	36	7.9
E.Cavan, Monaghan, Armagh	14	3.6	182	46.8	144	37.0	8	2.0	21	5.4
Antrim, Down	2	1.3	71	46.7	54	35.5	4	2.6	13	8.6
N. Fermanagh, E.Donegal, Tyrone, Londonderry	9	2.8	129	40.6	121	38.0	5	1.6	32	10.1
Total	246	2.8	3536	39.8	3082	34.7	469	5.3	793	8.9

TABLE IV-13. HAIR COLOR, HEAD, BY COUNTY SUBGROUPS (Cont.)

	Ash brown No.	%	Golden No.	%	Ash No.	%	Red No.	%	White No.	%	Total No.
W. Donegal	-	-	1	.5	-	-	14	6.6	5	2.4	212
Mayo	2	.3	6	1.0	2	.3	29	5.0	12	2.1	580
Sligo, Leitrim, S. Fermanagh, W. Cavan	4	.6	4	.6	-	-	53	7.4	38	5.3	714
W. Galway	1	.2	3	.7	-	-	19	4.4	11	2.5	432
Aran Islands	-	-	-	-	-	-	9	6.7	3	2.2	135
Clare	3	.3	8	.8	-	-	45	4.8	27	2.8	945
Kerry	3	.6	11	2.0	-	-	16	3.0	16	3.0	539
Cork	-	-	9	1.6	1	.2	18	3.1	19	3.3	575
Limerick	1	.3	5	1.5	-	-	12	3.5	9	2.6	339
E. Galway, Roscommon	1	.2	5	1.0	-	-	28	5.4	17	3.3	515
Longford, Westmeath	8	1.2	8	1.2	5	.8	29	4.4	15	2.2	665
Offaly, Leix, Kildare	3	.6	4	.8	-	-	18	3.4	11	2.1	530
Tipperary, Kilkenny	2	.3	6	.9	1	.2	25	3.8	21	3.2	650
Waterford, Wexford	4	.9	3	.6	2	.4	7	1.5	22	4.8	463
Wicklow, Carlow	3	1.1	-	-	1	.4	9	3.2	7	2.5	278
Meath, Louth, Dublin	1	.2	1	.2	-	-	17	3.7	10	2.2	458
E.Cavan, Monaghan, Armagh	3	.8	3	.8	-	-	9	2.3	5	1.3	389
Antrim, Down	-	-	1	.6	-	-	4	2.6	3	2.0	152
N. Fermanagh, E.Donegal, Tyrone, Londonderry	3	.9	3	.9	1	.3	9	2.8	6	1.9	318
Total	42	.5	81	.9	13	.1	370	4.2	257	2.9	8889

TABLE IV-14. EYE COLOR BY COUNTY SUBGROUPS

	Dark brown, Dark-light brown Light brown No.	%	Gray-brown No.	%	Green-brown No.	%	Blue-brown No.	%
W. Donegal	-	-	10	4.7	6	2.8	105	49.5
Mayo	1	.2	23	4.0	15	2.6	287	49.5
Sligo, Leitrim, S. Fermanagh, W. Cavan	7	1.0	17	2.4	25	3.5	323	45.1
W. Galway	1	.2	20	4.6	13	3.0	191	44.2
Aran Islands	-	-	1	.7	-	-	77	55.4
Clare	-	-	59	6.2	17	1.8	434	45.9
Kerry	1	.2	28	5.2	17	3.2	294	54.5
Cork	2	.3	36	6.3	8	1.4	316	55.0
Limerick	1	.3	17	5.0	6	1.8	167	49.1
E. Galway, Roscommon	1	.2	17	3.3	15	2.9	227	44.1
Longford, Westmeath	8	1.2	33	4.9	29	4.3	280	41.4
Offaly, Leix, Kildare	6	1.1	27	5.1	25	4.7	213	40.1
Tipperary, Kilkenny	2	.3	39	6.0	26	4.0	277	42.6
Waterford, Wexford	2	.4	35	7.6	31	6.7	151	32.6
Wicklow, Carlow	1	.4	13	4.7	13	4.7	94	33.8
Meath, Louth, Dublin	6	1.3	28	6.1	20	4.4	175	38.2
E.Cavan, Monaghan, Armagh	1	.2	10	2.6	10	2.6	148	38.0
Antrim, Down	1	.6	10	6.6	12	7.9	51	33.6
N. Fermanagh, E.Donegal, Tyrone, Londonderry	-	-	18	5.7	11	3.4	103	32.4
Total	41	.5	441	5.0	299	3.4	3913	43.9

TABLE IV-14. EYE COLOR BY COUNTY SUBGROUPS (Continued)

	Gray, gray-blue		Blue		Unmatched		Total
	No.	%	No.	%	No.	%	No.
W. Donegal	5	2.4	85	40.1	1	.5	212
Mayo	16	2.8	236	40.7	2	.3	580
Sligo, Leitrim, S. Fermanagh, W. Cavan	22	3.1	318	44.4	4	.6	716
W. Galway	14	3.2	192	44.4	1	.2	432
Aran Islands	3	2.2	58	41.7	–	–	139
Clare	42	4.4	391	41.3	3	.3	946
Kerry	8	1.5	186	34.5	5	.9	539
Cork	17	3.0	192	33.4	4	.7	575
Limerick	10	2.9	138	40.6	1	.3	340
E. Galway, Roscommon	15	2.9	237	46.0	3	.6	515
Longford, Westmeath	48	7.1	278	41.1	–	–	676
Offaly, Leix, Kildare	37	7.0	221	41.6	2	.4	531
Tipperary, Kilkenny	41	6.3	261	40.2	4	.6	650
Waterford, Wexford	29	6.3	213	46.0	2	.4	463
Wicklow, Carlow	18	6.5	138	49.6	1	.4	278
Meath, Louth, Dublin	27	5.9	201	43.9	1	.2	458
E.Cavan, Monaghan, Armagh	14	3.6	200	51.4	6	1.5	389
Antrim, Down	6	3.9	70	46.0	2	1.3	152
N. Fermanagh, E.Donegal, Tyrone, Londonderry	25	7.9	159	50.0	2	.6	318
Total	397	4.4	3774	42.4	44	.5	8909

TABLE IV-15. PIGMENT, MIXED EYES, BY COUNTY SUBGROUPS

	Very pronouncedly dark		Pronouncedly dark		Even		Pronouncedly light		Very pronouncedly light		Total
	No.	%	No.	%	No.	%	No.	%	No.	%	No.
W. Donegal	4	3.2	10	8.0	12	9.6	27	21.6	72	57.6	125
Mayo	11	3.2	13	3.8	39	11.5	60	17.7	216	63.7	339
Sligo, Leitrim, S. Fermanagh, W. Cavan	16	4.2	28	7.3	31	8.1	81	21.2	225	59.0	381
W. Galway	6	2.5	17	7.2	31	13.1	37	15.7	145	61.4	236
Aran Islands	1	1.3	6	7.6	6	7.6	22	27.8	44	55.7	79
Clare	20	3.6	31	5.6	64	11.7	113	20.6	320	58.4	548
Kerry	8	2.3	26	7.5	38	11.0	65	18.8	209	60.4	346
Cork	6	1.6	20	5.3	45	12.0	58	15.5	246	65.6	375
Limerick	5	2.5	8	4.0	17	8.5	41	20.6	128	64.3	199
E. Galway, Roscommon	10	3.7	14	5.1	28	10.2	63	23.1	158	57.9	273
Longford, Westmeath	16	4.2	35	9.2	72	18.9	57	15.0	200	52.6	380
Offaly, Leix, Kildare	7	2.4	30	10.1	40	13.5	39	13.2	180	60.8	296
Tipperary, Kilkenny	7	1.8	30	7.8	48	12.5	68	17.8	230	60.0	383
Waterford, Wexford	14	5.7	35	14.2	33	13.4	39	15.8	125	50.8	246
Wicklow, Carlow	3	2.2	10	7.4	16	11.8	19	14.1	87	64.4	135
Meath, Louth, Dublin	12	4.9	15	6.1	46	18.8	37	15.2	134	54.9	244
E.Cavan, Monaghan, Armagh	4	2.2	11	6.1	24	13.2	30	16.6	112	61.9	181
Antrim, Down	6	7.7	10	12.8	10	12.8	13	16.7	39	50.0	78
N. Fermanagh, E.Donegal, Tyrone, Londonderry	3	2.0	12	7.8	20	13.1	26	17.0	92	60.1	153
Total	159	3.2	361	7.2	620	12.4	895	17.9	2962	59.3	4997

TABLE IV-16. IRIS BY COUNTY SUBGROUPS

	Clear		Rayed		Zoned		Spotted	
	No.	%	No.	%	No.	%	No.	%
W. Donegal	49	23.3	49	23.3	4	1.9	2	1.0
Mayo	145	25.1	95	16.4	5	.9	19	3.3
Sligo, Leitrim, S. Fermanagh, W. Cavan	203	28.5	133	18.7	10	1.4	14	2.0
W. Galway	110	25.8	86	20.1	16	3.7	11	2.6
Aran Islands	53	38.1	33	23.7	5	3.6	5	3.6
Clare	178	18.9	169	17.9	17	1.8	24	2.5
Kerry	47	8.8	117	21.9	5	.9	14	2.6
Cork	89	15.6	116	20.3	5	.9	19	3.3
Limerick	66	19.5	68	20.1	3	.9	9	2.7
E. Galway, Roscommon	152	29.5	83	16.1	9	1.7	15	2.9
Longford, Westmeath	275	40.7	167	24.7	28	4.1	3	.5
Offaly, Leix, Kildare	121	23.0	155	29.5	14	2.7	25	4.8
Tipperary, Kilkenny	100	15.4	156	24.1	5	.8	24	3.7
Waterford, Wexford	76	16.5	161	34.9	1	.2	23	5.0
Wicklow, Carlow	45	16.3	72	26.1	5	1.8	12	4.3
Meath, Louth, Dublin	99	21.6	107	23.4	10	2.2	11	2.4
E.Cavan, Monaghan, Armagh	78	20.4	85	22.2	3	.8	7	1.8
Antrim, Down	29	19.3	30	20.0	2	1.3	4	2.7
N. Fermanagh, E.Donegal, Tyrone, Londonderry	60	18.9	68	21.4	2	.6	7	2.2
Total	1975	22.3	1950	22.0	149	1.7	248	2.8

TABLE IV-16. IRIS BY COUNTY SUBGROUPS (Continued)

	Diffuse		Scalloped		Total
	No.	%	No.	%	No.
W. Donegal	85	40.5	21	10.0	210
Mayo	242	41.9	72	12.4	578
Sligo, Leitrim, S. Fermanagh, W. Cavan	230	32.3	122	17.1	712
W. Galway	138	32.3	66	15.4	427
Aran Islands	23	16.5	20	14.4	139
Clare	370	39.2	185	19.6	943
Kerry	223	41.7	129	24.1	535
Cork	232	40.6	110	19.3	571
Limerick	125	37.0	67	19.8	338
E. Galway, Roscommon	168	32.6	88	17.1	515
Longford, Westmeath	170	25.1	33	4.9	676
Offaly, Leix, Kildare	126	24.0	85	16.2	526
Tipperary, Kilkenny	211	32.6	151	23.3	647
Waterford, Wexford	124	26.9	76	16.5	461
Wicklow, Carlow	60	21.7	82	29.7	276
Meath, Louth, Dublin	127	27.7	104	22.7	458
E.Cavan, Monaghan, Armagh	104	27.2	106	27.7	383
Antrim, Down	51	34.0	34	22.7	150
N. Fermanagh, E.Donegal, Tyrone, Londonderry	76	24.0	104	32.8	317
Total	2885	32.6	1655	18.7	8862

TABLE IV-17. EYEFOLDS, EXTERNAL, BY COUNTY SUBGROUPS

	Absent		Submedium		Medium		Pronounced		Total
	No.	%	No.	%	No.	%	No.	%	No.
W. Donegal	194	91.5	15	7.1	3	1.4	-	-	212
Mayo	503	86.7	30	5.2	43	7.4	4	.7	580
Sligo, Leitrim, S. Fermanagh, W. Cavan	619	86.6	56	7.8	31	4.3	9	1.2	715
W. Galway	378	87.5	9	2.1	40	9.3	5	1.2	432
Aran Islands	124	89.2	8	5.8	3	2.2	4	2.9	139
Clare	822	86.9	63	6.6	53	5.6	8	.8	946
Kerry	488	90.5	22	4.1	27	5.0	2	.4	539
Cork	496	86.3	33	5.7	36	6.3	10	1.7	575
Limerick	298	87.6	18	5.3	21	6.2	3	.9	340
E. Galway, Roscommon	452	87.8	28	5.4	23	4.5	12	2.3	515
Longford, Westmeath	597	88.3	38	5.6	26	3.8	15	2.2	676
Offaly, Leix, Kildare	455	85.7	35	6.6	37	7.0	4	.8	531
Tipperary, Kilkenny	520	80.0	62	9.5	58	8.9	10	1.5	650
Waterford, Wexford	385	83.2	41	8.8	29	6.3	8	1.7	463
Wicklow, Carlow	254	91.4	14	5.0	10	3.6	-	-	278
Meath, Louth, Dublin	400	87.3	29	6.3	26	5.7	3	.6	458
E.Cavan, Monaghan, Armagh	335	86.1	38	9.8	12	3.1	4	1.0	389
Antrim, Down	132	86.8	11	7.2	8	5.3	1	.6	152
N. Fermanagh, E.Donegal, Tyrone, Londonderry	270	84.9	26	8.2	18	5.7	4	1.2	318
Total	7722	86.7	576	6.5	504	5.6	106	1.2	8908

TABLE IV-18. EYEFOLDS, MEDIAN, BY COUNTY SUBGROUPS

	Absent		Submedium		Medium		Pronounced		Total
	No.	%	No.	%	No.	%	No.	%	No.
W. Donegal	209	98.6	-	-	2	.9	1	.5	212
Mayo	564	97.2	4	.7	9	1.6	3	.5	580
Sligo, Leitrim, S. Fermanagh, W. Cavan	696	97.2	11	1.5	8	1.1	1	.1	716
W. Galway	422	97.7	7	1.6	3	.7	-	-	432
Aran Islands	137	98.6	1	.7	-	-	1	.7	139
Clare	926	97.9	5	.5	11	1.2	4	.4	946
Kerry	531	98.5	2	.4	5	.9	1	.2	539
Cork	556	96.7	4	.7	8	1.4	7	1.2	575
Limerick	335	98.5	-	-	1	.3	4	1.2	340
E. Galway, Roscommon	500	97.5	4	.8	5	1.0	4	.8	513
Longford, Westmeath	646	95.6	13	1.9	9	1.3	8	1.2	676
Offaly, Leix, Kildare	513	96.6	6	1.1	10	1.9	2	.4	531
Tipperary, Kilkenny	613	94.3	12	1.8	18	2.8	7	1.1	650
Waterford, Wexford	451	97.4	5	1.1	4	.9	3	.6	463
Wicklow, Carlow	268	96.4	4	1.4	6	2.2	-	-	278
Meath, Louth, Dublin	445	97.2	4	.9	7	1.5	2	.4	458
E.Cavan, Monaghan, Armagh	376	96.6	7	1.8	6	1.5	-	-	389
Antrim, Down	147	96.7	3	2.0	2	1.3	-	-	152
N. Fermanagh, E.Donegal, Tyrone, Londonderry	309	97.2	3	.9	4	1.2	2	.6	318
Total	8644	97.0	95	1.1	118	1.3	50	.6	8907

TABLE IV-19. EYEFOLDS, INTERNAL, BY COUNTY SUBGROUPS

	Absent		Submedium		Medium, pronounced		Total
	No.	%	No.	%	No.	%	No.
W. Donegal	207	97.6	5	2.4	-	-	212
Mayo	575	99.1	4	.7	1	.2	580
Sligo, Leitrim, S. Fermanagh, W. Cavan	711	99.4	4	.6	-	-	715
W. Galway	430	99.5	2	.5	-	-	432
Aran Islands	138	99.3	-	-	1	.7	139
Clare	944	99.8	2	.2	-	-	946
Kerry	536	99.4	2	.4	1	.2	539
Cork	571	99.5	3	.5	-	-	574
Limerick	340	100.0	-	-	-	-	340
E. Galway, Roscommon	511	99.2	2	.4	2	.4	515
Longford, Westmeath	659	97.5	15	2.2	2	.3	676
Offaly, Leix, Kildare	521	98.1	9	1.7	1	.2	531
Tipperary, Kilkenny	643	98.9	7	1.1	-	-	650
Waterford, Wexford	462	99.8	1	.2	-	-	463
Wicklow, Carlow	275	98.9	3	1.1	-	-	278
Meath, Louth, Dublin	452	98.9	2	.4	3	.6	457
E.Cavan, Monaghan, Armagh	381	97.9	8	2.0	-	-	389
Antrim, Down	151	99.3	1	.6	-	-	152
N. Fermanagh, E.Donegal, Tyrone, Londonderry	312	98.4	5	1.6	-	-	317
Total	8819	99.0	75	.8	11	.1	8905

TABLE IV-20. EYE OBLIQUITY BY COUNTY SUBGROUPS

	Absent		Submedium		Medium		Pronounced		Down		Total
	No.	%	No.	%	No.	%	No.	%	No.	%	No.
W. Donegal	142	67.0	42	19.8	11	5.2	1	.5	16	7.5	212
Mayo	433	74.6	94	16.2	25	4.3	2	.3	26	4.5	580
Sligo, Leitrim, S. Fermanagh, W. Cavan	517	72.2	127	17.7	32	4.5	1	.1	39	5.4	716
W. Galway	318	73.6	58	13.4	17	3.9	4	.9	35	8.1	432
Aran Islands	126	90.6	7	5.0	4	2.9	-	-	2	1.4	139
Clare	657	69.4	177	18.7	31	3.3	6	.6	75	7.9	946
Kerry	331	61.4	137	25.4	31	5.8	4	.7	36	6.7	539
Cork	375	65.2	137	23.8	26	4.5	8	1.4	29	5.0	575
Limerick	213	62.6	79	23.2	24	7.0	4	1.2	20	5.9	340
E. Galway, Roscommon	375	72.8	88	17.1	22	4.3	2	.4	28	5.4	515
Longford, Westmeath	568	84.0	58	8.6	24	3.6	-	-	26	3.8	676
Offaly, Leix, Kildare	285	53.7	179	33.7	39	7.3	-	-	28	5.3	531
Tipperary, Kilkenny	359	55.2	216	33.2	33	5.1	7	1.1	35	5.4	650
Waterford, Wexford	249	53.8	157	33.9	31	6.7	4	.9	22	4.8	463
Wicklow, Carlow	131	47.1	110	39.6	18	6.5	3	1.1	16	5.8	278
Meath, Louth, Dublin	255	55.7	154	33.6	19	4.1	3	.6	27	5.9	458
E.Cavan, Monaghan, Armagh	189	48.6	152	39.1	15	3.8	3	.8	30	7.7	389
Antrim, Down	73	48.0	64	42.1	4	2.6	3	2.0	8	5.3	152
N. Fermanagh, E.Donegal, Tyrone, Londonderry	142	44.6	137	43.1	15	4.7	2	.6	22	6.9	318
Total	5738	64.4	2173	24.4	421	4.7	57	.6	520	5.8	8909

TABLE IV-21. EYE OPENING HEIGHT BY COUNTY SUBGROUPS

	Submedium		Medium		Pronounced		Total
	No.	%	No.	%	No.	%	No.
W. Donegal	6	2.8	197	92.9	9	4.2	212
Mayo	26	4.5	539	92.9	15	2.6	580
Sligo, Leitrim, S. Fermanagh, W. Cavan	45	6.3	651	90.9	20	2.8	716
W. Galway	36	8.3	388	89.8	8	1.8	432
Aran Islands	6	4.3	132	95.0	1	.7	139
Clare	71	7.5	859	91.1	13	1.4	943
Kerry	19	3.5	499	92.6	21	3.9	539
Cork	33	5.7	524	91.1	18	3.1	575
Limerick	13	3.8	315	92.6	12	3.5	340
E. Galway, Roscommon	21	4.1	485	94.2	9	1.7	515
Longford, Westmeath	40	6.0	603	89.7	29	4.3	672
Offaly, Leix, Kildare	34	6.4	481	90.6	16	3.0	531
Tipperary, Kilkenny	37	5.7	585	90.0	28	4.3	650
Waterford, Wexford	53	11.4	394	85.1	16	3.4	463
Wicklow, Carlow	18	6.5	250	89.9	10	3.6	278
Meath, Louth, Dublin	25	5.5	418	91.5	14	3.1	457
E.Cavan, Monaghan, Armagh	24	6.2	352	90.5	13	3.3	389
Antrim, Down	10	6.6	139	91.4	3	2.0	152
N. Fermanagh, E.Donegal, Tyrone, Londonderry	16	5.0	292	91.8	10	3.1	318
Total	533	6.0	8103	91.0	265	3.0	8901

TABLE IV-22. EYEBROW THICKNESS BY COUNTY SUBGROUPS

	Submedium		Medium		Pronounced, very pro.		Total
	No.	%	No.	%	No.	%	No.
W. Donegal	2	.9	208	98.1	2	.9	212
Mayo	9	1.6	563	97.1	8	1.4	580
Sligo, Leitrim, S. Fermanagh, W. Cavan	6	.8	689	96.2	21	2.9	716
W. Galway	10	2.3	401	92.8	21	4.9	432
Aran Islands	4	2.9	131	94.2	4	2.9	139
Clare	36	3.8	888	93.9	22	2.3	946
Kerry	16	3.0	507	94.1	16	3.0	539
Cork	16	2.8	538	93.6	21	3.6	575
Limerick	12	3.5	314	92.6	13	3.8	339
E. Galway, Roscommon	8	1.6	481	93.4	26	5.0	515
Longford, Westmeath	21	3.1	622	92.0	33	4.9	676
Offaly, Leix, Kildare	25	4.7	481	90.6	25	4.7	531
Tipperary, Kilkenny	23	3.5	604	92.9	23	3.5	650
Waterford, Wexford	31	6.7	416	89.8	16	3.4	463
Wicklow, Carlow	15	5.4	249	89.6	14	5.0	278
Meath, Louth, Dublin	19	4.1	410	89.5	29	6.3	458
E.Cavan, Monaghan, Armagh	18	4.6	359	92.3	12	3.1	389
Antrim, Down	2	1.3	144	94.7	6	3.9	152
N. Fermanagh, E.Donegal, Tyrone, Londonderry	14	4.4	291	91.5	13	4.1	318
Total	287	3.2	8296	93.1	325	3.6	8908

TABLE IV-23. EYEBROW CONCURRENCY BY COUNTY SUBGROUPS

	Absent		Submedium		Medium		Pronounced		Total
	No.	%	No.	%	No.	%	No.	%	No.
W. Donegal	1	.5	52	24.5	141	66.5	18	8.5	212
Mayo	8	1.4	123	21.2	417	71.9	32	5.5	580
Sligo, Leitrim, S. Fermanagh, W. Cavan	11	1.5	156	21.8	465	64.9	84	11.7	716
W. Galway	12	2.8	81	18.8	298	69.0	41	9.5	432
Aran Islands	1	.7	29	20.9	92	66.2	17	12.2	139
Clare	24	2.5	201	21.2	633	66.9	88	9.3	946
Kerry	8	1.5	130	24.1	356	66.0	45	8.3	539
Cork	8	1.4	138	24.0	379	65.9	50	8.7	575
Limerick	5	1.5	91	26.8	216	63.7	27	8.0	339
E. Galway, Roscommon	16	3.1	83	16.1	349	67.8	67	13.0	515
Longford, Westmeath	14	2.1	152	22.5	428	63.3	82	12.1	676
Offaly, Leix, Kildare	10	1.9	142	26.7	313	58.9	66	12.4	531
Tipperary, Kilkenny	10	1.5	158	24.3	424	65.2	58	8.9	650
Waterford, Wexford	9	1.9	130	28.1	282	60.9	42	9.1	463
Wicklow, Carlow	5	1.8	75	27.0	174	62.6	24	8.6	278
Meath, Louth, Dublin	5	1.1	120	26.2	263	57.4	70	15.3	458
E.Cavan, Monaghan, Armagh	4	1.0	117	30.1	223	57.3	45	11.6	389
Antrim, Down	1	.6	27	17.8	109	71.7	15	9.9	152
N. Fermanagh, E.Donegal, Tyrone, Londonderry	4	1.2	64	20.1	205	64.5	45	14.2	318
Total	156	1.8	2069	23.2	5767	64.7	916	10.3	8908

TABLE IV-24. BROW RIDGES BY COUNTY SUBGROUPS

	Absent		Submedium		Medium		Pronounced		Very pro.		Total
	No.	%	No.	%	No.	%	No.	%	No.	%	No.
W. Donegal	5	2.4	51	24.0	120	56.6	35	16.5	1	.5	212
Mayo	5	.9	106	18.3	389	67.1	78	13.4	2	.3	580
Sligo, Leitrim, S. Fermanagh, W. Cavan	12	1.7	140	19.6	437	61.0	126	17.6	1	.1	716
W. Galway	2	.5	75	17.4	306	70.8	49	11.3	-	-	432
Aran Islands	-	-	25	18.0	67	48.2	46	33.1	1	.7	139
Clare	3	.3	151	16.0	618	65.3	172	18.2	2	.2	946
Kerry	9	1.7	89	16.5	291	54.0	147	27.3	3	.6	539
Cork	9	1.6	69	12.0	352	61.3	142	24.7	2	.3	574
Limerick	5	1.5	67	19.7	211	62.0	55	16.2	2	.6	340
E. Galway, Roscommon	1	.2	77	15.0	326	63.3	110	21.4	1	.2	515
Longford, Westmeath	1	.1	124	18.4	413	61.2	129	19.1	8	1.2	675
Offaly, Leix, Kildare	26	4.9	114	21.5	274	51.6	115	21.6	2	.4	531
Tipperary, Kilkenny	20	3.1	128	19.7	326	50.2	174	26.8	2	.3	650
Waterford, Wexford	17	3.7	68	14.7	271	58.5	106	22.9	1	.2	463
Wicklow, Carlow	10	3.6	73	26.2	130	46.8	62	22.3	3	1.1	278
Meath, Louth, Dublin	18	3.9	118	25.8	215	46.9	104	22.7	3	.6	458
E.Cavan, Monaghan, Armagh	27	6.9	125	32.1	192	49.4	45	11.6	-	-	389
Antrim, Down	3	2.0	37	24.3	69	45.4	43	28.3	-	-	152
N. Fermanagh, E.Donegal, Tyrone, Londonderry	22	6.9	88	27.7	128	40.2	80	25.2	-	-	318
Total	195	2.2	1725	19.4	5135	57.6	1818	20.4	34	.4	8907

TABLE IV-25. FOREHEAD HEIGHT BY COUNTY SUBGROUPS

	Submedium		Medium		Pronounced		Total
	No.	%	No.	%	No.	%	No.
W. Donegal	6	2.8	73	34.4	133	62.7	212
Mayo	17	2.9	250	43.2	312	53.9	579
Sligo, Leitrim, S. Fermanagh, W. Cavan	36	5.0	333	46.5	347	48.5	716
W. Galway	9	2.1	250	57.9	173	40.0	432
Aran Islands	5	3.6	100	71.9	34	24.5	139
Clare	28	3.0	541	57.2	377	39.8	946
Kerry	20	3.7	172	31.9	347	64.4	539
Cork	24	4.2	205	35.6	346	60.2	575
Limerick	18	5.3	122	35.9	200	58.8	340
E. Galway, Roscommon	18	3.5	258	50.3	237	46.2	513
Longford, Westmeath	46	6.8	387	57.6	239	35.6	672
Offaly, Leix, Kildare	21	4.0	188	35.4	322	60.6	531
Tipperary, Kilkenny	28	4.3	213	32.8	409	62.9	650
Waterford, Wexford	17	3.7	178	38.4	268	57.9	463
Wicklow, Carlow	10	3.6	91	32.7	177	63.7	278
Meath, Louth, Dublin	14	3.0	155	33.8	289	63.1	458
E.Cavan, Monaghan, Armagh	8	2.0	122	31.4	259	66.6	389
Antrim, Down	4	2.6	46	30.3	102	67.1	152
N. Fermanagh, E.Donegal, Tyrone, Londonderry	4	1.2	102	32.1	212	66.7	318
Total	333	3.7	3786	42.5	4783	53.7	8902

TABLE IV-26. FOREHEAD SLOPE BY COUNTY SUBGROUPS

	Forward		Absent		Submedium		Medium	
	No.	%	No.	%	No.	%	No.	%
W. Donegal	1	.5	17	8.0	121	57.1	62	29.2
Mayo	7	1.2	44	7.6	301	51.9	191	32.8
Sligo, Leitrim, S. Fermanagh, W. Cavan	18	2.5	47	6.6	344	48.0	276	38.5
W. Galway	5	1.2	14	3.2	168	38.9	207	47.9
Aran Islands	1	.7	4	2.9	32	23.0	92	66.2
Clare	7	.7	38	4.0	391	41.4	447	47.3
Kerry	3	.6	27	5.0	274	50.8	200	37.1
Cork	2	.3	30	5.2	251	43.6	234	40.7
Limerick	4	1.2	30	8.8	157	46.2	119	35.0
E. Galway, Roscommon	7	1.4	23	4.5	214	41.6	236	45.8
Longford, Westmeath	14	2.1	48	7.1	226	33.4	352	52.1
Offaly, Leix, Kildare	7	1.3	38	7.2	247	46.5	204	38.4
Tipperary, Kilkenny	10	1.5	68	10.5	311	47.8	204	31.4
Waterford, Wexford	6	1.3	33	7.1	196	42.3	171	36.9
Wicklow, Carlow	1	.4	16	5.8	131	47.1	100	36.0
Meath, Louth, Dublin	3	.6	31	6.8	222	48.5	168	36.7
E.Cavan, Monaghan, Armagh	6	1.5	36	9.2	208	53.5	113	29.0
Antrim, Down	-	-	6	3.9	84	55.3	46	30.3
N. Fermanagh, E.Donegal, Tyrone, Londonderry	4	1.2	37	11.6	170	53.4	81	25.5
Total	106	1.2	587	6.6	4048	45.4	3503	39.3

TABLE IV-26. FOREHEAD SLOPE BY COUNTY SUBGROUPS (Continued)

	Pronounced		Very pro.		Total
	No.	%	No.	%	No.
W. Donegal	11	5.2	-	-	212
Mayo	37	6.4	-	-	580
Sligo, Leitrim, S. Fermanagh, W. Cavan	31	4.3	-	-	716
W. Galway	38	8.8	-	-	432
Aran Islands	10	7.2	-	-	139
Clare	62	6.6	-	-	945
Kerry	35	6.5	-	-	539
Cork	58	10.1	-	-	575
Limerick	30	8.8	-	-	340
E. Galway, Roscommon	35	6.8	-	-	515
Longford, Westmeath	35	5.2	1	.1	676
Offaly, Leix, Kildare	33	6.2	2	.4	531
Tipperary, Kilkenny	52	8.0	5	.8	650
Waterford, Wexford	52	11.2	5	1.1	463
Wicklow, Carlow	27	9.7	3	1.1	278
Meath, Louth, Dublin	33	7.2	1	.2	458
E.Cavan, Monaghan, Armagh	24	6.2	2	.5	389
Antrim, Down	15	9.9	1	.6	152
N. Fermanagh, E.Donegal, Tyrone, Londonderry	24	7.5	2	.6	318
Total	642	7.2	22	.2	8908

TABLE IV-27. NASION DEPRESSION BY COUNTY SUBGROUPS

	Absent No.	Absent %	Very small No.	Very small %	Submedium No.	Submedium %	Medium No.	Medium %
W. Donegal	-	-	1	.5	31	14.6	130	61.3
Mayo	1	.2	2	.3	91	15.7	335	57.8
Sligo, Leitrim, S. Fermanagh, W. Cavan	2	.3	14	2.0	119	16.6	463	64.7
W. Galway	-	-	3	.7	61	14.2	297	69.1
Aran Islands	1	.7	-	-	23	16.5	88	63.3
Clare	1	.1	11	1.2	134	14.2	604	63.8
Kerry	-	-	3	.6	50	9.3	309	57.3
Cork	2	.3	9	1.6	54	9.4	338	58.8
Limerick	-	-	10	2.9	40	11.8	205	60.3
E. Galway, Roscommon	-	-	9	1.7	84	16.3	328	63.7
Longford, Westmeath	7	1.0	14	2.1	140	20.7	420	62.1
Offaly, Leix, Kildare	-	-	2	.4	61	11.5	329	62.0
Tipperary, Kilkenny	1	.2	17	2.6	76	11.7	371	57.1
Waterford, Wexford	1	.2	8	1.7	47	10.2	275	59.4
Wicklow, Carlow	2	.7	1	.4	25	9.0	164	59.0
Meath, Louth, Dublin	1	.2	14	3.0	60	13.1	265	57.9
E.Cavan, Monaghan, Armagh	1	.2	5	1.3	34	8.7	257	66.1
Antrim, Down	-	-	1	.6	15	9.9	77	50.6
N. Fermanagh, E.Donegal, Tyrone, Londonderry	-	-	9	2.8	36	11.3	158	49.7
Total	20	.2	133	1.5	1181	13.2	5413	60.8

TABLE IV-27. NASION DEPRESSION BY COUNTY SUBGROUPS (Continued)

	Pronounced No.	Pronounced %	Very pro. No.	Very pro. %	Total No.
W. Donegal	50	23.6	-	-	212
Mayo	147	25.3	4	.7	580
Sligo, Leitrim, S. Fermanagh, W. Cavan	108	15.1	10	1.4	716
W. Galway	63	14.6	6	1.4	430
Aran Islands	27	19.4	-	-	139
Clare	187	19.8	9	1.0	946
Kerry	166	30.8	11	2.0	539
Cork	157	27.3	15	2.6	575
Limerick	82	24.1	3	.9	340
E. Galway, Roscommon	92	17.9	2	.4	515
Longford, Westmeath	93	13.8	2	.3	676
Offaly, Leix, Kildare	129	24.3	10	1.9	531
Tipperary, Kilkenny	174	26.8	11	1.7	650
Waterford, Wexford	125	27.0	7	1.5	463
Wicklow, Carlow	81	29.1	5	1.8	278
Meath, Louth, Dublin	110	24.0	8	1.7	458
E.Cavan, Monaghan, Armagh	86	22.1	6	1.5	389
Antrim, Down	57	37.5	2	1.3	152
N. Fermanagh, E.Donegal, Tyrone, Londonderry	107	33.6	8	2.5	318
Total	2041	22.9	119	1.3	8907

TABLE IV-28. NASAL ROOT HEIGHT BY COUNTY SUBGROUPS

	Very small, submedium No.	Very small, submedium %	Medium No.	Medium %	Pronounced No.	Pronounced %	Very pro. No.	Very pro. %	Total No.
W. Donegal	8	3.8	154	72.6	50	23.6	-	-	212
Mayo	24	4.1	465	80.2	89	15.3	2	.3	580
Sligo, Leitrim, S. Fermanagh, W. Cavan	25	3.5	549	76.7	139	19.4	3	.4	716
W. Galway	11	2.5	352	81.5	68	15.7	1	.2	432
Aran Islands	-	-	101	72.7	38	27.3	-	-	139
Clare	20	2.1	766	81.0	149	15.8	10	1.0	945
Kerry	19	3.5	406	75.5	103	19.1	10	1.8	538
Cork	13	2.3	437	76.0	118	20.5	7	1.2	575
Limerick	6	1.8	269	79.1	63	18.5	2	.6	340
E. Galway, Roscommon	12	2.3	380	73.8	113	21.9	10	1.9	515
Longford, Westmeath	31	4.6	548	81.1	94	13.9	3	.4	676
Offaly, Leix, Kildare	17	3.2	436	82.1	77	14.5	1	.2	531
Tipperary, Kilkenny	19	2.9	461	71.1	160	24.7	8	1.2	648
Waterford, Wexford	12	2.6	333	72.1	114	24.7	3	.6	462
Wicklow, Carlow	8	2.9	198	71.2	65	23.4	7	2.5	278
Meath, Louth, Dublin	16	3.5	331	72.3	107	23.4	4	.9	458
E.Cavan, Monaghan, Armagh	13	3.3	313	80.5	61	15.7	2	.5	389
Antrim, Down	2	1.3	125	82.2	24	15.8	1	.6	152
N. Fermanagh, E.Donegal, Tyrone, Londonderry	12	3.8	253	79.6	53	16.7	-	-	318
Total	268	3.0	6877	77.2	1685	18.9	74	.8	8904

TABLE IV-29. NASAL ROOT BREADTH BY COUNTY SUBGROUPS

	Very small, submedium		Medium		Pronounced		Very pro.		Total
	No.	%	No.	%	No.	%	No.	%	No.
W. Donegal	10	4.7	144	67.9	57	26.9	1	.5	212
Mayo	11	1.9	410	70.7	154	26.6	5	.9	580
Sligo, Leitrim, S. Fermanagh, W. Cavan	19	2.6	542	75.8	151	21.1	3	.4	715
W. Galway	8	1.8	317	73.4	105	24.3	2	.5	432
Aran Islands	6	4.3	100	71.9	33	23.7	-	-	139
Clare	20	2.1	724	76.6	195	20.6	6	.6	945
Kerry	15	2.8	393	73.0	121	22.5	9	1.7	538
Cork	9	1.6	415	72.2	147	25.6	4	.7	575
Limerick	7	2.0	259	76.2	71	20.9	3	.9	340
E. Galway, Roscommon	10	1.9	388	75.3	115	22.3	2	.4	515
Longford, Westmeath	12	1.8	572	84.6	91	13.5	1	.1	676
Offaly, Leix, Kildare	10	1.9	380	71.6	140	26.4	1	.2	531
Tipperary, Kilkenny	9	1.4	413	63.7	215	33.2	11	1.7	648
Waterford, Wexford	12	2.6	279	60.4	161	34.8	10	2.2	462
Wicklow, Carlow	10	3.6	186	66.9	78	28.0	4	1.4	278
Meath, Louth, Dublin	3	.6	321	70.1	130	28.4	4	.9	458
E.Cavan, Monaghan, Armagh	2	.5	261	67.1	119	30.6	7	1.8	389
Antrim, Down	2	1.3	110	72.4	40	26.3	-	-	152
N. Fermanagh, E.Donegal, Tyrone, Londonderry	4	1.2	223	70.1	89	28.0	2	.6	318
Total	179	2.0	6437	72.3	2212	24.8	75	.8	8903

TABLE IV-30. NASAL BRIDGE HEIGHT BY COUNTY SUBGROUPS

	Very small, submedium		Medium		Pronounced		Very pro.		Total
	No.	%	No.	%	No.	%	No.	%	No.
W. Donegal	9	4.2	161	75.9	40	18.9	2	.9	212
Mayo	22	3.8	482	83.2	73	12.6	2	.3	579
Sligo, Leitrim, S. Fermanagh, W. Cavan	20	2.8	593	82.8	97	13.5	6	.8	716
W. Galway	9	2.1	372	86.1	49	11.3	2	.5	432
Aran Islands	1	.7	111	79.8	26	18.7	1	.7	139
Clare	26	2.8	744	78.8	162	17.2	12	1.3	944
Kerry	21	3.9	366	68.0	137	25.5	14	2.6	538
Cork	11	1.9	399	69.4	154	26.8	11	1.9	575
Limerick	8	2.4	262	77.0	67	19.7	3	.9	340
E. Galway, Roscommon	8	1.6	425	82.5	75	14.6	7	1.4	515
Longford, Westmeath	24	3.6	580	85.8	69	10.2	3	.4	676
Offaly, Leix, Kildare	18	3.4	418	78.7	91	17.1	4	.8	531
Tipperary, Kilkenny	20	3.1	432	66.7	177	27.3	19	2.9	648
Waterford, Wexford	13	2.8	316	68.4	124	26.8	9	1.9	462
Wicklow, Carlow	12	4.3	173	62.2	84	30.2	9	3.2	278
Meath, Louth, Dublin	19	4.1	324	70.7	112	24.4	3	.6	458
E.Cavan, Monaghan, Armagh	21	5.4	279	71.7	86	22.1	3	.8	389
Antrim, Down	4	2.6	112	73.7	33	21.7	3	2.0	152
N. Fermanagh, E.Donegal, Tyrone, Londonderry	13	4.1	239	75.2	64	20.1	2	.6	318
Total	279	3.1	6788	76.2	1720	19.3	115	1.3	8902

TABLE IV-31. NASAL BRIDGE BREADTH BY COUNTY SUBGROUPS

	Submedium		Medium		Pronounced		Very pro.		Total
	No.	%	No.	%	No.	%	No.	%	No.
W. Donegal	6	2.8	178	84.0	27	12.7	1	.5	212
Mayo	1	.2	481	83.1	93	16.1	4	.7	579
Sligo, Leitrim, S. Fermanagh, W. Cavan	6	.8	612	85.6	95	13.3	2	.3	715
W. Galway	3	.7	373	86.5	55	12.8	-	-	431
Aran Islands	-	-	124	89.2	15	10.8	-	-	139
Clare	14	1.5	752	79.7	171	18.1	7	.7	944
Kerry	7	1.3	405	75.3	122	22.7	4	.7	538
Cork	3	.5	416	72.3	154	26.8	2	.3	575
Limerick	2	.6	277	81.5	61	17.9	-	-	340
E. Galway, Roscommon	4	.8	448	87.0	62	12.0	1	.2	515
Longford, Westmeath	9	1.3	591	87.6	74	11.0	1	.1	675
Offaly, Leix, Kildare	2	.4	393	74.0	134	25.2	2	.4	531
Tipperary, Kilkenny	5	.8	469	72.4	169	26.1	5	.8	648
Waterford, Wexford	4	.9	312	67.5	141	30.5	5	1.1	462
Wicklow, Carlow	2	.7	205	73.7	71	25.5	-	-	278
Meath, Louth, Dublin	4	.9	308	67.2	145	31.6	1	.2	458
E.Cavan, Monaghan, Armagh	-	-	275	70.7	112	28.8	2	.5	389
Antrim, Down	1	.6	107	70.4	44	28.9	-	-	152
N. Fermanagh, E.Donegal, Tyrone, Londonderry	1	.3	229	72.0	86	27.0	2	.6	318
Total	74	.8	6955	78.2	1831	20.6	39	.4	8899

TABLE IV-32.   NASAL SEPTUM BY COUNTY SUBGROUPS

	Straight, concave		Convex		Total
	No.	%	No.	%	No.
W. Donegal	56	26.4	156	73.6	212
Mayo	187	32.5	389	67.5	576
Sligo, Leitrim, S. Fermanagh, W. Cavan	251	35.2	462	64.8	713
W. Galway	139	33.2	280	66.8	419
Aran Islands	64	46.4	74	53.6	138
Clare	286	30.5	652	69.5	938
Kerry	165	30.7	373	69.3	538
Cork	190	33.0	385	67.0	575
Limerick	103	30.4	236	69.6	339
E. Galway, Roscommon	189	37.2	319	62.8	508
Longford, Westmeath	275	40.7	401	59.3	676
Offaly, Leix, Kildare	267	50.3	264	49.7	531
Tipperary, Kilkenny	238	36.8	409	63.2	647
Waterford, Wexford	191	41.3	271	58.6	462
Wicklow, Carlow	146	52.5	132	47.5	278
Meath, Louth, Dublin	211	46.2	246	53.8	457
E.Cavan, Monaghan, Armagh	204	52.4	185	47.6	389
Antrim, Down	68	44.7	84	55.3	152
N. Fermanagh, E.Donegal, Tyrone, Londonderry	167	52.5	151	47.5	318
Total	3397	38.3	5469	61.7	8866

TABLE IV-33. NASAL TIP, THICKNESS, BY COUNTY SUBGROUPS

	Submedium		Medium		Pronounced		Very pro.		Total
	No.	%	No.	%	No.	%	No.	%	No.
W. Donegal	3	1.4	167	78.8	41	19.3	1	.5	212
Mayo	11	1.9	417	71.9	150	25.9	2	.3	580
Sligo, Leitrim, S. Fermanagh, W. Cavan	16	2.2	534	74.6	164	22.9	2	.3	716
W. Galway	6	1.4	348	80.6	77	17.8	1	.2	432
Aran Islands	-	-	121	87.0	18	12.9	-	-	139
Clare	15	1.6	724	76.7	199	21.1	6	.6	944
Kerry	13	2.4	371	69.0	151	28.1	3	.6	538
Cork	9	1.6	397	69.0	164	28.5	5	.9	575
Limerick	3	.9	268	78.8	69	20.3	-	-	340
E. Galway, Roscommon	10	1.9	420	81.6	84	16.3	1	.2	515
Longford, Westmeath	19	2.8	562	83.1	95	14.0	-	-	676
Offaly, Leix, Kildare	7	1.3	368	69.3	155	29.2	1	.2	531
Tipperary, Kilkenny	10	1.5	466	71.9	169	26.1	3	.5	648
Waterford, Wexford	4	.9	304	65.8	148	32.0	6	1.3	462
Wicklow, Carlow	3	1.1	187	67.3	86	30.9	2	.7	278
Meath, Louth, Dublin	10	2.2	286	62.4	162	35.4	-	-	458
E.Cavan, Monaghan, Armagh	6	1.5	257	66.1	126	32.4	-	-	389
Antrim, Down	3	2.0	103	67.8	46	30.3	-	-	152
N. Fermanagh, E.Donegal, Tyrone, Londonderry	3	.9	212	66.7	99	31.1	4	1.2	318
Total	151	1.7	6512	73.1	2203	24.7	37	.4	8903

TABLE IV-34. NASAL TIP, INCLINATION, BY COUNTY SUBGROUPS

	Up, medium		Up, submedium		Horizontal		Down, submedium		Down, medium		Total
	No.	%	No.	%	No.	%	No.	%	No.	%	No.
W. Donegal	21	9.9	185	87.3	4	1.9	1	.5	1	.5	212
Mayo	46	8.0	501	86.7	24	4.2	6	1.0	1	.2	578
Sligo, Leitrim, S. Fermanagh, W. Cavan	67	9.4	614	85.9	21	2.9	11	1.5	2	.3	715
W. Galway	39	9.0	361	83.6	23	5.3	8	1.8	1	.2	432
Aran Islands	10	7.2	116	83.4	9	6.5	3	2.2	1	.7	139
Clare	91	9.6	775	82.2	52	5.5	16	1.7	9	1.0	943
Kerry	69	12.8	440	81.8	20	3.7	6	1.1	3	.6	538
Cork	60	10.4	486	84.5	18	3.1	9	1.6	2	.3	575
Limerick	42	12.4	272	80.0	19	5.6	6	1.8	1	.3	340
E. Galway, Roscommon	51	9.9	436	84.8	17	3.3	7	1.4	3	.6	514
Longford, Westmeath	136	20.2	506	75.2	23	3.4	7	1.0	1	.1	673
Offaly, Leix, Kildare	77	14.5	429	80.8	18	3.4	6	1.1	1	.2	531
Tipperary, Kilkenny	70	10.8	530	81.8	34	5.2	10	1.5	4	.6	648
Waterford, Wexford	50	10.8	377	81.6	25	5.4	8	1.7	2	.4	462
Wicklow, Carlow	31	11.2	234	84.2	9	3.2	3	1.1	1	.4	278
Meath, Louth, Dublin	68	14.8	366	79.9	20	4.4	4	.9	-	-	458
E.Cavan, Monaghan, Armagh	37	9.5	328	84.3	22	5.6	2	.5	-	-	389
Antrim, Down	18	11.8	122	80.3	8	5.3	3	2.0	1	.6	152
N. Fermanagh, E.Donegal, Tyrone, Londonderry	20	9.1	270	84.9	15	4.7	3	.9	1	.3	318
Total	1012	11.4	7348	82.6	381	4.3	119	1.3	35	.4	8895

TABLE IV-35. NASAL WINGS BY COUNTY SUBGROUPS

| | Compressed | | Medium | | Flaring | | Total |
	No.	%	No.	%	No.	%	No.
W. Donegal	9	4.2	194	91.5	9	4.2	212
Mayo	33	5.7	513	88.4	34	5.9	580
Sligo, Leitrim, S. Fermanagh, W. Cavan	41	5.7	604	84.4	71	9.9	716
W. Galway	11	2.6	392	91.0	28	6.5	431
Aran Islands	13	9.4	120	86.3	6	4.3	139
Clare.	72	7.6	802	85.1	68	7.2	942
Kerry	36	6.7	466	86.8	35	6.5	537
Cork	17	3.0	526	91.5	32	5.6	575
Limerick	18	5.3	306	90.0	16	4.7	340
E. Galway, Roscommon	28	5.4	451	87.6	36	7.0	515
Longford, Westmeath	50	7.4	577	85.7	46	6.8	673
Offaly, Leix, Kildare.	29	5.5	472	88.9	30	5.6	531
Tipperary, Kilkenny	25	3.8	587	90.6	36	5.6	648
Waterford, Wexford	29	6.3	410	88.7	23	5.0	462
Wicklow, Carlow	10	3.6	251	90.3	17	6.1	278
Meath, Louth, Dublin	22	4.8	406	88.6	30	6.6	458
E.Cavan, Monaghan, Armagh	6	1.5	366	94.1	17	4.4	389
Antrim, Down	5	3.3	140	92.1	7	4.6	152
N. Fermanagh, E.Donegal, Tyrone, Londonderry	8	2.5	293	92.4	16	5.0	317
Total	462	5.2	7876	88.5	557	6.3	8895

TABLE IV-36. NOSTRIL VISIBILITY, FRONTAL, BY COUNTY SUBGROUPS

| | Absent | | Submedium, medium | | Pronounced | | Total |
	No.	%	No.	%	No.	%	No.
W. Donegal	5	2.4	207	97.6	-	-	212
Mayo	29	5.0	547	94.5	3	.5	579
Sligo, Leitrim, S. Fermanagh, W. Cavan	21	2.9	688	96.1	7	1.0	716
W. Galway	20	4.6	410	95.1	1	.2	431
Aran Islands	5	3.6	128	92.1	6	4.3	139
Clare.	69	7.3	873	92.5	2	.2	944
Kerry	23	4.3	510	95.0	4	.7	537
Cork	29	5.0	544	94.6	2	.3	575
Limerick	19	5.6	318	93.5	3	.9	340
E. Galway, Roscommon	17	3.3	495	96.1	3	.6	515
Longford, Westmeath	15	2.2	638	94.6	21	3.1	674
Offaly, Leix, Kildare.	19	3.6	506	95.6	4	.8	529
Tipperary, Kilkenny	40	6.2	601	92.7	7	1.1	648
Waterford, Wexford	34	7.4	427	92.4	1	.2	462
Wicklow, Carlow	12	4.3	266	95.7	-	-	278
Meath, Louth, Dublin	19	4.1	436	95.2	3	.6	458
E.Cavan, Monaghan, Armagh . . . . . . :.	23	5.9	365	93.8	1	.2	389
Antrim, Down	11	7.2	140	92.1	1	.6	152
N. Fermanagh, E.Donegal, Tyrone, Londonderry	20	6.3	296	93.4	1	.3	317
Total	430	4.8	8395	94.4	70	.8	8895

TABLE IV-37. NASAL PROFILE BY COUNTY SUBGROUPS

| | Concave | | Concave, snub tip | | Straight | | Straight, snub tip | |
	No.	%	No.	%	No.	%	No.	%
W. Donegal	18	8.5	1	.5	76	35.8	6	2.8
Mayo	52	9.0	5	.9	233	40.4	26	4.5
Sligo, Leitrim, S. Fermanagh, W. Cavan	51	7.1	4	.6	342	47.8	21	2.9
W. Galway	33	7.6	4	.9	165	38.3	13	3.0
Aran Islands	3	2.2	-	-	84	60.4	5	3.6
Clare.	73	7.7	5	.5	353	37.4	35	3.7
Kerry	47	8.7	4	.7	207	38.5	14	2.6
Cork	35	6.1	3	.5	228	39.6	12	2.1
Limerick	24	7.0	2	.6	121	35.6	9	2.6
E. Galway, Roscommon	33	6.4	4	.8	234	45.4	27	5.2
Longford, Westmeath	24	3.6	12	1.8	402	59.6	40	5.9
Offaly, Leix, Kildare.	37	7.0	6	1.1	261	49.2	19	3.6
Tipperary, Kilkenny	52	8.0	6	.9	261	40.3	26	4.0
Waterford, Wexford	22	4.8	1	.2	222	48.0	13	2.8
Wicklow, Carlow	14	5.0	-	-	120	43.2	13	4.7
Meath, Louth, Dublin	31	6.8	4	.9	204	44.5	19	4.1
E.Cavan, Monaghan, Armagh	25	6.4	-	-	184	47.3	4	1.0
Antrim, Down	9	5.9	1	.6	68	44.7	8	5.3
N. Fermanagh, E.Donegal, Tyrone, Londonderry	12	3.8	1	.3	151	47.5	12	3.8
Total	595	6.7	63	.7	3916	44.0	322	3.6

TABLE IV-37. NASAL PROFILE BY COUNTY SUBGROUPS (Continued)

	Convex		Convex, snub tip		Total
	No.	%	No.	%	No.
W. Donegal	96	45.3	15	7.1	212
Mayo	236	40.9	25	4.3	577
Sligo, Leitrim, S. Fermanagh, W. Cavan	266	37.2	31	4.3	715
W. Galway	180	41.8	36	8.4	431
Aran Islands	46	33.1	1	.7	139
Clare	424	44.9	54	5.7	944
Kerry	228	42.4	38	7.1	538
Cork	258	44.9	39	6.8	575
Limerick	164	48.2	20	5.9	340
E. Galway, Roscommon	190	36.9	27	5.2	515
Longford, Westmeath	176	26.1	21	3.1	675
Offaly, Leix, Kildare	193	36.3	15	2.8	531
Tipperary, Kilkenny	264	40.7	39	6.0	648
Waterford, Wexford	184	39.8	20	4.3	462
Wicklow, Carlow	119	42.8	12	4.3	278
Meath, Louth, Dublin	188	41.0	12	2.6	458
E.Cavan, Monaghan, Armagh	159	40.9	17	4.4	389
Antrim, Down	62	40.8	4	2.6	152
N. Fermanagh, E.Donegal, Tyrone, Londonderry	131	41.2	11	3.4	318
Total	3564	40.0	437	4.9	8897

TABLE IV-38. LIPS, INTEGUMENTAL THICKNESS, BY COUNTY SUBGROUPS

	Submedium		Medium		Pronounced		Total
	No.	%	No.	%	No.	%	No.
W. Donegal	1	.5	204	96.2	7	3.3	212
Mayo	1	.2	547	94.3	32	5.5	580
Sligo, Leitrim, S. Fermanagh, W. Cavan	14	2.0	679	94.8	23	3.2	716
W. Galway	3	.7	411	95.1	18	4.2	432
Aran Islands	2	1.4	132	95.0	5	3.6	139
Clare	4	.4	916	96.8	26	2.7	946
Kerry	1	.2	523	97.0	15	2.8	539
Cork	6	1.0	547	95.1	22	3.8	575
Limerick	2	.6	327	96.2	11	3.2	340
E. Galway, Roscommon	8	1.6	482	93.6	25	4.8	515
Longford, Westmeath	8	1.2	636	94.1	32	4.7	676
Offaly, Leix, Kildare	12	2.2	497	93.6	22	4.1	531
Tipperary, Kilkenny	8	1.2	616	94.8	26	4.0	650
Waterford, Wexford	3	.6	447	96.5	13	2.8	463
Wicklow, Carlow	7	2.5	260	93.5	11	4.0	278
Meath, Louth, Dublin	4	.9	425	92.8	29	6.3	458
E.Cavan, Monaghan, Armagh	2	.5	362	93.0	25	6.4	389
Antrim, Down	4	2.6	135	88.8	13	8.6	152
N. Fermanagh, E.Donegal, Tyrone, Londonderry	12	3.8	294	92.4	12	3.8	318
Total	102	1.1	8440	94.7	367	4.1	8909

TABLE IV-39. UPPER LIP, MEMBRANOUS THICKNESS, BY COUNTY SUBGROUPS

	Very small		Submedium		Medium		Pronounced		Total
	No.	%	No.	%	No.	%	No.	%	No.
W. Donegal	5	2.4	32	15.1	169	79.7	6	2.8	212
Mayo	13	2.2	87	15.0	466	80.3	14	2.4	580
Sligo, Leitrim, S. Fermanagh, W. Cavan	7	1.0	133	18.6	552	77.1	24	3.4	716
W. Galway	1	.2	77	17.8	351	81.2	3	.7	432
Aran Islands	-	-	57	41.0	79	56.8	3	2.2	139
Clare	19	2.0	276	29.2	634	67.0	17	1.8	946
Kerry	2	.4	113	21.0	408	75.8	15	2.8	538
Cork	4	.7	147	25.6	406	70.6	18	3.1	575
Limerick	4	1.2	74	21.8	256	75.3	6	1.8	340
E. Galway, Roscommon	5	1.0	120	23.3	381	74.1	8	1.6	514
Longford, Westmeath	5	.7	143	21.2	513	76.0	14	2.1	675
Offaly, Leix, Kildare	5	.9	135	25.4	379	71.4	12	2.2	531
Tipperary, Kilkenny	11	1.7	163	25.1	461	70.9	15	2.3	650
Waterford, Wexford	8	1.7	127	27.4	319	68.9	9	1.9	463
Wicklow, Carlow	5	1.8	78	28.0	189	68.0	6	2.2	278
Meath, Louth, Dublin	6	1.3	105	22.9	327	71.4	20	4.4	458
E.Cavan, Monaghan, Armagh	5	1.3	85	21.8	285	73.3	14	3.6	389
Antrim, Down	1	.6	36	23.7	103	67.8	12	7.9	152
N. Fermanagh, E.Donegal, Tyrone, Londonderry	-	-	79	24.8	216	67.9	23	7.2	318
Total	106	1.2	2067	23.2	6494	72.9	239	2.7	8906

TABLE IV-40.   LIPS, EVERSION, BY COUNTY SUBGROUPS

| | Submedium | | Medium | | Pronounced | | Total |
	No.	%	No.	%	No.	%	No.
W. Donegal	37	17.4	166	78.3	9	4.2	212
Mayo	95	16.4	461	79.5	24	4.1	580
Sligo, Leitrim, S. Fermanagh, W. Cavan	109	15.2	572	80.0	34	4.8	715
W. Galway	73	16.9	352	81.5	7	1.6	432
Aran Islands	9	6.5	124	89.2	6	4.3	139
Clare	284	30.0	631	66.7	31	3.3	946
Kerry	111	20.6	405	75.1	23	4.3	539
Cork	150	26.1	396	68.9	29	5.0	575
Limerick	74	21.8	259	76.2	7	2.0	340
E. Galway, Roscommon	109	21.2	394	76.6	11	2.1	514
Longford, Westmeath	98	14.5	562	83.1	16	2.4	676
Offaly, Leix, Kildare	133	25.0	383	72.1	15	2.8	531
Tipperary, Kilkenny	170	26.2	455	70.0	25	3.8	650
Waterford, Wexford	132	28.5	319	68.9	12	2.6	463
Wicklow, Carlow	79	28.4	192	69.1	7	2.5	278
Meath, Louth, Dublin	108	23.6	323	70.5	27	5.9	458
E.Cavan, Monaghan, Armagh	85	21.8	283	72.8	21	5.4	389
Antrim, Down	34	22.4	104	68.4	14	9.2	152
N. Fermanagh, E.Donegal, Tyrone, Londonderry	78	24.5	210	66.0	30	9.4	318
Total	1968	22.1	6591	74.0	348	3.9	8907

TABLE IV-41.   LIP SEAM BY COUNTY SUBGROUPS

| | Absent | | Submedium | | Medium | | Total |
	No.	%	No.	%	No.	%	No.
W. Donegal	210	99.0	2	.9	-	-	212
Mayo	576	99.3	4	.7	-	-	580
Sligo, Leitrim, S. Fermanagh, W. Cavan	683	95.6	26	3.6	5	.7	714
W. Galway	426	98.6	5	1.2	1	.2	432
Aran Islands	137	98.6	1	.7	1	.7	139
Clare	935	98.8	10	1.0	1	.1	946
Kerry	531	98.5	8	1.5	-	-	539
Cork	559	97.2	15	2.6	1	.2	575
Limerick	336	98.8	4	1.2	-	-	340
E. Galway, Roscommon	504	97.9	10	1.9	1	.2	515
Longford, Westmeath	642	95.5	25	3.7	5	.7	672
Offaly, Leix, Kildare	522	98.3	8	1.5	1	.2	531
Tipperary, Kilkenny	636	97.8	14	2.2	-	-	650
Waterford, Wexford	456	98.5	6	1.3	1	.2	463
Wicklow, Carlow	272	97.8	6	2.2	-	-	278
Meath, Louth, Dublin	444	97.2	13	2.8	-	-	457
E.Cavan, Monaghan, Armagh	379	97.4	9	2.3	1	.2	389
Antrim, Down	149	98.0	3	2.0	-	-	152
N. Fermanagh, E.Donegal, Tyrone, Londonderry	315	99.0	3	.9	-	-	318
Total	8712	97.9	172	1.9	18	.2	8902

TABLE IV-42.   ALVEOLAR PROGNATHISM BY COUNTY SUBGROUPS

| | Absent | | Submedium | | Medium, pronounced | | Total |
	No.	%	No.	%	No.	%	No.
W. Donegal	211	99.5	-	-	1	.5	212
Mayo	576	99.3	2	.3	2	.3	580
Sligo, Leitrim, S. Fermanagh, W. Cavan	691	96.5	12	1.7	13	1.8	716
W. Galway	425	98.8	3	.7	2	.5	430
Aran Islands	138	99.3	-	-	1	.7	139
Clare	942	99.6	3	.3	1	.1	946
Kerry	538	99.8	1	.2	-	-	539
Cork	568	98.8	4	.7	3	.5	575
Limerick	338	99.4	2	.6	-	-	340
E. Galway, Roscommon	507	98.4	2	.4	6	1.2	515
Longford, Westmeath	621	92.0	14	2.1	40	5.9	675
Offaly, Leix, Kildare	514	97.0	12	2.3	4	.8	530
Tipperary, Kilkenny	636	97.8	10	1.5	4	.6	650
Waterford, Wexford	450	97.2	12	2.6	1	.2	463
Wicklow, Carlow	261	93.9	15	5.4	2	.7	278
Meath, Louth, Dublin	449	98.0	7	1.5	2	.4	458
E.Cavan, Monaghan, Armagh	382	98.2	7	1.8	-	-	389
Antrim, Down	143	94.1	8	5.3	1	.6	152
N. Fermanagh, E.Donegal, Tyrone, Londonderry	309	97.2	7	2.2	2	.6	318
Total	8699	97.7	121	1.4	85	1.0	8905

TABLE IV-43. MID-FACIAL PROGNATHISM BY COUNTY SUBGROUPS

	Absent No.	%	Submedium No.	%	Medium No.	%	Pronounced No.	%	Total No.
W. Donegal	198	93.4	11	5.2	2	.9	1	.5	212
Mayo	567	97.8	11	1.9	2	.3	-	-	580
Sligo, Leitrim, S. Fermanagh, W. Cavan	673	94.2	32	4.5	8	1.1	1	.1	714
W. Galway	407	94.2	22	5.1	2	.5	1	.2	432
Aran Islands	137	98.6	1	.7	1	.7	-	-	139
Clare	914	96.6	27	2.8	4	.4	1	.1	946
Kerry	519	96.3	16	3.0	4	.7	-	-	539
Cork	537	93.6	28	4.9	8	1.4	1	.2	574
Limerick	324	95.3	12	3.5	3	.9	1	.3	340
E. Galway, Roscommon	483	94.0	27	5.2	4	.8	-	-	514
Longford, Westmeath	615	91.2	52	7.7	6	.9	1	.1	674
Offaly, Leix, Kildare	455	85.7	63	11.9	11	2.1	2	.4	531
Tipperary, Kilkenny	572	88.0	64	9.8	13	2.0	1	.2	650
Waterford, Wexford	394	85.1	49	10.6	18	3.9	2	.4	463
Wicklow, Carlow	212	76.2	41	14.7	21	7.6	4	1.4	278
Meath, Louth, Dublin	406	88.6	41	9.0	11	2.4	-	-	458
E.Cavan, Monaghan, Armagh	342	87.9	40	10.3	7	1.8	-	-	389
Antrim, Down	138	90.8	14	9.2	-	-	-	-	152
N. Fermanagh, E.Donegal, Tyrone, Londonderry	298	93.7	15	4.7	5	1.6	-	-	318
Total	8191	92.0	566	6.4	130	1.5	16	.2	8903

TABLE IV-44. CHIN PROMINENCE BY COUNTY SUBGROUPS

	Submedium No.	%	Medium No.	%	Pronounced No.	%	Total No.
W. Donegal	30	14.2	169	79.7	13	6.1	212
Mayo	57	9.8	484	83.4	39	6.7	580
Sligo, Leitrim, S. Fermanagh, W. Cavan	93	13.0	583	81.5	39	5.4	715
W. Galway	58	13.4	352	81.5	22	5.1	432
Aran Islands	6	4.3	117	84.2	16	11.5	139
Clare	82	8.7	775	81.9	89	9.4	946
Kerry	50	9.3	417	77.4	72	13.4	539
Cork	50	8.7	442	76.9	83	14.4	575
Limerick	24	7.0	270	79.4	46	13.5	340
E. Galway, Roscommon	55	10.7	424	82.5	35	6.8	514
Longford, Westmeath	68	10.1	525	77.8	82	12.1	675
Offaly, Leix, Kildare	57	10.7	430	81.0	44	8.3	531
Tipperary, Kilkenny	83	12.8	487	75.0	79	12.2	649
Waterford, Wexford	39	8.4	373	80.6	51	11.0	463
Wicklow, Carlow	31	11.2	218	78.4	29	10.4	278
Meath, Louth, Dublin	55	12.0	371	81.0	32	7.0	458
E.Cavan, Monaghan, Armagh	68	17.5	295	75.8	26	6.7	389
Antrim, Down	16	10.5	126	82.9	10	6.6	152
N. Fermanagh, E.Donegal, Tyrone, Londonderry	52	16.4	248	78.0	18	5.7	318
Total	974	10.9	7106	79.8	825	9.3	8905

TABLE IV-45. CHIN TYPE BY COUNTY SUBGROUPS

	Median No.	%	Bilateral No.	%	Total No.
W. Donegal	10	4.7	202	95.3	212
Mayo	17	2.9	562	97.1	579
Sligo, Leitrim, S. Fermanagh, W. Cavan	12	1.7	703	98.3	715
W. Galway	30	6.9	402	93.0	432
Aran Islands	5	3.6	133	96.4	138
Clare	44	4.6	901	95.3	945
Kerry	12	2.2	527	97.8	539
Cork	21	3.6	554	96.3	575
Limerick	9	2.6	331	97.4	340
E. Galway, Roscommon	11	2.1	503	97.8	514
Longford, Westmeath	15	2.2	661	97.8	676
Offaly, Leix, Kildare	16	3.0	514	97.0	530
Tipperary, Kilkenny	25	3.8	625	96.2	650
Waterford, Wexford	23	5.0	440	95.0	463
Wicklow, Carlow	15	5.4	263	94.6	278
Meath, Louth, Dublin	16	3.5	441	96.5	457
E.Cavan, Monaghan, Armagh	19	4.9	370	95.1	389
Antrim, Down	4	2.6	148	97.4	152
N. Fermanagh, E.Donegal, Tyrone, Londonderry	1	.3	317	99.7	318
Total	305	3.4	8597	96.6	8902

TABLE IV-46.   TEETH, ERUPTION, BY COUNTY SUBGROUPS

	Complete No.	%	Partial No.	%	Total No.
W. Donegal	141	66.8	70	33.2	211
Mayo	405	70.2	172	29.8	577
Sligo, Leitrim, S. Fermanagh, W. Cavan	427	65.8	222	34.2	649
W. Galway	331	77.2	98	22.8	429
Aran Islands	85	63.0	50	37.0	135
Clare	788	84.4	146	15.6	934
Kerry	408	76.0	129	24.0	537
Cork	445	77.7	128	22.3	573
Limerick	244	72.0	95	28.0	339
E. Galway, Roscommon	350	72.2	135	27.8	485
Longford, Westmeath	380	60.5	248	39.5	628
Offaly, Leix, Kildare	367	70.2	156	29.8	523
Tipperary, Kilkenny	499	77.1	148	22.9	647
Waterford, Wexford	368	79.6	94	20.3	462
Wicklow, Carlow	208	75.4	68	24.6	276
Meath, Louth, Dublin	328	74.4	113	25.6	441
E.Cavan, Monaghan, Armagh	270	70.3	114	29.7	384
Antrim, Down	112	74.2	39	25.8	151
N. Fermanagh, E.Donegal, Tyrone, Londonderry	220	70.1	94	29.9	314
Total	6376	73.3	2319	26.7	8695

TABLE IV-47.   BITE BY COUNTY SUBGROUPS

	Under No.	%	Edge-to-edge No.	%	Submedium over No.	%	Pronounced over No.	%	Total No.
W. Donegal	1	.6	-	-	168	97.1	4	2.3	173
Mayo	2	.4	1	.2	455	95.8	17	3.6	475
Sligo, Leitrim, S. Fermanagh, W. Cavan	-	-	-	-	576	98.0	12	2.0	588
W. Galway	4	1.1	4	1.1	340	94.7	11	3.1	359
Aran Islands	-	-	2	1.5	130	96.3	3	2.2	135
Clare	14	2.1	3	.4	611	93.3	27	4.1	655
Kerry	2	.5	3	.7	412	97.4	6	1.4	423
Cork	6	1.5	3	.8	382	95.7	8	2.0	399
Limerick	2	.8	1	.4	234	93.6	13	5.2	250
E. Galway, Roscommon	1	.2	1	.2	419	97.2	10	2.3	431
Longford, Westmeath	1	.2	3	.5	600	96.6	17	2.7	621
Offaly, Leix, Kildare	1	.2	-	-	388	96.8	12	3.0	401
Tipperary, Kilkenny	4	.8	2	.4	442	94.8	18	3.9	466
Waterford, Wexford	2	.7	2	.7	268	95.0	10	3.5	282
Wicklow, Carlow	-	-	-	-	188	93.5	13	6.5	201
Meath, Louth, Dublin	-	-	1	.3	334	96.2	12	3.4	347
E.Cavan, Monaghan, Armagh	-	-	1	.3	281	96.9	8	2.8	290
Antrim, Down	-	-	-	-	124	99.2	1	.8	125
N. Fermanagh, E.Donegal, Tyrone, Londonderry	2	.8	-	.4	243	96.8	5	2.0	251
Total	42	.6	28	.4	6595	96.0	207	3.0	6872

TABLE IV-48.   TEETH, WEAR, BY COUNTY SUBGROUPS

	Absent, submedium No.	%	Medium No.	%	Pronounced, Very pro. No.	%	Total No.
W. Donegal	134	77.9	30	17.4	8	4.6	172
Mayo	353	74.5	92	19.4	29	6.1	474
Sligo, Leitrim, S. Fermanagh, W. Cavan	458	77.9	107	18.2	23	3.9	588
W. Galway	255	72.2	83	23.5	15	4.2	353
Aran Islands	100	74.1	33	24.4	2	1.5	135
Clare	467	73.8	124	19.6	42	6.6	633
Kerry	270	64.1	102	24.2	49	11.6	421
Cork	266	67.2	108	27.3	22	5.6	396
Limerick	167	66.8	65	26.0	18	7.2	250
E. Galway, Roscommon	338	79.2	79	18.5	10	2.3	427
Longford, Westmeath	494	80.1	108	17.5	15	2.4	617
Offaly, Leix, Kildare	327	81.8	63	15.8	10	2.5	400
Tipperary, Kilkenny	353	76.6	97	21.0	11	2.4	461
Waterford, Wexford	212	75.7	51	18.2	17	6.1	280
Wicklow, Carlow	149	74.1	36	17.9	16	8.0	201
Meath, Louth, Dublin	271	78.1	64	18.4	12	3.4	347
E.Cavan, Monaghan, Armagh	231	79.6	48	16.6	11	3.8	290
Antrim, Down	107	85.6	15	12.0	3	2.4	125
N. Fermanagh, E.Donegal, Tyrone, Londonderry	217	86.8	30	12.0	3	1.2	250
Total	5169	75.8	1335	19.6	316	4.6	6820

TABLE IV-49.   TEETH, LOSS, BY COUNTY SUBGROUPS

	None		Very small (1-4)		Submedium (5-8)		Medium (9-16)		Pronounced (17-)		Total
	No.	%	No.	%	No.	%	No.	%	No.	%	No.
W. Donegal	33	15.6	78	36.8	56	26.4	6	2.8	39	18.4	212
Mayo	56	9.7	243	42.0	143	24.7	33	5.7	104	18.0	579
Sligo, Leitrim, S. Fermanagh, W. Cavan	72	10.0	311	43.4	133	18.6	65	9.1	135	18.8	716
W. Galway	41	9.5	183	42.4	103	23.8	24	5.6	81	18.8	432
Aran Islands	17	12.2	78	56.1	21	15.1	16	11.5	7	5.0	139
Clare	40	4.2	326	34.5	228	24.1	49	5.2	303	32.0	946
Kerry	37	6.9	204	37.8	122	22.6	52	9.6	124	23.0	539
Cork	30	5.2	191	33.2	124	21.6	50	8.7	180	31.3	575
Limerick	16	4.7	134	39.4	82	24.1	18	5.3	90	26.5	340
E. Galway, Roscommon	44	8.6	216	42.0	120	23.3	44	8.6	90	17.5	514
Longford, Westmeath	57	8.5	266	39.6	156	23.2	85	12.6	108	16.1	672
Offaly, Leix, Kildare	32	6.0	249	46.9	81	15.2	28	5.3	141	26.6	531
Tipperary, Kilkenny	69	10.6	247	38.0	111	17.1	33	5.1	190	29.2	650
Waterford, Wexford	38	8.2	149	32.2	74	16.0	21	4.5	181	39.1	463
Wicklow, Carlow	24	8.6	93	33.4	66	23.7	18	6.5	77	27.7	278
Meath, Louth, Dublin	26	5.7	198	43.2	81	17.7	36	7.9	117	25.5	458
E.Cavan, Monaghan, Armagh	30	7.7	163	41.9	70	18.0	27	6.9	99	25.4	389
Antrim, Down	9	5.9	69	45.4	39	25.6	8	5.3	27	17.8	152
N. Fermanagh, E.Donegal, Tyrone, Londonderry	39	12.3	138	43.4	61	19.2	14	4.4	66	20.8	318
Total	710	8.0	3536	39.7	1871	21.0	627	7.0	2159	24.2	8903

TABLE IV-50. TEETH, CARIES, BY COUNTY SUBGROUPS

	Absent		Very small		Submedium		Medium		Pronounced		Total
	No.	%	No.	%	No.	%	No.	%	No.	%	No.
W. Donegal	1	.6	17	9.8	96	55.5	45	26.0	14	8.1	173
Mayo	3	.6	30	6.3	274	57.6	92	19.3	77	16.2	476
Sligo, Leitrim, S. Fermanagh, W. Cavan	4	.7	82	13.9	331	56.0	119	20.1	55	9.3	591
W. Galway	1	.3	39	11.0	181	50.8	93	26.1	42	11.8	356
Aran Islands	2	1.5	24	17.8	69	51.1	33	24.4	7	5.2	135
Clare	-	-	19	2.9	344	53.1	154	23.8	131	20.2	648
Kerry	-	-	18	4.3	217	51.5	121	28.7	65	15.4	421
Cork	2	.5	10	2.5	216	54.4	129	32.5	40	10.1	397
Limerick	1	.4	8	3.2	125	50.0	79	31.6	37	14.8	250
E. Galway, Roscommon	2	.5	43	10.0	248	57.7	91	21.2	46	10.7	430
Longford, Westmeath	8	1.3	96	15.4	292	47.0	136	21.9	89	14.3	621
Offaly, Leix, Kildare	3	.7	46	11.5	236	58.8	85	21.2	31	7.7	401
Tipperary, Kilkenny	6	1.3	28	6.1	279	60.5	118	25.6	30	6.5	461
Waterford, Wexford	6	2.1	25	8.9	157	55.7	67	23.8	27	9.6	282
Wicklow, Carlow	1	.5	13	6.5	107	53.2	59	29.4	21	10.4	201
Meath, Louth, Dublin	3	.9	25	7.2	203	58.5	86	24.8	30	8.6	347
E.Cavan, Monaghan, Armagh	6	2.1	33	11.4	172	59.3	62	21.4	17	5.9	290
Antrim, Down	-	-	12	9.6	85	68.0	22	17.6	6	4.8	125
N. Fermanagh, E.Donegal, Tyrone, Londonderry	9	3.6	42	16.7	146	57.9	49	19.4	6	2.4	252
Total	58	.8	610	8.9	3778	55.1	1640	23.9	771	11.2	6857

TABLE   IV-51. FACE SHORTENING BY COUNTY SUBGROUPS

	Absent		Submedium		Medium		Pronounced		Total
	No.	%	No.	%	No.	%	No.	%	No.
W. Donegal	171	80.7	4	1.9	23	10.8	14	6.6	212
Mayo	467	80.5	27	4.6	61	10.5	25	4.3	580
Sligo, Leitrim, S. Fermanagh, W. Cavan	521	72.9	82	11.5	81	11.3	31	4.3	715
W. Galway	322	74.5	36	8.3	45	10.4	29	6.7	432
Aran Islands	113	83.1	18	13.2	4	2.9	1	.7	136
Clare	623	66.1	84	8.9	163	17.3	73	7.7	943
Kerry	416	77.3	26	4.8	43	8.0	53	9.8	538
Cork	394	68.6	49	8.5	87	15.2	44	7.7	574
Limerick	246	72.4	24	7.0	38	11.2	32	9.4	340
E. Galway, Roscommon	398	78.5	36	7.1	45	8.9	28	5.5	507
Longford, Westmeath	538	81.1	79	11.9	39	5.9	7	1.0	663
Offaly, Leix, Kildare	379	72.0	39	7.4	93	17.7	15	2.8	526
Tipperary, Kilkenny	450	69.3	47	7.2	108	16.6	44	6.8	649
Waterford, Wexford	275	59.4	43	9.3	115	24.8	30	6.5	463
Wicklow, Carlow	194	69.8	20	7.2	44	15.8	20	7.2	278
Meath, Louth, Dublin	332	72.6	40	8.8	70	15.3	15	3.3	457
E.Cavan, Monaghan, Armagh	287	73.8	30	7.7	56	14.4	16	4.1	389
Antrim, Down	123	80.9	7	4.6	12	7.9	10	6.6	152
N. Fermanagh, E.Donegal, Tyrone, Londonderry	250	78.9	28	8.8	31	9.8	8	2.5	317
Total	6499	73.3	719	8.1	1158	13.0	495	5.6	8871

TABLE IV-52. TEETH, CROWDING, BY COUNTY SUBGROUPS

	Absent		Medium		Pronounced		Total
	No.	%	No.	%	No.	%	No.
W. Donegal	79	45.7	84	48.6	10	5.8	173
Mayo	213	44.9	232	48.9	29	6.1	474
Sligo, Leitrim, S. Fermanagh, W. Cavan	279	47.2	288	48.7	24	4.1	591
W. Galway	184	51.5	158	44.2	15	4.2	357
Aran Islands	79	58.5	51	37.8	5	3.7	135
Clare	270	41.7	327	50.5	51	7.9	648
Kerry	161	38.2	237	56.3	23	5.5	421
Cork	147	37.0	225	56.7	25	6.3	397
Limerick	100	40.0	134	53.6	16	6.4	250
E. Galway, Roscommon	156	36.2	257	59.6	18	4.2	431
Longford, Westmeath	302	48.6	298	48.0	21	3.4	621
Offaly, Leix, Kildare	158	39.4	222	55.4	21	5.2	401
Tipperary, Kilkenny	200	43.4	228	49.4	33	7.2	461
Waterford, Wexford	118	41.8	137	48.6	27	9.6	282
Wicklow, Carlow	68	33.7	114	56.4	20	9.9	202
Meath, Louth, Dublin	129	37.1	195	56.0	24	6.9	348
E.Cavan, Monaghan, Armagh	120	41.4	149	51.4	21	7.2	290
Antrim, Down	43	34.4	78	62.4	4	3.2	125
N. Fermanagh, E.Donegal, Tyrone, Londonderry	116	46.0	128	50.8	8	3.2	252
Total	2922	42.6	3542	51.6	395	5.8	6859

TABLE IV-53. MALARS, FRONTAL PROJECTION, BY COUNTY SUBGROUPS

	Absent, submedium		Medium		Pronounced		Total
	No.	%	No.	%	No.	%	No.
W. Donegal	-	-	173	81.6	39	18.4	212
Mayo	3	.5	468	80.7	109	18.8	580
Sligo, Leitrim, S. Fermanagh, W. Cavan	8	1.1	559	78.1	149	20.8	716
W. Galway	1	.2	317	73.4	114	26.4	432
Aran Islands	1	.7	116	83.4	22	15.8	139
Clare	2	.2	819	86.6	125	13.2	946
Kerry	3	.6	417	77.5	118	21.9	538
Cork	-	-	508	88.3	67	11.6	575
Limerick	2	.6	252	74.1	86	25.3	340
E. Galway, Roscommon	5	1.0	421	81.9	88	17.1	514
Longford, Westmeath	9	1.3	582	86.1	85	12.6	676
Offaly, Leix, Kildare	4	.8	442	83.2	85	16.0	531
Tipperary, Kilkenny	-	-	541	83.2	109	16.8	650
Waterford, Wexford	2	.4	403	87.0	58	12.5	463
Wicklow, Carlow	2	.7	234	84.2	42	15.1	278
Meath, Louth, Dublin	4	.9	393	85.8	61	13.3	458
E.Cavan, Monaghan, Armagh	1	.2	331	85.1	57	14.6	389
Antrim, Down	-	-	129	84.9	23	15.1	152
N. Fermanagh, E.Donegal, Tyrone, Londonderry	-	-	282	88.7	36	11.3	318
Total	47	.5	7387	82.9	1473	16.5	8907

TABLE IV-54. MALARS, LATERAL PROJECTION, BY COUNTY SUBGROUPS

	Absent		Medium		Pronounced		Very Pro.		Total
	No.	%	No.	%	No.	%	No.	%	No.
W. Donegal	-	-	121	57.1	84	39.6	7	3.3	212
Mayo	1	.2	300	51.7	267	46.0	12	2.1	580
Sligo, Leitrim, S. Fermanagh, W. Cavan	2	.3	487	68.0	215	30.0	12	1.7	716
W. Galway	-	-	232	53.8	170	39.4	29	6.7	431
Aran Islands	1	.7	117	84.2	21	15.1	-	-	139
Clare	3	.3	602	63.8	311	32.9	28	3.0	944
Kerry	2	.4	290	53.8	223	41.4	24	4.4	539
Cork	2	.3	350	60.9	218	37.9	5	.9	575
Limerick	-	-	183	53.8	143	42.0	14	4.1	340
E. Galway, Roscommon	6	1.2	328	63.7	172	33.4	9	1.7	515
Longford, Westmeath	8	1.2	538	79.6	129	19.1	1	.1	676
Offaly, Leix, Kildare	4	.8	406	76.6	116	21.9	4	.8	530
Tipperary, Kilkenny	1	.2	404	62.2	235	36.2	9	1.4	649
Waterford, Wexford	2	.4	330	71.3	129	27.9	2	.4	463
Wicklow, Carlow	-	-	190	68.3	81	29.1	7	2.5	278
Meath, Louth, Dublin	2	.4	316	69.0	138	30.1	2	.4	458
E.Cavan, Monaghan, Armagh	1	.2	272	69.9	115	29.6	1	.2	389
Antrim, Down	-	-	110	72.4	40	26.3	2	1.3	152
N. Fermanagh, E.Donegal, Tyrone, Londonderry	-	-	202	63.5	111	34.9	5	1.6	318
Total	35	.4	5778	64.9	2918	32.8	173	1.9	8904

TABLE IV-55. GONIAL ANGLES BY COUNTY SUBGROUPS

	Submedium		Medium		Pronounced		Very pro.		Total
	No.	%	No.	%	No.	%	No.	%	No.
W. Donegal	-	-	128	60.4	77	36.3	7	3.3	212
Mayo	4	.7	340	58.6	228	39.3	8	1.4	580
Sligo, Leitrim, S. Fermanagh, W. Cavan	32	4.5	473	66.1	199	27.8	12	1.7	716
W. Galway	15	3.5	269	62.3	136	31.5	12	2.8	432
Aran Islands	8	5.8	105	75.5	25	18.0	1	.7	139
Clare	22	2.3	613	64.8	292	30.9	19	2.0	946
Kerry	11	2.0	297	55.1	222	41.2	9	1.7	539
Cork	11	1.9	358	62.3	197	34.3	9	1.6	575
Limerick	7	2.0	188	55.3	137	40.3	8	2.4	340
E. Galway, Roscommon	11	2.1	356	69.1	137	26.6	11	2.1	515
Longford, Westmeath	34	5.0	493	73.1	144	21.4	3	.4	674
Offaly, Leix, Kildare	12	2.2	387	72.9	122	23.0	10	1.9	531
Tipperary, Kilkenny	7	1.1	429	66.0	202	31.1	12	1.8	650
Waterford, Wexford	7	1.5	320	69.1	133	28.7	3	.6	463
Wicklow, Carlow	8	2.9	178	64.0	87	31.3	5	1.8	278
Meath, Louth, Dublin	24	5.2	287	62.7	144	31.4	3	.6	458
E.Cavan, Monaghan, Armagh	20	5.1	247	63.5	118	30.3	4	1.0	389
Antrim, Down	4	2.6	89	58.6	55	36.2	4	2.6	152
N. Fermanagh, E.Donegal, Tyrone, Londonderry	10	3.1	185	58.2	118	37.1	5	1.6	318
Total	247	2.8	5742	64.5	2773	31.1	145	1.6	8907

TABLE IV-56. EAR HELIX BY COUNTY SUBGROUPS

	Very small		Submedium		Medium		Pronounced		Total
	No.	%	No.	%	No.	%	No.	%	No.
W. Donegal	-	-	61	28.8	150	70.8	1	.5	212
Mayo	2	.3	164	28.3	405	69.8	9	1.6	580
Sligo, Leitrim, S. Fermanagh, W. Cavan	1	.1	86	12.0	586	81.8	43	6.0	716
W. Galway	2	.5	63	14.6	355	82.2	12	2.8	432
Aran Islands	-	-	11	7.9	121	87.0	7	5.0	139
Clare	13	1.4	244	25.8	658	69.6	31	3.3	946
Kerry	1	.2	132	24.5	392	72.7	14	2.6	539
Cork	8	1.4	162	28.2	383	66.6	22	3.8	575
Limerick	2	.6	92	27.0	237	69.7	9	2.6	340
E. Galway, Roscommon	-	-	78	15.1	420	81.6	17	3.3	515
Longford, Westmeath	-	-	101	14.9	539	79.7	36	5.3	676
Offaly, Leix, Kildare	1	.2	90	16.9	411	77.4	29	5.5	531
Tipperary, Kilkenny	2	.3	176	27.1	452	69.5	20	3.1	650
Waterford, Wexford	1	.2	127	27.4	319	68.9	16	3.4	463
Wicklow, Carlow	4	1.4	89	32.0	178	64.0	7	2.5	278
Meath, Louth, Dublin	2	.4	93	20.3	335	73.1	28	6.1	458
E.Cavan, Monaghan, Armagh	5	1.3	87	22.4	268	68.9	29	7.4	389
Antrim, Down	-	-	37	24.3	101	66.4	14	9.2	152
N. Fermanagh, E.Donegal, Tyrone, Londonderry	5	1.6	94	29.6	197	61.9	22	6.9	318
Total	49	.6	1987	22.3	6507	73.0	366	4.1	8909

TABLE IV-57. EAR ANTIHELIX BY COUNTY SUBGROUPS

	Absent		Submedium		Medium		Pronounced		Total
	No.	%	No.	%	No.	%	No.	%	No.
W. Donegal	-	-	8	3.8	176	83.0	28	13.2	212
Mayo	-	-	16	2.8	506	87.4	57	9.8	579
Sligo, Leitrim, S. Fermanagh, W. Cavan	4	.6	39	5.4	604	84.4	69	9.6	516
W. Galway	1	.2	17	3.9	384	88.9	30	6.9	432
Aran Islands	1	.7	9	6.5	94	67.6	35	25.2	139
Clare	3	.3	65	6.9	812	85.8	66	7.0	946
Kerry	1	.2	24	4.4	414	76.8	100	18.6	539
Cork	-	-	30	5.2	466	81.0	79	13.7	575
Limerick	-	-	13	3.8	273	80.3	54	15.9	340
E. Galway, Roscommon	1	.2	27	5.2	434	84.3	53	10.3	515
Longford, Westmeath	4	.6	48	7.1	527	78.3	94	14.0	673
Offaly, Leix, Kildare	-	-	18	3.4	434	81.7	79	14.9	531
Tipperary, Kilkenny	1	.2	22	3.4	503	77.4	124	19.1	650
Waterford, Wexford	-	-	21	4.5	374	80.8	68	14.7	463
Wicklow, Carlow	-	-	17	6.1	225	80.9	36	12.9	278
Meath, Louth, Dublin	-	-	16	3.5	382	83.4	60	13.1	458
E.Cavan, Monaghan, Armagh	-	-	9	2.3	341	87.7	39	10.0	389
Antrim, Down	-	-	5	3.3	124	81.6	23	15.1	152
N. Fermanagh, E.Donegal, Tyrone, Londonderry	-	-	12	3.8	263	82.7	43	13.5	318
Total	16	.2	416	4.7	7336	82.4	1137	12.8	8905

TABLE IV-58. DARWIN'S POINT BY COUNTY SUBGROUPS

	Absent No.	%	Submedium No.	%	Medium No.	%	Pronounced No.	%	Total No.
W. Donegal	163	76.9	45	21.2	4	1.9	-	-	212
Mayo	460	79.4	100	17.3	18	3.1	1	.2	579
Sligo, Leitrim, S. Fermanagh, W. Cavan	503	70.3	191	26.7	21	2.9	-	-	715
W. Galway	330	76.6	86	20.0	14	3.2	1	.2	431
Aran Islands	122	87.8	12	8.6	5	3.6	-	-	139
Clare	721	76.4	198	21.0	25	2.6	-	-	944
Kerry	439	81.4	87	16.1	12	2.2	1	.2	539
Cork	452	78.6	109	19.0	14	2.4	-	-	575
Limerick	263	77.6	71	20.9	5	1.5	-	-	339
E. Galway, Roscommon	361	70.4	142	27.7	8	1.6	2	.2	513
Longford, Westmeath	392	58.2	246	36.6	30	4.4	5	.7	673
Offaly, Leix, Kildare	406	76.4	104	19.6	17	3.2	4	.8	531
Tipperary, Kilkenny	506	77.8	124	19.1	18	2.8	2	.3	650
Waterford, Wexford	352	76.0	92	19.9	19	4.1	-	-	463
Wicklow, Carlow	196	70.8	70	25.3	10	3.6	1	.4	277
Meath, Louth, Dublin	330	72.0	113	24.7	15	3.3	-	-	458
E.Cavan, Monaghan, Armagh	272	69.9	110	28.3	7	1.8	-	-	389
Antrim, Down	112	73.7	39	25.6	1	.6	-	-	152
N. Fermanagh, E.Donegal, Tyrone, Londonderry	231	72.6	82	25.8	4	1.2	1	.3	318
Total	6611	74.3	2021	22.7	247	2.8	18	.2	8897

TABLE IV-59. EAR LOBE ATTACHMENT BY COUNTY SUBGROUPS

	Soldered No.	%	Attached No.	%	Free No.	%	Total No.
W. Donegal	1	.5	95	44.8	116	54.7	212
Mayo	5	.9	243	41.9	332	57.2	580
Sligo, Leitrim, S. Fermanagh, W. Cavan	9	1.2	229	32.0	478	66.8	716
W. Galway	2	.5	171	39.6	259	60.0	432
Aran Islands	1	.7	31	22.3	107	77.0	139
Clare	17	1.8	348	36.8	581	61.4	946
Kerry	13	2.4	273	50.6	253	46.9	539
Cork	5	.9	280	48.7	290	50.4	575
Limerick	2	.6	169	49.7	169	49.7	340
E. Galway, Roscommon	9	1.8	148	28.8	357	69.4	514
Longford, Westmeath	6	.9	140	20.7	530	78.4	676
Offaly, Leix, Kildare	14	2.6	212	39.9	305	57.4	531
Tipperary, Kilkenny	11	1.7	332	51.1	307	47.2	650
Waterford, Wexford	11	2.4	197	42.6	254	55.0	462
Wicklow, Carlow	4	1.4	135	48.6	139	50.0	278
Meath, Louth, Dublin	5	1.1	194	42.4	259	56.6	458
E.Cavan, Monaghan, Armagh	3	.8	175	45.0	211	54.2	389
Antrim, Down	2	1.3	66	43.4	84	55.3	152
N. Fermanagh, E.Donegal, Tyrone, Londonderry	7	2.2	161	50.6	150	47.2	318
Total	127	1.4	3599	40.4	5181	58.2	8907

TABLE IV-60. EAR LOBE SIZE BY COUNTY SUBGROUPS

	Absent, submedium No.	%	Medium No.	%	Pronounced No.	%	Total No.
W. Donegal	-	-	116	54.7	96	45.3	212
Mayo	2	.3	356	61.4	222	38.3	580
Sligo, Leitrim, S. Fermanagh, W. Cavan	2	.3	408	57.1	305	42.6	715
W. Galway	2	.5	273	63.3	156	36.2	431
Aran Islands	1	.7	75	54.0	63	45.3	139
Clare	4	.4	586	61.9	356	37.6	946
Kerry	2	.4	290	53.8	247	45.8	539
Cork	2	.3	264	45.9	309	53.7	575
Limerick	4	1.2	169	49.7	167	49.1	340
E. Galway, Roscommon	9	1.7	319	61.9	187	36.3	515
Longford, Westmeath	4	.6	383	56.6	289	42.8	676
Offaly, Leix, Kildare	3	.6	270	50.8	258	48.6	531
Tipperary, Kilkenny	1	.2	324	49.8	325	50.0	650
Waterford, Wexford	-	-	189	40.8	274	59.2	463
Wicklow, Carlow	1	.4	126	45.3	151	54.3	278
Meath, Louth, Dublin	3	.6	248	54.1	207	45.2	458
E.Cavan, Monaghan, Armagh	-	-	191	49.1	198	50.9	389
Antrim, Down	-	-	76	50.1	76	50.0	152
N. Fermanagh, E.Donegal, Tyrone, Londonderry	2	.6	171	53.8	145	45.6	318
Total	42	.5	4834	54.3	4031	45.2	8907

TABLE IV-61. EAR PROTRUSION BY COUNTY SUBGROUPS

	Submedium		Medium		Pronounced		Total
	No.	%	No.	%	No.	%	No.
W. Donegal	2	.9	179	84.4	31	14.6	212
Mayo	2	.3	501	86.4	77	13.3	580
Sligo, Leitrim, S. Fermanagh, W. Cavan	3	.4	610	85.2	103	14.4	716
W. Galway	1	.2	340	78.7	91	21.1	432
Aran Islands	-	-	110	79.1	29	20.9	139
Clare	6	.6	715	75.6	225	23.8	946
Kerry	3	.6	403	74.8	133	24.7	539
Cork	3	.5	429	74.6	143	24.9	575
Limerick	3	.9	245	72.0	92	27.0	340
E. Galway, Roscommon	-	-	425	83.0	87	17.0	512
Longford, Westmeath	6	.9	539	79.8	130	19.2	675
Offaly, Leix, Kildare	3	.6	398	75.1	129	24.3	530
Tipperary, Kilkenny	7	1.1	497	76.5	146	22.5	650
Waterford, Wexford	7	1.5	364	78.6	92	19.9	463
Wicklow, Carlow	3	1.1	209	75.2	66	23.7	278
Meath, Louth, Dublin	3	.6	348	76.0	107	23.4	458
E.Cavan, Monaghan, Armagh	5	1.3	280	72.0	104	26.7	389
Antrim, Down	2	1.3	102	67.1	48	31.6	152
N. Fermanagh, E.Donegal, Tyrone, Londonderry	1	.3	202	63.5	115	36.2	318
Total	60	.7	6896	77.4	1948	21.9	8904

TABLE IV-62. TEMPORAL FULLNESS BY COUNTY SUBGROUPS

	Submedium		Medium		Pronounced		Total
	No.	%	No.	%	No.	%	No.
W. Donegal	40	18.9	127	59.9	45	21.2	212
Mayo	118	20.3	311	53.6	151	26.0	580
Sligo, Leitrim, S. Fermanagh, W. Cavan	88	12.3	427	59.6	201	28.1	716
W. Galway	76	17.6	237	54.9	119	27.5	432
Aran Islands	7	5.0	110	79.1	22	15.8	139
Clare	239	25.3	503	53.3	202	21.4	944
Kerry	108	20.0	280	51.9	151	28.0	539
Cork	116	20.2	305	53.0	154	26.8	575
Limerick	65	19.1	183	53.8	92	27.0	340
E. Galway, Roscommon	65	12.6	306	59.4	144	28.0	515
Longford, Westmeath	30	4.4	460	68.0	186	27.5	676
Offaly, Leix, Kildare	59	11.1	376	70.8	96	18.1	531
Tipperary, Kilkenny	89	13.7	416	64.0	145	22.3	650
Waterford, Wexford	68	14.7	312	67.4	83	17.9	463
Wicklow, Carlow	38	13.7	201	72.3	39	14.0	278
Meath, Louth, Dublin	75	16.4	304	66.4	79	17.2	458
E.Cavan, Monaghan, Armagh	64	16.4	249	64.0	76	19.5	389
Antrim, Down	19	12.5	107	70.4	26	17.1	152
N. Fermanagh, E.Donegal, Tyrone, Londonderry	42	13.2	217	68.2	59	18.6	318
Total	1406	15.8	5431	61.0	2070	23.2	8907

TABLE IV-63. OCCIPITAL PROTRUSION BY COUNTY SUBGROUPS

	Absent, submedium		Medium		Pronounced		Total
	No.	%	No.	%	No.	%	No.
W. Donegal	31	14.6	124	58.5	57	26.9	212
Mayo	42	7.2	467	80.5	71	12.2	580
Sligo, Leitrim, S. Fermanagh, W. Cavan	47	6.6	571	79.7	98	13.7	716
W. Galway	45	10.4	347	80.3	40	9.2	432
Aran Islands	3	2.2	130	93.5	6	4.3	139
Clare	105	11.1	699	74.0	141	14.9	945
Kerry	61	11.3	397	73.6	81	15.0	539
Cork	40	7.0	453	78.8	82	14.3	575
Limerick	25	7.4	259	76.2	56	16.5	340
E. Galway, Roscommon	49	9.5	402	78.0	64	12.4	515
Longford, Westmeath	49	7.2	542	80.3	84	12.4	675
Offaly, Leix, Kildare	33	6.2	387	73.0	110	20.8	530
Tipperary, Kilkenny	54	8.3	452	69.5	144	22.2	650
Waterford, Wexford	33	7.1	309	66.7	121	26.1	463
Wicklow, Carlow	21	7.6	186	66.9	71	25.5	278
Meath, Louth, Dublin	27	5.9	305	66.6	126	27.5	458
E.Cavan, Monaghan, Armagh	17	4.4	259	66.6	113	29.0	389
Antrim, Down	5	3.3	117	77.0	30	19.7	152
N. Fermanagh, E.Donegal, Tyrone, Londonderry	26	8.2	216	67.9	76	23.9	318
Total	713	8.0	6622	74.4	1571	17.6	8906

TABLE IV-64. LAMBDOID FLATTENING BY COUNTY SUBGROUPS

	Absent No.	%	Submedium No.	%	Medium No.	%	Pronounced No.	%	Total No.
W. Donegal	7	3.3	24	11.3	124	58.5	57	26.9	212
Mayo	33	5.7	85	14.7	293	50.7	167	28.9	578
Sligo, Leitrim, S. Fermanagh, W. Cavan	113	15.8	83	11.6	390	54.6	128	17.9	714
W. Galway	28	6.5	47	10.9	222	51.4	135	31.2	432
Aran Islands	8	5.8	22	15.9	44	31.9	64	46.4	138
Clare	70	7.4	122	12.9	405	42.8	349	36.9	946
Kerry	25	4.6	35	6.5	315	58.6	163	30.3	538
Cork	30	5.2	52	9.0	300	52.2	193	33.6	575
Limerick	13	3.8	23	6.8	152	44.7	152	44.7	340
E. Galway, Roscommon	61	11.8	63	12.2	254	49.3	137	26.6	515
Longford, Westmeath	36	5.3	147	21.8	299	44.3	193	28.6	675
Offaly, Leix, Kildare	140	26.4	28	5.3	236	44.4	127	23.9	531
Tipperary, Kilkenny	224	34.6	55	8.5	242	37.3	127	19.6	648
Waterford, Wexford	206	44.5	10	2.2	149	32.2	98	21.2	463
Wicklow, Carlow	96	34.5	5	1.8	116	41.7	61	21.9	278
Meath, Louth, Dublin	145	31.6	40	8.7	194	42.4	79	17.2	458
E.Cavan, Monaghan, Armagh	158	40.6	46	11.8	131	33.7	54	13.9	389
Antrim, Down	106	70.2	5	3.3	28	18.5	12	7.9	151
N. Fermanagh, E.Donegal, Tyrone, Londonderry	202	63.9	20	6.3	78	24.7	16	5.1	316
Total	1701	19.1	912	10.2	3972	44.6	2312	26.0	8897

TABLE IV-65. OCCIPITAL FLATTENING BY COUNTY SUBGROUPS

	Absent No.	%	Medium No.	%	Pronounced No.	%	Total No.
W. Donegal	183	86.3	23	10.8	6	2.8	212
Mayo	517	89.3	44	7.6	18	3.1	579
Sligo, Leitrim, S. Fermanagh, W. Cavan	617	86.2	77	10.8	22	3.1	716
W. Galway	395	91.4	32	7.4	5	1.2	432
Aran Islands	131	94.2	8	5.8	-	-	139
Clare	825	87.3	80	8.5	40	4.2	945
Kerry	465	86.3	65	12.0	9	1.7	539
Cork	503	87.6	57	9.9	14	2.4	574
Limerick	276	81.2	49	14.4	15	4.4	340
E. Galway, Roscommon	460	89.3	37	7.2	18	3.5	515
Longford, Westmeath	567	83.9	86	12.7	23	3.4	676
Offaly, Leix, Kildare	432	81.4	74	13.9	25	4.7	531
Tipperary, Kilkenny	479	73.7	130	20.0	41	6.3	650
Waterford, Wexford	317	68.5	102	22.0	44	9.5	463
Wicklow, Carlow	206	74.1	48	17.3	24	8.6	278
Meath, Louth, Dublin	363	79.2	68	14.8	27	5.9	458
E.Cavan, Monaghan, Armagh	266	68.6	101	26.0	21	5.4	388
Antrim, Down	67	44.1	65	42.8	20	13.2	152
N. Fermanagh, E.Donegal, Tyrone, Londonderry	177	55.7	107	33.6	34	10.7	318
Total	7246	81.4	1253	14.1	406	4.6	8905

TABLE IV-66. FACIAL ASYMMETRY BY COUNTY SUBGROUPS

	Absent No.	%	Left No.	%	Right No.	%	Total No.
W. Donegal	149	70.6	18	8.5	44	20.8	211
Mayo	435	75.1	58	10.0	86	14.8	579
Sligo, Leitrim, S. Fermanagh, W. Cavan	549	77.0	44	6.2	120	16.8	713
W. Galway	348	80.6	22	5.1	62	14.4	432
Aran Islands	135	97.1	-	-	4	2.9	139
Clare	604	63.9	94	9.9	247	26.1	945
Kerry	378	70.4	51	9.5	108	20.1	537
Cork	387	67.3	43	7.5	145	25.2	575
Limerick	222	65.5	36	10.6	81	23.9	339
E. Galway, Roscommon	393	76.3	34	6.6	88	17.1	515
Longford, Westmeath	562	83.9	47	7.0	61	9.1	670
Offaly, Leix, Kildare	409	77.2	33	6.2	88	16.6	530
Tipperary, Kilkenny	446	68.7	56	8.6	147	22.6	649
Waterford, Wexford	334	72.3	45	9.7	83	18.0	462
Wicklow, Carlow	215	77.3	23	8.3	40	14.4	278
Meath, Louth, Dublin	355	77.5	33	7.2	70	15.3	458
E.Cavan, Monaghan, Armagh	315	81.0	23	5.9	51	13.1	389
Antrim, Down	106	69.7	14	9.2	32	21.0	152
N. Fermanagh, E.Donegal, Tyrone, Londonderry	240	75.5	23	7.2	55	17.3	318
Total	6582	74.0	697	7.8	1612	18.1	8891

TABLE V-1. WEIGHT BY COUNTY SUBGROUPS

	Mean
1. E. Galway, Roscommon	161.00
2. Mayo	160.80
3. W. Galway	160.60
4. Kerry	160.50
5. Cork	159.60
6. Clare	159.10
7. Sligo, Leitrim, S. Fermanagh W.Cavan	158.50
8. Limerick	157.90
9. Tipperary, Kilkenny	157.70
10. Waterford, Wexford	156.50
11. Aran Islands	156.30
12. N.Fermanagh, E. Donegal, Tyrone, Londonderry	155.60
13. W. Donegal	155.30
14. Wicklow, Carlow	154.80
15. Antrim, Down	154.50
16. E.Cavan, Monaghan, Armagh	154.30
17. Offaly, Leix, Kildare	154.20
18. Meath, Louth, Dublin	153.00
19. Longford, Westmeath	151.00
Total	157.30

TABLE V-2. STATURE BY COUNTY SUBGROUPS

	Mean
1. Aran Islands	174.48
2. E. Galway, Roscommon	173.16
3. Kerry	173.04
4. W. Galway	172.98
5. Cork	172.47
6. Clare	172.20
7. Mayo	172.17
8. Limerick	171.96
9. Sligo, Leitrim, S. Fermanagh W. Cavan	171.84
10. Tipperary, Kilkenny	171.81
11. N.Fermanagh, E. Donegal, Tyrone, Londonderry	171.78
12. Antrim, Down	171.51
13. W. Donegal	171.48
14. Offaly, Leix, Kildare	171.42
15. Longford, Westmeath	171.36
16. Waterford, Wexford	171.00
17. Wicklow, Carlow	170.79
18. E. Cavan, Monagh, Armagh	170.79
19. Meath, Louth, Dublin	170.52
Total	171.90

TABLE V-3. THORACIC INDEX BY COUNTY SUBGROUPS

	Mean
1. Wicklow, Carlow	83.18
2. Waterford, Wexford	82.94
3. E.Cavan, Monaghan, Armagh	81.94
4. Tipperary, Kilkenny	81.90
5. Meath, Louth, Dublin	81.78
6. Offaly, Leix, Kildare	81.14
7. Cork	80.94
8. N.Fermanagh, E. Donegal, Tyrone, Londonderry	80.86
9. Antrim, Down	80.74
10. W.Donegal	80.50
11. Kerry	80.34
12. Sligo, Leitrim, S.Fermanagh, W.Cavan	80.06
13. Mayo	80.02
14. Clare	79.94
14. Limerick	79.94
15. E.Galway, Roscommon	79.54
17. W.Galway	78.74
18. Longford, Westmeath	78.74
19. Aran Islands	76.78
Total	80.54

TABLE V-4: HEAD LENGTH BY COUNTY SUBGROUPS

	Mean
1. Aran Islands	198.36
2. W.Galway	196.62
3. E. Galway, Roscommon	196.59
4. Sligo, Leitrim, S. Fermanagh, W. Cavan	196.11
5. Cork	195.90
6. E.Cavan, Monghan, Armagh	195.75
7. Longford, Westmeath	195.69
8. Clare	195.66
8. Meath, Louth, Dublin	195.66
10. Limerick	195.54
11. Mayo	195.48
12. N.Fermanagh, E. Donegal, Tyrone, Londonderry	195.42
13. Tipperary, Kilkenny	195.15
14. Kerry	195.12
15. Wicklow, Carlow	195.00
16. Antrim, Down	194.97
17. W.Donegal	194.94
17. Offaly, Leix, Kildare	194.94
19. Waterford, Wexford	194.76
Total	195.63

TABLE V-5. HEAD BREADTH BY COUNTY SUBGROUPS

	Mean
1. Kerry	155.92
2. Clare	155.65
3. Cork	155.56
4. Limerick	155.50
5. Mayo	155.14
6. W.Donegal	154.42
7. W.Galway	154.27
7. Aran Islands	154.27
9. E.Galway, Roscommon	154.36
10. Sligo, Leitrim, S. Fermanagh, W. Cavan	154.18
11. Tipperary, Kilkenny	154.12
12. N. Fermanagh, E. Donegal, Tyrone, Londonderry,	153.94
13. Antrim, Down	153.46
14. Waterford, Wexford	153.16
15. Wicklow, Carlow	152.47
16. Offaly, Leix, Kildare	152.44
16. E. Cavan, Monaghan, Armagh	152.44
18. Longford, Westmeath	152.41
19. Meath, Louth, Dublin	152.14
Total	154.12

TABLE V-6. CEPHALIC INDEX BY COUNTY SUBGROUPS

Dolichocephaly (59-76)		Brachycephaly (83-94)		Mesocephaly (77-82)	
Average mean	23.3	Average mean	12.5	Average mean	64.1
Arans	35.0	Kerry	21.4	Limerick	70.8
Longford, Westmeath	34.5	Clare	18.2	Antrim, Down	67.8
Meath, Louth, Dublin	33.5	Mayo	16.9	Wicklow, Carlow	67.3
E. Cavan, etc.	32.6	Cork	15.6	Cork	67.1
Offaly, Leix, Kildare	29.8	W. Donegal	15.1	Kerry	66.9
W. Galway	25.7	Limerick	14.7	W. Galway	66.0
Wicklow, Carlow	25.5	Tipperary, Kilkenny	14.0	Clare	65.6
N. Fermanagh, etc.	24.5	Antrim, Down	12.5	Sligo, Leitrim, etc.	65.3
Waterford, Wexford	24.4	N. Fermanagh, etc.	12.3	Mayo	65.3
E. Galway, Rosc.	24.4	Waterford, Wexford	11.4	E. Galway, Rosc.	65.3
Sligo, etc.	23.8	Sligo, etc.	11.0	W. Donegal	65.1
Tipperary Kilkenny	23.1	E. Galway, Rosc.	10.3	Waterford, Wexford	64.1
W. Donegal	19.8	Offaly, Leix, Kildare	9.2	N. Fermanagh, etc.	63.2
Antrim Down	19.7	E. Cavan, etc.	8.5	Tipperary, Kilkenny	62.9
Mayo	17.8	W. Galway	8.3	Meath, Louth, Dublin	61.5
Cork	17.2	Arans	8.0	Offaly, Leix, Kildare	60.9
Clare	16.2	Longford, Westmeath	7.7	E. Cavan, etc.	58.9
Limerick	14.4	Wicklow, Carlow	7.2	Longford, Westmeath	57.8
Kerry	11.7	Meath, Louth, Dublin	5.0	Arans	56.9

TABLE V-7. LENGTH-HEIGHT INDEX BY SUBGROUPS

	Mean
1. N. Fermanagh, E. Donegal, Tyrone, Londonderry	64.85
2. West Donegal	64.52
3. Offaly, Leix, Kildare	64.46
4. Tipperary, Kilkenny	64.43
4. Wicklow, Carlow	64.43
6. Antrim, Down	64.40
7. Waterford, Wexford	64.34
8. Limerick	64.28
9. Cork	64.07
10. Meath, Louth, Dublin	63.98
10. Clare	63.98
12. Mayo	63.92
12. Kerry	63.92
14. E. Cavan, Monaghan, Armagh	63.86
15. West Galway	63.53
16. East Galway, Roscommon	63.47
17. Sligo, Leitrim, S.Fermanagh, W. Cavan	63.32
18. Longford, Westmeath	62.87
19. Aran Islands	60.50
Total	63.89

TABLE V-8. BIZYGOMATIC DIAMETER BY COUNTY SUBGROUPS

	Mean
1. Kerry	142.30
2. Clare	142.00
2. Cork	142.00
4. Mayo	141.75
5. E. Galway, Roscommon	141.65
6. Limerick	141.40
6. W. Galway	141.40
8. Aran Islands	141.05
9. Sligo, Leitrim, S. Fermanagh, W. Cavan	140.95
10. Tipperary, Kilkenny	140.50
11. W. Donegal	140.40
12. N. Fermanagh, E. Donegal, Tyrone, Londonderry	140.25
13. Waterford, Wexford	140.00
14. Antrim, Down	139.95
15. Wicklow, Carlow	139.65
16. E. Cavan, Monaghan, Armagh	139.60
17. Meath, Louth, Dublin	139.25
18. Longford, Westmeath	139.20
19. Offaly, Leix, Kildare	139.10
Total	140.80

TABLE V-9. TOTAL FACE HEIGHT BY COUNTY SUBGROUPS

	Mean
1. Aran Islands	129.85
2. W. Galway	128.60
3. E. Cavan, Monaghan, Armagh	127.90
4. Kerry	127.45
5. Wicklow, Carlow	127.35
6. Mayo	127.25
7. Sligo, Leitrim, S.Fermanagh, W. Cavan	127.20
7. Tipperary, Kilkenny	127.20
9. E. Galway, Roscommon	127.15
10. W. Donegal	127.10
10. Cork	127.10
12. Offaly, Leix, Kildare	126.90
13. Waterford, Wexford	126.85
14. Limerick	126.70
15. Clare	126.55
16. Meath, Louth, Dublin	126.50
16. Antrim, Down	126.50
18. N. Fermanagh, E. Donegal, Tyrone, Londonderry	126.45
19. Longford Westmeath	126.35
Total	127.10

TABLE V-10. UPPER FACE HEIGHT BY COUNTY SUBGROUPS

	Mean
1. Kerry	73.85
2. Cork	73.70
2. Tipperary, Kilkenny	73.70
4. E.Cavan, Monaghan, Armagh	73.65
5. Wicklow, Carlow	73.60
5. Antrim, Down	73.60
7. N. Fermanagh, E. Donegal, Tyrone, Londonderry	73.50
8. W. Donegal	73.30
9. Waterford, Wexford	73.25
10. Offaly, Leix, Kildare	73.05
11. Mayo	73.00
12. W. Galway	72.80
12. Limerick	72.80
14. Clare	72.65
15. Aran Islands	72.50
16. Meath, Louth, Dublin	72.45
17. Sligo, Leitrim, S.Fermanagh, W. Cavan	71.90
18. E. Galway, Roscommon	71.80
19. Longford, Westmeath	70.60
Total	72.80

TABLE V-11. FACIAL INDEX BY COUNTY SUBGROUPS

	Mean
1. Aran Islands	91.70
2. E. Cavan, Monaghan, Arnagh	91.40
3. Offaly, Leix, Kildare	91.10
4. Wicklow, Carlow	91.00
5. West Galway	90.90
6. Meath, Louth, Dublin	90.70
7. Longford, Westmeath	90.65
8. Waterford, Wexford	90.45
9. West Donegal	90.40
9. Tipperary, Kilkenny	90.40
11. Sligo, Leitrim, S.Fermanagh, W. Cavan	90.30
12. Antrim, Down	90.20
13. N. Fermanagh, E. Donegal, Tyrone, Londonderry	90.05
14. East Galway, Roscommon	89.70
15. Mayo	89.60
16. Kerry	89.50
17. Limerick	89.45
18. Cork	89.35
19. Clare	89.25
Total	90.20

TABLE V-12. NOSE HEIGHT BY COUNTY SUBGROUPS

	Mean
1. Aran Islands	57.10
2. Kerry	56.94
3. Cork	56.90
4. Clare	56.86
5. Tipperary, Kilkenny	56.82
6. West Galway	56.74
7. Waterford, Wexford	56.58
8. Wicklow, Carlow	56.54
9. Mayo	56.30
10. E. Cavan, Monaghan, Armagh	56.18
11. West Donegal	56.14
12. Limerick	56.10
13. East Galway, Roscommon	56.06
14. Antrim, Down	56.02
15. Offaly, Leix, Kildare	55.98
16. Meath, Louth, Dublin	55.78
17. N. Fermanagh, E. Donegal, Tyrone, Londonderry	55.74
18. Sligo, Leitrim, S. Fermanagh, W. Cavan	55.70
19. Longford, Westmeath	55.30
Total	56.30

TABLE V-13. NOSE BREADTH BY COUNTY SUBGROUPS

	Mean
1. West Galway	36.59
2. Cork	36.47
3. Aran Islands	36.35
4. Offaly, Leix, Kildare	36.26
4. Kerry	36.26
6. N. Fermanagh, E. Donegal, Tyrone, Londonderry	36.23
7. Wicklow, Carlow	36.20
7. E. Cavan, Monaghan, Armagh	36.20
9. Mayo	36.11
10. Clare	36.05
11. Meath, Louth, Dublin	35.99
12. Waterford, Wexford	35.96
13. Tipperary, Kilkenny	35.90
13. East Galway, Roscommon	35.90
13. Sligo, Leitrim, S. Fermanagh, W. Cavan	35.90
16. Antrim, Down	35.78
17. Limerick	35.60
18. West Donegal	35.39
10. Longford, Westmeath	35.24
Total	36.02

TABLE V-14. NASAL INDEX BY COUNTY SUBGROUPS

	Mean
1. N. Fermanagh, E. Donegal, Tyrone, Londonderry	65.14
2. West Galway	65.10
3. Meath, Louth, Dublin	64.98
4. Sligo, Leitrim, S. Fermanagh, W. Cavan	64.94
5. Offaly, Leix, Kildare	64.86
6. E. Cavan, Monaghan, Armagh	64.82
7. Mayo	64.66
8. East Galway, Roscommon	64.46
9. Cork	64.42
10. Longford, Westmeath	64.30
11. Wicklow, Carlow	64.18
12. Antrim, Down	64.10
13. Waterford, Wexford	63.98
13. Kerry	63.98
13. Clare	63.98
16. Aran Islands	63.90
17. West Donegal	63.78
18. Limerick	63.70
19. Tipperary, Kilkenny	63.66
Total	64.38

TABLE V-15. FRONTO-PARIETAL INDEX BY COUNTY SUBGROUPS

	Mean
1. E. Cavan, Monaghan, Armagh	71.62
2. Waterford, Wexford	71.50
3. Meath, Louth, Dublin	71.44
4. Tipperary, Kilkenny	71.41
5. West Donegal	71.38
6. West Galway	71.35
7. Offaly, Leix, Kildare	71.29
8. Wicklow, Carlow	71.26
8. Mayo	71.26
10. Clare	71.08
11. Cork	71.05
12. N. Fermanagh, E. Donegal, Tyrone, Londonderry	71.02
13. East Galway, Roscommon	70.90
14. Sligo, Leitrim, S. Fermanagh, W. Cavan	70.66
15. Limerick	70.63
16. Longford, Westmeath	70.54
16. Antrim, Down	70.54
18. Kerry	70.39
19. Aran Islands	70.36
Total	71.05

TABLE V-16. ZYGO-FRONTAL INDEX BY COUNTY SUBGROUPS

	Mean
1. Tipperary, Kilkenny	78.46
2. West Donegal	78.38
3. E. Cavan, Monaghan, Armagh	78.22
4. Offaly, Leix, Kildare	78.14
4. Waterford, Wexford	78.14
6. Wicklow, Carlow	78.10
7. Meath, Louth, Dublin	78.06
8. N. Fermanagh, E. Donegal, Tyrone, Londonderry	78.02
9. Clare	77.90
9. West Galway	77.90
11. Mayo	77.86
12. Cork	77.70
13. Limerick	77.54
14. Antrim, Down	77.46
15. Sligo, Leitrim, S. Fermanagh, W. Cavan	77.34
16. Longford, Westmeath	77.30
17. East Galway, Roscommon	77.22
18. Kerry	77.02
19. Aran Islands	76.94
Total	77.78

TABLE V-17. SKIN COLOR, INNER ARM; COMBINED BRUNET AND SWARTHY, BY COUNTY SUBGROUPS

	No.	%
1. Longford, Westmeath	126	18.6
2. Aran Islands	20	14.4
3. Meath, Louth, Dublin	47	10.2
4. Offaly, Leix, Kildare	51	9.6
5. East Galway, Roscommon . .	43	8.4
6. West Galway	35	8.1
7. Wicklow, Carlow	22	8.0
8. Waterford, Wexford	35	7.6
8. West Donegal	16	7.6
10. Kerry	40	7.4
11. Sligo, Leitrim, S. Farmanagh, W. Cavan	52	7.3
12. Tipperary, Kilkenny	44	6.8
13. Cork	38	6.6
14. Limerick	22	6.5
15. Clare	59	6.2
16. E. Cavan, Monaghan, Armagh	23	5.9
17. Antrim, Down	8	5.3
17. N. Fermanagh, E. Donegal, Tyrone, Londonderry . .	17	5.3
19. Mayo	16	4.1
Total	722	8.1

TABLE V-19. HAIR FORM; STRAIGHT, BY COUNTY SUBGROUPS

	No.	%
1. Wicklow, Carlow	113	40.6
2. N. Fermanagh, E. Donegal, Tyrone, Londonderry . .	124	29.0
3. Aran Islands	52	37.4
4. Waterford, Wexford	172	37.1
5. E. Cavan, Monaghan, Armagh	144	37.0
6. Tipperary, Kilkenny	236	36.3
7. Cork	190	33.2
8. West Donegal	70	33.0
9. Kerry	175	32.5
10. Meath, Louth, Dublin	145	31.6
11. Limerick	100	29.5
12. Offaly, Leix, Kildare	147	27.7
13. West Galway	116	26.8
14. Antrim, Down	40	26.3
15. Clare	242	25.6
16. Sligo, Leitrim, S. Fermanagh, W. Cavan	157	21.9
17. Mayo	126	21.7
18. East Galway, Roscommon . .	110	21.4
19. Longford, Westmeath	96	14.2

Hair Form by County Subgroups; Deep Waves, Curly, Frizzly, Woolly

	No.	%
1. Longford, Westmeath	187	27.6
2. Offaly, Leix, Kildare	135	25.5
3. Cork	145	25.3
4. Antrim, Down	38	25.0
5. Mayo	138	23.8
6. West Donegal	49	23.1
6. East Galway, Roscommon . .	119	23.1
6. Meath, Louth, Dublin	106	23.1
9. Clare	203	21.4
10. Tipperary, Kilkenny	131	20.2
11. Sligo, Leitrim, S. Fermanagh W. Cavan	144	20.1
12. Kerry	107	19.9
13. West Galway	81	18.7
14. Limerick	63	18.6
15. N. Fermanagh, E. Donegal, Tyrone, Londonderry . .	59	18.5
16. Aran Islands	25	18.0
17. Wicklow, Carlow	46	16.6
18. E. Cavan, Monaghan, Armagh	63	16.2
19. Waterford, Wexford	74	16.0
Total	1913	21.5

TABLE V-18. FRECKLES; COMBINED MEDIUM AND PRONOUNCED, BY COUNTY SUBGROUPS

	No.	%
1. West Donegal	67	31.5
2. Aran Islands	36	25.9
3. Mayo	131	22.6
4. Kerry	121	22.5
5. Limerick	61	17.9
6. Cork	94	16.3
7. Sligo, Leitrim, S. Fermanagh, W. Cavan	106	14.8
8. Antrim, Down	22	14.5
9. Longford, Westmeath	97	14.4
10. West Galway	61	14.2
11. N. Fermanagh, E. Donegal, Tyrone, Londonderry . .	43	13.5
12. Clare	126	13.3
13. East Galway, Roscommon . .	60	11.6
14. Offaly, Leix, Kildare	51	9.6
15. Tipperary, Kilkenny	51	7.9
16. Meath, Louth, Dublin	36	7.8
17. Waterford, Wexford	33	7.1
18. E. Cavan, Monaghan, Armagh	23	5.9
19. Wicklow, Carlow	14	5.0
Total	1233	13.8

TABLE V-20. HAIR COLOR; COMBINED BLACK AND DARK BROWN, BY COUNTY SUBGROUPS

	No.	%
1. E. Cavan, Monaghan, Armagh	196	50.4
2. Waterford, Wexford	232	50.0
3. Meath, Louth, Dublin	223	48.7
4. Mayo	281	48.4
5. Antrim, Down	73	48.0
6. Wicklow, Carlow	132	47.5
7. Kerry	253	46.9
8. West Donegal	99	46.7
9. Offaly, Leix, Kildare	246	46.4
10. Tipperary, Kilkenny	300	46.1
11. N. Fermanagh, E. Donegal, Tyrone, Londonderry . .	138	43.4
11. Limerick	147	43.4
13. Clare	407	43.0
14. Cork	235	40.9
15. West Galway	172	39.8
16. Sligo, Leitrim, S. Fermanagh W. Cavan	258	36.1
17. E. Galway, Roscommon	173	33.6
18. Longford, Westmeath	185	27.8
19. Aran Islands	32	23.7
Total	3782	42.6

TABLE V-21. HAIR COLOR; COMBINED BROWN AND RED-BROWN, BY COUNTY SUBGROUPS

	No.	%
1. Aran Islands	81	60.0
2. Longford, Westmeath	327	49.2
3. East Galway, Roscommon . .	238	46.2
4. West Galway	180	41.7
5. Clare	391	41.4
6. Sligo, Leitrim, S. Fermanagh W. Cavan	291	40.7
7. Limerick	137	40.4
8. West Donegal	84	39.6
8. N. Fermanagh, E. Donegal, Tyrone, Londonderry . .	126	39.6
10. Cork	224	39.0
10. E. Cavan, Monaghan, Armagh	152	39.0
12. Offaly, Leix, Kildare	205	38.6
13. Wicklow, Carlow	107	38.4
14. Antrim, Down	58	38.1
15. Mayo	218	37.6
16. Meath, Louth, Dublin	170	37.1
17. Kerry	197	36.5
18. Tipperary, Kilkenny	231	35.6
19. Waterford, Wexford	134	28.9
Total	3551	40.0

TABLE V-22. HAIR COLOR; COMBINED GOLDEN BROWN, ASH BROWN, AND GOLDEN, BY COUNTY SUBGROUPS

	No.	%
1. Longford, Westmeath	104	15.6
2. Waterford, Wexford	66	14.2
3. Cork	78	13.6
4. N. Fermanagh, E. Donegal, Tyrone, Londonderry	38	11.9
5. East Galway, Roscommon	59	11.5
5. West Galway	50	11.5
7. Tipperary, Kilkenny	72	11.0
8. Kerry	57	10.6
9. Sligo, Leitrim, S. Fermanagh W. Cavan	74	10.4
10. Limerick	34	10.0
11. Offaly, Leix, Kildare	50	9.5
12. Antrim, Down	14	9.2
13. Meath, Louth, Dublin	38	8.3
14. Clare	75	7.9
14. Wicklow, Carlow	22	7.9
16. Aran Islands	10	7.4
17. East Cavan, Monaghan, Armagh	27	7.0
18. Mayo	38	6.5
19. West Donegal	10	4.7
Total	916	10.3

TABLE V-23. EYE COLOR; COMBINED GRAY-BROWN, GREEN-BROWN, AND BLUE-BROWN, BY COUNTY SUBGROUPS

	No.	%
1. Kerry	339	62.9
2. Cork	360	62.7
3. West Donegal	121	57.0
4. Mayo	325	56.1
4. Aran Islands	78	56.1
6. Limerick	190	55.9
7. Clare	510	53.9
8. Tipperary, Kilkenny	342	52.6
9. West Galway	224	51.8
10. Sligo, Leitrim, S. Fermanagh W. Cavan	365	51.0
11. Longford, Westmeath	342	50.6
12. East Galway, Roscommon	259	50.3
13. Offaly, Leix, Kildare	265	49.9
14. Meath, Louth, Dublin	223	48.7
15. Antrim, Down	73	48.1
16. Waterford, Wexford	217	46.9
17. Wicklow, Carlow	120	43.2
17. E. Cavan, Monaghan, Armagh	168	43.2
19. N. Fermanagh, E. Donegal, Tyrone, Londonderry	132	41.5
Total	4653	52.3

TABLE V-24. COMBINED LIGHT EYES, (GRAY, GRAY-BLUE, BLUE), BY COUNTY SUBGROUPS

Eye Color	No.	%
1. N. Fermanagh, E. Donegal, Tyrone, Londonderry	184	57.9
2. Wicklow, Carlow	156	56.1
3. E. Cavan, Monaghan, Armagh	214	55.0
4. Waterford, Wexford	242	52.3
5. Antrim, Down	76	49.9
6. Meath, Louth, Dublin	228	49.8
7. E. Galway, Roscommon	252	48.9
8. Offaly, Leix, Kildare	258	48.6
9. Longford, Westmeath	326	48.2
10. W. Galway	206	47.6
11. Sligo, Leitrim, S. Fermanagh W. Cavan	340	47.5
12. Tipperary, Kilkenny	302	46.5
13. Clare	432	45.7
14. Aran Islands	61	43.9
15. Mayo	252	43.5
15. Limerick	148	43.5
17. W. Donegal	90	42.5
18. Cork	209	36.4
19. Kerry	194	36.0
Total	4171	46.8

TABLE V-25. BROWN RIDGES; COMBINED ABSENT AND SUBMEDIUM, COMBINED PRONOUNCED AND VERY PRONOUNCED BY COUNTY SUBGROUPS

Absent and Submedium	No.	%
1. E. Cavan, Monaghan, Armagh	152	39.0
2. N. Fermanagh, E. Donegal, Tyrone, Londonderry	110	34.6
3. Wicklow, Carlow	83	29.8
4. Meath, Louth, Dublin	136	29.7
5. West Donegal	56	26.4
5. Offaly, Leix, Kildare	140	26.4
7. Antrim, Down	40	26.3
8. Tipperary, Kilkenny	148	22.8
9. Sligo, Leitrim, S. Fermanagh, W. Cavan	152	21.3
10. Limerick	72	21.2
11. Mayo	111	19.2
12. Longford, Westmeath	125	18.5
13. Waterford, Wexford	85	18.4
14. Kerry	98	18.2
15. Aran Islands	25	18.0
16. West Galway	77	17.9
17. Clare	154	16.3
18. East Galway, Roscommon	78	15.2
19. Cork	78	13.6
Total	1920	21.6

Pronounced and Very Pronounced	No.	%
1. Aran Islands	47	33.8
2. Antrim, Down	43	28.3
3. Kerry	150	27.9
4. Tipperary, Kilkenny	176	27.1
5. N. Fermanagh, E. Donegal, Tyrone, Londonderry	80	25.2
6. Cork	144	25.0
7. Wicklow, Carlow	65	23.4
8. Meath, Louth, Dublin	107	23.3
9. Waterford, Wexford	107	23.1
10. Offaly, Leix, Kildare	140	22.0
11. East Galway, Roscommon	111	21.6
12. Longford, Westmeath	137	20.3
13. Clare	174	18.4
14. Sligo, Leitrim, S. Fermanagh W. Cavan	127	17.7
15. West Donegal	36	17.0
16. Limerick	57	16.8
17. Mayo	80	13.7
18. E. Cavan, Monaghan, Armagh	45	11.6
Total	1852	20.8

TABLE V-26. BROW RIDGES; EXCESS PERCENTAGES OF PRONOUNCED AND VERY PRONOUNCED OVER ABSENT AND SUBMEDIUM, BY COUNTY SUBGROUPS

	%
1. Aran Islands	15.8
2. Cork	11.4
3. Kerry	9.7
4. E. Galway	6.4
5. Waterford, Wexford	4.7
6. Tipperary, Kilkenny	4.3
7. Clare	2.1
8. Antrim, Down	2.0
9. Longford, Westmeath	1.8
10. Sligo, Leitrim, S. Fermanagh, West Cavan	-3.6
11. Offaly, Leix, Kildare	-4.4
12. Limerick	-4.8
13. Mayo	-5.5
14. W. Galway	-6.4
14. Wicklow, Carlow	-6.4
14. Meath, Louth, Dublin	-6.4
17. W. Donegal	-9.4
18. N. Fermanagh, E. Donegal, Tyrone, Londonderry	-9.4
19. E. Cavan, Monaghan, Armagh	-27.4

TABLE V-27. FOREHEAD HEIGHT BY COUNTY SUBGROUPS

Submedium and Medium	No.	%
1. Aran Islands	105	75.5
2. Longford, Westmeath	433	64.4
3. Clare	569	60.2
4. West Galway	259	60.0
5. East Galway, Roscommon	276	53.8
6. Sligo, Leitrim, S.Fermanagh, W. Cavan	369	51.5
7. Mayo	267	46.1
8. Waterford, Wexford	195	42.1
9. Limerick	140	41.2
10. Cork	229	39.8
11. Offaly, Leix, Kildare	209	39.4
12. West Donegal	79	37.2
13. Tipperary, Kilkenny	241	37.1
14. Meath, Louth, Dublin	169	36.8
15. Wicklow, Carlow	101	36.3
16. Kerry	192	35.6
17. E. Cavan, Monaghan, Armagh	130	33.4
18. N. Fermanagh, E. Donegal, Tyrone, Londonderry	106	33.3
19. Antrim, Down	50	32.9
Total	4119	46.2

Pronounced	No.	%
1. Antrim, Down	102	67.1
2. N. Fermanagh, E. Donegal, Tyrone, Londonderry	212	66.7
3. E. Cavan, Monaghan, Armagh	259	66.6
4. Kerry	347	64.4
5. Wicklow, Carlow	177	63.7
6. Meath, Louth, Dublin	289	63.1
7. Tipperary, Kilkenny	409	62.9
8. West Donegal	133	62.7
9. Offaly, Leix, Kildare	322	60.6
10. Cork	346	60.2
11. Limerick	200	58.8
12. Waterford, Wexford	268	57.9
13. Mayo	312	53.9
14. Sligo, Leitrim, S.Fermanagh, West Cavan	347	48.5
15. East Galway, Roscommon	237	46.2
16. West Galway	173	40.0
17. Clare	377	39.8
18. Longford, We stmeath	239	35.6
19. Aran Islands	34	24.5
Total	4783	53.7

TABLE V-28. FOREHEAD HEIGHT; EXCESS PERCENTAGES OF PRONOUNCED OVER SUBMEDIUM AND MEDIUM, BY COUNTY SUBGROUPS

	%
1. Antrim, Down	34.2
2. N. Fermanagh, etc.	33.4
3. E. Cavan, Monagh. Arm.	33.2
4. Kerry	28.8
5. Wicklow, Carlow	27.4
6. Meath, Louth, Dublin	26.3
7. Tipperary, Kilkenny	25.8
8. W. Donegal	25.5
9. Offaly, Leix, Kildare	21.2
10. Cork	20.4
11. Limerick	17.6
12. Waterford, Wexford	15.8
13. Mayo	7.8
14. Sligo, Leitrim, etc.	- 3.0
15. E. Galway, Roscommon	- 7.6
16. W. Galway	- 20.0
17. Clare	- 20.4
18. Longford, Westmeath	- 28.8
19. Aran Islands	- 51.0

TABLE V-29. FOREHEAD SLOPE; FORWARD, ABSENT, SUBMEDIUM (A) MINUS PRONOUNCED, VERY PRONOUNCED (B), BY COUNTY SUBGROUPS

	A	B	A-B
1. W. Donegal	65.6	5.2	60.4
2. N. Fermanagh, etc.	66.2	8.1	58.1
3. E. Cavan, etc.	64.2	6.7	57.5
4. Mayo	60.7	6.4	54.3
5. Sligo, etc.	57.1	4.3	52.8
6. Tipperary, Kilkenny	59.8	8.8	51.0
7. Kerry	56.4	6.5	49.9
8. Antrim, Down	59.2	10.5	48.7
9. Meath, Louth, Dublin	55.9	7.4	48.5
10. Offaly, Leix, Kildare	55.0	6.6	48.4
11. Limerick	56.2	8.8	47.4
12. Wicklow, Carlow	53.3	10.8	42.5
13. E. Galway, Roscommon	47.5	6.8	40.7
14. Clare	46.1	6.6	39.5
15. Cork	49.1	10.1	39.0
16. Waterford, Wexford	50.7	12.3	38.4
17. Longford, Westmeath	42.6	5.3	37.3
18. W. Galway	43.3	8.8	34.5
19. Arans	26.6	7.2	19.4
Totals	53.2	7.4	45.8

TABLE V-30. NASION DEPRESSION; EXCESS PERCENTAGES OF PRONOUNCED OVER ABSENT AND SUBMEDIUM, BY COUNTY SUBGROUPS

	%
1. Kerry	22.9
2. Wicklow, Carlow	20.8
3. Cork	18.6
4. Antrim, Down	18.3
5. Waterford, Wexford	16.4
6. Offaly, Leix, Kildare	14.3
7. Tipperary, Kilkenny	14.0
8. E. Cavan, Monaghan, Armagh	13.4
9. N. Fermanagh, E. Donegal, Tyrone, Londonderry	12.0
10. Limerick	10.3
11. Mayo	9.8
12. Longford, Westmeath	9.7
13. Meath, Louth, Dublin	9.4
14. West Donegal	8.5
15. Clare	5.3
16. Aran Islands	2.2
17. West Galway	1.1
18. East Galway, Roscommon	.3
19. Sligo, Leitrim, S. Fermanagh, West Cavan	- 2.4
Total	9.3

TABLE V-31. NASAL ROOT HEIGHT; COMBINED PRONOUNCED AND VERY PRONOUNCED, BY COUNTY SUBGROUPS

	No.	%
1. Aran Islands	38	27.3
2. Tipperary, Kilkerry	168	25.9
3. Wicklow, Carlow	72	25.9
4. Waterford, Wexford	117	25.3
5. Meath, Louth, Dublin	111	24.3
6. East Galway, Roscommon	123	23.8
7. West Donegal	50	23.6
8. Cork	125	21.7
9. Kerry	113	20.9
10. Sligo, Leitrim, S.Fermanagh, W. Cavan	142	19.8
11. Limerick	65	19.1
12. Clare	159	16.8
13. N. Fermanagh, E. Donegal, Tyrone, Londonderry	53	16.7
14. Antrim, Down	25	16.4
15. E. Cavan, Monaghan, Armagh	63	16.2
16. West Galway	69	15.9
17. Mayo	91	15.6
18. Offaly, Leix, Kildare	78	14.7
19. Longford, Westmeath	97	14.3
Total	1759	19.7

TABLE V-32. NASAL ROOT BREADTH; COMBINED PRONOUNCED AND VERY PRONOUNCED, BY COUNTY SUBGROUPS

	No.	%
1. Waterford, Wexford	171	37.0
2. Tipperary, Kilkerry	226	34.9
3. E. Cavan, Monaghan, Armagh	126	32.4
4. Wicklow, Carlow	82	29.4
5. Meath, Louth, Dublin	134	29.3
6. N. Fermanagh, E. Donegal, Tyrone, Londonderry	91	28.6
7. Mayo	159	27.5
8. West Donegal	58	27.4
9. Offaly, Leix, Kildare	141	26.6
10. Cork	151	26.3
10. Antrim, Down	40	26.3
12. West Galway	107	24.8
13. Kerry	130	24.2
14. Aran Islands	33	23.7
15. East Galway, Roscommon	117	22.7
16. Limerick	74	21.8
17. Sligo, Leitrim, S.Fermanagh, W. Cavan	154	21.5
18. Clare	201	21.2
19. Longford, Westmeath	92	13.6
Total	2287	25.6

TABLE V-33. NASAL BRIDGE HEIGHT; COMBINED PRONOUNCED AND VERY PRONOUNCED, BY COUNTY SUBGROUPS

	No.	%
1. Wicklow, Carlow	93	33.4
2. Tipperary, Kilkerry	196	30.2
3. Waterford, Wexford	133	28.7
3. Cork	165	28.7
5. Kerry	151	28.1
6. Meath, Louth, Dublin	115	25.0
7. Antrim, Down	36	23.7
8. E. Cavan, Monaghan, Armagh	89	22.9
9. N. Fermanagh, E. Donegal, Tyrone, Londonderry	66	20.7
10. Limerick	70	20.6
11. West Donegal	42	19.8
12. Aran Islands	27	19.4
13. Clare	174	18.5
14. Offaly, Leix, Kildare	95	17.8
15. East Galway, Roscommon	82	16.0
16. Sligo, Leitrim, S.Fermanagh, W. Cavan	103	14.3
17. Mayo	75	12.9
18. West Galway	51	11.8
19. Longford, Westmeath	72	10.6
Total	1835	20.6

TABLE V-34. NASAL BRIDGE BREADTH; COMBINED PRONOUNCED AND VERY PRONOUNCED, BY COUNTY SUBGROUPS

	No.	%
1. Meath, Louth, Dublin	146	31.8
2. Waterford, Wexford	146	31.6
3. E.Cavan, Monaghan, Armagh	114	29.3
4. Antrim, Down	44	28.9
5. N. Fermanagh, E. Donegal, Tyrone, Londonderry	88	27.6
6. Cork	156	27.1
7. Tipperary, Kilkerry	174	26.9
8. Offaly, Leix, Kildare	136	25.6
9. Wicklow, Carlow	71	25.5
10. Kerry	126	23.4
11. Clare	178	18.8
12. Limerick	61	17.9
13. Mayo	97	16.8
14. Sligo, Leitrim, S. Fermanagh, W. Cavan	97	13.6
15. West Donegal	28	13.2
16. West Galway	55	12.8
17. East Galway, Roscommon	63	12.2
18. Longford, Westmeath	75	11.1
19. Aran Islands	15	10.8
Total	1870	21.0

TABLE V-35. NASAL TIP, THICKNESS; COMBINED PRONOUNCED AND VERY PRONOUNCED, BY COUNTY SUBGROUPS

	No.	%
1. Meath, Louth, Dublin	162	35.4
2. Waterford, Wexford	154	33.3
3. E.Cavan, Monaghan, Armagh	126	32.4
4. N. Fermanagh, E. Donegal, Tyrone, Londonderry	103	32.3
5. Wicklow, Carlow	88	31.6
6. Antrim, Down	46	30.3
7. Offaly, Leix, Kildare	156	29.4
7. Cork	169	29.4
9. Kerry	154	28.7
10. Tipperary, Kilkerry	172	26.6
11. Mayo	152	26.2
12. Sligo, Leitrim, S. Fermanagh, W. Cavan	166	23.2
13. Clare	105	21.7
14. Limerick	69	20.3
15. West Donegal	42	19.8
16. West Galway	78	18.0
17. East Galway, Roscommon	85	16.5
18. Longford, Westmeath	95	14.0
19. Aran Islands	18	12.9
Total	2240	25.1

TABLE V-36. NASAL PROFILE; EXCESS OF CONCAVE OVER CONVEX, BY COUNTY SUBGROUPS

	%
1. Longford, Westmeath	41.7
2. East Galway, Roscommon	33.7
3. Aran Islands	32.2
4. Offaly, Leix, Kildare	21.8
5. Sligo, Leitrim, S. Fermanagh, W. Cavan	16.9
6. Antrim, Down	13.1
7. Meath, Louth, Dublin	12.7
8. Waterford, Wexford	11.7
9. N. Fermanagh, E. Donegal, Tyrone, Londonderry	10.8
10. Mayo	9.6
11. E. Cavan, Monaghan, Armagh	9.4
12. Tipperary, Kilkenny	6.5
13. Wicklow, Carlow	5.8
14. Kerry	1.0
15. West Galway	- .4
16. Clare	-1.3
17. Cork	-3.4
18. West Donegal	-4.8
19. Limerick	-8.3
Total	10.1

TABLE V-37. MID-FACIAL PROGNATHISM; COMBINED SUBMEDIUM, MEDIUM, AND PRONOUNCED, BY COUNTY SUBGROUPS

	No.	%
1. Wicklow, Carlow	66	23.7
2. Waterford, Wexford	69	14.9
3. Offaly, Leix, Kildare	76	14.4
4. E. Cavan, Monaghan, Armagh	47	12.1
5. Tipperary, Kilkenny	78	12.0
6. Meath, Louth, Dublin	52	11.4
7. Antrim, Down	14	9.2
8. Longford, Westmeath	59	8.7
9. West Donegal	14	6.6
10. Cork	37	6.5
11. N. Fermanagh, E. Donegal, Tyrone, Londonderry	20	6.3
12. E. Galway, Roscommon	31	6.0
13. West Galway	25	5.8
14. Sligo, Leitrim, S. Farmanagh, W. Cavan	41	5.7
15. Limerick	16	4.7
16. Kerry	20	3.7
17. Clare	32	3.3
18. Mayo	13	2.2
19. Aran Islands	2	1.4
Total	712	8.1

TABLE V-38. TEETH, LOSS; NONE, VERY SMALL, SUBMEDIUM (A), OVER MEDIUM PRONOUNCED (B), BY COUNTY SUBGROUPS

	A	B	A-B
1. Aran Islands	83.4	16.5	66.9
2. N. Fermanagh, E. Donegal, Tyrone, Londonderry	74.9	25.2	59.7
3. W. Donegal	78.8	21.2	57.6
4. Antrim, Down	76.9	23.1	53.8
5. Mayo	76.4	23.7	52.7
6. W. Galway	75.7	24.4	51.3
7. E. Galway, Roscommon	73.9	26.1	47.8
8. Sligo, Leitrim, S. Fermanagh W. Cavan	72.0	27.9	44.1
9. Longford, Westmeath	71.3	28.7	42.6
10. Limerick	68.2	31.8	36.4
11. Offaly, Leix, Kildare	68.1	31.9	36.2
12. E. Cavan, Monaghan, Armagh	67.6	32.3	35.3
13. Kerry	67.3	32.6	34.7
14. Meath, Louth, Dublin	66.6	33.4	33.2
15. Wicklow, Carlow	65.7	34.2	31.5
16. Tipperary, Kilkenny	65.7	34.3	31.4
17. Clare	62.8	37.2	25.6
18. Cork	60.0	40.0	20.0
19. Waterford, Wexford	56.4	43.6	12.8
Total	68.7	31.2	37.5

TABLE V-39. TEETH, CARIES; NONE, VERY SMALL, SUBMEDIUM (A), MINUS MEDIUM PRONOUNCED (B), BY COUNTY SUBGROUPS

	A	B	A-B
1. N. Fermanagh, E. Donegal, Tyrone, Londonderry	78.2	21.8	56.4
2. Antrim, Down	77.6	22.4	55.2
3. E. Cavan, Monaghan, Armagh	72.8	27.3	45.5
4. Offaly, Leix, Kildare	71.0	28.9	42.1
5. Sligo, Leitrim, S. Fermanagh, W. Cavan	70.6	29.4	41.2
6. Aran Islands	70.4	29.6	40.8
7. E. Galway, Roscommon	68.2	31.9	36.3
8. Tipperary, Kilkenny	67.9	32.1	35.8
9. Waterford, Wexford	66.7	33.4	33.3
10. Meath, Louth, Dublin	66.6	33.4	33.2
11. West Donegal	65.9	34.1	31.8
12. Mayo	64.5	35.5	31.0
13. Longford, Westmeath	63.7	36.2	27.5
14. W. Galway	62.1	37.9	24.2
15. Wicklow, Carlow	60.2	39.8	20.4
16. Cork	57.4	42.6	14.8
17. Clare	56.0	44.0	12.0
18. Kerry	55.8	44.1	11.7
19. Limerick	53.6	46.4	7.2
Total	64.8	35.1	29.7

TABLE V-40. MALARS, LATERAL PROJECTION, COMBINED AND VERY PRONOUNCED, BY COUNTY SUBGROUPS

	No.	%
1. Mayo	279	48.1
2. Limerick	157	46.1
2. West Galway	199	46.1
4. Kerry	247	45.8
5. West Donegal	91	42.9
6. Cork	223	38.8
7. Tipperary, Kilkenny	244	37.6
8. N. Fermanagh, E. Donegal, Tyrone, Londonderry	116	36.5
9. Clare	339	35.9
10. East Galway, Roscommon	181	34.8
11. Sligo, Leitrim, S. Fermanagh, W. Cavan	227	31.7
12. Wicklow, Carlow	88	31.6
13. Meath, Louth, Dublin	140	30.5
14. E. Cavan, Monaghan, Armagh	116	29.8
15. Waterford, Wexford	131	28.3
16. Antrim, Down	42	27.6
17. Offaly, Leix, Kildare	120	22.7
18. Longford, Westmeath	130	19.2
19. Aran Islands	21	15.1
Total	3091	34.7

TABLE V-41. GONIAL ANGLES; COMBINED PRONOUNCED AND VERY PRONOUNCED, BY COUNTY SUBGROUPS

	No.	%
1. Kerry	231	42.9
2. Limerick	145	42.7
3. Mayo	236	40.7
4. West Donegal	84	39.6
5. Antrim, Down	59	38.8
6. N. Fermanagh, E. Donegal, Tyrone, Londonderry	123	38.7
7. Cork	206	35.9
8. West Galway	158	34.3
9. Wicklow, Carlow	92	33.1
10. Tipperary, Kilkenny	214	32.9
10. Clare	311	32.9
12. Meath, Louth, Dublin	147	32.0
13. E. Cavan, Monaghan, Armagh	122	31.3
14. Sligo, Leitrim, S. Fermanagh, W. Cavan	211	29.5
15. Waterford, Wexford	136	29.3
16. East Galway, Roscommon	148	28.7
17. Offaly, Leix, Kildare	132	24.9
18. Longford, Westmeath	147	21.8
19. Aran Islands	26	18.7
Total	2918	32.7

TABLE V-42. EAR HELIX; COMBINED VERY SMALL AND SUBMEDIUM, BY COUNTY SUBGROUPS

	No.	%
1. Wicklow, Carlow	93	33.4
2. N. Fermanagh, E. Donegal, Tyrone, Londonderry	99	31.2
3. Cork	170	29.6
4. West Donegal	61	28.8
5. Mayo	166	28.6
6. Limerick	94	27.6
6. Waterford, Wexford	128	27.6
8. Tipperary, Kilkenry	178	27.4
9. Clare	257	27.2
10. Kerry	133	24.7
11. Antrim, Down	37	24.3
12. E. Cavan, Monaghan, Armagh	92	23.7
13. Meath, Louth, Dublin	95	20.7
14. Offaly, Leix, Kildare	91	17.1
15. East Galway, Roscommon	78	15.1
15. West Galway	65	15.1
17. Longford, Westmeath	101	14.9
18. Sligo, Leitrim, S. Fermanagh, W. Cavan	87	12.1
19. Aran Islands	11	7.9
Total	2016	22.9

TABLE V-43. OCCIPITAL PROTRUSION; ABSENT, SUBMEDIUM (A), OVER PRONOUNCED (B), BY COUNTY SUBGROUPS

	A	B	A-B
1. E. Cavan, Monaghan, Armagh	4.4	29.0	24.6
2. Meath, Louth, Dublin	5.9	27.5	21.6
3. Waterford, Wexford	7.1	26.1	19.0
4. Wicklow, Carlow	7.6	25.5	17.9
5. Antrim, Down	3.3	19.7	16.4
6. N. Fermanagh, E. Donegal, Tyrone, Londonderry	8.2	23.9	15.7
7. Offaly, Leix, Kildare	6.2	20.8	14.6
8. Tipperary, Kilkenny	8.3	22.2	13.9
9. W. Donegal	14.6	26.9	12.3
10. Limerick	7.4	16.5	9.1
11. Cork	7.0	14.3	7.3
12. Sligo, Leitrim, S. Fermanagh, W. Cavan	6.6	13.7	7.1
13. Longford, Westmeath	7.2	12.4	5.2
14. Mayo	7.2	12.2	5.0
15. Clare	11.1	14.9	3.8
16. Kerry	11.3	15.0	3.7
17. E. Galway, Roscommon	9.5	12.4	2.9
18. Aran Islands	2.2	4.3	2.1
19. W. Galway	10.4	9.2	-1.2
Totals	8.0	17.6	9.6

TABLE V-44. COUNTY MAYO, COMPARATIVE DATA.

	Clare Island, Inishturk		Browne Ballycroy		Mullet, Inishkea, Portacloy		Dupertuis Mayo Sample	
	No.	Mean	No.	Mean	No.	Mean	No.	Mean
Age	56	19-63*	45	19-70*	58	17-60*	580	35.25
Stature	56	169.6	50	172.1	62	172.5	578	172.17
Relative Sitting Height	56	52.1	49	53.1	62	51.3	578	53.22
Relative Span	56	105.7	50	105.75	61	104.36	572	105.88
Cephalic Index	56	79.4	50	80.5	62	79.4	580	79.41
Nasal Index	56	67.6	50	63.9	62	64.0	579	64.66

*Range

TABLE V-45. COUNTY MAYO, COMPARATIVE DATA.

Observations	Clare Island, Inishturk		Browne Ballycroy		Mullet, Inishkea, Portacloy		Total		Dupertuis Mayo Sample	
	No.	%	No.	%	No.	%	No.	%	No.	%
Eye Color:										
Light	54	72.97	119	78.81	179	86.89	352	81.67	252	43.60
Medium	20	27.03	23	15.23	19	9.22	62	14.39	325	56.23
Dark	0	0.00	9	5.96	8	3.89	17	3.94	1	0.17
Total	74	100.00	151	100.00	206	100.00	431	100.00	578	100.00
Hair Color:										
Red	0	0.00	6	3.97	5	2.43	11	2.55	29	5.11
Fair	6	8.10	17	11.25	14	6.79	37	8.59	8	1.41
Brown	35	47.30	45	29.81	83	40.29	163	37.82	250	44.01
Dark	26	35.14	65	43.05	88	42.72	179	41.53	261	45.95
Black	7	9.46	18	11.92	16	7.77	41	9.51	20	3.52
Total	74	100.00	151	100.00	206	100.00	431	100.00	568	100.00

TABLE V-46. COUNTY GALWAY, COMPARATIVE DATA

	Garumna and Lettermullen		Browne Inishbofin and Inishshark		Carna and Mweenish, Connemara		Dupertuis West Galway Sample	
	No.	Mean	No.	Mean	No.	Mean	No.	Mean
Age	65	19-60*	38	17-63*	38	30.6	432	36.35
Stature	65	173.9	40	163.3	38	171.6	432	172.98
Relative Sitting Height	65	52.2	-	-	38	52.0	429	52.88
Relative Span	65	104.7	36	104.9	38	105.8	420	105.14
Cephalic Index	65	76.9	40	80.4	38	79.2	432	78.45
Nasal Index	65	63.4	40	64.9	38	63.1	432	65.10

*Range (see V-44)

TABLE V-47. COUNTY GALWAY, COMPARATIVE DATA

Observations	Garumna and Lettermullen		Browne Inishbofin and Inishshark		Carna and Mweenish, Connemara		Total		Dupertuis West Galway Sample	
	No.	%	No.	%	No.	%	No.	%	No.	%
Eye Color:										
Light	165	88.70	68	81.93	147	80.77	380	84.26	206	47.80
Medium	19	10.22	10	12.05	24	13.18	53	11.75	224	51.97
Dark	2	1.08	5	6.02	11	6.05	18	3.99	1	0.23
Total	186	100.00	83	100.00	182	100.00	451	100.00	431	100.00
Hair Color:										
Red	6	3.23	4	4.82	3	1.64	13	2.88	19	4.51
Fair	21	11.29	3	3.62	19	10.45	43	9.54	3	0.71
Brown	108	58.06	33	39.76	98	53.84	239	52.99	227	53.92
Dark	44	23.66	38	45.78	51	28.02	133	29.49	168	39.91
Black	7	3.76	5	6.02	11	6.05	23	5.10	4	0.95
Total	186	100.00	83	100.00	182	100.00	451	100.00	421	100.00

TABLE V-48. ARAN ISLANDS, COMPARATIVE DATA.

		Browne			Dupertuis	
	No.	Range	Mean	No.	Range	Mean
Age	27	17–75	42.2	139	15–84	34.50 + 1.00
Stature	27	156.5–187.5	164.5	139	158–193	174.48 ∓ 0.40
Relative Sitting Height. . .	-	-	-	138	46–57	52.28 ∓ 0.09
Relative Span.	22	97.01–106.0	101.9	137	98–111	104.06 ∓ 0.14
Cephalic Index.	27	71.6–85.1	77.1	137	68–88	77.79 ∓ 0.19
Nasal Index	27	50.0–68.5	58.5	139	52–83	63.90 ∓ 0.36

TABLE V-49. ARAN ISLANDS, COMPARATIVE DATA

Observations	Browne		Dupertuis	
	No.	%	No.	%
Eye Color:				
Light	119	88.80	61	43.88
Medium	11	8.21	78	56.12
Dark	4	2.99	0	0.00
Total	134	100.00	139	100.00
Hair Color:				
Red.	5	3.73	9	6.82
Fair	8	5.97	0	0.00
Brown.	85	63.43	91	68.94
Dark.	34	25.37	31	23.48
Black	2	1.50	1	0.76
Total	134	100.00	132	100.00

TABLE V-50. ANTRIM-DOWN, COMPARATIVE DATA

	Ballycastle[1]		Ballymoney[2]		Dupertuis Antrim, Down Sample		Presbyterians	
	No.	%	No.	%	No.	%	No.	%
Eyes:								
Dark	11	7.10	18	15.65	1	0.66	3	0.94
Mixed	103	66.45	77	66.96	73	48.67	148	46.39
Light	41	26.45	20	17.39	76	50.67	168	52.67
Total	155	100.00	115	100.00	150	100.00	319	100.00
Hair:								
Black.	17	10.97	14	12.17	2	1.34	11	3.53
Dark Brown	44	28.39	35	30.43	71	47.65	111	35.58
Brown	76	49.03	54	46.96	71	47.65	178	57.05
Fair	17	10.97	10	8.70	1	0.67	4	1.28
Red.	1	0.64	2	1.74	4	2.69	8	2.56
Total	155	100.00	115	100.00	149	100.00	312	100.00
	No.	Mean	No.	Mean	No.	Mean	No.	Mean
Head Length	155	198.5	115	197.4	152	194.97	321	196.56
Head Breadth.	155	153.6	115	152.7	152	153.46	321	153.01
Head Height.	155	139.7	114	136.8	152	125.62	321	126.22
Minimum Frontal Diameter . . .	154	108.2	115	107.0	152	108.06	321	107.86
Bizygomatic Diameter.	155	141.3	115	140.3	152	139.95	320	140.05
Bigonial Diameter	155	104.8	115	106.1	152	108.18	320	108.50
Nose Length	152	54.6	115	54.4	152	56.02	321	56.70
Nose Breadth.	152	34.8	115	35.0	152	35.78	321	36.44
Stature	154	173.0	115	172.0	152	171.51	320	173.31
Span.	155	177.7	115	177.0	151	180.09	311	183.18
Chest Breadth	154	29.4	115	29.0	152	28.80	316	29.04
Chest Depth.	153	22.8	115	22.4	152	23.12	316	23.50
Biacromial Diameter	155	39.3	115	38.8	151	38.66	319	38.90
Sitting Height.	153	91.7	113	92.0	152	90.94	319	91.81
Weight	155	151.5	-	-	152	154.50	320	160.30
Cephalic Index.	155	77.5	115	77.2	152	78.96	321	77.97
Breadth-Height Index	155	91.0	115	89.6	152	81.68	321	82.37

[1]Gamble, Walmsley, and Mogey, 1943, pp. 114, 123.
[2]Gamble, Walmsley, and Mogey, 1942, pp. 101, 115.

TABLE VI-1. COUNTY AFFINITIES BY RANK; WEST DONEGAL

	Measurements and Indices	Morphology
Mayo	3	10
Sligo, Leitrim, S. Fermanagh, W. Cavan	1	2
W. Galway	2	4
Aran Islands	2	4
Clare	2	4
Kerry	4	9
Cork	2	9
Limerick	7	9
E. Galway, Roscommon	2	3
Longford, Westmeath	2	1
Offaly, Leix, Kildare	7	5
Tipperary, Kilkenny	9	5
Waterford, Wexford	4	2
Wicklow, Carlow	3	1
Meath, Louth, Dublin	3	6
E. Cavan, Monaghan, Armagh	3	4
Antrim, Down	8	3
N. Fermanagh, E. Donegal, Tyrone, Londonderry	8	6

TABLE VI-2. COUNTY AFFINITIES BY RANK; N. FERMANAGH, E. DONEGAL, TYRONE, LONDONDERRY

	Measurements and Indices	Morphology
W. Donegal	9	6
Mayo	4	3
Sligo, Leitrim, S. Fermanagh, W. Cavan	4	1
W. Galway	3	2
Aran Islands	1	5
Clare	3	3
Kerry	1	1
Cork	4	7
Limerick	5	7
E. Galway, Roscommon	5	2
Longford, Westmeath	3	-
Offaly, Leix, Kildare	5	3
Tipperary, Kilkenny	5	4
Waterford, Wexford	5	5
Wicklow, Carlow	8	8
Meath, Louth, Dublin	6	2
E. Cavan, Monaghan, Armagh	3	12
Antrim, Down	9	13

TABLE VI-3. COUNTY AFFINITIES BY RANK; ANTRIM, DOWN

	Measurements and Indices	Morphology
W. Donegal	7	4
Mayo	1	5
Sligo, Leitrim, S. Fermanagh, W. Cavan	5	1
W. Galway	3	2
Aran Islands	-	2
Clare	2	2
Kerry	2	3
Cork	1	5
Limerick	3	2
E. Galway, Roscommon	5	3
Longford, Westmeath	7	3
Offaly, Leix, Kildare	5	7
Tipperary, Kilkenny	6	1
Waterford, Wexford	10	7
Wicklow, Carlow	9	5
Meath, Louth, Dublin	5	10
E. Cavan, Monaghan, Armagh	2	13
N. Fermanagh, E. Donegal, Tyrone, Londonderry	8	12

TABLE VI-4. COUNTY AFFINITIES BY RANK; EAST CAVAN,
MONAGHAN, ARMAGH

	Measurements and Indices	Morphology
W. Donegal	5	4
Mayo	6	6
Sligo, Leitrim, S. Fermanagh, W. Cavan	3	2
W. Galway	4	3
Aran Islands	2	1
Clare	2	1
Kerry	6	3
Cork	3	2
Limerick	-	1
E. Galway, Roscommon	1	3
Longford, Westmeath	4	1
Offaly, Leix, Kildare	11	4
Tipperary, Kilkenny	8	6
Waterford, Wexford	6	13
Wicklow, Carlow	7	7
Meath, Louth, Dublin	5	6
Antrim, Down	2	10
N. Fermanagh, E. Donegal, Tyrone, Londonderry	2	10

TABLE VI-5. COUNTY AFFINITIES BY RANK; MEATH,
LOUTH, DUBLIN

	Measurements and Indices	Morphology
W. Donegal	3	5
Mayo	2	3
Sligo, Leitrim, S. Fermanagh, W. Cavan	3	2
W. Galway	3	-
Aran Islands	4	1
Clare	6	2
Kerry	1	6
Cork	2	-
Limerick	5	3
E. Galway, Roscommon	-	4
Longford, Westmeath	6	1
Offaly, Leix, Kildare	7	8
Tipperary, Kilkenny	3	8
Waterford, Wexford	5	9
Wicklow, Carlow	9	13
E. Cavan, Monaghan, Armagh	4	7
Antrim, Down	3	10
N. Fermanagh, E. Donegal, Tyrone, Londonderry	4	2

TABLE VI-6. COUNTY AFFINITIES BY RANK; LONGFORD,
WESTMEATH

	Measurements and Indices	Morphology
W. Donegal	2	1
Mayo	-	10
Sligo, Leitrim, S. Fermanagh, W. Cavan	8	8
W. Galway	3	8
Aran Islands	5	15
Clare	2	5
Kerry	1	-
Cork	3	4
Limerick	4	1
E. Galway, Roscommon	6	9
Offaly, Leix, Kildare	5	10
Tipperary, Kilkenny	1	1
Waterford, Wexford	5	5
Wicklow, Carlow	3	1
Meath, Louth, Dublin	8	2
E. Cavan, Monaghan, Armagh	7	1
Antrim, Down	9	3
N. Fermanagh, E. Donegal, Tyrone, Londonderry	4	

TABLE VI-7. COUNTY AFFINITIES BY RANK; OFFALY LEIX, KILDARE

	Measurements and Indices	Morphology
W. Donegal	8	5
Mayo	4	2
Sligo, Leitrim, S. Fermanagh, W. Cavan	4	6
W. Galway	3	4
Aran Islands	2	2
Clare	-	3
Kerry	2	-
Cork	5	7
Limerick	1	5
E. Galway, Roscommon	1	9
Longford, Westmeath	2	8
Tipperary, Kilkenny	3	6
Waterford, Wexford	8	5
Wicklow, Carlow	9	4
Meath, Louth, Dublin	6	8
E. Cavan, Monaghan, Armagh	8	4
Antrim, Down	5	5
N. Fermanagh, E. Donegal, Tyrone, Londonderry	3	3

TABLE VI-8. COUNTY AFFINITIES BY RANK; WICKLOW, CARLOW

	Measurements and Indices	Morphology
W. Donegal	2	1
Mayo	3	2
Sligo, Leitrim, S. Fermanagh, W. Cavan	1	1
W. Galway	4	3
Aran Islands	-	3
Clare	2	4
Kerry	3	5
Cork	1	7
Limerick	4	2
E. Galway, Roscommon	2	3
Longford, Westmeath	3	1
Offaly, Leix, Kildare	10	5
Tipperary, Kilkenny	4	8
Waterford, Wexford	8	10
Meath, Louth, Dublin	8	13
E. Cavan, Monaghan, Armagh	8	6
Antrim, Down	8	5
N. Fermanagh, E. Donegal, Tyrone, Londonderry	3	6

TABLE VI-9. COUNTY AFFINITIES BY RANK; WATERFORD, WEXFORD

	Measurements and Indices	Morphology
W. Donegal	4	2
Mayo	4	3
Sligo, Leitrim, S. Fermanagh, W. Cavan	3	2
W. Galway	2	-
Aran Islands	2	2
Clare	2	4
Kerry	3	2
Cork	2	5
Limerick	5	4
E. Galway, Roscommon	3	2
Longford, Westmeath	5	5
Offaly, Leix, Kildare	8	5
Tipperary, Kilkenny	5	7
Wicklow, Carlow	7	10
Meath, Louth, Dublin	5	9
E. Cavan, Monaghan, Armagh	6	13
Antrim, Down	10	6
N. Fermanagh, E. Donegal, Tyrone, Londonderry	6	4

TABLE VI-10. COUNTY AFFINITIES BY RANK; TIPPERARY, KILKENNY

	Measurements and Indices	Morphology
W. Donegal	9	5
Mayo	4	2
Sligo, Leitrim, S. Fermanagh, W. Cavan	5	6
W. Galway	2	4
Aran Islands	-	2
Clare	5	6
Kerry	4	7
Cork	6	7
Limerick	5	2
E. Galway, Roscommon	3	2
Longford, Westmeath	1	2
Offaly, Leix, Kildare	3	6
Waterford, Wexford	5	7
Wicklow, Carlow	4	8
Meath, Louth, Dublin	3	8
E. Cavan, Monaghan, Armagh	8	7
Antrim, Down	4	1
N. Fermanagh, E. Donegal, Tyrone, Londonderry	6	4

TABLE VI-11. COUNTY AFFINITIES BY RANK; KERRY

	Measurements and Indices	Morphology
W. Donegal	4	10
Mayo	4	5
Sligo, Leitrim, S. Fermanagh, W. Cavan	3	4
W. Galway	5	5
Aran Islands	6	2
Clare	9	8
Cork	11	9
Limerick	3	9
E. Galway, Roscommon	8	2
Longford, Westmeath	-	-
Offaly, Leix, Kildare	2	1
Tipperary, Kilkenny	5	8
Waterford, Wexford	1	3
Wicklow, Carlow	3	6
Meath, Louth, Dublin	1	6
E. Cavan, Monaghan, Armagh	5	3
Antrim, Down	1	3
N. Fermanagh, E. Donegal, Tyrone, Londonderry	1	2

TABLE VI-12. COUNTY AFFINITIES BY RANK; CORK

	Measurements and Indices	Morphology
W. Donegal	2	10
Mayo	5	1
Sligo, Leitrim, S. Fermanagh, W. Cavan	3	2
W. Galway	4	3
Aran Islands	2	1
Clare	16	8
Kerry	7	8
Limerick	7	8
E. Galway, Roscommon	3	4
Longford, Westmeath	2	2
Offaly, Leix, Kildare	3	6
Tipperary, Kilkenny	5	6
Waterford, Wexford	1	4
Wicklow, Carlow	2	5
Meath, Louth, Dublin	2	1
E. Cavan, Monaghan, Armagh	4	2
Antrim, Down	-	5
N. Fermanagh, E. Donegal, Tyrone, Londonderry	3	8

TABLE VI-13. COUNTY AFFINITIES BY RANK; CLARE

	Measurements and Indices	Morphology
W. Donegal	2	4
Mayo	10	3
Sligo, Leitrim, S. Fermanagh, W. Cavan	2	8
W. Galway	6	12
Aran Islands	2	3
Kerry	8	8
Cork	16	7
Limerick	8	6
E. Galway, Roscommon	-	6
Longford, Westmeath	1	5
Offaly, Leix, Kildare	-	3
Tipperary, Kilkenny	3	6
Waterford, Wexford	1	1
Wicklow, Carlow	3	5
Meath, Louth, Dublin	7	3
E. Cavan, Monaghan, Armagh	1	1
Antrim, Down	1	2
N. Fermanagh, E. Donegal, Tyrone, Londonderry	1	4

TABLE VI-14. COUNTY AFFINITIES BY RANK; LIMERICK

	Measurements and Indices	Morphology
W. Donegal	9	9
Mayo	5	9
Sligo, Leitrim, S. Fermanagh, W. Cavan	3	8
W. Galway	5	3
Aran Islands	2	2
Clare	7	6
Kerry	4	9
Cork	7	11
E. Galway, Roscommon	4	2
Longford, Westmeath	1	1
Offaly, Leix, Kildare	2	6
Tipperary, Kilkenny	6	1
Waterford, Wexford	6	4
Wicklow, Carlow	1	2
Meath, Louth, Dublin	5	4
E. Cavan, Monaghan, Armagh	-	1
Antrim, Down	3	2
N. Fermanagh, E. Donegal, Tyrone, Londonderry	6	7

TABLE VI-15. COUNTY AFFINITIES BY RANK; MAYO

	Measurements and Indices	Morphology
W. Donegal	3	8
Sligo, Leitrim, S. Fermanagh, W. Cavan	6	9
W. Galway	7	7
Aran Islands	1	6
Clare	13	3
Kerry	3	4
Cork	7	-
Limerick	8	8
E. Galway, Roscommon	6	4
Longford, Westmeath	-	7
Offaly, Leix, Kildare	5	2
Tipperary, Kilkenny	2	2
Waterford, Wexford	1	3
Wicklow, Carlow	4	2
Meath, Louth, Dublin	4	3
E. Cavan, Monaghan, Armagh	7	6
Antrim, Down	1	5
N. Fermanagh, E. Donegal, Tyrone, Londonderry	3	4

TABLE VI-16. COUNTY AFFINITIES BY RANK; SLIGO, LEITRIM S. FERMANAGH, W. CAVAN

	Measurements and Indices	Morphology
W. Donegal	3	4
Mayo	5	9
W. Galway	2	7
Aran Islands	6	3
Clare	3	8
Kerry	1	5
Cork	2	2
Limerick	4	7
E. Galway, Roscommon	12	13
Longford, Westmeath	7	7
Offaly, Leix, Kildare	6	4
Tipperary, Kilkenny	7	6
Waterford, Wexford	2	2
Wicklow, Carlow	1	1
Meath, Louth, Dublin	3	1
E. Cavan, Monaghan, Armagh	3	2
Antrim, Down	6	1
N. Fermanagh, E. Donegal, Tyrone, Londonderry	3	1

TABLE VI-17. COUNTY AFFINITIES BY RANK; WEST GALWAY

	Measurements and Indices	Morphology
W. Donegal	4	4
Mayo	7	8
Sligo, Leitrim, S. Fermanagh, W. Cavan	2	7
Aran Islands	10	6
Clare	4	11
Kerry	6	4
Cork	4	4
Limerick	5	5
E. Galway, Roscommon	7	14
Longford, Westmeath	2	7
Offaly, Leix, Kildare	3	3
Tipperary, Kilkenny	2	2
Waterford, Wexford	2	-
Wicklow, Carlow	2	3
Meath, Louth, Dublin	3	-
E. Cavan, Monaghan, Armagh	4	3
Antrim, Down	2	3
N. Fermanagh, E. Donegal, Tyrone, Londonderry	4	3

TABLE VI-18. COUNTY AFFINITIES BY RANK; ARAN ISLANDS

	Measurements and Indices	Morphology
W. Donegal	3	5
Mayo	1	8
Sligo, Leitrim, S.Fermanagh, W. Cavan	10	4
W. Galway	13	6
Clare	4	7
Kerry	7	4
Cork	3	1
Limerick	4	2
E. Galway, Roscommon	6	9
Longford, Westmeath	8	17
Offaly, Leix, Kildare	5	4
Tipperary, Kilkenny	-	2
Waterford, Wexford	3	4
Wicklow, Carlow	-	4
Meath, Louth, Dublin	3	1
E. Cavan, Monaghan, Armagh	3	1
Antrim, Down	1	2
N. Fermanagh, E. Donegal, Tyrone, Londonderry	1	5

TABLE VI-19.   COUNTY AFFINITIES BY RANK; EAST GALWAY, ROSCOMMON

	Measurements and Indices	Morphology
W. Donegal	2	3
Mayo	6	4
Sligo, Leitrim, S.Fermanagh, W. Cavan	12	13
W. Galway	11	13
Aran Islands	4	4
Clare	1	5
Kerry	8	2
Cork	4	3
Limerick	5	3
Longford, Westmeath	5	7
Offaly, Leix, Kildare	1	9
Tipperary, Kilkenny	3	1
Waterford, Wexford	2	2
Wicklow, Carlow	2	3
Meath, Louth, Dublin	-	4
E. Cavan, Monaghan, Armagh	2	4
Antrim, Down	4	2
N. Fermanagh, E. Donegal, Tyrone, Londonderry	4	2

COMPOSITION OF THE PROTESTANT SERIES

TABLE VII-1.   COMPARISON OF CATHOLIC AND PROTESTANTS; BIRTHPLACE

Birthplace	Total Church of Ireland No.	%	Total Presbyterian No.	%	Total Protestant No.	%	Total Catholic No.	%
W. Donegal	10	2.0	5	1.6	15	1.8	212	2.4
Mayo	4	.8	-	-	4	.5	580	6.5
Sligo, Leitrim, S. Fermanagh, W. Cavan	38	7.5	4	1.2	42	5.1	716	8.0
W. Galway	-	-	-	-	-	-	432	4.8
Aran Islands	-	-	-	-	-	-	139	1.6
Clare	5	1.0	1	.3	6	.7	946	10.6
Kerry	5	1.0	-	-	5	.6	539	6.0
Cork	15	3.0	-	-	15	1.8	575	6.4
Limerick	3	.6	-	-	3	.4	340	3.8
E. Galway, Roscommon	2	.4	-	-	2	.2	515	5.8
Longford, Westmeath	8	1.6	1	.3	9	1.1	676	7.6
Offaly, Leix, Kildare	12	2.4	2	.6	14	1.7	531	6.0
Tipperary, Kilkenny	13	2.6	-	-	13	1.6	650	7.3
Waterford, Wexford	8	1.6	-	-	8	1.0	463	5.2
Wicklow, Carlow	24	4.7	-	-	24	2.9	278	3.1
Meath, Louth, Dublin	15	3.0	6	1.9	21	2.5	458	5.1
E.Cavan, Monaghan, Armagh	75	14.8	43	13.4	118	14.2	389	4.4
Antrim, Down	118	23.2	142	44.2	260	31.4	152	1.7
N. Fermanagh, E.Donegal, Tyrone, Londonderry	153	30.1	117	36.4	270	32.6	318	3.6
Total	508		321		829		8909	

TABLE VIII-1. COMPARISON OF CATHOLICS AND PROTESTANTS: EDUCATION

Education	Total Church of Ireland No.	%	Total Presbyterian No.	%	Total Protestant No.	%	Total Catholic No.	%
Illiterate	7	1.4	–	–	7	.8	294	3.3
Read and write	4	.8	–	–	4	.5	104	1.2
National School	406	79.9	260,	81.5	666	80.5	7260	81.7
Secondary School	83	16.3	52	16.3	135	16.3	1026	11.6
University	8	1.6	7	2.2	15	1.8	198	2.2
Total	508		319		827		8882	
Educational Ranking								
A (Illiterate + read and write)	11	2.2	–	–	11	1.3	398	4.5
B (Secondary School + University)	91	17.9	59	18.5	150	18.1	1224	13.8
B/A		8.1		–		13.9		3.1

TABLE VIII-2. COMPARISON OF CATHOLICS AND PROTESTANTS: LANGUAGE

Language	Total Church of Ireland No.	%	Total Presbyterian No.	%	Total Protestant No.	%	Total Catholic No.	%
No. Irish	455	89.9	308	96.0	763	92.3	4881	54.8
Native speaker	2	.4	–	–	2	.2	1230	13.8
Irish only	–	–	–	–	–	–	85	1.0
School Irish	49	9.7	13	4.0	62	7.5	2704	30.4
Total	506		321		827		8900	

TABLE VIII-3. COMPARISON OF CATHOLICS AND PROTESTANTS: OCCUPATION

Occupation	Total Church of Ireland No.	%	Total Presbyterian No.	%	Total Protestant No.	%	Total Catholic No.	%
Hired laborer, tinker	25	5.8	19	6.8	44	6.2	666	7.8
Herdsman, small, medium, and large farmer, farm steward, gardener	71	16.4	47	16.9	118	16.6	1252	14.6
Farm dependant	17	3.9	8	2.9	25	3.5	663	7.7
Fisherman	11	2.5	1	.4	12	1.7	226	2.6
Navvy	39	9.0	22	7.9	61	8.6	1989	23.2
Semi-skilled	56	12.9	35	12.6	91	12.8	689	8.0
Transportation	28	6.5	22	7.9	50	7.0	382	4.4
Factory	20	4.6	12	4.3	32	4.5	118	1.4
Skilled	25	5.8	17	6.1	42	5.9	227	2.6
Shop assistants, small shopkeepers, merchants	88	20.3	62	22.3	150	21.1	874	10.2
Clerks	19	4.4	10	3.6	29	4.1	154	1.8
Professional, teachers, clergy	7	1.6	6	2.2	13	1.8	207	2.4
Soldiers	17	3.9	13	4.7	30	4.2	1001	11.6
Students	10	2.3	4	1.4	14	2.0	138	1.6
Total	433		278		711		8586	

TABLE IX-1.   COMPARISON OF CATHOLICS AND
PROTESTANTS: MEASUREMENTS

	No.	Range	Mean	S. D.
Age				
Total Church of Ireland	508	15- 84	36.60 + 0.46	15.55
Total Presbyterian...	321	15- 89	36.05 ∓ 0.55	14.70
Total Protestant	829	15- 89	36.40 ∓ 0.36	15.20
Total Catholic	8909	15- 94	35.70 ∓ 0.11	15.40
Weight				
Total Church of Ireland	507	91-280	157.60 + 0.74	24.60
Total Presbyterian...	320	101-230	160.30 ∓ 0.84	22.40
Total Protestant.....	827	91-280	158.60 ∓ 0.56	23.80
Total Catholic	8906	91-290	157.30 ∓ 0.16	22.50
Stature				
Total Church of Ireland	507	152-202	172.08 + 0.21	7.02
Total Presbyterian...	320	149-196	173.31 ∓ 0.26	7.05
Total Protestant	827	149-202	172.56 ∓ 0.17	7.08
Total Catholic	8902	146-202	171.90 ∓ 0.05	6.84
Span				
Total Church of Ireland	494	158-217	181.17 + 0.26	8.46
Total Presbyterian ..	311	158-211	183.18 ∓ 0.32	8.31
Total Protestant	805	158-217	181.95 ∓ 0.20	8.46
Total Catholic	8675	146-211	181.14 ∓ 0.06	7.92
Relative Span				
Total Church of Ireland	494	96-113	105.18 + 0.07	2.40
Total Presbyterian...	311	98-113	105.68 ∓ 0.10	2.56
Total Protestant	805	96-113	105.38 ∓ 0.06	2.48
Total Catholic	8671	94-115	105.32 ∓ 0.02	2.52
Biacromial Diameter				
Total Church of Ireland	506	31- 45	38.42 + 0.06	2.13
Total Presbyterian...	319	31- 45	38.90 ∓ 0.08	2.01
Total Protestant.....	825	31- 45	38.60 ∓ 0.05	2.10
Total Catholic	8880	28- 48	38.57 ∓ 0.01	2.07
Relative Shoulder Breadth				
Total Church of Ireland	506	20- 27	22.38 + 0.03	1.12
Total Presbyterian...	319	20- 25	22.44 ∓ 0.04	1.06
Total Protestant	825	20- 27	22.40 ∓ 0.02	1.10
Total Catholic	8875	18- 27	22.44 ∓ 0.01	1.12
Chest Breadth				
Total Church of Ireland	499	20- 40	28.62 + 0.07	2.43
Total Presbyterian...	316	23- 40	29.04 ∓ 0.09	2.46
Total Protestant.....	815	20- 40	28.80 ∓ 0.06	2.43
Total Catholic	8854	20- 40	28.86 ∓ 0.02	2.43
Chest Depth				
Total Church of Ireland	499	16- 33	23.48 + 0.06	2.06
Total Presbyterian ...	316	18- 29	23.50 ∓ 0.07	1.96
Total Protestant.....	815	16- 33	23.50 ∓ 0.05	2.02
Total Catholic	8849	18- 33	23.20 ∓ 0.01	2.02
Thoracic Index				
Total Church of Ireland	499	65-108	82.10 + 0.19	6.24
Total Presbyterian ...	316	57-100	80.90 ∓ 0.23	6.08
Total Protestant.....	815	57-108	81.62 ∓ 0.15	6.24
Total Catholic	8845	53-108	80.54 ∓ 0.05	6.72
Sitting Height				
Total Church of Ireland	506	81-101	91.48 + 0.10	3.48
Total Presbyterian ...	319	81-101	91.81 ∓ 0.14	3.66
Total Protestant.....	825	81-101	91.60 ∓ 0.08	3.54
Total Catholic	8884	75-107	91.48 ∓ 0.02	3.60
Relative Sitting Height				
Total Church of Ireland	506	48- 57	53.14 + 0.04	1.44
Total Presbyterian ...	319	48- 57	53.00 ∓ 0.05	1.32
Total Protestant.....	825	48- 57	53.08 ∓ 0.03	1.40
Total Catholic	8881	46- 59	53.22 ∓ 0.01	1.48
Head Length				
Total Church of Ireland	508	173-220	195.87 + 0.19	6.45
Total Presbyterian ...	321	173-223	196.56 ∓ 0.24	6.33
Total Protestant.....	829	173-223	196.14 ∓ 0.15	6.42
Total Catholic	8900	170-223	195.63 ∓ 0.05	6.51
Head Breadth				
Total Church of Ireland	507	132-176	152.65 + 0.17	5.67
Total Presbyterian ...	321	132-170	153.01 ∓ 0.20	5.37
Total Protestant.....	828	132-176	152.80 ∓ 0.13	5.55
Total Catholic	8895	126-185	154.12 ∓ 0.04	5.73

TABLE IX-1.   COMPARISON OF CATHOLICS AND PROTESTANTS: MEASUREMENTS (Cont.)

	No.	Range	Mean	S. D.
Cephalic Index				
Total Church of Ireland	507	62- 88	78.00 ± 0.09	3.06
Total Presbyterian . . .	321	65- 88	77.97 ± 0.12	3.12
Total Protestant	828	62- 88	78.00 ± 0.07	3.09
Total Catholic.	8892	65- 94	78.84 ± 0.02	3.30
Head Circumference				
Total Church of Ireland	492	520-639	569.90 ± 0.50	16.50
Total Presbyterian . . .	313	520-624	571.25 ± 0.59	15.45
Total Protestant	805	520-639	570.50 ± 0.38	16.20
Total Catholic	8244	505-654	572.15 ± 0.12	16.50
Head Height				
Total Church of Ireland	508	102-153	125.66 ± 0.19	6.32
Total Presbyterian . .	321	110-149	126.22 ± 0.23	6.16
Total Protestant	829	102-153	125.86 ± 0.15	6.24
Total Catholic.	8898	102-149	124.98 ± 0.04	6.04
Length-Height Index				
Total Church of Ireland	508	52- 75	64.07 ± 0.10	3.30
Total Presbyterian . .	321	55- 75	64.19 ± 0.11	3.03
Total Protestant	829	52- 75	64.13 ± 0.08	3.21
Total Catholic.	8891	52- 78	63.89 ± 0.02	3.33
Breadth-Height Index				
Total Church of Ireland	507	70- 96	82.16 ± 0.12	4.17
Total Presbyterian . .	321	70- 96	82.37 ± 0.16	4.29
Total Protestant	828	70- 96	82.25 ± 0.10	4.23
Total Catholic.	8887	67-102	81.05 ± 0.03	4.26
Bizygomatic Diameter				
Total Church of Ireland	507	120-159	139.25 ± 0.18	6.00
Total Presbyterian. . .	320	125-154	140.05 ± 0.18	4.90
Total Protestant	827	120-159	139.55 ± 0.13	5.60
Total Catholic.	8891	110-169	140.80 ± 0.04	5.95
Cephalo-Facial Index				
Total Church of Ireland	506	82-105	91.25 ± 0.10	3.18
Total Presbyterian. . .	320	82-105	91.46 ± 0.12	3.09
Total Protestant	826	82-105	91.34 ± 0.07	3.15
Total Catholic.	8880	76-108	91.40 ± 0.02	3.30
Total Face Height				
Total Church of Ireland	508	100-149	125.85 ± 0.22	7.50
Total Presbyterian. . .	321	105-154	126.75 ± 0.28	7.35
Total Protestant	829	100-154	126.20 ± 0.17	7.45
Total Catholic.	8897	95-154	127.10 ± 0.05	6.95
Upper Face Height				
Total Church of Ireland	508	55- 94	72.95 ± 0.14	4.60
Total Presbyterian. . .	320	60- 89	73.80 ± 0.18	4.70
Total Protestant	828	55- 94	73.30 ± 0.11	4.65
Total Catholic.	8894	50- 89	72.80 ± 0.03	4.50
Facial Index				
Total Church of Ireland	507	70-109	90.25 ± 0.16	5.45
Total Presbyterian. . .	320	75-109	90.35 ± 0.21	5.65
Total Protestant	827	70-109	90.30 ± 0.13	5.50
Total Catholic	8879	70-114	90.20 ± 0.04	5.50
Upper Facial Index				
Total Church of Ireland	507	40- 63	52.28 ± 0.10	3.45
Total Presbyterian . . .	319	43- 66	52.49 ± 0.13	3.42
Total Protestant	826	40- 66	52.37 ± 0.08	3.45
Total Catholic	8876	37- 69	51.62 ± 0.02	3.45
Nose Height				
Total Church of Ireland	508	40- 71	55.78 ± 0.13	4.28
Total Presbyterian . . .	321	44- 71	56.70 ± 0.16	4.16
Total Protestant.	829	40- 71	56.14 ± 0.10	4.24
Total Catholic	8898	40- 71	56.30 ± 0.03	4.08
Nose Breadth				
Total Church of Ireland	508	28- 48	35.78 ± 0.10	3.36
Total Presbyterian . . .	321	28- 45	36.44 ± 0.12	3.24
Total Protestant.	829	28- 48	36.05 ± 0.08	3.33
Total Catholic	8904	25- 57	36.02 ± 0.02	3.09
Nasal Index				
Total Church of Ireland	508	48- 91	64.54 ± 0.20	6.60
Total Presbyterian . . .	321	44- 87	64.58 ± 0.25	6.60
Total Protestant.	829	44- 91	64.54 ± 0.15	6.60
Total Catholic	8896	44- 99	64.38 ± 0.05	6.48

TABLE IX-1.   COMPARISON OF CATHOLICS AND PROTESTANTS:
MEASUREMENTS (Cont.)

	No.	Range	Mean	S. D.
Minimum Frontal Diameter				
Total Church of Ireland	508	89-128	108.46 + 0.14	4.56
Total Presbyterian . . .	321	93-124	107.86 ∓ 0.17	4.64
Total Protestant	829	89-128	108.22 ∓ 0.11	4.60
Total Catholic	8898	89-128	109.22 ∓ 0.03	4.84
Fronto-Parietal Index				
Total Church of Ireland	507	60- 80	71.05 + 0.09	2.97
Total Presbyterian . . .	321	63- 83	70.57 ∓ 0.11	2.94
Total Protestant	828	60- 83	70.87 ∓ 0.07	2.97
Total Catholic	8886	60- 86	71.05 ∓ 0.02	3.09
Zygo-Frontal Index				
Total Church of Ireland	507	64- 87	77.98 + 0.09	3.12
Total Presbyterian . . .	320	68- 87	77.06 ∓ 0.12	3.16
Total Protestant	827	64- 87	77.62 ∓ 0.07	3.16
Total Catholic	8882	64- 95	77.78 ∓ 0.02	3.32
Bigonial Diameter				
Total Church of Ireland	508	86-129	108.14 + 0.17	5.72
Total Presbyterian . . .	320	94-137	108.50 ∓ 0.19	5.12
Total Protestant	828	86-137	108.30 ∓ 0.13	5.48
Total Catholic	8897	86-133	109.26 ∓ 0.04	5.64
Zygo-Gonial Index				
Total Church of Ireland	507	63- 89	77.65 + 0.10	3.42
Total Presbyterian . . .	319	66- 92	77.56 ∓ 0.12	3.33
Total Protestant	826	63- 92	77.62 ∓ 0.08	3.39
Total Catholic	8880	63- 92	77.56 ∓ 0.02	3.48
Fronto-Gonial Index				
Total Church of Ireland	508	80-119	99.75 + 0.16	5.20
Total Presbyterian . . .	320	85-119	100.50 ∓ 0.21	5.55
Total Protestant	828	80-119	100.05 ∓ 0.12	5.35
Total Catholic	8888	80-124	99.90 ∓ 0.04	5.50

TABLE IX-2.   METRIC CHARACTERS IN WHICH
CHURCH OF IRELAND DIFFERS
FROM TOTAL CATHOLICS

	c.r.	M.D.+se^d
Smaller chest breadth	3.42	-.24+.07
Greater chest depth	3.33	.20∓.06
Greater thoracic index	7.80	1.56∓.20
Smaller head breadth	8.16	-1.47∓.18
Smaller cephalic index	9.33	-.84∓.09
Smaller head circumference	4.41	-2.25∓.51
Greater head height	3.40	.68∓.20
Greater breadth-height index	9.25	1.11∓.12
Smaller bizygomatic diameter . . .	8.15	-1.55∓.19
Smaller total face height	5.43	-1.25∓.23
Greater upper facial index	6.60	.66∓.10
Smaller nose height	4.00	-.52∓.13
Smaller minimum frontal diameter	5.43	-.76∓.14
Smaller bigonial diameter	6.22	-1.12∓.18

TABLE IX-3.   METRIC CHARACTERS IN WHICH
PRESBYTERIANS DIFFER
SIGNIFICANTLY FROM TOTAL
CATHOLICS

	c.r.	M.D.+se^d
Greater weight	3.48	3.00+.86
Greater stature	5.22	1.41∓.27
Greater span	6.18	2.04∓.33
Greater relative span	3.60	.36∓.10
Greater biacromial diameter	4.12	.33∓.08
Greater chest depth	4.28	.30∓.07
Smaller relative sitting height . . .	4.40	-.22∓.05
Greater head length	3.72	.93∓.25
Smaller head breadth	5.55	-1.11∓.20
Smaller cephalic index	7.25	-.87∓.12
Greater head height	5.39	1.24∓.23
Greater breadth-height index	8.25	1.32∓.16
Smaller bizygomatic diameter . . .	4.17	-.75∓.18
Greater upper face height	5.55	1.00∓.18
Greater upper facial index	6.69	.87∓.13
Greater nose breadth	3.50	.42∓.12
Smaller min. fron. diameter	8.00	-1.36∓.17
Smaller fronto-parietal index	4.36	-.48∓.11
Smaller zygo-frontal index	6.00	-.72∓.12
Smaller bigonial diameter	4.00	-.76∓.19

TABLE IX-4.   METRIC CHARACTERS IN WHICH BOTH CHURCH
OF IRELAND AND PRESBYTERIANS DIFFER
SIGNIFICANTLY FROM TOTAL CATHOLICS

	Church of Ireland critical ratio	Presbyterian critical ratio
Greater chest depth	3.33	4.28
Smaller head breadth	8.16	5.55
Smaller cephalic index	9.33	7.25
Greater head height	3.40	5.39
Greater breadth-height index	9.25	8.25
Smaller bizygomatic diameter.	8.15	4.17
Greater upper facial index	6.60	6.69
Smaller min. fron. diameter	5.43	8.00
Smaller Bigonial diameter	6.22	4.00

TABLE IX-5.   METRIC CHARACTERS IN WHICH CHURCH OF
IRELAND AND PRESBYTERIANS DIFFER SIGNI-
FICANTLY FROM EACH OTHER

	Church of Ireland critical ratio	MD±se[d]
Smaller stature	3.61	-1.23±.34
Smaller span	4.90	-2.01±.41
Smaller relative span.	4.17	-.50±.12
Smaller biacromial	4.80	-.48±.10
Smaller chest breadth	3.82	-.42±.11
Greater thoracic index	4.00	1.20±.30
Smaller bizygomatic diameter.	3.20	-.80±.25
Smaller upper face height	3.70	-.85±.23
Smaller nose height	4.60	-.92±.20
Smaller nose breadth.	4.40	-.66±.15
Greater fronto-parietal index	3.43	.48±.14
Greater zygo-frontal index	6.13	.92±.15

TABLE X-1.   COMPARISON OF CATHOLICS AND PROTESTANTS:
               MORPHOLOGICAL OBSERVATIONS

	Total Church of Ireland		Total Presbyterian		Total Protestant		Total Catholic	
	No.	%	No.	%	No.	%	No.	%
Skin Color, Inner Arm								
Pale	1	.2	-	-	1	.1	26	.3
Pink	476	93.7	300	93.4	776	93.6	8160	91.6
Brunet	31	6.1	18	5.6	49	5.9	694	7.8
Swarthy	-	-	3	.9	3	.4	28	.3
Total	508		321		829		8908	
Vascularity								
Absent, submedium	2	.4	-	-	2	.2	63	.7
Medium	375	73.8	223	69.5	598	72.1	6686	75.1
Pronounced	131	25.8	98	30.5	229	27.6	2158	24.2
Total	508		321		829		8907	
Freckles								
Absent	311	61.2	176	54.8	487	58.7	5371	60.3
Submedium	149	29.3	124	38.6	273	32.9	2300	25.8
Medium	41	8.1	19	5.9	60	7.2	973	10.9
Pronounced, massed	7	1.4	2	.6	9	1.1	260	2.9
Total	508		321		829		8904	
Moles								
Absent	480	94.5	312	97.2	792	95.5	8359	93.9
Few	26	5.1	9	2.8	35	4.2	495	5.6
Many	2	.4	-	-	2	.2	47	.5
Total	508		321		829		8901	
Hair Form								
Straight	227	44.8	142	44.2	369	44.6	2555	28.7
Low waves	209	41.2	122	38.0	331	40.0	4437	49.8
Deep waves	56	11.0	47	14.6	103	12.4	1606	18.0
Curly	14	2.8	10	3.1	24	2.9	292	3.3
Frizzly, woolly	1	.2	-	-	1	.1	15	.2
Total	507		321		828		8905	
Hair Texture								
Coarse	19	3.7	12	3.7	31	3.7	415	4.6
Medium	475	93.7	300	93.4	775	93.6	8242	92.5
Fine	13	2.6	9	2.8	22	2.6	249	2.8
Total	507		321		828		8906	
Hair Quantity, Head								
Submedium	5	1.0	5	1.6	10	1.2	208	2.3
Medium	488	96.2	301	93.8	789	95.3	8468	95.1
Pronounced	14	2.8	15	4.7	29	3.5	229	2.6
Total	507		321		828		8905	
Baldness								
Absent	263	51.9	178	55.6	441	53.3	5267	59.2
Submedium	130	25.6	73	22.8	203	24.5	2030	22.8
Medium	53	10.4	41	12.8	94	11.4	968	10.9
Pronounced	61	12.0	28	8.8	89	10.8	639	7.2
Total	507		320		827		8904	
Hair Quantity, Beard								
Very small, submedium	37	7.3	17	5.3	54	6.5	522	5.8
Medium	459	90.5	279	86.9	738	89.1	8074	90.6
Pronounced, very pronounced	11	2.2	25	7.8	36	4.3	312	3.5
Total	507		321		828		8908	
Hair Quantity, Body								
Absent	-		-	-	-	-	33	.4
Submedium	36	7.1	18	5.6	54	6.5	528	5.9
Medium	465	91.7	284	88.5	749	90.4	8112	91.1
Pronounced	6	1.2	19	5.9	25	3.0	234	2.6
Total	507		321		828		8907	

TABLE X-1.   COMPARISON OF CATHOLICS AND PROTESTANTS:
MORPHOLOGICAL OBSERVATIONS (Cont.)

	Total Church of Ireland		Total Presbyterian		Total Protestant		Total Catholic	
	No.	%	No.	%	No.	%	No.	%
Grayness, Head								
Absent	265	52.3	173	53.9	438	52.9	4813	54.0
Submedium	123	24.3	74	23.0	197	23.8	1934	21.7
Medium	64	12.6	45	14.0	109	13.2	1200	13.5
Pronounced	55	10.8	29	9.0	84	10.1	959	10.8
Total	507		321		828		8906	
Grayness, Beard								
Absent	304	60.0	198	61.7	502	60.6	5813	65.3
Submedium	79	15.6	45	14.0	124	15.0	900	10.1
Medium	75	14.8	48	15.0	123	14.8	1361	15.3
Pronounced	49	9.7	30	9.3	79	9.5	831	9.3
Total	507		321		828		8905	
Hair Color, Head								
Black	10	2.0	11	3.4	21	2.5	246	2.8
Dark brown	190	37.5	111	34.6	301	36.4	3536	39.8
Brown	201	39.7	123	38.3	324	39.2	3082	34.7
Red-brown	13	2.6	8	2.5	21	2.5	469	5.3
Golden brown	47	9.3	46	14.3	93	11.2	793	8.9
Ash brown	1	.2	1	.3	2	.2	42	.5
Golden	5	1.0	3	.9	8	1.0	81	.9
Ash	5	1.0	1	.3	6	.7	13	.1
Red	22	4.3	8	2.5	30	3.6	370	4.2
White	12	2.4	9	2.8	21	2.5	257	2.9
Total	506		321		827		8889	
Eye Color;								
dark brown, dark-light brown, light brown	3	.6	3	.9	6	.7	41	.5
Gray-brown	37	7.3	20	6.2	57	6.9	441	5.0
Green-brown	37	7.3	19	5.9	56	6.8	299	3.4
Blue-brown	186	36.6	109	34.0	295	35.6	3913	43.9
Gray, gray-blue	35	6.9	23	7.2	58	7.0	397	4.4
Blue	204	40.2	145	45.2	349	42.1	3774	42.4
Unmatched.	6	1.2	2	.6	8	1.0	44	.5
Total	508		321		829		8909	
Pigment, Mixed Eyes								
Very pronouncedly dark . .	13	4.4	6	3.6	19	4.1	159	3.2
Pronouncedly dark	41	14.0	19	11.4	60	13.1	361	7.2
Even	48	16.4	26	15.6	74	16.1	620	12.4
Pronouncedly light	42	14.4	29	17.4	71	15.5	895	17.9
Very pronouncedly light . . .	148	50.7	87	52.1	235	51.2	3963	59.3
Total	292		167		459		4997	
Iris								
Clear	74	14.8	44	13.8	118	14.4	1975	22.3
Rayed.	87	17.4	69	21.6	156	19.0	1950	22.0
Zoned.	3	.6	4	1.2	7	.8	149	1.7
Spotted	9	1.8	5	1.6	14	1.7	248	2.8
Diffuse	175	34.9	107	33.5	282	34.4	2885	32.6
Scalloped.	153	30.5	90	28.2	243	29.6	1655	18.7
Total	501		319		820		8862	
Eyefolds, External								
Absent	420	82.7	261	81.3	681	82.1	7722	86.7
Submedium	50	9.8	33	10.3	83	10.0	576	6.5
Medium	34	6.7	24	7.5	58	7.0	504	5.6
Pronounced	4	.8	3	.9	7	.8	106	1.2
Total	508		321		829		8908	
Eyefolds, Median								
Absent	490	96.4	314	97.8	804	97.0	8644	97.0
Submedium	8	1.6	2	.6	10	1.2	95	1.1
Medium	7	1.4	4	1.2	11	1.3	118	1.3
Pronounced	3	.6	1	.3	4	.5	50	.6
Total	508		321		829		8907	

TABLE X-1.   COMPARISON OF CATHOLICS AND PROTESTANTS:
MORPHOLOGICAL OBSERVATIONS (Cont.)

	Total Church of Ireland		Total Presbyterian		Total Protestant		Total Catholic	
	No.	%	No.	%	No.	%	No.	%
Eyefolds, Internal								
Absent	500	98.4	318	99.1	818	98.7	8819	99.0
Submedium	8	1.6	3	.9	11	1.3	75	.8
Medium, pronounced	-	-	-	-	-	-	11	.1
Total	508		321		829		8905	
Eye Obliquity								
Absent	226	44.5	131	40.8	357	43.1	5738	64.4
Submedium	219	43.1	146	45.5	365	44.0	2173	24.4
Medium	32	6.3	21	6.5	53	6.4	421	4.7
Pronounced	2	.4	3	.9	5	.6	57	.6
Down	29	5.7	20	6.2	49	5.9	520	5.8
Total	508		321		829		8909	
Eye Opening Height								
Submedium	37	7.3	24	7.5	61	7.4	533	6.0
Medium	456	89.9	288	89.7	744	89.8	8103	91.0
Pronounced	14	2.8	9	2.8	23	2.8	265	3.0
Total	507		321		828		8901	
Eyebrow Thickness								
Submedium	31	6.1	19	5.9	50	6.0	287	3.2
Medium	462	91.1	296	92.2	758	91.5	8296	93.1
Pronounced, very pronounced	14	2.8	6	1.9	20	2.4	325	3.6
Total	507		321		828		8908	
Eyebrow Concurrency								
Absent	14	2.8	9	2.8	23	2.8	156	1.8
Submedium	132	26.0	68	21.2	200	24.1	2069	23.2
Medium	319	62.8	218	67.9	537	64.8	5767	64.7
Pronounced	43	8.5	26	8.1	69	8.3	916	10.3
Total	508		321		829		8908	
Brow Ridges								
Absent	25	4.9	14	4.4	39	4.7	195	2.2
Submedium	116	22.8	86	26.8	202	24.4	1725	19.4
Medium	232	45.7	136	42.4	368	44.4	5135	57.6
Pronounced	135	26.6	81	25.2	216	26.0	1818	20.4
Very pronounced	-	-	4	1.2	4	.5	34	.4
Total	508		321		829		8907	
Forehead Height								
Submedium	13	2.6	6	1.9	19	2.3	333	3.7
Medium	149	29.3	96	29.9	245	29.6	3786	42.5
Pronounced	346	68.1	219	68.2	565	68.2	4783	53.7
Total	508		321		829		8902	
Forehead Slope								
Forward	3	.6	5	1.6	8	1.0	106	1.2
Absent	34	6.7	24	7.5	58	7.0	587	6.6
Submedium	257	50.6	156	48.6	413	49.8	4048	45.4
Medium	159	31.3	92	28.7	251	30.3	3503	39.3
Pronounced	48	9.4	42	13.1	90	10.8	642	7.2
Very pronounced	7	1.4	2	.6	9	1.1	22	.2
Total	508		321		829		8908	
Nasion Depression								
Absent	3	.6	1	.3	4	.5	20	.2
Very small	9	1.8	4	1.2	13	1.6	133	1.5
Submedium	43	8.5	34	10.6	77	9.3	1181	13.2
Medium	276	54.3	158	49.2	434	52.4	5413	60.8
Pronounced	172	33.8	116	36.1	288	34.7	2041	22.9
Very pronounced	5	1.0	8	2.5	13	1.6	119	1.3
Total	508		321		829		8907	
Nasal Root Height								
Very small, submedium . .	11	2.2	13	4.0	24	2.9	268	3.0
Medium	405	79.7	232	72.3	637	76.8	6877	77.2
Pronounced	89	17.5	75	23.4	164	19.8	1685	18.9
Very pronounced	3	.6	1	.3	4	.5	74	.8
Total	508		321		829		8904	

TABLE X-1. COMPARISON OF CATHOLICS AND PROTESTANTS:
MORPHOLOGICAL OBSERVATIONS (Cont.)

	Total Church of Ireland No.	%	Total Presbyterian No.	%	Total Protestant No.	%	Total Catholic No.	%
Nasal Root Breadth								
Very small, submedium ..	5	1.0	4	1.2	9	1.1	179	2.0
Medium	353	69.5	222	69.2	575	69.4	6437	72.3
Pronounced	143	28.1	92	28.7	235	28.3	2212	24.8
Very pronounced	7	1.4	3	.9	10	1.2	75	.8
Total	508		321		829		8903	
Nasal Septum								
Straight, concave	238	46.9	148	46.1	386	46.6	3397	38.3
Convex	269	53.0	173	53.9	442	53.4	5469	61.7
Total	507		321		828		8866	
Nasal Bridge Height								
Very small, submedium ..	12	2.4	15	4.7	27	3.3	279	3.1
Medium	382	75.3	210	65.4	592	71.5	6788	76.2
Pronounced	105	20.7	93	29.0	198	23.9	1720	19.3
Very pronounced	8	1.6	3	.9	11	1.3	115	1.3
Total	507		321		828		8902	
Nasal Bridge Breadth								
Submedium	1	.2	3	.9	4	.5	74	.8
Medium	351	69.2	217	67.6	568	68.6	6955	78.2
Pronounced	152	30.0	99	30.8	251	30.3	1831	20.6
Very pronounced	3	.6	2	.6	5	.6	39	.4
Total	507		321		828		8899	
Nasal Profile								
Concave	29	5.7	17	5.3	46	5.6	595	6.7
Concave, snub tip	2	.4	3	.9	5	.6	63	.7
Straight	242	47.7	126	39.2	368	44.4	3916	44.0
Straight, snub tip	15	3.0	6	1.9	21	2.5	322	3.6
Convex	203	40.0	146	45.5	349	42.1	3564	40.0
Convex, snub tip......	16	3.2	23	7.2	39	4.7	437	4.9
Total .	507		321		828		8897	
Nasal Tip, Thickness								
Submedium	8	1.6	3	.9	11	1.3	151	1.7
Medium	350	69.0	204	63.6	554	66.9	6512	73.1
Pronounced	149	29.4	114	35.5	263	31.8	2203	24.7
Very pronounced	-	-	-	-	-	-	37	.4
Total .	507		321		828		8903	
Nasal Tip, Inclination								
Up, medium	44	8.7	19	5.9	63	7.6	1012	11.4
Up, submedium	426	84.2	275	85.7	701	84.8	7348	82.6
Horizontal..........	30	5.9	23	7.2	53	6.4	381	4.3
Down, submedium.....	5	1.0	3	.9	8	1.0	119	1.3
Down, medium	1	.2	1	.3	2	.2	35	.4
Total .	506		321		827		8895	
Nasal Wings								
Compressed	16	3.2	7	2.2	23	2.8	462	5.2
Medium	474	93.5	296	92.2	770	93.0	7876	88.5
Flaring............	17	3.4	18	5.6	35	4.2	557	6.3
Total .	507		321		828		8895	
Nostril Visibility, Frontal								
Absent	37	7.3	26	8.1	63	7.6	430	4.8
Submedium, medium ...	469	92.5	295	91.9	764	92.3	8395	94.4
Pronounced	1	.2	-	-	1	.1	70	.8
Total .	507		321		828		8895	
Lips, Integumental Thickness								
Submedium	11	2.2	12	3.7	23	2.8	102	1.1
Medium	474	93.3	291	90.6	765	92.3	8440	94.7
Pronounced	23	4.5	18	5.6	41	4.9	367	4.1
Total .	508		321		829		8909	
Lips, Membranous Thickness, Upper								
Very small	4	.8	3	.9	7	.8	106	1.2
Submedium	135	26.6	85	26.5	220	26.5	2067	23.2
Medium	329	64.8	209	65.1	538	64.9	6494	72.9
Pronounced	40	7.9	24	7.5	64	7.7	239	2.7
Total .	508		321		829		8906	
Lips, Eversion								
Submedium	135	26.6	88	27.4	223	26.9	1968	22.1
Medium	331	65.2	208	64.8	539	65.0	6591	74.0
Pronounced	42	8.3	25	7.8	67	8.1	348	3.9
Total .	508		321		829		8907	
Mid-facial Prognathism								
Absent	460	90.6	292	91.0	752	90.7	8191	92.0
Submedium	44	8.7	27	8.4	71	8.6	566	6.4
Medium	4	.8	2	.6	6	.7	130	1.5
Pronounced	-	-	-	-	-	-	16	.2
Total .	508		321		829		8903	
Alveolar Prognathism								
Absent	501	98.6	315	98.1	816	98.4	8699	97.7
Submedium	5	1.0	5	1.6	10	1.2	121	1.4
Medium, pronounced	2	.4	1	.3	3	.4	85	1.0
Total .	508		321		829		8905	

TABLE X-1.   COMPARISON OF CATHOLICS AND PROTESTANTS:
MORPHOLOGICAL OBSERVATIONS (Cont.)

	Total Church of Ireland		Total Presbyterian		Total Protestant		Total Catholic	
	No.	%	No.	%	No.	%	No.	%
Chin Prominence								
Submedium	54	10.6	34	10.6	88	10.6	974	10.9
Medium	405	79.7	249	77.6	654	78.9	7106	79.8
Pronounced	49	9.6	38	11.8	87	10.5	825	9.3
Total	508		321		829		8905	
Teeth Eruption								
Complete	371	74.2	248	77.5	619	75.5	6376	73.3
Partial	129	25.8	72	22.5	201	24.5	2319	26.7
Total	500		320		820		8695	
Bite								
Under	3	.8	3	1.3	6	1.0	42	.6
Edge-to-edge	5	1.4	1	.4	6	1.0	28	.4
Submedium over	352	96.7	215	96.4	567	96.6	6595	96.0
Pronounced over	4	1.1	4	1.8	8	1.4	207	3.0
Total	364		223		587		6872	
Teeth, Loss								
None	39	7.7	22	6.8	61	7.4	710	8.0
Very small	209	41.1	114	35.5	323	39.0	3536	39.7
Submedium	80	15.7	67	20.9	147	17.7	1871	21.0
Medium	32	6.3	20	6.2	52	6.3	627	7.0
Pronounced	148	29.1	98	30.5	246	29.7	2159	24.2
Total	508		321		829		8903	
Teeth, Wear								
Absent, submedium	300	82.4	189	84.8	489	83.3	5169	75.8
Medium	51	14.0	30	13.4	81	13.8	1335	19.6
Pronounced, very pronounced	13	3.6	4	1.8	17	2.9	316	4.6
Total	364		223		587		6820	
Teeth, Caries								
Absent	9	2.5	6	2.7	15	2.6	58	.8
Very small	37	10.2	20	9.0	57	9.7	610	8.9
Submedium	224	61.5	145	65.0	369	62.9	3778	55.1
Medium	67	18.4	45	20.2	112	19.1	1640	23.9
Pronounced	27	7.4	7	3.1	34	5.8	771	11.2
Total	364		223		587		6857	
Face Shortening								
Absent	358	70.9	223	69.5	581	70.3	6499	71.9
Submedium	58	11.5	39	12.1	97	11.7	719	8.1
Medium	63	12.5	40	12.5	103	12.5	1158	13.0
Pronounced	26	5.1	19	5.9	45	5.4	495	5.6
Total	506		321		826		8871	
Teeth, Crowding								
Absent	153	41.9	92	41.2	245	41.7	2922	42.6
Medium	198	54.2	122	54.7	320	54.4	3542	51.6
Pronounced	14	3.8	9	4.0	23	3.9	395	5.8
Total	365		223		588		6859	
Malars, Frontal Projection								
Absent, submedium	-	-	1	.3	1	.1	47	.5
Medium	465	91.5	288	89.7	753	90.8	7387	82.9
Pronounced	43	8.5	32	10.0	75	9.0	1473	16.5
Total	508		321		829		8907	
Malars, Lateral Projection								
Absent, submedium	1	.2	1	.3	2	.2	35	.4
Medium	380	74.8	230	71.6	610	73.6	5778	64.9
Pronounced	126	24.8	88	27.4	214	25.8	2918	32.8
Very pronounced	1	.2	2	.6	3	.4	173	1.9
Total	508		321		829		8904	
Gonial Angles								
Submedium	16	3.1	12	3.7	28	3.4	247	2.8
Medium	331	65.2	199	62.0	530	63.9	5742	64.5
Pronounced	153	30.1	105	32.7	258	31.1	2773	31.1
Very pronounced	8	1.6	5	1.6	13	1.6	145	1.6
Total	508		321		829		8907	
Ear Helix								
Very small	4	.8	8	2.5	12	1.4	49	.6
Submedium	118	23.2	78	24.3	196	23.6	1987	22.3
Medium	363	71.4	208	64.8	571	68.9	6507	73.0
Pronounced	23	4.5	27	8.4	50	6.0	366	4.1
Total	508		321		829		8909	
Ear Antihelix								
Absent	-	-	-	-	-	-	16	.2
Submedium	10	2.0	10	3.1	20	2.4	416	4.7
Medium	423	83.3	268	83.5	691	83.4	7336	82.4
Pronounced	75	14.8	43	13.4	118	14.2	1137	12.8
Total	508		321		329		8905	
Darwin's Point								
Absent	370	72.8	236	73.5	606	73.1	6611	74.3
Submedium	127	25.0	75	23.4	202	24.4	2021	22.7
Medium	10	2.0	10	3.1	20	2.4	247	2.8
Pronounced	1	.2	-	-	1	.1	18	.2
Total	580		321		829		8897	

TABLE X-1. COMPARISON OF CATHOLICS AND PROTESTANTS:
MORPHOLOGICAL OBSERVATIONS (Cont.)

	Total Church of Ireland		Total Presbyterian		Total Protestant		Total Catholic	
	No.	%	No.	%	No.	%	No.	%
Ear Lobe Attachment								
Soldered	6	1.2	8	2.5	14	1.7	127	1.4
Attached	223	43.9	135	42.0	358	43.2	3599	40.4
Free	279	54.9	178	55.4	457	55.1	5181	58.2
Total	508		321		829		8907	
Ear Lobe Size								
Absent, submedium	3	.6	-	-	3	.4	42	.5
Medium	255	50.2	161	50.2	416	50.2	4834	54.3
Pronounced	250	49.2	160	49.8	410	49.4	4031	45.2
Total	508		321		829		8907	
Ear Protrusion								
Submedium	10	2.0	2	.6	12	1.4	60	.7
Medium	364	71.6	223	69.5	587	70.8	6896	77.4
Pronounced	134	26.4	96	29.9	230	27.7	1948	21.9
Total	508		321		829		8904	
Temporal Fullness								
Submedium	65	12.8	55	17.1	120	14.5	1406	15.8
Medium	387	76.2	227	70.7	614	74.1	5431	61.0
Pronounced	56	11.0	39	12.1	95	11.4	2070	23.2
Total	508		321		829		8907	
Occipital Protrusion								
Absent, submedium	15	3.0	13	4.0	28	3.4	713	8.0
Medium	361	71.1	228	71.0	589	71.0	6622	74.4
Pronounced	132	26.0	80	24.9	212	25.6	1571	17.6
Total	508		321		829		8906	
Lambdoid Flattening								
Absent	303	59.9	234	72.9	537	64.9	1701	19.1
Submedium	35	6.9	15	4.7	50	6.0	912	10.2
Medium	128	25.3	59	18.4	187	22.6	3972	44.6
Pronounced	40	7.9	13	4.0	53	6.4	2312	26.0
Total	506		321		827		8897	
Occipital Flattening								
Absent	313	61.6	183	57.0	496	59.8	7246	81.4
Medium	148	29.1	98	30.5	246	29.7	1253	14.1
Pronounced	47	9.2	40	12.5	87	10.5	406	4.6
Total	508		321		829		8905	
Facial Asymmetry								
Absent	396	78.0	233	72.6	629	75.9	6582	74.0
Left	33	6.5	27	8.4	60	7.2	697	7.8
Right	79	15.6	61	19.0	140	16.9	1612	18.1
Total	508		321		829		8891	

TABLE X-2. MORPHOLOGICAL CHARACTERS IN WHICH CHURCH OF IRELAND DIFFERS SIGNIFICANTLY FROM TOTAL CATHOLICS

	critical ratio	M.D.+se[d]
Hair		
More straight hair	10.59	16.1+1.52
Less low waves	5.66	- 8.6∓1.52
Less deep waves	7.14	- 7.0∓ .98
Less absent baldness	4.74	- 7.3∓1.54
Less absent grayness, beard	3.53	- 5.3∓1.50
More brown hair	3.33	5.0∓1.50
Eyes		
Less blue-brown eyes	4.93	- 7.3+1.48
More pron. dark pigment, mixed eyes	4.89	6.8∓1.39
Less very pron. lt. pigm..."...."	4.24	- 8.6∓2.03
Less clear irides	5.86	- 6.5∓1.11
More scalloped irides	8.31	−11.8∓1.42
Eye Slits		
Less absent external eyefolds	3.45	- 4.0+1.16
Less absent eye obliquity	13.09	-19.9∓1.52
Forehead		
More pronounced brow ridges	4.56	6.2+1.36
More pronounced forehead height	10.00	14.4∓1.44
More submedium forehead slope	3.38	55.2∓1.54
Nose		
More pron. nasion depression	7.52	10.9+1.45
Less convex nasal septum	5.65	- 8.7∓1.54
More pron. nasal bridge breadth	6.71	9.4∓1.40
More pron. nasal tip thickness	3.36	4.7∓1.40
More absent nostrils vis., frontal	3.13	2.5∓1.80
Lips		
More pron. up. lips., membran. thickn.	6.34	5.2+ .82
More pronounced lip eversion	5.24	4.4∓ .84
Teeth		
More pronounced tooth loss	3.50	4.9+1.40
More abs., submed. tooth wear	4.75	6.6∓1.39
More submedium caries	3.62	6.4∓1.77
Less medium caries	3.87	- 5.5∓1.42
Less pronounced caries	3.96	- 3.8∓ .96
Malars		
Less pron. malars, fron. projection	9.09	- 8.0+ .88
Less pron. malars, lateral ."	5.97	- 8.0∓1.34
Ears		
More pron. ear protrusion	3.33	4.5+1.35
Cranial Shape		
Less pronounced temporal fullness	12.57	-12.2+ .98
More pron. occipital protrusion	6.27	8.4∓1.34
More absent lambdoid flattening	27.50	40.8∓1.50
Less absent occipital flattening	13.38	19.8∓1.48

TABLE X-3. MORPHOLOGICAL CHARACTERS IN WHICH PRESBYTERIANS DIFFER SIGNIFICANTLY FROM TOTAL CATHOLICS

	critical ratio	M.D.+se[d]
Skin		
More pronounced vascularity	3.18	6.3+1.98
Hair		
More straight hair	8.16	15.5+1.90
Less low waves	6.34	-11.8∓1.86
More golden brown hair	4.02	5.4∓1.34
Eyes		
Less blue-brown eyes	5.44	- 9.9+1.82
Less clear irides	6.34	- 8.5∓1.34
More scalloped irides	5.52	9.5∓1.72
Less absent external eyefolds	3.62	- 5.4∓1.49
Less absent eye obliquity	12.55	-23.6∓1.88
Forehead		
More submedium brow ridges	4.39	7.4+1.69
More pronounced forehead height	8.10	14.5∓1.79
More pronounced forehead slope	4.57	5.9∓1.29
Nose		
More pronounced nasion depressions	7.21	13.2+1.83
Less convex nasal septum	4.08	- 7.8∓1.91
More pron. nasal bridge height	5.61	9.7∓1.73
More pron. nasal bridge breadth	5.80	10.2∓1.76
More convex nasal profile	4.06	7.8∓1.92
More pronounced nasal tip thickness	5.90	10.8∓1.83
More abs. nostril vis., frontal	3.17	3.3∓1.04
Lips		
More pron. up. lips., mem. thickn.	4.80	4.8+1.00
More submed. lip eversion	3.10	5.3∓1.71
More pron. lip eversion	3.82	3.9∓1.02
Teeth		
More pron. tooth loss	3.60	6.3+1.76
More abs., submed. tooth wear	5.42	9.0∓1.66
More submed. tooth caries	4.52	9.9∓2.19
Less pron. tooth caries	9.76	- 8.1∓ .83
Malars		
Less pron. malars, fron. proj.	5.60	- 6.5+1.16
Less pron. malars, lat. proj.	3.16	- 5.4∓1.71
Ears		
More pron. ear protrusion	4.57	8.0+1.75
Cranial Shape		
Less pron. temporal fullness	8.74	-11.1+1.27
More pron. occipital protrusion	4.42	7.3∓1.65
More absent lambdoid flattening	3.18	53.8∓1.69
Less absent occipital flattening	12.91	-24.4∓1.89

TABLE X-4. MORPHOLOGICAL CHARACTERS IN WHICH BOTH CHURCH OF IRELAND AND PRESBYTERIANS DIFFER FROM TOTAL CATHOLICS SIGNIFICANTLY

	Church of Ireland critical ratio	Presbyterian critical ratio	M.D.$\pm$se^d
Hair			
More straight hair	10.59	8.16	see
Less low waves	5.66	6.34	previous
Eyes			pages
Less blue-brown eyes	4.93	5.44	
Less clear irides	5.86	6.34	
More scalloped irides.......	8.31	5.52	
Less absent external eyefolds .	3.45	3.62	
Less absent eye obliquity	13.09	12.55	
Forehead			
More pronounced forehead height	10.00	8.10	
Nose			
More pron. nasion depression .	7.52	7.21	
Less convex nasal septum . . .	5.65	4.08	
More pron. nasal bridge br. . .	6.71	5.80	
More pron. nasal tip thickness .	3.36	5.90	
More absent nostril vis., frontal	3.13	3.17	
Lips			
More pron. up. lips, mem. thickn.	6.34	4.80	
More pron. lip eversion	5.24	3.82	
Teeth			
More pron. tooth loss	3.50	3.60	
More abs., submed. tooth wear.	4.75	5.42	
More submedium caries	3.62	4.52	
Less pronounced caries	3.96	9.76	
Malars			
Less pron. malars, fron. proj..	9.09	5.60	
Less pron. malars, lat. proj...	5.97	3.16	
Ears			
More pron. ear protrusion ...	3.33	4.57	
Cranial Shape			
Less pron. temporal fullness .	12.57	8.74	
More pron. occipital protrusion	6.27	4.42	
More absent lambdoid flattening	27.20	3.18	
Less absent occipital flattening	13.38	12.91	

TABLE X-5. MORPHOLOGICAL CHARACTERS IN WHICH CHURCH OF IRELAND DIFFERS SIGNIFICANTLY FROM PRESBYTERIANS

	Church of Ireland critical ratio	M.D.$\pm$se^d
Hair		
Less pron., very pron. hair quantity, beard	5.09	$- 5.6 + 1.10$
Less pron. hair quantity, body ..	5.00	$- 4.7 \mp .94$
Less golden brown hair	3.16	$- 5.0 \mp 1.58$
Nose		
Less pron. nasal root height....	3.01	$- 5.9 + 1.96$
Less pron. nasal bridge height ..	3.95	$- 8.3 \mp 2.10$
More straight nasal profile	4.03	9.6 ∓ 2.38
Less convex nasal profile	3.97	$- 9.5 \mp 2.39$
Ears		
Less pron. ear helix	3.20	$- 3.9 \mp 1.22$
Cranial Shape		
Less absent lambdoid flattening .	5.83	-13.0 ∓ 2.23

TABLE XI-1. TOTAL SUBCATEGORIES OF MORPHOLOGY IN WHICH EACH RELIGIOUS GROUP HAS SIGNIFICANT DIFFERENCES

	Total Subcategories	Ch.of I.	Presby.	Prot.	Ch.I./Presby.
Skin	4	-	1	-	-
Hair	9	4	2	1	3
Eyes	3	3	2	2	-
Eye slits ...	5	2	2	2	-
Eyebrows ..	2	-	-	-	-
Forehead ..	3	3	3	1	-
Nose	11	5	7	5	3
Lips	3	2	2	2	-
Prognathism.	3	-	-	-	-
Teeth	7	3	3	3	-
Malars	3	2	2	2	-
Ears	6	1	1	1	1
Cranial shape	4	4	4	4	1
Total	63	29	29	23	8
		46.03%	46.03%	36.50%	12.70%

TABLE XI-2.   SUMMARY OF DIFFERENCES BETWEEN CHURCH OF IRELAND AND CATHOLICS

Metric Differences

Measurements - 18
Greater than Catholics in 2 - 11.11%
Smaller than Catholics in 8 - 44.44%
Indices - 15
Differ from Catholics in 4 - 16.67%

Morphologic Differences

Total		Excess	Deficiency
4	Skin	-	-
9	Hair	4	-
3	Eyes	2	1
5	Eye slits	1	-
2	Eyebrows . . .	-	-
3	Forehead . . .	3	-
11	Nose	5	-
3	Lips	2	-
3	Prognathism .	-	-
7	Teeth	2	1
3	Malars	-	2
6	Ears	1	-
4	Cranial shape	3	1
63	. . . .	23 36.51%	5 7.94%

TABLE XI-4.   SUMMARY OF DIFFERENCES BETWEEN PROTESTANTS AND CATHOLICS

Metric Differences, in the same direction (paired but not combined)

Measurements - 18
Greater than Catholics in 2 - 11.11%
Smaller than Catholics in 4 - 22.22%
Indices - 15
Differ from Catholics in 3 - 20.00%

Morphological Differences (paired but not combined)

Total		Excess	Deficiency
4	Skin	-	-
9	Hair	1	-
3	Eyes	1	2
5	Eye slits . .	2	-
2	Eyebrows . .	-	-
3	Forehead .	1	-
11	Nose	5	-
3	Lips	2	-
3	Prognathism	-	-
7	Teeth	3	1
3	Malars . . .	-	2
6	Ears	1	-
4	Cranial shape	3	1
63	. . . .	18 28.57%	6 9.52%

TABLE XI-3.   SUMMARY OF DIFFERENCES BETWEEN PRESBYTERIANS AND CATHOLICS

Metric Differences

Measurements - 18
Greater than Catholics in 9 - 50.00%
Smaller than Catholics in 4 - 22.22%
Indices - 15
Differ from Catholics in 7 - 46.67%

Morphological Differences

Total		Excess	Deficiency
4	Skin	1	-
9	Hair	2	-
3	Eyes	1	2
5	Eye slits . . .	2	-
2	Eyebrows . . .	-	-
3	Forehead . . .	3	-
11	Nose	6	1
3	Lips	3	-
3	Prognathism .	-	-
7	Teeth	3	-
3	Malars	-	2
6	Ears	1	-
4	Cranial shape	3	1
63	. . . .	25 39.68%	6 9.52%

TABLE XI-5.   SUMMARY OF DIFFERENCES BETWEEN CHURCH OF IRELAND AND PRESBYTERIANS

Metric Differences

Measurements - 18
Greater than Presbyterians in 0 - 0
Smaller than Presbyterians in 8 - 44.44%
Indices - 15
Differ from Presbyterians in 4 - 16.67%

Morphological Differences

Total		Excess	Deficiency
4	Skin	-	-
9	Hair . . .	-	3
3	Eyes . . .	-	-
5	Eye slits .	-	-
2	Eyebrows	-	-
3	Forehead	-	-
11	Nose . . .	1	2
3	Lips	-	-
3	Prognathism	-	-
7	Teeth . . .	-	-
3	Malars . .	-	-
6	Ears . . .	-	1
4	Cranial shape	1	1
63	. . . .	2 3.17%	6 9.52%

TABLE XIII-1. BIRTHPLACE BY MORPHOLOGICAL TYPES (by percentages of total
series in each county subgroup

	West Donegal No.	%	Mayo No.	%	Sligo,Leitrim, So.Fermanagh West Cavan No.	%	West Galway No.	%	Aran Islands No.	%
Pure Nordic	-	-	5	9.1	3	5.4	3	5.4	-	-
Predominantly Nordic	6	.9	18	2.8	62	9.6	35	5.4	7	1.1
Keltic	54	2.2	113	4.7	192	8.0	116	4.8	44	1.8
East Baltic	2	1.9	8	7.6	9	8.6	3	2.9	1	1.0
Dinaric	46	2.6	129	7.3	115	6.5	56	3.2	20	1.1
Nordic Mediterranean	73	2.6	171	6.2	214	7.8	128	4.6	43	1.6
Pure Mediterranean	-	-	1	3.0	8	24.2	1	3.0	-	-
Nordic Alpine	37	2.1	128	7.3	131	7.5	90	5.1	14	.8
Total	218	2.3	573	6.0	734	7.7	432	4.5	129	1.4

	Clare No.	%	Kerry No.	%	Cork No.	%	Limerick No.	%	East Galway, Roscommon No.	%
Pure Nordic	2	3.6	-	-	5	9.1	3	5.4	2	3.6
Predominantly Nordic	43	6.6	29	4.5	35	5.4	21	3.2	39	6.0
Keltic	200	8.3	79	3.3	94	3.9	58	2.4	135	5.6
East Baltic	10	9.5	13	12.4	10	9.5	3	2.9	3	2.9
Dinaric	260	14.7	134	7.6	124	7.0	76	4.3	82	4.6
Nordic Mediterranean	235	8.5	133	4.8	170	6.2	94	3.4	154	5.6
Pure Mediterranean	2	6.1	-	-	-	-	-	-	1	3.0
Nordic Alpine	198	11.3	130	7.4	131	7.5	75	4.3	88	5.0
Total	950	10.0	518	5.4	569	6.0	330	3.5	504	5.3

	Longford, Westmeath No.	%	Offaly, Leix Kildare No.	%	Tipperary, Kilkenny No.	%	Waterford, Wexford No.	%	Wicklow, Carlow No.	%
Pure Nordic	9	16.4	2	3.6	3	5.4	4	7.3	1	1.8
Predominantly Nordic	80	12.3	33	5.1	37	5.7	42	6.5	18	2.8
Keltic	174	7.2	160	6.6	156	6.5	107	4.4	109	4.5
East Baltic	8	7.6	4	3.8	7	6.7	4	3.8	3	2.9
Dinaric	104	5.9	77	4.4	146	8.2	88	5.0	40	2.3
Nordic Mediterranean	226	8.2	162	5.9	171	6.2	120	4.4	78	2.8
Pure Mediterranean	6	18.2	4	12.1	1	3.0	1	3.0	1	3.0
Nordic Alpine	93	5.3	86	4.9	82	4.7	114	6.5	44	2.5
Total	700	7.4	528	5.5	603	6.3	480	5.0	294	3.1

	Meath, Louth, Dublin No.	%	East Cavan, Monaghan, Armagh No.	%	Antrim No.	%	Down No.	%	No. Fermanagh, East Donegal, Tyrone, Londonderry No.	%	Total No.	%
Pure Nordic	1	1.8	3	5.4	2	3.6	7	12.7	55	.6		
Predominantly Nordic	33	5.1	33	5.1	33	5.1	45	6.9	649	6.8		
Keltic	158	6.6	172	7.1	116	4.8	171	7.1	2408	25.3		
East Baltic	2	1.9	2	1.9	3	2.9	10	9.5	105	1.1		
Dinaric	58	3.3	68	3.8	57	3.2	88	5.0	1768	18.6		
Nordic Mediterranean	152	5.5	144	5.2	136	4.9	145	5.3	2749	28.9		
Pure Mediterranean	3	9.1	-	-	3	9.1	1	3.0	33	.3		
Nordic Alpine	60	3.4	76	4.3	63	3.6	114	6.5	1754	18.4		
Total	467	4.9	498	5.2	413	4.3	581	6.1	9521			

TABLE XIII-2. BIRTHPLACE BY COMBINED MORPHOLOGICAL TYPES

	West Donegal No.	%	Mayo No.	%	Sligo, Leitrim, West Cavan, So. Fermanagh No.	%	West Galway No.	%	Aran Islands No.	%
Pure + Predominantly Nordic	6	.8	23	3.3	65	9.2	38	5.4	7	1.0

	Clare No.	%	Kerry No.	%	Cork No.	%	Limerick No.	%	East Galway Roscommon No.	%
Pure + Predominantly Nordic	45	6.4	29	4.1	40	5.7	24	3.4	41	5.8

TABLE XIII-2.   BIRTHPLACE BY COMBINED MORPHOLOGICAL TYPES (Cont.)

	Longford, Westmeath/		Offaly, Leix, Kildare		Tipperary, Kilkenny		Waterford, Wexford		Wicklow, Carlow	
	No.	%	No.	%	No.	%	No.	%	No.	%
Pure + Predominantly Nordic	89	12.6	35	5.0	40	5.7	46	6.5	19	2.7

	Meath, Louth, Dublin		East Cavan, Monaghan, Armagh		Antrim, Down		No. Fermanagh, East Donegal, Tyrone, Londonderry		Total	
	No.	%	No.	%	No.	%	No.	%	No.	
Pure + Predominantly Nordic	34	4.8	36	5.1	35	5.0	52	7.4	704	

TABLE XIII-3.   BIRTHPLACE BY MORPHOLOGICAL TYPES (by ratios of each type in county subgroups to total distribution of that type).

	West Donegal		Mayo		Sligo, Leitrim, West Cavan So. Fermanagh		West Galway		Aran Islands	
	No.	%	No.	%	No.	%	No.	%	No.	%
Pure Nordic	-	-	5	1.5	3	.7	3	1.2	-	-
Predominantly Nordic	6	.4	18	.5	62	1.2	35	1.2	7	.8
Keltic	54	1.0	113	.8	192	1.0	116	1.1	44	1.3
East Baltic	2	.8	8	1.3	9	1.1	3	.6	1	.7
Dinaric	46	1.1	129	1.2	115	.8	56	.7	20	.8
Nordic Mediterranean	73	1.1	171	1.0	314	1.0	128	1.0	43	1.1
Pure Mediterranean	-	-	1	.5	8	3.1	1	.7	-	-
Nordic Alpine	37	.9	128	1.2	131	1.0	90	1.1	14	.6
Total	218	2.3	573	6.0	734	7.7	432	4.5	129	1.4

	Clare		Kerry		Cork		Limerick		East Galway, Roscommon	
	No.	%	No.	%	No.	%	No.	%	No.	%
Pure Nordic	2	.4	-	-	5	1.5	3	1.5	2	.7
Predominantly Nordic	43	.7	29	.8	35	.9	21	.9	39	1.1
Keltic	200	.8	79	.6	94	.6	58	.7	135	1.0
East Baltic	10	1.0	13	2.3	10	1.6	3	.8	3	.5
Dinaric	260	1.5	134	1.4	124	1.2	76	1.2	82	.9
Nordic Mediterranean	235	.8	133	.9	170	1.0	94	1.0	154	1.0
Pure Mediterranean	2	.6	-	-	-	-	-	-	1	.6
Nordic Alpine	198	1.1	130	1.4	131	1.2	75	1.2	88	.9
Total	950	10.0	518	5.4	569	6.0	330	3.5	504	5.3

	Longford, Westmeath		Offaly, Leix, Kildare		Tipperary, Kilkenny		Waterford, Wexford		Wicklow, Carlow	
	No.	%	No.	%	No.	%	No.	%	No.	%
Pure Nordic	9	2.2	2	.6	3	.8	4	1.5	1	.6
Predominantly Nordic	80	1.7	33	.9	37	.9	42	1.3	18	.9
Keltic	174	1.0	160	1.2	156	1.0	107	.9	109	1.4
East Baltic	8	1.0	4	.7	7	1.1	4	.8	3	.9
Dinaric	104	.8	77	.8	146	1.3	88	1.0	40	.7
Nordic Mediterranean	226	1.1	162	1.1	171	1.0	120	.9	78	.9
Pure Mediterranean	6	2.4	4	2.2	1	.5	1	.6	1	1.0
Nordic Alpine	93	.7	86	.9	82	.7	114	1.3	44	.8
Total	700	7.4	528	5.5	603	6.3	480	5.0	294	3.1

	Meath, Louth, Dublin		East Cavan, Monaghan, Armagh		Antrim, Down		No. Fermanagh, East Donegal, Tyrone, Londonderry		Total	
	No.	%	No.	%	No.	%	No.	%	No.	
Pure Nordic	1	.4	3	1.0	2	.8	7	2.1	55	
Predominantly Nordic	33	1.0	33	1.0	33	1.2	45	1.1	649	
Keltic	158	1.3	172	1.4	116	1.1	171	1.2	2408	
East Baltic	2	.4	2	.4	3	.7	10	1.6	105	
Dinaric	58	.7	68	.7	57	.7	88	.8	1768	
Nordic Mediterranean	152	1.1	144	1.0	136	1.1	145	.9	2749	
Pure Mediterranean	3	1.8	-	-	3	2.1	1	.5	33	
Nordic Alpine	60	.7	76	.8	63	.8	114	1.1	1754	
Total	467	4.9	498	5.2	413	4.3	581	6.1	9521	

TABLE XIII-4.   BIRTHPLACE BY COMBINED MORPHOLOGICAL TYPES

	West Donegal		Mayo		Sligo, Leitrim, West Cavan, So. Fermanagh		West Galway		Aran Islands	
	No.	%	No.	%	No.	%	No.	%	No.	%
Pure + Predominantly Nordic	6	.3	23	.6	65	1.2	38	1.2	7	.7

	Clare		Kerry		Cork		Limerick		East Galway, Roscommon	
	No.	%	No.	%	No.	%	No.	%	No.	%
Pure + Predominantly Nordic	45	.6	29	.8	40	1.0	24	1.0	41	1.1

	Longford, Westmeath		Offaly, Leix, Kildare		Tipperary, Kilkenny		Waterford, Wexford		Wicklow, Carlow	
	No.	%	No.	%	No.	%	No.	%	No.	%
Pure + Predominantly Nordic	89	1.7	35	.9	40	.9	46	1.3	19	.9

	Meath, Louth, Dublin		East Cavan, Monaghan, Armagh		Antrim, Down		No. Fermanagh, East Donegal, Tyrone, Londonderry		Total	
	No.	%	No.	%	No.	%	No.	%	No.	
Pure + Predominantly Nordic	34	1.0	36	1.0	35	1.2	52	1.2	704	

TABLE XIII-5.   BIRTHPLACE BY MORPHOLOGICAL TYPES (by absolute percentages of total county subseries)

	West Donegal		Mayo		Sligo, Leitrim, So. Fermanagh, West Cavan		West Galway		Aran Islands	
	No.	%	No.	%	No.	%	No.	%	No.	%
Pure Nordic	-	-	5	.9	3	.4	3	.7	-	-
Predominantly Nordic	6	2.8	18	3.1	62	8.4	35	8.1	7	5.4
Keltic	54	24.8	113	19.7	192	26.2	116	26.8	44	34.1
East Baltic	2	.9	8	1.4	9	1.2	3	.7	1	.8
Dinaric	46	21.1	129	22.5	115	15.7	56	13.0	20	15.5
Nordic Mediterranean	73	33.5	171	29.8	214	29.2	128	29.6	43	33.3
Pure Mediterranean	-	-	1	.2	8	1.1	1	.2	-	-
Nordic Alpine	37	17.0	128	22.3	131	17.8	90	20.8	14	10.8
Total	218		573		734		432		129	

	Clare		Kerry		Cork		Limerick		East Galway, Roscommon	
	No.	%	No.	%	No.	%	No.	%	No.	%
Pure Nordic	2	.2	-	-	5	.9	3	.9	2	.4
Predominantly Nordic	43	4.5	29	5.6	35	6.2	21	6.4	39	7.7
Keltic	200	21.0	79	15.2	94	16.5	58	17.6	135	26.8
East Baltic	10	1.0	13	2.5	10	1.8	3	.9	3	.6
Dinaric	260	27.4	134	25.9	124	21.8	76	23.0	82	16.3
Nordic Mediterranean	235	24.7	133	25.7	170	29.9	94	28.5	154	30.6
Pure Mediterranean	2	.2	-	-	-	-	-	-	1	.2
Nordic Alpine	198	20.8	130	25.1	131	23.0	75	22.7	88	17.5
Total	950		518		569		330		504	

	Longford, Westmeath		Offaly Leix, Kildare		Tipperary, Kilkenny		Waterford, Wexford		Wicklow, Carlow	
	No.		No.		No.		No.		No.	
Pure Nordic	9	1.3	2	.4	3	.5	4	.8	1	.3
Predominantly Nordic	80	11.4	33	6.2	37	6.1	42	8.7	18	6.1
Keltic	174	24.8	160	30.3	156	25.9	107	22.3	109	37.1
East Baltic	8	1.1	4	.8	7	1.2	4	.8	3	1.0
Dinaric	104	14.8	77	14.6	146	24.2	88	18.3	40	13.6
Nordic Mediterranean	226	32.3	162	30.7	171	28.4	120	25.0	78	26.5
Pure Mediterranean	6	.8	4	.8	1	.2	1	.2	1	.3
Nordic Alpine	93	13.3	86	16.3	82	13.6	114	23.7	44	15.0
Total	700		528		603		480		294	

TABLE XIII-5. BIRTHPLACE BY MORPHOLOGICAL TYPES (Cont.)

	Meath, Louth, Dublin		East Cavan, Monaghan, Armagh		Antrim, Down		No. Fermanagh, East Donegal, Tyrone, Londonderry		Total	
	No.	%	No.	%	No.	%	No.	%	No.	%
Pure Nordic	1	.2	3	.6	2	.5	7	1.2	55	.6
Predominantly Nordic	33	7.1	33	6.6	33	8.0	45	7.7	649	6.8
Keltic	158	33.8	172	34.5	116	28.1	171	29.4	2408	25.3
East Baltic	2	.4	2	.4	3	.7	10	1.7	105	1.1
Dinaric	58	12.4	68	13.6	57	13.8	88	15.1	1768	18.6
Nordic Mediterranean	152	32.5	144	28.9	136	32.9	145	25.0	2749	28.9
Pure Mediterranean	3	.6	-	-	3	.7	1	.2	33	.3
Nordic Alpine	60	12.8	76	15.3	63	15.2	114	19.6	1754	18.4
Total	467		498		413		581		9521	

TABLE XIII-6. BIRTHPLACE BY COMBINED MORPHOLOGICAL TYPES (Cont.)

	West Donegal		Mayo		Sligo, Leitrim, West Cavan, So. Fermanagh		West Galway		Aran Islands	
	No.	%	No.	%	No.	%	No.	%	No.	%
Pure + Predominantly Nordic	6	2.8	23	4.0	65	8.8	38	8.8	7	5.4

	Clare		Kerry		Cork		Limerick		East Galway, Roscommon	
	No.	%	No.	%	No.	%	No.	%	No.	%
Pure + Predominantly Nordic	45	4.7	29	5.6	40	7.0	24	7.3	41	8.1

	Longford, Westmeath		Offaly, Leix, Kildare		Tipperary, Kilkenny		Waterford, Wexford		Wicklow, Carlow	
	No.	%	No.	%	No.	%	No.	%	No.	%
Pure + Predominantly Nordic	89	12.7	35	6.6	40	6.6	46	9.6	19	6.5

	Meath, Louth, Dublin		East Cavan, Monaghan, Armagh		Antrim, Down		No. Fermanagh, East Donegal, Tyrone, Londonderry		Total	
	No.	%	No.	%	No.	%	No.	%	No.	%
Pure + Predominantly Nordic	34	7.3	36	7.2	35	8.5	52	9.0	704	7.4

TABLE XIV-1.   EDUCATION BY MORPHOLOGICAL TYPES

	Illiterate No.	%	Read and write No.	%	National school No.	%	Secondary school No.	%	University No.	%	Total No.	%
Pure Nordic	-	-	-	-	41	75.9	13	24.1	-	-	54	.6
Predominantly Nordic	3	.5	4	.6	539	83.3	84	13.0	17	2.6	647	6.8
Keltic	107	4.5	38	1.6	2019	84.3	193	8.0	38	1.6	2395	25.3
East Baltic	1	1.0	-	-	78	75.0	18	17.3	7	6.7	104	1.1
Dinaric	30	1.7	14	.8	1366	77.3	300	17.0	56	3.2	1766	18.6
Nordic Mediterranean	83	3.0	25	.9	2270	83.0	310	11.3	45	1.6	2733	28.8
Pure Mediterranean	1	3.0	1	3.0	26	78.8	4	12.1	1	3.0	33	.3
Nordic Alpine	40	2.3	14	.8	1401	80.2	242	13.9	49	2.8	1746	18.4
Total	265	2.8	96	1.0	7740	81.7	1164	12.3	213	2.2	9478	

TABLE XIV-2. EDUCATIONAL RANKING BY MORPHOLOGICAL
TYPES (Illiterate, Read and write (A), over Secondary
School, University (B))

	A (Illiterate + Read and write) %	B (Secondary school + University) %	B/A
1. Pure Nordic	-	24.1	-
2. East Baltic	1.0	24.0	24.0
3. Predominantly Nordic	1.1	15.6	14.2
4. Dinaric	2.5	20.2	8.1
5. Nordic Alpine	3.1	16.7	5.4
6. Nordic Mediterranean	4.0	13.0	3.2
7. Pure Mediterranean	6.0	15.2	2.5
8. Keltic	6.0	9.6	1.6
Total series	3.8	14.5	3.8

TABLE XIV-3. LANGUAGE BY MORPHOLOGICAL TYPES

	No Irish No.	%	Native speaker No.	%	Irish only No.	%	School Irish No.	%	Total No.	%
Pure Nordic	31	56.4	4	7.3	-	-	20	36.4	55	.6
Predominantly Nordic	343	52.9	64	9.9	1	.2	240	37.0	648	6.8
Keltic	1530	63.6	273	11.3	32	1.3	571	23.7	2406	25.3
East Baltic	55	52.4	16	15.2	-	-	34	32.4	105	1.1
Dinaric	929	52.6	206	11.7	12	.7	619	35.0	1766	18.6
Nordic Mediterranean	1641	59.7	356	13.0	25	.9	726	26.4	2748	28.9
Pure Mediterranean	20	60.6	1	3.0	1	3.0	11	33.3	33	.3
Nordic Alpine	932	53.2	249	14.2	15	.8	557	31.8	1753	18.4
Total	5481	57.6	1169	12.3	86	.9	2778	29.2	9514	

TABLE XIV-4. OCCUPATION OF INDIVIDUAL BY MORPHOLOGICAL TYPES

	Hired laborer, tinker No.	%	Herdsman, farmer farm steward, gardener No.	%	Farm dependent No.	%	Fisherman No.	%	Navvy No.	%
Pure Nordic	2	3.8	-	-	6	11.5	1	1.9	12	23.1
Predominantly Nordic	43	7.1	66	10.8	61	10.0	12	2.0	130	21.3
Keltic	248	10.8	387	16.8	147	6.4	58	2.5	557	24.2
East Baltic	3	2.9	13	12.7	10	9.8	1	1.0	16	15.7
Dinaric	93	5.6	228	13.7	128	7.7	39	2.3	335	20.1
Nordic Mediterranean	175	6.6	344	13.0	188	7.1	69	2.6	646	24.5
Pure Mediterranean	-	-	5	15.2	2	6.1	-	-	7	21.2
Nordic Alpine	123	7.3	254	15.2	144	8.6	44	2.6	302	18.0
Total	687	7.6	1297	14.3	686	7.6	224	2.5	2005	22.1

TABLE XIV-4. OCCUPATION OF INDIVIDUAL BY MORPHOLOGICAL TYPES (Cont.)

	Semi-skilled trades		Transportation		Factory		Skilled trades		Shop assistants Sm. shopkeepers merchants	
	No.	%	No.	%	No.	%	No.	%	No.	%
Pure Nordic.......	9	17.3	1	1.9	-	-	3	5.8	8	15.4
Predominantly Nordic	46	7.6	26	4.3	8	1.3	26	4.3	70	11.5
Keltic	189	8.2	114	5.0	43	1.9	40	1.7	222	9.6
East Baltic........	8	7.8	6	5.9	2	2.0	2	2.0	13	12.7
Dinaric	134	8.0	64	3.8	24	1.4	58	3.5	209	12.5
Nordic Mediterranean	237	9.0	107	4.0	39	1.5	80	3.0	290	11.0
Pure Mediterranean .	-	-	4	12.1	-	-	1	3.0	8	24.2
Nordic Alpine	133	7.9	101	6.0	32	1.9	58	3.5	187	11.2
Total	756	8.3	423	4.6	148	1.6	268	3.0	1007	11.1

	Clerks		Professional, teachers, clergy		Soldiers		Students		Total
	No.	%	No.	%	No.	%	No.	%	No.
Pure Nordic	-	-	2	3.8	7	13.5	1	1.9	52
Predominantly Nordic	19	3.1	15	2.5	72	11.8	15	2.5	609
Keltic	31	1.3	41	1.8	202	8.8	24	1.0	2303
East Baltic	2	2.0	5	4.9	17	16.7	4	3.9	102
Dinaric	35	2.1	53	3.2	232	13.9	36	2.2	1668
Nordic Mediterranean	66	2.5	47	1.8	316	12.0	37	1.4	2641
Pure Mediterranean .	-	-	-	-	6	18.2	-	-	33
Nordic Alpine......	29	1.7	53	3.2	173	10.3	41	2.4	1674
Total	182	2.0	216	2.4	1025	11.3	158	1.7	9082

TABLE XIV-5. OCCUPATION OF INDIVIDUAL, RURAL AND URBAN, BY MORPHOLOGICAL TYPES

	Rural		Urban		Total
	No.	%	No.	%	No.
Pure Nordic	9	17.3	43	82.7	52
Predominantly Nordic	182	29.9	427	70.1	609
Keltic	840	36.5	1463	63.5	2303
East Baltic	27	26.5	75	73.5	102
Dinaric	488	29.2	1180	70.7	1668
Nordic Mediterranean	776	29.4	1865	70.6	2641
Pure Mediterranean .	7	21.2	26	78.8	33
Nordic Alpine	565	33.8	1109	66.2	1674
Total	2894	31.9	6188	68.1	9082

TABLE XIV-6. RELIGION BY MORPHOLOGICAL TYPES

	Catholic		Church of Ireland		Presbyterian		Total
	No.	%	No.	%	No.	%	No.
Pure Nordic	46	86.8	5	9.4	2	3.8	53
Predominantly Nordic	556	87.4	41	6.4	39	6.1	636
Keltic	2136	90.4	136	5.8	90	3.8	2362
East Baltic	91	90.1	8	7.9	2	2.0	101
Dinaric..........	1617	93.5	73	4.2	39	2.2	1729
Nordic Mediterranean	2428	90.8	160	6.0	87	3.2	2675
Pure Mediterranean .	26	83.9	2	6.4	3	9.7	31
Nordic Alpine	1615	93.8	60	3.5	47	2.7	1722
Total	8515	91.5	485	5.2	309	3.3	9309

TABLE XV-1. AGE GROUPS BY MORPHOLOGICAL TYPES

	15-19		20-24		25-29		30-34		35-39		40-44		45-49	
	No.	%	No.	%	No.	%	No.	%	No.	%	No.	%	No.	%
Pure Nordic	14	25.4	16	29.1	7	12.7	7	12.7	7	12.7	3	5.4	1	1.8
Predominantly Nordic	101	15.6	210	32.4	136	21.0	89	13.7	36	5.5	25	3.8	15	2.3
Keltic	174	7.2	375	15.6	306	12.7	269	11.2	256	10.6	228	9.5	180	7.5
East Baltic	13	12.4	38	36.2	15	14.3	14	13.3	7	6.7	2	1.9	4	3.8
Dinaric	180	10.2	383	21.7	275	15.6	270	15.3	184	10.4	136	7.7	90	5.1
Nordic Mediterranean	262	9.5	559	20.3	366	13.3	325	11.8	305	11.1	237	8.6	181	6.6
Pure Mediterranean	3	9.1	4	12.1	4	12.1	4	12.1	3	9.1	2	1.9	4	12.1
Nordic Alpine	213	12.1	404	23.0	245	14.0	211	12.0	186	10.6	135	7.7	83	4.7
Total	960	10.1	1989	20.9	1354	14.2	1189	12.5	984	10.3	768	8.1	558	5.9

	50-54		55-59		60-64		65-69		70-74		75-79		80-94		Total
	No.	%	No.	%	No.	%	No.	%	No.	%	No.		No.		No.
Pure Nordic	-	-	-	-	-	-	-	-	-	-	-		-		55
Predominantly Nordic	12	1.8	13	2.0	3	.5	6	.9	-	-	3	.5	-	-	649
Keltic	178	7.4	161	6.7	123	5.1	83	3.4	48	2.0	17	.7	10	.4	2408
East Baltic	2	1.9	6	5.7	3	2.9	-	-	1	1.0	-	-	-	-	105
Dinaric	84	4.8	69	3.9	43	2.4	29	1.6	18	1.0	5	.3	2	.1	1768
Nordic Mediterranean	160	5.8	117	4.2	106	3.8	71	2.6	35	1.3	18	.6	7	.2	2749
Pure Mediterranean	4	12.1	1	3.0	2	6.1	1	3.0	-	-	1	3.0	-	-	33
Nordic Alpine	84	4.8	65	3.7	76	4.3	36	2.0	9	.5	3	.2	4	.2	1754
Total	524	5.5	432	4.5	356	3.7	226	2.4	111	1.2	47	.5	23	.2	9521

TABLE XV-2. AGE BY MORPHOLOGICAL TYPES

	No.	Range	Mean	S.D.
Pure Nordic	55	15-49	26.10 + 0.74	8.20
Predominantly Nordic	649	15-79	27.95 ∓ 0.28	10.55
Keltic	2408	15-94	38.55 ∓ 0.21	15.45
East Baltic	105	15-74	29.95 ∓ 0.83	12.65
Dinaric	1768	15-89	33.40 ∓ 0.21	13.35
Nordic Mediterranean	2749	15-89	35.50 ∓ 0.19	14.70
Pure Mediterranean	33	15-79	39.10 ∓ 1.82	15.55
Nordic Alpine	1754	15-89	33.50 ∓ 0.22	14.00
Total	9521	15-94	34.90 + 0.10	14.50

TABLE XV-3. AGE BY MORPHOLOGICAL TYPES

	Mean Ages in Ascending Order
Pure Nordic	26.10
Predominantly Nordic	27.95
East Baltic	29.95
Dinaric	33.40
Nordic Alpine	33.50
Nordic Mediterranean	35.50
Keltic	38.55
Pure Mediterranean	39.10
Total	34.90

TABLE XV-4. WEIGHT BY MORPHOLOGICAL TYPES

	No.	Range	Mean	S.D.
Pure Nordic	55	111-210	151.10 + 1.76	19.40
Predominantly Nordic	649	101-250	155.50 ∓ 0.55	20.80
Keltic	2407	91-260	156.60 ∓ 0.30	21.70
East Baltic	105	101-250	156.70 ∓ 1.63	24.80
Dinaric	1767	101-280	157.30 ∓ 0.37	23.00
Nordic Mediterranean	2749	91-290	157.30 ∓ 0.28	22.20
Pure Mediterranean	33	111-200	150.30 ∓ 2.40	20.40
Nordic Alpine	1754	91-270	158.80 ∓ 0.38	23.50
Total	9519	91-290	157.20 + 0.15	22.40

TABLE XV-5. STATURE BY MORPHOLOGICAL TYPES

	No.	Range	Mean	S.D.
Pure Nordic	55	155-187	172.08 + 0.55	6.03
Predominantly Nordic	649	152-202	173.25 ∓ 0.17	6.54
Keltic	2407	146-199	171.87 ∓ 0.09	6.84
East Baltic	105	155-187	171.78 ∓ 0.44	6.75
Dinaric	1764	149-202	172.47 ∓ 0.11	6.78
Nordic Mediterranean	2748	149-202	172.14 ∓ 0.09	6.81
Pure Mediterranean	33	161-184	170.91 ∓ 0.62	5.31
Nordic Alpine	1754	146-196	171.36 ∓ 0.11	6.93
Total	9515	146-202	172.05 + 0.05	6.84

TABLE XV-6. SPAN BY MORPHOLOGICAL TYPES

	No.	Range	Mean	S.D.
Pure Nordic	55	164-199	180.54 + 0.69	7.62
Predominantly Nordic	642	158-205	181.86 ∓ 0.21	7.95
Keltic	2341	146-208	181.23 ∓ 0.11	7.98
East Baltic	104	161-202	180.57 ∓ 0.54	8.22
Dinaric	1738	155-217	181.77 ∓ 0.13	8.04
Nordic Mediterranean	2686	146-211	181.26 ∓ 0.10	7.92
Pure Mediterranean	31	170-205	180.30 ∓ 0.84	6.96
Nordic Alpine	1712	152-208	180.69 ∓ 0.13	7.86
Total	9309	146-217	181.26 + 0.06	7.95

TABLE XV-7. RELATIVE SPAN BY MORPHOLOGICAL TYPES

	No.	Range	Mean	S.D.
Pure Nordic	55	98-111	104.98 + 0.25	2.72
Predominantly Nordic	642	98-115	105.02 ∓ 0.07	2.56
Keltic	2341	96-115	105.42 ∓ 0.04	2.56
East Baltic	104	98-113	105.32 ∓ 0.17	2.52
Dinaric	1736	96-115	105.32 ∓ 0.04	2.54
Nordic Mediterranean	2685	94-115	105.26 ∓ 0.03	2.52
Pure Mediterranean	31	100-113	105.60 ∓ 0.27	2.20
Nordic Alpine	1712	96-115	105.44 ∓ 0.04	2.48
Total	9306	94-115	105.32 + 0.02	2.52

TABLE XV-8. BIACROMIAL DIAMETER BY MORPHOLOGICAL TYPES

	No.	Range	Mean	S.D.
Pure Nordic	55	31-42	37.85 + 0.20	2.25
Predominantly Nordic	647	28-45	38.51 ∓ 0.06	2.13
Keltic	2401	28-45	38.57 ∓ 0.03	1.98
East Baltic	104	34-42	38.30 ∓ 0.13	1.95
Dinaric	1762	31-48	38.69 ∓ 0.03	2.13
Nordic Mediterranean	2742	31-48	38.54 ∓ 0.03	2.04
Pure Mediterranean	33	34-42	37.91 ∓ 0.24	2.01
Nordic Alpine	1750	31-45	38.69 ∓ 0.03	2.10
Total	9494	28-48	38.60 + 0.01	2.07

TABLE XV-9. RELATIVE SHOULDER BREADTH BY MORPHOLOGICAL TYPES

	No.	Range	Mean	S.D.
Pure Nordic	55	20-25	22.10 + 0.10	1.10
Predominantly Nordic	647	18-27	22.22 ∓ 0.03	1.12
Keltic	2401	18-27	22.46 ∓ 0.02	1.12
East Baltic	104	20-25	22.52 ∓ 0.07	1.12
Dinaric	1759	18-27	22.42 ∓ 0.02	1.14
Nordic Mediterranean	2741	18-27	22.40 ∓ 0.01	1.12
Pure Mediterranean	33	20-25	22.02 ∓ 0.12	0.98
Nordic Alpine	1750	18-27	22.56 ∓ 0.02	1.12
Total	9490	18-27	22.42 + 0.01	1.12

TABLE XV-10. CHEST BREADTH BY MORPHOLOGICAL TYPES

	No.	Range	Mean	S.D.
Pure Nordic	54	23-34	27.93 + 0.17	1.89
Predominantly Nordic	649	20-40	28.50 ∓ 0.06	2.37
Keltic	2381	20-40	28.83 ∓ 0.03	2.34
East Baltic	105	23-37	28.62 ∓ 0.17	2.64
Dinaric	1761	20-40	28.86 ∓ 0.04	2.46
Nordic Mediterranean	2736	20-40	28.83 ∓ 0.03	2.37
Pure Mediterranean	32	23-37	28.14 ∓ 0.29	2.46
Nordic Alpine	1746	20-40	28.92 ∓ 0.04	2.46
Total	9464	20-40	28.83 + 0.02	2.40

TABLE XV-11. CHEST DEPTH BY MORPHOLOGICAL TYPES

	No.	Range	Mean	S.D.
Pure Nordic	54	18-29	22.46 + 0.14	1.56
Predominantly Nordic	649	18-31	22.72 ∓ 0.05	1.86
Keltic	2381	18-31	23.32 ∓ 0.03	1.98
East Baltic	104	18-29	22.58 ∓ 0.14	2.06
Dinaric	1759	18-33	23.04 ∓ 0.03	2.00
Nordic Mediterranean	2734	16-31	23.22 ∓ 0.02	1.98
Pure Mediterranean	32	18-27	22.94 ∓ 0.23	1.92
Nordic Alpine	1746	18-31	23.22 ∓ 0.03	2.02
Total	9459	16-33	23.16 + 0.01	1.98

TABLE XV-12. THORACIC INDEX BY MORPHOLOGICAL TYPES

	No.	Range	Mean	S.D.
Pure Nordic	54	69- 92	80.66 + 0.46	5.04
Predominantly Nordic	649	61-100	80.02 ∓ 0.17	6.52
Keltic	2380	57-108	81.10 ∓ 0.09	6.72
East Baltic	104	57-100	78.86 ∓ 0.43	6.52
Dinaric	1758	57-104	79.86 ∓ 0.10	6.48
Nordic Mediterranean	2732	53-108	80.74 ∓ 0.08	6.64
Pure Mediterranean	32	57-104	82.38 ∓ 0.98	8.20
Nordic Alpine	1746	57-104	80.38 ∓ 0.11	6.60
Total	9455	53-108	80.54 + 0.05	6.64

TABLE XV-13. SITTING HEIGHT BY MORPHOLOGICAL TYPES

	No.	Range	Mean	S.D.
Pure Nordic	55	84-101	91.54 + 0.29	3.24
Predominantly Nordic	646	81-107	92.14 ∓ 0.09	3.42
Keltic	2400	78-104	91.36 ∓ 0.05	3.57
East Baltic	105	81-101	91.78 ∓ 0.23	3.57
Dinaric	1759	78-104	91.75 ∓ 0.06	3.45
Nordic Mediterranean	2745	75-107	91.60 ∓ 0.05	3.60
Pure Mediterranean	33	81-101	90.28 ∓ 0.40	3.39
Nordic Alpine	1751	75-104	91.48 ∓ 0.06	3.66
Total	9494	75-107	91.57 + 0.02	3.57

TABLE XV-14. RELATIVE SITTING HEIGHT BY MORPHOLOGICAL TYPES

	No.	Range	Mean	S.D.
Pure Nordic	55	50-57	53.00 + 0.12	1.28
Predominantly Nordic	646	48-59	53.20 ∓ 0.04	1.50
Keltic	2400	46-59	53.18 ∓ 0.02	1.50
East Baltic	105	48-57	53.42 ∓ 0.09	1.40
Dinaric	1758	48-57	53.18 ∓ 0.02	1.44
Nordic Mediterranean	2744	48-59	53.22 ∓ 0.02	1.46
Pure Mediterranean	33	50-57	52.80 ∓ 0.17	1.42
Nordic Alpine	1751	48-59	53.34 ∓ 0.02	1.46
Total	9492	46-59	53.22 + 0.01	1.46

TABLE XV-15. HEAD LENGTH BY MORPHOLOGICAL TYPES

	No.	Range	Mean	S.D.
Pure Nordic	55	185-214	196.74 ± 0.59	6.51
Predominantly Nordic	649	173-223	197.46 ± 0.17	6.36
Keltic.	2408	176-220	197.58 ± 0.08	5.91
East Baltic	105	173-208	193.05 ± 0.39	6.00
Dinaric.	1768	170-214	192.27 ± 0.10	5.94
Nordic Mediterranean	2749	176-223	197.70 ± 0.08	5.94
Pure Mediterranean	33	179-214	197.46 ± 0.80	6.78
Nordic Alpine	1754	173-220	192.69 ± 0.10	6.12
Total	9521	170-223	195.66 ± 0.04	6.51

TABLE XV-16. HEAD BREADTH BY MORPHOLOGICAL TYPES

	No.	Range	Mean	S.D.
Pure Nordic	55	141-170	151.12 ± 0.45	4.98
Predominantly Nordic	649	132-167	151.66 ± 0.13	5.07
Keltic.	2408	129-167	151.57 ± 0.06	4.74
East Baltic	105	147-185	157.96 ± 0.34	5.22
Dinaric.	1768	138-179	157.54 ± 0.08	5.19
Nordic Mediterranean	2749	126-170	151.90 ± 0.06	4.89
Pure Mediterranean	33	141-167	152.56 ± 0.58	4.95
Nordic Alpine	1754	141-179	157.63 ± 0.08	5.04
Total	9521	126-185	153.97 ± 0.04	5.76

TABLE XV-17. HEAD CIRCUMFERENCE BY MORPHOLOGICAL TYPES

	No.	Range	Mean	S.D.
Pure Nordic	50	535-624	570.20 ± 1.83	19.20
Predominantly Nordic	615	520-639	571.85 ± 0.46	17.10
Keltic.	2221	505-639	571.70 ± 0.23	16.05
East Baltic	101	535-639	574.70 ± 1.13	16.80
Dinaric.	1655	505-639	571.25 ± 0.27	16.50
Nordic Mediterranean	2570	520-654	572.30 ± 0.22	16.50
Pure Mediterranean	33	520-624	573.80 ± 2.38	20.25
Nordic Alpine	1614	520-654	572.45 ± 0.28	16.80
Total	8859	505-654	572.00 ± 0.12	16.50

TABLE XV-18. CEPHALIC INDEX BY MORPHOLOGICAL TYPES

	No.	Range	Mean	S.D.
Pure Nordic	55	71-79	76.65 ± 0.17	1.89
Predominantly Nordic	649	65-79	76.62 ± 0.05	1.86
Keltic.	2408	65-79	76.59 ± 0.02	1.86
East Baltic	105	80-91	82.08 ± 0.13	1.92
Dinaric.	1768	80-94	82.20 ± 0.03	1.89
Nordic Mediterranean	2749	62-79	76.65 ± 0.02	1.95
Pure Mediterranean	33	71-79	77.01 ± 0.19	1.59
Nordic Alpine	1754	80-91	82.17 ± 0.03	1.95
Total	9521	62-94	78.75 ± 0.02	3.30

TABLE XV-19. HEAD HEIGHT BY MORPHOLOGICAL TYPES

	No.	Range	Mean	S.D.
Pure Nordic	55	110-137	125.02 ± 0.52	5.68
Predominantly Nordic	646	106-145	125.26 ± 0.16	6.08
Keltic.	2407	102-149	124.62 ± 0.08	6.04
East Baltic	105	110-141	125.54 ± 0.37	5.64
Dinaric.	1765	106-145	125.34 ± 0.10	6.12
Nordic Mediterranean	2749	102-149	125.06 ± 0.08	6.00
Pure Mediterranean	33	114-137	124.34 ± 0.54	4.60
Nordic Alpine	1754	106-153	125.50 ± 0.10	6.16
Total	9514	102-153	125.10 ± 0.04	6.08

TABLE XV-20. LENGTH-HEIGHT INDEX BY MORPHOLOGICAL TYPES

	No.	Range	Mean	S.D.
Pure Nordic	55	52-72	63.65 + 0.28	3.12
Predominantly Nordic	646	52-75	63.38 ∓ 0.08	3.12
Keltic	2407	52-75	63.08 ∓ 0.04	3.21
East Baltic	105	58-75	65.12 ∓ 0.21	3.21
Dinaric	1765	52-78	65.12 ∓ 0.05	3.30
Nordic Mediterranean	2749	52-75	63.26 ∓ 0.04	3.03
Pure Mediterranean	33	55-69	62.99 ∓ 0.30	2.52
Nordic Alpine	1754	55-75	65.15 ∓ 0.05	3.30
Total	9514	52-78	63.95 + 0.02	3.33

TABLE XV-21. BREADTH-HEIGHT INDEX BY MORPHOLOGICAL TYPES

	No.	Range	Mean	S.D.
Pure Nordic	55	70-93	82.94 + 0.35	3.87
Predominantly Nordic	646	70-96	82.55 ∓ 0.11	4.14
Keltic	2407	67-96	82.10 ∓ 0.06	4.14
East Baltic	105	73-90	79.58 ∓ 0.25	3.84
Dinaric	1765	67-93	79.46 ∓ 0.06	3.99
Nordic Mediterranean	2749	67-99	82.28 ∓ 0.05	4.02
Pure Mediterranean	33	76-93	81.44 ∓ 0.41	3.48
Nordic Alpine	1754	67-93	79.55 ∓ 0.06	3.96
Total	9514	67-99	81.20 + 0.03	4.26

TABLE XV-22. MINIMUM FRONTAL DIAMETER BY MORPHOLOGICAL TYPES

	No.	Range	Mean	S.D.
Pure Nordic	55	97-124	108.82 + 0.44	4.88
Predominantly Nordic	649	97-128	108.62 ∓ 0.12	4.64
Keltic	2407	89-128	108.46 ∓ 0.06	4.60
East Baltic	105	101-124	110.02 ∓ 0.30	4.60
Dinaric	1767	93-128	109.54 ∓ 0.08	4.92
Nordic Mediterranean	2746	89-128	108.75 ∓ 0.06	4.68
Pure Mediterranean	32	97-116	107.74 ∓ 0.48	4.04
Nordic Alpine	1752	93-128	110.54 ∓ 0.08	4.92
Total	9513	89-128	109.14 + 0.03	4.80

TABLE XV-23. FRONTO-PARIETAL INDEX BY MORPHOLOGICAL TYPES

	No.	Range	Mean	S.D.
Pure Nordic	55	66-77	72.07 + 0.22	2.43
Predominantly Nordic	649	60-86	71.80 ∓ 0.08	3.00
Keltic	2407	60-86	71.68 ∓ 0.04	3.03
East Baltic	105	63-77	69.82 ∓ 0.19	2.85
Dinaric	1767	60-80	69.73 ∓ 0.05	2.91
Nordic Mediterranean	2746	60-86	71.71 ∓ 0.04	2.97
Pure Mediterranean	32	63-80	70.75 ∓ 0.38	3.18
Nordic Alpine	1752	60-80	70.27 ∓ 0.05	2.91
Total	9513	60-86	71.05 + 0.02	3.09

TABLE XV-24. ZYGO-FRONTAL INDEX BY MORPHOLOGICAL TYPES

	No.	Range	Mean	S.D.
Pure Nordic	55	68-87	78.50 + 0.28	3.08
Predominantly Nordic	646	68-91	78.22 ∓ 0.08	3.16
Keltic	2403	64-95	77.98 ∓ 0.04	3.28
East Baltic	105	68-87	77.42 ∓ 0.20	3.00
Dinaric	1763	64-95	77.38 ∓ 0.05	3.36
Nordic Mediterranean	2743	68-95	77.98 ∓ 0.04	3.24
Pure Mediterranean	32	64-83	76.74 ∓ 0.42	3.52
Nordic Alpine	1749	64-91	77.62 ∓ 0.05	3.24
Total	9496	64-95	77.82 + 0.02	3.24

TABLE XV-25. BIZYGOMATIC DIAMETER BY MORPHOLOGICAL TYPES

	No.	Range	Mean	S.D.
Pure Nordic	55	125-159	138.65 + 0.51	5.65
Predominantly Nordic	646	120-159	139.05 ∓ 0.15	5.55
Keltic	2404	110-159	139.45 ∓ 0.08	5.60
East Baltic	105	125-159	142.80 ∓ 0.43	6.55
Dinaric	1764	110-164	142.00 ∓ 0.10	5.95
Nordic Mediterranean	2746	120-169	139.80 ∓ 0.07	5.70
Pure Mediterranean	33	125-154	139.60 ∓ 0.69	5.90
Nordic Alpine	1751	120-164	142.60 ∓ 0.10	5.90
Total	9504	110-169	140.60 + 0.04	5.90

TABLE XV-26. CEPHALO-FACIAL INDEX BY MORPHOLOGICAL TYPES

	No.	Range	Mean	S.D.
Pure Nordic	55	85- 99	91.67 + 0.22	2.40
Predominantly Nordic	646	79-105	91.73 ∓ 0.08	3.00
Keltic	2404	76-105	92.03 ∓ 0.04	3.18
East Baltic	105	79-102	90.38 ∓ 0.23	3.45
Dinaric	1764	76-105	90.14 ∓ 0.05	3.15
Nordic Mediterranean	2746	76-108	92.06 ∓ 0.04	3.18
Pure Mediterranean	33	82- 99	91.46 ∓ 0.45	3.81
Nordic Alpine	1751	76-105	90.50 ∓ 0.05	3.09
Total	9504	76-108	91.37 + 0.02	3.27

TABLE XV-27. TOTAL FACE HEIGHT BY MORPHOLOGICAL TYPES

	No.	Range	Mean	S.D.
Pure Nordic	55	105-154	126.10 + 0.67	7.35
Predominantly Nordic	648	100-149	127.40 ∓ 0.18	6.85
Keltic	2405	95-154	127.20 ∓ 0.10	7.10
East Baltic	105	105-144	124.40 ∓ 0.49	7.45
Dinaric	1767	100-149	128.30 ∓ 0.10	6.55
Nordic Mediterranean	2746	100-154	127.30 ∓ 0.09	7.00
Pure Mediterranean	33	110-139	123.80 ∓ 0.85	7.25
Nordic Alpine	1751	95-154	125.10 ∓ 0.11	6.65
Total	9510	95-154	127.00 + 0.05	6.95

TABLE XV-28. UPPER FACE HEIGHT BY MORPHOLOGICAL TYPES

	No.	Range	Mean	S.D.
Pure Nordic	54	60-84	71.25 + 0.36	3.90
Predominantly Nordic	648	55-89	72.55 ∓ 0.12	4.50
Keltic	2405	50-89	73.05 ∓ 0.06	4.60
East Baltic	105	60-84	71.10 ∓ 0.28	4.20
Dinaric	1767	60-94	73.90 ∓ 0.07	4.15
Nordic Mediterranean	2747	55-89	73.00 ∓ 0.06	4.55
Pure Mediterranean	33	60-84	71.85 ∓ 0.53	4.50
Nordic Alpine	1747	55-89	71.40 ∓ 0.07	4.25
Total	9506	50-94	72.80 + 0.03	4.50

TABLE XV-29. FACIAL INDEX BY MORPHOLOGICAL TYPES

	No.	Range	Mean	S.D.
Pure Nordic	55	80-109	91.10 + 0.42	4.65
Predominantly Nordic	645	75-109	91.50 ∓ 0.14	5.20
Keltic	2401	70-114	91.10 ∓ 0.08	5.60
East Baltic	105	75- 99	87.25 ∓ 0.34	5.10
Dinaric	1763	70-114	90.30 ∓ 0.08	5.15
Nordic Mediterranean	2743	70-114	90.95 ∓ 0.07	5.40
Pure Mediterranean	33	75- 99	89.25 ∓ 0.71	6.05
Nordic Alpine	1748	70-104	87.65 ∓ 0.08	4.95
Total	9493	70-114	90.25 + 0.04	5.50

TABLE XV-30. UPPER FACIAL INDEX BY MORPHOLOGICAL TYPES

	No.	Range	Mean	S.D.
Pure Nordic	54	43-57	51.29 + 0.28	3.09
Predominantly Nordic	645	40-66	52.04 ∓ 0.09	3.33
Keltic.	2401	37-69	52.28 ∓ 0.05	3.60
East Baltic	105	40-60	49.79 ∓ 0.20	3.03
Dinaric	1763	40-69	51.95 ∓ 0.05	3.09
Nordic Mediterranean	2744	37-66	52.07 ∓ 0.04	3.42
Pure Mediterranean	33	43-60	51.56 ∓ 0.39	3.30
Nordic Alpine	1744	37-66	50.00 ∓ 0.05	3.09
Total	9489	37-69	51.68 + 0.02	3.45

TABLE XV-31. NOSE HEIGHT BY MORPHOLOGICAL TYPES

	No.	Range	Mean	S.D.
Pure Nordic	55	44-63	54.46 + 0.36	3.96
Predominantly Nordic	648	40-67	55.74 ∓ 0.11	4.12
Keltic.	2405	44-71	56.34 ∓ 0.06	4.08
East Baltic	105	44-63	54.22 ∓ 0.25	3.76
Dinaric.	1768	44-71	58.22 ∓ 0.06	3.56
Nordic Mediterranean	2746	40-71	56.30 ∓ 0.05	4.08
Pure Mediterranean	33	48-67	56.66 ∓ 0.43	3.68
Nordic Alpine	1754	40-71	54.42 ∓ 0.06	3.68
Total	9514	40-71	56.22 + 0.03	4.08

TABLE XV-32. NOSE BREADTH BY MORPHOLOGICAL TYPES

	No.	Range	Mean	S.D.
Pure Nordic	55	31-42	35.06 + 0.26	2.88
Predominantly Nordic	648	28-48	35.81 ∓ 0.08	2.97
Keltic.	2407	28-48	36.14 ∓ 0.04	3.18
East Baltic	105	28-45	36.53 ∓ 0.19	2.91
Dinaric. :	1768	25-45	34.13 ∓ 0.04	2.31
Nordic Mediterranean	2747	25-57	36.17 ∓ 0.04	3.12
Pure Mediterranean	33	31-45	36.35 ∓ 0.38	3.24
Nordic Alpine	1754	28-57	37.37 ∓ 0.04	2.82
Total	9517	25-57	35.96 + 0.02	3.09

TABLE XV-33. NASAL INDEX BY MORPHOLOGICAL TYPES

	No.	Range	Mean	S.D.
Pure Nordic	55	52-83	64.70 + 0.54	5.96
Predominantly Nordic	647	48-99	64.62 ∓ 0.18	6.64
Keltic.	2405	44-95	64.58 ∓ 0.09	6.52
East Baltic	105	52-91	68.42 ∓ 0.36	5.48
Dinaric.	1768	44-63	58.86 ∓ 0.05	3.28
Nordic Mediterranean	2745	44-95	64.62 ∓ 0.08	6.52
Pure Mediterranean	33	48-83	64.42 ∓ 0.80	6.84
Nordic Alpine	1754	64-99	69.02 ∓ 0.07	4.40
Total	9512	44-99	64.38 + 0.04	6.48

TABLE XV-34. BIGONIAL DIAMETER BY MORPHOLOGICAL TYPES

	No.	Range	Mean	S.D.
Pure Nordic	55	98-125	107.34 + 0.46	5.12
Predominantly Nordic	648	94-129	108.14 ∓ 0.14	5.20
Keltic.	2402	86-133	108.78 ∓ 0.08	5.48
East Baltic	105	94-133	109.66 ∓ 0.39	5.92
Dinaric.	1768	90-133	109.50 ∓ 0.09	5.68
Nordic Mediterranean	2747	90-137	108.94 ∓ 0.07	5.48
Pure Mediterranean	33	94-121	107.50 ∓ 0.68	5.76
Nordic Alpine	1754	86-133	109.86 ∓ 0.09	5.88
Total	9512	86-137	109.10 + 0.04	5.60

TABLE XV-35. ZYGO-GONIAL INDEX BY MORPHOLOGICAL TYPES

	No.	Range	Mean	S.D.
Pure Nordic	55	69-86	77.47 + 0.31	3.39
Predominantly Nordic	645	66-92	77.65 ∓ 0.09	3.33
Keltic	2398	66-92	77.92 ∓ 0.05	3.45
East Baltic	105	69-89	76.75 ∓ 0.22	3.42
Dinaric	1764	63-92	77.11 ∓ 0.06	3.48
Nordic Mediterranean	2744	66-92	77.86 ∓ 0.04	3.42
Pure Mediterranean	33	63-86	77.26 ∓ 0.48	4.05
Nordic Alpine	1751	66-92	77.05 ∓ 0.05	3.39
Total	9495	63-92	77.56 + 0.02	3.45

TABLE XV-36. FRONTO-GONIAL INDEX BY MORPHOLOGICAL TYPES

	No.	Range	Mean	S.D.
Pure Nordic	55	85-114	98.35 + 0.43	4.70
Predominantly Nordic	648	80-119	99.40 ∓ 0.15	5.55
Keltic	2401	80-124	100.15 ∓ 0.07	5.45
East Baltic	105	85-119	99.20 ∓ 0.35	5.35
Dinaric	1767	80-124	99.85 ∓ 0.09	5.60
Nordic Mediterranean	2744	80-124	99.95 ∓ 0.07	5.50
Pure Mediterranean	32	90-114	99.80 ∓ 0.60	5.00
Nordic Alpine	1752	85-119	99.30 ∓ 0.08	5.25
Total	9504	80-124	99.80 + 0.04	5.50

MORPHOLOGICAL OBSERVATIONS

TABLE XVI-1. SKIN COLOR, INNER ARM, BY MORPHOLOGICAL TYPES

	Pale No.	Pale %	Pink No.	Pink %	Brunet No.	Brunet %	Swarthy No.	Swarthy %	Total No.
Pure Nordic	-	-	55	100.0	-	-	-	-	55
Predominantly Nordic	2	.3	646	99.5	1	.2	-	-	649
Keltic	8	.3	2320	96.4	78	3.2	1	.04	2407
East Baltic	1	1.0	104	99.0	-	-	-	-	105
Dinaric	2	.1	1621	91.7	134	7.6	11	.6	1768
Nordic Mediterranean	9	.3	2370	86.2	361	13.1	9	.3	2749
Pure Mediterranean	-	-	12	36.4	17	51.5	4	12.1	33
Nordic Alpine	2	.1	1577	89.9	168	9.6	7	.4	1754
Total	24	.2	8705	91.4	759	8.0	32	.3	9520

TABLE XVI-2. VASCULARITY BY MORPHOLOGICAL TYPES

	Submedium No.	Submedium %	Medium No.	Medium %	Pronounced No.	Pronounced %	Total No.
Pure Nordic	-	-	31	56.4	24	43.6	55
Predominantly Nordic	4	.6	466	71.8	179	27.6	649
Keltic	17	.7	1762	73.2	629	26.1	2408
East Baltic	-	-	55	52.9	49	47.1	104
Dinaric	9	.5	1333	75.4	425	24.0	1767
Nordic Mediterranean	19	.7	2179	79.3	551	20.0	2749
Pure Mediterranean	-	-	29	87.9	4	12.1	33
Nordic Alpine	8	.4	1321	75.3	425	24.2	1754
Total	57	.6	7176	75.4	2286	24.0	9519

TABLE XVI-3. FRECKLES BY MORPHOLOGICAL TYPES

	Absent		Submedium		Medium		Pronounced, massed		Total
	No.	%	No.	%	No.	%	No.	%	No.
Pure Nordic	32	58.2	11	20.0	10	18.2	2	3.6	55
Predominantly Nordic	327	50.4	186	28.6	103	15.9	33	5.1	649
Keltic.	1540	64.0	619	25.7	192	8.0	56	2.3	2407
East Baltic	34	32.4	24	22.9	37	35.2	10	9.5	105
Dinaric.	1027	58.2	484	27.4	207	11.7	48	2.7	1766
Nordic Mediterranean	1698	61.8	716	26.1	268	9.8	65	2.4	2747
Pure Mediterranean	23	69.7	7	21.2	3	9.1	-	-	33
Nordic Alpine	1031	58.8	490	27.9	189	10.8	44	2.5	1754
Total	5712	60.0	2537	26.7	1009	10.6	258	2.7	9516

TABLE XVI-4. MOLES BY MORPHOLOGICAL TYPES

	Absent		Few		Many		Total
	No.	%	No.	%	No.	%	No.
Pure Nordic	51	92.7	3	5.4	1	1.8	55
Predominantly Nordic	598	92.1	47	7.2	4	.6	649
Keltic.	2301	95.6	98	4.1	8	.3	2407
East Baltic	99	94.3	5	4.8	1	1.0	105
Dinaric.	1651	93.4	106	6.0	10	.6	1767
Nordic Mediterranean	2559	93.2	165	6.0	21	.8	2745
Pure Mediterranean	32	97.0	1	3.0	-	-	33
Nordic Alpine	1637	93.4	109	6.2	6	.3	1752
Total	8928	93.8	534	5.6	51	.5	9513

TABLE XVI-5. HAIR FORM BY MORPHOLOGICAL TYPES

	Straight		Low waves		Deep waves		Curly		Frizzly, woolly		Total
	No.	%	No.	%	No.	%	No.	%	No.	%	No.
Pure Nordic	19	34.6	25	45.4	10	18.2	1	1.8	-	-	55
Predominantly Nordic	191	29.4	293	45.1	142	21.9	23	3.5	-	-	649
Keltic.	783	32.5	1160	48.2	377	15.6	86	3.4	2	.1	2408
East Baltic	23	22.1	48	46.2	28	26.9	5	4.8	-	-	104
Dinaric.	479	27.1	910	51.5	318	18.0	54	3.0	6	.3	1767
Nordic Mediterranean	835	30.4	1350	49.1	473	17.2	85	3.1	5	.2	2748
Pure Mediterranean	9	27.3	15	45.4	9	27.3	-	-	-	-	33
Nordic Alpine	473	27.0	867	49.4	345	19.7	66	3.8	3	.2	1754
Total	2812	29.5	4668	49.0	1702	17.9	320	3.4	16	.2	9518

TABLE XVI-6. HAIR TEXTURE BY MORPHOLOGICAL TYPES

	Coarse		Medium		Fine		Total
	No.	%	No.	%	No.	%	No.
Pure Nordic	-	-	48	87.3	7	12.7	55
Predominantly Nordic.	24	3.7	589	90.8	36	5.5	649
Keltic.	108	4.5	2229	92.6	71	2.9	2408
East Baltic	17	16.2	85	81.0	3	2.9	105
Dinaric.	78	4.4	1643	93.0	46	2.6	1767
Nordic Mediterranean	111	4.0	2570	93.6	65	2.4	2746
Pure Mediterranean	1	3.0	31	93.9	1	3.0	33
Nordic Alpine	87	5.0	1624	92.6	42	2.4	1753
Total	426	4.5	8819	92.7	271	2.8	9516

TABLE XVI-7. HAIR QUANTITY, HEAD, BY MORPHOLOGICAL TYPES

	Submedium		Medium		Pronounced		Total
	No.	%	No.	%	No.	%	No.
Pure Nordic	-	-	52	94.6	3	5.4	55
Predominantly Nordic	7	1.1	623	96.0	19	2.9	649
Keltic.	54	2.2	2301	95.6	53	2.2	2408
East Baltic	3	2.9	98	93.3	4	3.8	105
Dinaric.	44	2.5	1668	94.3	56	3.2	1768
Nordic Mediterranean	56	2.0	2623	95.5	67	2.4	2746
Pure Mediterranean	1	3.0	32	97.0	-	-	33
Nordic Alpine	47	2.7	1651	94.2	55	3.1	1753
Total	212	2.2	9048	95.1	257	2.7	9517

TABLE XVI-8. HAIR QUANTITY, BEARD, BY MORPHOLOGICAL TYPES

	Very small, submedium No.	%	Medium No.	%	Pronounced, Very Pro. No.	%	Total No.
Pure Nordic	3	5.4	52	94.6	-	-	55
Predominantly Nordic	62	9.6	572	88.3	14	2.2	648
Keltic	117	4.8	2213	91.9	78	3.2	2408
East Baltic	6	5.7	95	90.5	4	3.8	105
Dinaric	113	6.4	1598	90.4	57	3.2	1768
Nordic Mediterranean	161	5.8	2464	89.7	123	4.5	2748
Pure Mediterranean	5	15.2	27	81.8	1	3.0	33
Nordic Alpine	117	6.7	1569	89.4	68	3.9	1754
Total	584	6.1	8590	90.2	345	3.6	9519

TABLE XVI-9. HAIR QUANTITY, BODY, BY MORPHOLOGICAL TYPES

	Absent No.	%	Submedium No.	%	Medium No.	%	Pronounced No.	%	Total No.
Pure Nordic	-	-	3	5.4	52	94.6	-	-	55
Predominantly Nordic	6	.9	54	8.3	579	89.4	9	1.4	648
Keltic	3	.1	117	4.8	2231	92.6	57	2.4	2408
East Baltic	-	-	7	6.7	95	90.5	3	2.9	105
Dinaric	5	.3	111	6.3	1607	90.9	45	2.5	1768
Nordic Mediterranean	10	.4	167	6.1	2479	90.2	93	3.4	2749
Pure Mediterranean	-	-	6	18.2	26	78.8	1	3.0	33
Nordic Alpine	12	.7	124	7.1	1570	89.5	48	2.7	1754
Total	36	.4	589	6.2	8639	90.7	256	2.7	9520

TABLE XVI-10. BALDNESS BY MORPHOLOGICAL TYPES

	Absent No.	%	Submedium No.	%	Medium No.	%	Pronounced No.	%	Total No.
Pure Nordic	44	80.0	9	16.4	2	3.6	-	-	55
Predominantly Nordic	485	74.7	100	15.4	44	6.8	20	3.1	649
Keltic	1287	53.5	635	26.4	284	11.8	201	8.4	2407
East Baltic	73	69.5	17	16.2	8	7.6	7	6.7	105
Dinaric	1082	61.2	425	24.0	171	9.7	90	5.1	1768
Nordic Mediterranean	1615	58.8	625	22.8	316	11.5	190	6.9	2746
Pure Mediterranean	21	63.6	8	24.2	3	9.1	1	3.0	33
Nordic Alpine	1126	64.3	360	20.5	157	9.0	109	6.2	1752
Total	5733	60.2	2179	22.9	985	10.4	618	6.5	9515

TABLE XVI-11. GRAYNESS, HEAD, BY MORPHOLOGICAL TYPES

	Absent No.	%	Submedium No.	%	Medium No.	%	Pronounced No.	%	Total No.
Pure Nordic	49	89.1	5	9.1	1	1.8	-	-	55
Predominantly Nordic	537	82.7	56	8.6	36	5.5	20	3.1	649
Keltic	1112	46.2	603	25.0	430	17.8	263	10.9	2408
East Baltic	82	78.1	11	10.5	7	6.7	5	4.8	105
Dinaric	1015	57.4	421	23.8	207	11.7	124	7.0	1767
Nordic Mediterranean	1442	52.5	679	24.7	409	14.9	218	7.9	2748
Pure Mediterranean	15	45.4	12	36.4	5	15.2	1	3.0	33
Nordic Alpine	1033	58.9	371	21.2	210	12.0	140	8.0	1754
Total	5285	55.5	2158	22.7	1305	13.7	771	8.1	9519

TABLE XVI-12. GRAYNESS, BEARD, BY MORPHOLOGICAL TYPES

	Absent No.	%	Submedium No.	%	Medium No.	%	Pronounced No.	%	Total No.
Pure Nordic	50	90.9	4	7.3	1	1.8	-	-	55
Predominantly Nordic	570	87.8	29	4.5	33	5.1	17	2.6	649
Keltic	1378	57.2	311	12.9	468	19.4	251	10.4	2408
East Baltic	87	83.6	4	3.8	9	8.6	4	3.8	104
Dinaric	1241	70.2	193	10.9	238	13.5	96	5.4	1768
Nordic Mediterranean	1775	64.7	324	11.8	459	16.7	187	6.8	2745
Pure Mediterranean	22	66.7	5	15.2	4	12.1	2	6.1	33
Nordic Alpine	1236	70.5	170	9.7	235	13.4	113	6.4	1754
Total	6359	66.8	1040	10.9	1447	15.2	670	7.0	9516

TABLE XVI-13. HAIR COLOR, HEAD, BY MORPHOLOGICAL TYPES

	Black No.	%	Dark brown No.	%	Brown No.	%	Red-brown No.	%	Golden brown No.	%
Pure Nordic	-	-	-	-	-	-	-	-	-	-
Predominantly Nordic	-	-	-	-	-	-	-	-	529	81.5
Keltic	36	1.5	956	39.7	1129	46.9	149	6.2	-	-
East Baltic	-	-	-	-	-	-	-	-	-	-
Dinaric	53	3.0	725	41.0	659	37.3	96	5.4	187	10.6
Nordic Mediterranean	130	4.7	1442	52.4	994	36.2	144	5.2	-	-
Pure Mediterranean	3	9.1	24	72.7	4	12.1	2	6.1	-	-
Nordic Alpine	44	2.5	734	41.8	684	39.0	107	6.1	180	10.3
Total	266	2.8	3881	40.8	3470	36.4	498	5.2	896	9.4

	Ash Brown No.	%	Golden No.	%	Ash No.	%	Red No.	%	Total No.
Pure Nordic	-	-	45	81.8	10	18.2	-	-	55
Predominantly Nordic	31	4.8	6	.9	1	.2	82	12.6	649
Keltic	-	-	-	-	-	-	138	5.7	2408
East Baltic	-	-	25	23.8	4	3.8	76	72.4	105
Dinaric	9	.5	-	-	-	-	39	2.2	1768
Nordic Mediterranean	-	-	-	-	-	-	39	1.4	2749
Pure Mediterranean	-	-	-	-	-	-	-	-	33
Nordic Alpine	5	.3	-	-	-	-	-	-	1754
Total	45	.5	76	.8	15	.2	374	3.9	9521

TABLE XVI-14. EYE COLOR BY MORPHOLOGICAL TYPES

	Dark brown, dark-light brown, light brown No.	%	Gray-brown No.	%	Green-brown No.	%	Blue-brown No.	%	Gray, Gray-blue No.	%	Blue No.	%	Total No.
Pure Nordic	-	-	-	-	-	-	-	-	5	9.1	50	90.9	55
Predominantly Nordic	-	-	11	1.7	15	2.3	256	39.4	29	4.5	338	52.1	649
Keltic	-	-	-	-	-	-	-	-	244	10.1	2164	89.9	2408
East Baltic	-	-	1	1.0	1	1.0	54	51.4	4	3.8	45	42.9	105
Dinaric	10	.6	86	4.9	60	3.4	803	45.4	70	4.0	739	41.8	1768
Nordic Mediterranean	-	-	305	11.1	208	7.6	2236	81.3	-	-	-	-	2749
Pure Mediterranean	33	100.0	-	-	-	-	-	-	-	-	-	-	33
Nordic Alpine	-	-	94	5.4	76	4.3	820	46.8	89	5.1	675	38.5	1754
Total	43	.4	497	5.2	360	3.8	4169	43.8	441	4.6	4011	42.1	9521

TABLE XVI-15. PIGMENT, MIXED EYES, BY MORPHOLOGICAL TYPES

	Very pronouncedly dark No.	%	Pronouncedly dark No.	%	Even No.	%	Pronouncedly light No.	%	Very pronouncedly light No.	%	Total No.
Pure Nordic	-	-	-	-	3	60.0	-	-	2	40.0	5
Predominantly Nordic	4	1.3	7	2.3	27	8.9	33	10.9	232	76.6	303
Keltic	-	-	3	1.4	78	36.4	8	3.7	125	58.4	214
East Baltic	-	-	-	-	4	6.7	6	10.0	50	83.3	60
Dinaric	35	3.5	69	6.8	121	12.0	186	18.4	600	59.3	1011
Nordic Mediterranean	103	3.8	261	9.5	331	12.0	525	19.1	1525	55.6	2745
Pure Mediterranean	-	-	-	-	-	-	-	-	-	-	-
Nordic Alpine	43	4.0	78	7.3	133	12.5	213	20.0	598	56.2	1065
Total	185	3.4	418	7.7	697	12.9	971	18.0	3132	58.0	5403

TABLE XVI-16. IRIS BY MORPHOLOGICAL TYPES

	Clear No.	%	Rayed No.	%	Zoned No.	%	Spotted No.	%	Diffuse No.	%	Scalloped No.	%	Total No.
Pure Nordic	30	54.6	7	12.7	1	1.8	-	-	-	-	17	30.9	55
Predominantly Nordic	189	29.2	167	25.8	9	1.4	12	1.8	148	22.9	122	18.8	647
Keltic	1021	42.4	443	18.4	46	1.9	3	.1	81	3.4	812	33.7	2406
East Baltic	23	21.9	28	26.7	6	5.7	2	1.9	34	32.4	12	11.4	105
Dinaric	355	20.2	365	20.7	30	1.7	37	2.1	632	35.9	342	19.4	1761
Nordic Mediterranean	56	2.0	674	24.6	45	1.6	137	5.0	1624	59.2	205	7.5	2741
Pure Mediterranean	24	72.7	8	24.2	-	-	-	-	1	3.0	-	-	33
Nordic Alpine	340	19.4	363	20.7	19	1.1	46	2.6	649	37.0	335	19.1	1752
Total	2038	21.4	2055	21.6	156	1.6	237	2.5	3169	33.4	1845	19.4	9500

TABLE XVI-17. EYEFOLDS, EXTERNAL, BY MORPHOLOGICAL TYPES

	Absent No.	%	Submedium No.	%	Medium No.	%	Pronounced No.	%	Total No.
Pure Nordic	47	85.4	6	10.9	2	3.6	-	-	55
Predominantly Nordic	565	87.0	45	6.9	36	5.5	3	.5	649
Keltic	2055	85.4	157	6.5	164	6.8	31	1.3	2407
East Baltic	91	86.7	9	8.6	5	4.8	-	-	105
Dinaric	1574	89.0	105	5.9	72	4.1	17	1.0	1768
Nordic Mediterranean	2376	86.4	204	7.4	138	5.0	31	1.1	2749
Pure Mediterranean	27	81.8	4	12.1	2	6.1	-	-	33
Nordic Alpine	1525	86.9	109	6.2	106	6.0	14	.8	1754
Total	8260	86.8	639	6.7	525	5.5	96	1.0	9520

TABLE XVI-18. EYEFOLDS, MEDIAN, BY MORPHOLOGICAL TYPES

	Absent No.	%	Submedium No.	%	Medium No.	%	Pronounced No.	%	Total No.
Pure Nordic	54	98.2	-	-	1	1.8	-	-	55
Predominantly Nordic	619	95.4	12	1.8	13	2.0	5	.8	649
Keltic	2349	97.6	22	.9	28	1.2	8	.3	2407
East Baltic	103	98.1	1	1.0	1	1.0	-	-	105
Dinaric	1740	98.4	13	.7	10	.6	5	.3	1768
Nordic Mediterranean	2653	96.5	37	1.3	39	1.4	20	.7	2749
Pure Mediterranean	33	100.0	-	-	-	-	-	-	33
Nordic Alpine	1692	96.5	21	1.2	31	1.8	9	.5	1753
Total	9243	97.1	106	1.1	123	1.3	47	.5	9519

TABLE XVI-19. EYEFOLDS, INTERNAL, BY MORPHOLOGICAL TYPES

	Absent No.	%	Submedium No.	%	Medium, pronounced No.	%	Total No.
Pure Nordic	54	98.2	1	1.8	-	-	55
Predominantly Nordic	641	98.8	7	1.1	1	.2	649
Keltic	2389	99.2	16	.7	2	.1	2407
East Baltic	104	99.0	1	1.0	-	-	105
Dinaric	1755	99.3	12	.7	1	.05	1768
Nordic Mediterranean	2719	98.9	26	.9	4	.1	2749
Pure Mediterranean	32	97.0	1	3.0	-	-	33
Nordic Alpine	1732	98.8	18	1.0	3	.2	1753
Total	9426	99.0	82	.9	11	.1	9519

TABLE XVI-20. EYE OBLIQUITY BY MORPHOLOGICAL TYPES

	Absent No.	%	Submedium No.	%	Medium No.	%	Pronounced No.	%	Down No.	%	Total No.
Pure Nordic	40	72.7	10	18.2	2	3.6	-	-	3	5.4	55
Predominantly Nordic	453	69.8	135	20.8	22	3.4	3	.5	36	5.5	649
Keltic	1453	60.3	702	29.2	115	4.8	15	.6	123	5.1	2408
East Baltic	75	71.4	15	14.3	4	3.8	-	-	11	10.5	105
Dinaric	1165	65.9	402	22.7	66	3.7	11	.6	124	7.0	1768
Nordic Mediterranean	1693	61.6	734	26.7	156	5.7	17	.6	149	5.4	2749
Pure Mediterranean	16	48.5	12	36.4	4	12.1	1	3.0	-	-	33
Nordic Alpine	1130	64.4	431	24.6	71	4.0	12	.7	110	6.3	1754
Total	6025	63.3	2441	25.6	440	4.6	59	.6	556	5.8	9521

TABLE XVI-21. EYE OPENING HEIGHT BY MORPHOLOGICAL TYPES

	Submedium No.	%	Medium No.	%	Pronounced No.	%	Total No.
Pure Nordic	1	1.8	53	96.4	1	1.8	55
Predominantly Nordic	29	4.5	603	93.0	16	2.5	648
Keltic	194	8.1	2135	88.9	73	3.0	2402
East Baltic	4	3.8	97	93.3	3	2.9	104
Dinaric	64	3.6	1629	92.2	73	4.1	1766
Nordic Mediterranean	172	6.2	2504	91.1	73	2.6	2749
Pure Mediterranean	-	-	32	97.0	1	3.0	33
Nordic Alpine	65	3.7	1639	93.4	50	2.8	1754
Total	529	5.6	8692	91.4	290	3.0	9511

TABLE XVI-22. EYEBROW THICKNESS BY MORPHOLOGICAL TYPES

	Submedium		Medium		Pronounced, very pronounced		Total
	No.	%	No.	%	No.	%	No.
Pure Nordic	1	1.8	54	98.2	-	-	55
Predominantly Nordic..	11	1.7	621	95.7	17	2.6	649
Keltic.............	85	3.5	2250	93.4	73	3.0	2408
East Baltic	3	2.9	101	96.2	1	1.0	105
Dinaric...........	62	3.5	1647	93.2	59	3.3	1768
Nordic Mediterranean..	79	2.9	2543	92.5	127	4.6	2749
Pure Mediterranean ...	3	9.1	28	84.8	2	6.1	33
Nordic Alpine	38	2.2	1654	94.3	62	3.5	1754
Total	282	3.0	8898	93.4	341	3.6	9521

TABLE XVI-23. EYEBROW CONCURRENCY BY MORPHOLOGICAL TYPES

	Absent		Submedium		Medium		Pronounced		Total
	No.	%	No.	%	No.	%	No.	%	No.
Pure Nordic	-	-	4	7.3	47	85.4	4	7.3	55
Predominantly Nordic	5	.8	118	18.2	433	66.7	93	14.3	649
Keltic	41	1.7	634	26.3	1530	63.5	203	8.4	2408
East Baltic	3	2.9	21	20.0	71	67.6	10	9.5	105
Dinaric	18	1.0	423	23.9	1176	66.5	151	8.5	1768
Nordic Mediterranean	38	1.4	584	21.2	1793	65.2	334	12.1	2749
Pure Mediterranean .	-	-	10	30.3	20	60.6	3	9.1	33
Nordic Alpine	26	1.5	346	19.7	1200	68.4	182	10.4	1754
Total	131	1.4	2140	22.5	6270	65.8	980	10.3	9521

TABLE XVI-24. BROW RIDGES BY MORPHOLOGICAL TYPES

	Absent		Submedium		Medium		Pronounced		Very Pro.		Total
	No.	%	No.	%	No.	%	No.	%	No.	%	No.
Pure Nordic	4	7.3	7	12.7	32	58.2	11	20.0	1	1.8	55
Predominantly Nordic	18	2.8	146	22.5	343	52.9	135	20.8	6	.9	648
Keltic	53	2.2	432	17.9	1318	54.7	594	24.7	11	.4	2408
East Baltic	3	2.9	19	18.1	59	56.2	24	22.9	-	-	105
Dinaric	41	2.3	432	24.4	1006	56.9	286	16.2	3	.2	1768
Nordic Mediterranean	66	2.4	496	18.0	1559	56.7	615	22.4	12	.4	2748
Pure Mediterranean .	1	3.0	7	21.2	18	54.6	6	18.2	1	3.0	38
Nordic Alpine......	47	2.7	362	20.6	1018	58.0	322	18.4	5	.3	1754
Total	233	2.4	1901	20.0	5353	56.2	1993	20.9	39	.4	9519

TABLE XVI-25. FOREHEAD HEIGHT BY MORPHOLOGICAL TYPES

	Submedium		Medium		Pronounced		Total
	No.	%	No.	%	No.	%	No.
Pure Nordic	1	1.8	19	34.6	35	63.6	55
Predominantly Nordic	23	3.5	253	39.0	372	57.4	648
Keltic	100	4.2	1053	43.7	1254	52.1	2407
East Baltic........	1	1.0	36	34.3	68	64.8	105
Dinaric	62	3.5	685	38.7	1021	57.7	1768
Nordic Mediterranean	116	4.2	1180	42.9	1452	52.8	2748
Pure Mediterranean .	2	6.1	18	54.6	13	39.4	33
Nordic Alpine	26	1.5	658	37.6	1068	61.0	1752
Total	331	3.5	3902	41.0	5283	55.5	9516

TABLE XVI-26. FOREHEAD SLOPE BY MORPHOLOGICAL TYPES

	Forward		Absent		Submedium		Medium		Pronounced		Very pro.		Total
	No.	%	No.	%	No.	%	No.	%	No.	%	No.	%	No.
Pure Nordic	2	3.6	1	1.8	27	49.1	23	41.8	2	3.6	-	-	55
Predominantly Nordic..	12	1.8	49	7.6	297	45.8	253	39.0	36	5.5	2	.3	649
Keltic.............	18	.7	126	5.2	1030	42.8	1001	41.6	219	9.1	13	.5	2407
East Baltic	-	-	10	9.5	51	48.6	39	37.1	5	4.8	-	-	105
Dinaric............	20	1.1	142	8.0	862	48.8	638	36.1	103	5.8	2	.1	1767
Nordic Mediterranean..	33	1.2	133	4.8	1210	44.0	1141	41.5	223	8.1	9	.3	2749
Pure Mediterranean ...	1	3.0	1	3.0	14	42.4	17	51.5	-	-	-	-	33
Nordic Alpine	29	1.6	175	10.0	872	49.7	577	32.9	98	5.6	2	.1	1753
Total	115	1.2	637	6.7	4363	45.8	3689	38.8	686	7.2	28	.3	9518

TABLE XVI-27. NASION DEPRESSION BY MORPHOLOGICAL TYPES

	Absent No.	%	Very small No.	%	Submedium No.	%	Medium No.	%	Pronounced No.	%	Very Pro. No.	%	Total No.
Pure Nordic	-	-	-	-	5	9.1	39	70.9	11	20.0	-	-	55
Predominantly Nordic ..	4	.6	20	3.1	108	16.7	373	57.6	137	21.1	6	.9	648
Keltic.............	6	.2	21	.9	247	10.2	1415	58.8	663	27.5	56	2.3	2408
East Baltic	-	-	-	-	23	21.9	59	56.2	20	19.0	3	2.9	105
Dinaric............	9	.5	43	2.4	292	16.5	1097	62.0	318	18.0	9	.5	1768
Nordic Mediterranean ..	6	.2	36	1.3	313	11.4	1655	60.2	705	25.6	34	1.2	2749
Pure Mediterranean ...	-	-	-	-	5	15.2	23	69.7	5	15.2	-	-	33
Nordic Alpine ,......	-	-	28	1.6	258	14.7	1055	60.2	395	22.5	17	1.0	1753
Total	25	.3	148	1.6	1251	13.1	5716	60.0	2254	23.7	125	1.3	9519

TABLE XVI-28. NASAL ROOT HEIGHT BY MORPHOLOGICAL TYPES

	Very small, submedium No.	%	Medium No.	%	Pronounced No.	%	Very Pro. No.	%	Total No.
Pure Nordic	4	7.3	40	72.7	11	20.0	-	-	55
Predominantly Nordic	25	3.8	484	74.6	134	20.6	6	.9	649
Keltic	76	3.2	1838	76.4	474	19.7	19	.8	2407
East Baltic	5	4.8	86	81.9	13	12.4	1	1.0	105
Dinaric..........	32	1.8	1334	75.5	377	21.3	24	1.4	1767
Nordic Mediterranean	73	2.6	2112	76.9	539	19.6	23	.8	2747
Pure Mediterranean .	-	-	26	78.8	7	21.2	-	-	33
Nordic Alpine	62	3.5	1421	81.1	266	15.2	4	.2	1753
Total	277	2.9	7341	77.1	1821	19.1	77	.8	9516

TABLE XVI-29. NASAL ROOT BREADTH BY MORPHOLOGICAL TYPES

	Very small, submedium No.	%	Medium No.	%	Pronounced No.	%	Very pro. No.	%	Total No.
Pure Nordic	-	-	37	67.3	17	30.9	1	1.8	55
Predominantly Nordic	6	.9	461	71.0	176	27.1	6	.9	649
Keltic	65	2.7	1707	70.9	614	25.5	21	.9	2407
East Baltic	-	-	76	72.4	29	27.6	-	-	105
Dinaric	41	2.3	1399	79.2	318	18.0	9	.5	1767
Nordic Mediterranean	42	1.5	1989	72.4	697	25.4	19	.7	2747
Pure Mediterranean	-	-	25	75.8	8	24.2	-	-	33
Nordic Alpine	23	1.3	1182	67.5	521	29.7	26	1.5	1752
Total	177	1.9	6876	72.3	2380	25.0	82	.9	9515

TABLE XVI-30. NASAL BRIDGE HEIGHT BY MORPHOLOGICAL TYPES

	Very small, submedium No.	%	Medium No.	%	Pronounced No.	%	Very pro. No.	%	Total No.
Pure Nordic	3	5.4	48	87.3	4	7.3	-	-	55
Predominantly Nordic	27	4.2	506	78.0	110	16.9	6	.9	649
Keltic	84	3.5	1799	74.7	493	20.5	31	1.3	2407
East Baltic	3	2.9	89	85.6	10	9.6	2	1.9	104
Dinaric	22	1.2	1242	70.3	455	25.7	48	2.7	1767
Nordic Mediterranean	79	2.9	2091	76.1	544	19.8	33	1.2	2747
Pure Mediterranean .	-	-	29	87.9	4	12.1	-	-	33
Nordic Alpine	77	4.4	1425	81.3	245	14.0	5	.3	1752
Total	295	3.1	7229	76.0	1865	19.6	125	1.3	9514

TABLE XVI-31. NASAL BRIDGE BREADTH BY MORPHOLOGICAL TYPES

	Submedium No.	%	Medium No.	%	Pronounced No.	%	Very Pro. No.	%	Total No.
Pure Nordic	1	1.8	40	72.7	14	25.4	-	-	55
Predominantly Nordic	2	.3	500	77.2	143	22.1	3	.5	648
Keltic	29	1.2	1807	75.1	557	23.2	13	.5	2406
East Baltic	-	-	84	80.8	19	18.3	1	1.0	104
Dinaric	26	1.5	1540	87.2	201	11.4	-	-	1767
Nordic Mediterranean	16	.6	2095	76.3	625	22.8	10	.4	2746
Pure Mediterranean	-	-	24	72.7	9	27.3	-	-	33
Nordic Alpine	7	.4	1279	73.0	454	25.9	12	.7	1752
Total	81	.8	7369	77.5	2022	21.2	39	.4	9511

TABLE XVI-32.   NASAL PROFILE BY MORPHOLOGICAL TYPES

	Concave No.	%	Concave snub tip No.	%	Straight No.	%	Straight, snub tip No.	%	Convex No.	%	Convex, snub tip No.	%	Total No.
Pure Nordic	4	7.3	-	-	28	50.9	3	5.4	16	29.1	4	7.3	55
Predominantly Nordic	46	7.1	3	.5	318	49.1	27	4.2	219	33.8	34	5.3	647
Keltic	158	6.6	23	1.0	1106	45.9	75	3.1	945	39.3	100	4.2	2407
East Baltic	13	12.5	-	-	47	45.2	6	5.8	34	32.7	4	3.8	104
Dinaric	46	2.6	8	.4	628	35.6	41	2.3	940	53.2	103	5.8	1766
Nordic Mediterranean	208	7.6	17	.6	1244	45.3	101	3.7	1049	38.2	126	4.6	2745
Pure Mediterranean	3	9.1	-	-	14	42.4	2	6.1	13	39.4	1	3.0	33
Nordic Alpine	168	9.6	17	1.0	827	47.2	84	4.8	553	31.6	103	5.9	1752
Total	646	6.8	68	.7	4212	44.3	339	3.6	3769	39.6	475	5.0	9509

TABLE XVI-33. NASAL SEPTUM BY MORPHOLOGICAL TYPES

	Straight concave No.	%	Convex No.	%	Total No.
Pure Nordic	26	47.3	29	52.7	55
Predominantly Nordic	256	39.7	389	60.3	645
Keltic	1011	42.2	1384	57.8	2395
East Baltic	36	34.3	69	65.7	105
Dinaric	616	35.0	1145	65.0	1761
Nordic Mediterranean	1048	38.3	1690	61.7	2738
Pure Mediterranean	11	33.3	22	66.7	33
Nordic Alpine	690	39.5	1056	60.5	1746
Total	3694	39.0	5784	61.0	9478

TABLE XVI-34. NASAL TIP, THICKNESS, BY MORPHOLOGICAL TYPES

	Submedium No.	%	Medium No.	%	Pronounced No.	%	Very pro. No.	%	Total No.
Pure Nordic	-	-	41	74.6	14	25.4	-	-	55
Predominantly Nordic	9	1.4	471	72.6	168	25.9	1	.2	649
Keltic	49	2.0	1713	71.2	636	26.4	9	.4	2407
East Baltic	2	1.9	77	74.0	23	22.1	2	1.9	104
Dinaric	42	2.4	1451	82.1	273	15.4	1	.05	1767
Nordic Mediterranean	34	1.2	1994	72.6	708	25.8	11	.4	2747
Pure Mediterranean	2	6.1	20	60.6	11	33.3	-	-	33
Nordic Alpine	14	.8	1177	67.2	552	31.5	9	.5	1752
Total	152	1.6	6944	73.0	2385	25.1	33	.3	9514

TABLE XVI-35. NASAL TIP, INCLINATION, BY MORPHOLOGICAL TYPES

| | Up, medium | | Up, submedium | | Horizontal | | Down, submedium | | Down, medium | | Total |
	No.	%	No.	%	No.	%	No.	%	No.	%	No.
Pure Nordic	7	12.7	48	87.3	-	-	-	-	-	-	55
Predominantly Nordic ..	91	14.0	532	82.1	19	2.9	4	.6	2	.3	648
Keltic.............	240	10.0	1990	82.7	125	5.2	38	1.6	12	.5	2405
East Baltic	21	20.2	80	76.9	2	1.9	-	-	1	1.0	104
Dinaric............	151	8.5	1521	86.1	73	4.1	18	1.0	4	.2	1767
Nordic Mediterranean ..	307	11.2	2273	82.8	113	4.1	41	1.5	11	.4	2745
Pure Mediterranean ...	5	15.2	25	75.8	3	9.1	-	-	-	-	33
Nordic Alpine	254	14.5	1385	79.2	83	4.7	22	1.2	5	.3	1749
Total	1076	11.3	7854	82.6	418	4.4	123	1.3	35	.4	9506

TABLE XVI-36. NASAL WINGS BY MORPHOLOGICAL TYPES

| | Compressed | | Medium | | Flaring | | Total |
	No.	%	No.	%	No.	%	No.
Pure Nordic	-	-	52	94.5	3	5.4	55
Predominantly Nordic	14	2.2	583	89.8	52	8.0	649
Keltic	135	5.6	2133	88.7	136	5.6	2404
East Baltic	3	2.9	94	90.4	7	6.7	104
Dinaric	124	7.0	1630	92.4	11	.6	1765
Nordic Mediterranean	137	5.0	2441	88.9	167	6.1	2745
Pure Mediterranean .	-	-	28	84.8	5	15.2	33
Nordic Alpine	50	2.8	1523	87.0	178	10.2	1751
Total	463	4.9	8484	89.2	559	5.9	9506

TABLE XVI-37. LIPS, INTEGUMENTAL THICKNESS, BY MORPHOLOGICAL TYPES

| | Submedium | | Medium | | Pronounced | | Total |
	No.	%	No.	%	No.	%	No.
Pure Nordic.......	-	-	51	92.7	4	7.3	55
Predominantly Nordic	8	1.2	609	93.8	32	4.9	649
Keltic	38	1.6	2263	94.0	107	4.4	2408
East Baltic	-	-	102	97.1	3	2.9	105
Dinaric..........	27	1.5	1681	95.1	60	3.4	1768
Nordic Mediterranean	27	1.0	2579	93.8	143	5.2	2749
Pure Mediterranean .	2	6.1	30	90.9	1	3.0	33
Nordic Alpine	12	.7	1675	95.5	67	3.8	1754
Total	114	1.2	8990	94.4	417	4.4	9521

TABLE XVI-38. UPPER LIP, MEMBRANOUS THICKNESS, BY MORPHOLOGICAL TYPES

| | Very small | | Submedium | | Medium | | Pronounced | | Total |
	No.	%	No.	%	No.	%	No.	%	No.
Pure Nordic	1	1.8	3	5.4	47	85.4	4	7.3	55
Predominantly Nordic	-	-	91	14.0	522	80.4	36	5.5	649
Keltic	31	1.3	640	26.6	1665	69.2	71	2.9	2407
East Baltic	2	1.9	15	14.3	79	75.2	9	8.6	105
Dinaric	17	1.0	391	22.1	1315	74.4	45	2.5	1768
Nordic Mediterranean	35	1.3	637	23.2	1976	71.9	101	3.7	2749
Pure Mediterranean .	1	3.0	15	45.4	17	51.5	-	-	33
Nordic Alpine	20	1.1	374	21.3	1313	74.9	45	2.6	1752
Total	107	1.1	2166	22.8	6934	72.8	311	3.3	9518

TABLE XVI-39. LIPS EVERSION, BY MORPHOLOGICAL TYPES

| | Submedium | | Medium | | Pronounced | | Total |
	No.	%	No.	%	No.	%	No.
Pure Nordic	3	5.4	46	83.6	6	10.9	55
Predominantly Nordic	80	12.3	526	81.0	43	6.6	649
Keltic	601	25.0	1714	71.2	92	3.8	2407
East Baltic	15	14.3	80	76.2	10	9.5	105
Dinaric	371	21.0	1336	75.6	61	3.4	1768
Nordic Mediterranean	605	22.0	2003	72.9	140	5.1	2748
Pure Mediterranean .	14	42.4	19	57.6	-	-	33
Nordic Alpine	371	21.2	1312	74.8	71	4.0	1754
Total	2060	21.6	7036	73.9	423	4.4	9519

TABLE XVI-40. MID-FACIAL PROGNATHISM BY MORPHOLOGICAL TYPES

	Absent		Submedium		Medium		Pronounced		Total
	No.	%	No.	%	No.	%	No.	%	No.
Pure Nordic	51	94.4	3	5.6	-	-	-	-	54
Predominantly Nordic	576	88.8	59	9.1	13	2.0	1	.2	649
Keltic.	2173	90.4	185	7.7	41	1.7	6	.2	2405
East Baltic.	99	94.3	5	4.8	-	-	1	1.0	105
Dinaric	1599	90.4	132	7.5	32	1.8	5	.3	1768
Nordic Mediterranean	2507	91.2	201	7.3	38	1.4	2	.1	2748
Pure Mediterranean .	30	90.9	2	6.1	1	3.0	-	-	33
Nordic Alpine	1692	96.5	50	2.8	10	.6	1	.05	1753
Total	8727	91.7	637	6.7	135	1.4	16	.2	9515

TABLE XVI-41. ALVEOLAR PROGNATHISM BY MORPHOLOGICAL TYPES

	Absent		Submedium		Medium, pronounced		Total
	No.	%	No.	%	No.	%	No.
Pure Nordic	54	98.2	-	-	1	1.8	55
Predominantly Nordic	635	98.0	8	1.2	5	.8	648
Keltic	2344	97.4	42	1.7	20	.8	2406
East Baltic.	103	98.1	1	1.0	1	1.0	105
Dinaric	1728	97.7	25	1.4	15	.8	1768
Nordic Mediterranean	2679	97.4	41	1.5	29	1.0	2749
Pure Mediterranean .	31	93.9	1	3.0	1	3.0	33
Nordic Alpine	1729	98.7	10	.6	13	.7	1752
Total	9303	97.8	128	1.3	85	.9	9516

TABLE XVI-42. CHIN PROMINENCE BY MORPHOLOGICAL TYPES

	Submedium		Medium		Pronounced		Total
	No.	%	No.	%	No.	%	No.
Pure Nordic	8	14.6	44	80.0	3	5.4	55
Predominantly Nordic	72	11.1	524	80.7	53	8.2	649
Keltic	283	11.8	1904	79.1	220	9.1	2407
East Baltic.	11	10.5	84	80.0	10	9.5	105
Dinaric	203	11.5	1377	77.9	187	10.6	1767
Nordic Mediterranean	340	12.4	2157	78.5	250	9.1	2747
Pure Mediterranean .	3	9.1	26	78.8	4	12.1	33
Nordic Alpine	134	7.6	1452	82.8	168	9.6	1754
Total	1054	11.1	7568	79.5	895	9.4	9517

TABLE XVI-43. TEETH, ERUPTION, BY MORPHOLOGICAL TYPES

	Complete		Partial		Total
	No.	%	No.	%	No.
Pure Nordic	29	52.7	26	47.3	55
Predominantly Nordic	373	58.4	266	41.6	639
Keltic	1855	79.2	486	20.8	2341
East Baltic	60	59.4	41	40.6	101
Dinaric	1258	72.1	487	27.9	1745
Nordic Mediterranean	1997	74.5	683	25.5	2680
Pure Mediterranean .	20	71.4	8	28.6	28
Nordic Alpine	1189	68.7	541	31.3	1730
Total	6781	72.8	2538	27.2	9319

TABLE XVI-44. TEETH, LOSS, BY MORPHOLOGICAL TYPES

	None		Very small		Submedium		Medium		Pronounced		Total
	No.	%	No.	%	No.	%	No.	%	No.	%	No.
Pure Nordic	8	14.6	26	47.3	13	23.6	2	3.6	6	10.9	55
Predominantly Nordic	89	13.7	350	53.9	111	17.1	33	5.1	66	10.2	649
Keltic	130	5.4	889	36.9	503	20.9	196	8.1	689	28.6	2407
East Baltic	7	6.7	57	54.3	22	21.0	4	3.8	15	14.3	105
Dinaric	160	9.1	741	42.0	402	22.8	99	5.6	364	20.6	1766
Nordic Mediterranean	196	7.1	1058	38.5	596	21.7	221	8.0	677	24.6	2748
Pure Mediterranean .	2	6.1	5	15.2	9	27.3	2	6.1	15	45.4	33
Nordic Alpine	180	10.3	754	43.0	355	20.3	91	5.2	372	21.2	1752
Total	772	8.1	3880	40.8	2011	21.1	648	6.8	2204	23.2	9515

TABLE XVI-45. TEETH, CARIES, BY MORPHOLOGICAL TYPES

	Absent No.	%	Very small No.	%	Submedium No.	%	Medium No.	%	Pronounced No.	%	Total No.
Pure Nordic	2	4.1	5	10.2	31	63.3	8	16.3	3	6.1	49
Predominantly Nordic	7	1.2	82	14.0	380	64.8	94	16.0	23	3.9	586
Keltic	20	1.1	129	7.4	924	53.0	449	25.7	222	12.7	1744
East Baltic	-	-	9	10.0	56	62.2	17	18.9	8	8.9	90
Dinaric	17	1.2	119	8.4	836	58.8	329	23.1	121	8.5	1422
Nordic Mediterranean	13	.6	184	8.7	1121	53.2	533	25.3	257	12.2	2108
Pure Mediterranean	-	-	2	10.0	10	50.0	6	30.0	2	10.0	20
Nordic Alpine	16	1.1	138	9.9	817	58.4	299	21.4	128	9.2	1398
Total	75	1.0	668	9.0	4175	56.3	1735	23.4	764	10.3	7417

TABLE XVI-46. TEETH, WEAR, BY MORPHOLOGICAL TYPES

	Absent, submedium No.	%	Medium No.	%	Pronounced, very pro. No.	%	Total No.
Pure Nordic	42	85.7	5	10.2	2	4.1	49
Predominantly Nordic	525	89.6	55	9.4	6	1.0	586
Keltic	1248	71.6	398	22.8	98	5.6	1744
East Baltic	79	88.8	7	7.9	3	3.4	89
Dinaric	1137	79.7	253	17.7	36	2.5	1426
Nordic Mediterranean	1571	74.8	414	19.7	114	5.4	2099
Pure Mediterranean	14	70.0	5	25.0	1	5.0	20
Nordic Alpine	1098	79.2	242	17.4	47	3.4	1387
Total	5714	77.2	1379	18.6	307	4.1	7400

TABLE XVI-47. TEETH, CROWDING, BY MORPHOLOGICAL TYPES

	Absent No.	%	Medium No.	%	Pronounced No.	%	Total No.
Pure Nordic	23	46.9	26	53.1	-	-	49
Predominantly Nordic	294	50.2	258	44.0	34	5.8	586
Keltic	707	40.2	943	53.7	107	6.1	1757
East Baltic	39	43.3	45	50.0	6	6.7	90
Dinaric	594	41.8	743	52.2	85	6.0	1422
Nordic Mediterranean	867	41.1	1110	52.7	130	6.2	2107
Pure Mediterranean	7	35.0	11	55.0	2	10.0	20
Nordic Alpine	656	47.0	684	49.0	57	4.1	1397
Total	3187	42 9	3820	51.4	421	5.7	7428

TABLE XVI-48. BITE BY MORPHOLOGICAL TYPES

	Under No.	%	Edge-to-edge No.	%	Submedium over No.	%	Pronounced over No.	%	Total No.
Pure Nordic	-	-	-	-	48	98.0	1	2.0	49
Predominantly Nordic	4	.7	9	1.5	556	94.9	17	2.9	586
Keltic	9	.5	4	.2	1671	95.6	63	3.6	1747
East Baltic	-	-	-	-	90	100.0	-	-	90
Dinaric	14	1.0	5	.4	1373	96.1	36	2.5	1428
Nordic Mediterranean	10	.5	6	.3	2028	96.2	64	3.0	2108
Pure Mediterranean	-	-	-	-	18	90.0	2	10.0	20
Nordic Alpine	11	.8	7	.5	1352	96.4	33	2.4	1403
Total	48	.6	31	.4	7136	96.0	216	2.9	7431

TABLE XVI-49. MALARS, FRONTAL PROJECTION, BY MORPHOLOGICAL TYPES

	Absent, submedium No.	%	Medium No.	%	Pronounced No.	%	Total No.
Pure Nordic	1	1.8	49	89.1	5	9.1	55
Predominantly Nordic	3	.5	538	82.9	108	16.6	649
Keltic	11	.4	2004	83.2	393	16.3	2408
East Baltic	-	-	91	86.7	14	13.3	105
Dinaric	7	.4	1484	84.0	275	15.6	1766
Nordic Mediterranean	19	.7	2277	82.9	452	16.4	2748
Pure Mediterranean	1	3.0	25	75.8	7	21.2	33
Nordic Alpine	5	.3	1493	85.1	256	14.6	1754
Total	47	.5	7961	83.6	1510	15.9	9518

TABLE XVI-50. MALARS, LATERAL PROJECTION, BY MORPHOLOGICAL TYPES

	Absent submedium No.	%	Medium No.	%	Pronounced No.	%	Very pro. No.	%	Total No.
Pure Nordic	-	-	39	70.9	15	27.3	1	1.8	55
Predominantly Nordic	-	-	479	73.8	161	24.8	9	1.4	649
Keltic	13	.5	1777	73.8	597	24.8	20	.8	2407
East Baltic	-	-	55	52.4	46	43.8	4	3.8	105
Dinaric	5	.3	994	56.2	724	41.0	44	2.5	1767
Nordic Mediterranean	14	.5	1967	71.6	730	26.6	37	1.3	2748
Pure Mediterranean	-	-	27	81.8	5	15.2	1	3.0	33
Nordic Alpine	4	.2	887	50.6	808	46.1	53	3.0	1752
Total	36	.4	6225	65.4	3086	32.4	169	1.8	9516

TABLE XVI-51. GONIAL ANGLES BY MORPHOLOGICAL TYPES

	Submedium No.	%	Medium No.	%	Pronounced No.	%	Very pro. No.	%	Total No.
Pure nordic	1	1.8	36	65.4	18	32.7	-	-	55
Predominantly Nordic	22	3.4	459	70.7	163	25.1	5	.8	649
Keltic	80	3.3	1685	70.0	619	25.7	23	1.0	2407
East Baltic	-	-	60	57.7	42	40.4	2	1.9	104
Dinaric	57	3.2	1044	59.0	628	35.5	39	2.2	1768
Nordic Mediterranean	71	2.6	1893	68.9	739	26.9	46	1.7	2749
Pure Mediterranean	1	3.0	27	81.8	5	15.2	-	-	33
Nordic Alpine	35	2.0	917	52.3	763	43.5	39	2.2	1754
Total	267	2.8	6121	64.3	2977	31.3	154	1.6	9519

TABLE XVI-52. EAR HELIX BY MORPHOLOGICAL TYPES

	Very small No.	%	Submedium No.	%	Medium No.	%	Pronounced No.	%	Total No.
Pure Nordic	1	1.8	14	25.4	38	69.1	2	3.6	55
Predominantly Nordic	3	.5	132	20.3	491	75.6	23	3.5	649
Keltic	16	.7	553	23.0	1730	71.8	109	4.5	2408
East Baltic	-	-	18	17.1	84	80.0	3	2.9	105
Dinaric	13	.7	422	23.9	1268	71.7	65	3.7	1768
Nordic Mediterranean	16	.6	653	23.8	1949	70.9	131	4.8	2749
Pure Mediterranean	-	-	4	12.1	28	84.8	1	3.0	33
Nordic Alpine	9	.5	344	19.6	1329	75.8	72	4.1	1754
Total	58	.6	2140	22.5	6917	72.6	406	4.3	9521

TABLE XVI-53. EAR ANTIHELIX BY MORPHOLOGICAL TYPES

	Absent No.	%	Submedium No.	%	Medium No.	%	Pronounced No.	%	Total No.
Pure Nordic	1	1.8	1	1.8	47	85.4	6	10.9	55
Predominantly Nordic	3	.5	26	4.0	528	81.4	92	14.2	649
Keltic	2	.1	117	4.9	1986	82.5	302	12.5	2407
East Baltic	-	-	5	4.8	85	81.7	14	13.5	104
Dinaric	3	.2	77	4.4	1450	82.0	238	13.5	1768
Nordic Mediterranean	3	.1	115	4.2	2266	82.4	364	13.2	2748
Pure Mediterranean	-	-	2	6.1	25	75.8	6	18.2	33
Nordic Alpine	3	.2	72	4.1	1487	84.9	190	10.8	1752
Total	15	.2	415	4.4	7874	82.7	1212	12.7	9516

TABLE XVI-54. DARWIN'S POINT BY MORPHOLOGICAL TYPES

	Absent		Submedium		Medium		Pronounced		Total
	No.	%	No.	%	No.	%	No.	%	No.
Pure Nordic	36	65.4	18	32.7	1	1.8	-	-	55
Predominantly Nordic	465	71.6	165	25.4	18	2.8	1	.2	649
Keltic	1775	73.7	550	22.8	79	3.3	3	.1	2407
East Baltic.	77	73.3	23	21.9	5	4.8	-	-	105
Dinaric	1290	73.0	437	24.7	38	2.2	1	.05	1766
Nordic Mediterranean	2037	74.2	627	22.8	71	2.6	10	.4	2745
Pure Mediterranean.	20	60.6	13	39.4	-	-	-	-	33
Nordic Alpine	1353	77.3	348	19.9	46	2.6	4	.2	1751
Total	7053	74.2	2181	22.9	258	2.7	19	.2	9511

TABLE XVI-55. EAR LOBE ATTACHMENT BY MORPHOLOGICAL TYPES

	Soldered		Attached		Free		Total
	No.	%	No.	%	No.	%	No.
Pure Nordic	1	1.8	28	50.9	26	47.3	55
Predominantly Nordic	14	2.2	253	39.0	382	58.8	649
Keltic	35	1.4	958	39.8	1415	58.8	2408
East Baltic.	2	1.9	41	39.0	62	59.0	105
Dinaric	27	1.5	725	41.0	1016	57.5	1768
Nordic Mediterranean	28	1.0	1118	40.7	1603	58.3	2749
Pure Mediterranean.	-	-	6	18.2	27	81.8	33
Nordic Alpine	33	1.9	747	42.6	973	55.5	1753
Total	140	1.5	3876	40.7	5504	57.8	9520

TABLE XVI-56. EAR LOBE SIZE BY MORPHOLOGICAL TYPES

	Absent, submedium		Medium		Pronounced		Total
	No.	%	No.	%	No.	%	No.
Pure Nordic	-	-	34	61.8	21	38.2	55
Predominantly Nordic	3	.5	387	59.6	259	39.9	649
Keltic	13	.5	1206	50.1	1189	49.4	2408
East Baltic	3	2.9	66	62.9	36	34.3	105
Dinaric	10	.5	1088	61.6	669	37.9	1767
Nordic Mediterranean	10	.4	1477	53.7	1261	45.9	2748
Pure Mediterranean.	-	-	12	36.4	21	63.6	33
Nordic Alpine	5	.3	935	53.3	814	46.4	1754
Total	44	.5	5205	54.7	4270	44.8	9519

TABLE XVI-57. EAR PROTRUSION BY MORPHOLOGICAL TYPES

	Submedium		Medium		Pronounced		Total
	No.	%	No.	%	No.	%	No.
Pure Nordic	1	1.8	40	72.7	14	25.4	55
Predominantly Nordic	5	.8	515	79.5	128	19.8	648
Keltic	15	.6	1789	74.3	604	25.1	2408
East Baltic	-	-	85	81.0	20	19.0	105
Dinaric	16	.9	1332	75.4	419	23.7	1767
Nordic Mediterranean	25	.9	2127	77.4	596	21.7	2748
Pure Mediterranean. .	2	6.1	24	72.7	7	21.2	33
Nordic Alpine	8	.4	1397	79.6	349	19.9	1754
Total	72	.8	7309	76.8	2137	22.4	9518

TABLE XVI-58. TEMPORAL FULLNESS BY MORPHOLOGICAL TYPES

	Submedium		Medium		Pronounced		Total
	No.	%	No.	%	No.	%	No.
Pure Nordic	6	10.9	42	76.4	7	12.7	55
Predominantly Nordic	67	10.3	493	76.0	89	13.7	649
Keltic	526	21.8	1645	68.3	237	9.8	2408
East Baltic	3	2.9	54	51.4	48	45.7	105
Dinaric	161	9.1	931	52.7	675	38.2	1767
Nordic Mediterranean	525	19.1	1883	68.5	340	12.4	2748
Pure Mediterranean .	5	15.2	25	75.8	3	9.1	33
Nordic Alpine.	127	7.2	889	50.7	738	42.1	1754
Total	1420	14.9	5962	62.6	2137	22.4	9519

TABLE XVI-59. OCCIPITAL PROTRUSION BY MORPHOLOGICAL TYPES

	Absent, submedium No.	%	Medium No.	%	Pronounced No.	%	Total No.
Pure Nordic	1	1.8	35	63.6	19	34.6	55
Predominantly Nordic	15	2.3	488	75.3	145	22.4	648
Keltic	58	2.4	1765	73.3	585	24.3	2408
East Baltic	15	14.3	81	77.1	9	8.6	105
Dinaric	265	15.0	1353	76.5	150	8.5	1768
Nordic Mediterranean	76	2.8	2013	73.2	659	24.0	2748
Pure Mediterranean .	2	6.1	27	81.8	4	12.1	33
Nordic Alpine	261	14.9	1354	77.2	139	7.9	1754
Total	693	7.3	7116	74.8	1710	18.0	9519

TABLE XVI-60. LAMBDOID FLATTENING BY MORPHOLOGICAL TYPES

	Absent No.	%	Submedium No.	%	Medium No.	%	Pronounced No.	%	Total No.
Pure Nordic	13	23.6	5	9.1	31	56.4	6	10.9	55
Predominantly Nordic	140	21.6	81	12.5	289	44.7	137	21.2	647
Keltic	614	25.5	219	9.1	1008	41.9	563	23.4	2404
East Baltic	15	14.3	13	12.4	58	55.2	19	18.1	105
Dinaric	391	22.1	160	9.1	744	42.1	471	26.7	1766
Nordic Mediterranean	559	20.4	308	11.2	1226	44.6	653	23.8	2746
Pure Mediterranean .	5	15.2	3	9.1	19	57.6	6	18.2	33
Nordic Alpine	430	24.6	172	9.8	706	40.3	443	25.3	1751
Total	2167	22.8	961	10.1	4081	42.9	2298	24.2	9507

TABLE XVI-61. OCCIPITAL FLATTENING BY MORPHOLOGICAL TYPES

	Absent No.	%	Medium No.	%	Pronounced No.	%	Total No.
Pure Nordic	49	89.1	5	9.1	1	1.8	55
Predominantly Nordic	564	86.9	72	11.1	13	2.0	649
Keltic	2004	83.3	326	13.6	75	3.1	2405
East Baltic	82	78.1	15	14.3	8	7.6	105
Dinaric	1288	72.8	345	19.5	135	7.6	1768
Nordic Mediterranean	2330	84.8	337	12.3	81	2.9	2748
Pure Mediterranean .	30	90.9	2	6.1	1	3.0	33
Nordic Alpine	1251	71.3	352	20.1	151	8.6	1754
Total	7598	79.8	1454	15.3	465	4.9	9517

TABLE XVI-62. FACIAL ASYMMETRY BY MORPHOLOGICAL TYPES

	Absent No.	%	Left No.	%	Right No.	%	Total No.
Pure Nordic	46	83.6	2	3.6	7	12.7	55
Predominantly Nordic	505	78.0	51	7.9	91	14.1	647
Keltic	1839	76.5	170	7.1	396	16.5	2405
East Baltic.	77	73.3	7	6.7	21	20.0	105
Dinaric	1206	68.4	170	9.6	387	22.0	1763
Nordic Mediterranean	2071	75.5	189	6.9	483	17.6	2743
Pure Mediterranean .	26	78.8	2	6.1	5	15.2	33
Nordic Alpine	1283	73.2	150	8.6	319	18.2	1752
Total	7053	74.2	741	7.8	1709	18.0	9503

TABLE XVIII-1. COMPARISON OF MEANS AND RANGES OF EARLY CHRISTIAN
IRISH CRANIA WITH THOSE OF LIVING IRISH

	Gallen Priory (40-120)	Offaly, Leix, Kildare (530)	Total Irish Catholic County (8900)
Glabello-occipital length ...	190.38 + 0.38	194.94 + 0.19	195.63 + 0.05
Maximum width	145.27 ∓ 0.31	152.44 ∓ 0.17	154.12 ∓ 0.04
Auricular height	115.50 ∓ 0.33	125.50 ∓ 0.18	124.98 ∓ 0.04
Horizontal circumference ..	535.06 ∓ 0.92	569.60 ∓ 0.49	572.15 ∓ 0.12
Minimum frontal diameter ..	98.48 ∓ 0.27	108.42 ∓ 0.13	109.22 ∓ 0.03
Bizygomatic diameter	135.64 ∓ 0.41	139.10 ∓ 0.18	140.80 ∓ 0.04
Bigonial diameter	102.67 ∓ 0.46	108.62 ∓ 0.16	109.26 ∓ 0.04
Nasion-menton height	117.78 ∓ 0.70	126.90 ∓ 0.21	127.10 ∓ 0.05
Nasion-prosthion height	72.03 ∓ 0.34	73.05 ∓ 0.12	72.50 ∓ 0.03
Nasal height	51.36 ∓ 0.26	55.98 ∓ 0.12	56.30 ∓ 0.03
Nasal breadth	24.23 ∓ 0.14	36.26 ∓ 0.09	36.02 ∓ 0.02
Cranial (length-breadth) index	76.38 ∓ 0.20	78.24 ∓ 0.10	78.84 ∓ 0.02
Auricular height-length index	60.79 ∓ 0.17	64.46 ∓ 0.10	63.89 ∓ 0.02
Fronto-parietal index	67.98 ∓ 0.20	71.29 ∓ 0.09	71.05 ∓ 0.02
Facial index	85.52 ∓ 0.72	91.10 ∓ 0.16	90.20 ∓ 0.04
Upper facial index	51.98 ∓ 0.37	52.37 ∓ 0.10	51.62 ∓ 0.02
Cranio-facial index	93.52 ∓ 0.32	91.37 ∓ 0.10	91.40 ∓ 0.02
Nasal index..............	47.52 ∓ 0.33	64.86 ∓ 0.17	64.38 ∓ 0.05
Fronto-gonial index	*106.34 ∓ 0.73	99.85 ∓ 0.16	99.90 ∓ 0.04
Zygo-gonial index	75.94 ∓ 0.44	78.04 ∓ 1.10	77.56 ∓ 0.02
Zygo-frontal index	72.67 ∓ 0.34	78.14 ∓ 0.10	77.78 ∓ 0.13
Stature	167 cm.**	171.42 ∓ 0.20	171.90 ∓ 0.05

*Howells divided this index in the opposite way to our procedure. The com-
  parable figure (calculated from the means of Howells's measurements)
  is 96.55.
**Reconstructed from Pearson's formulae

TABLE XVIII-2. CORRECTION OF GALLEN PRIORY MEANS

		Addition			Total Irish	Difference, Total Irish
Length	190.38	6.9	=	197.28	195.63	- 1.55
Width	145.27	9.1	=	154.37	154.12	- .25
Auricular height	115.50	8.5	=	124.00	124.98	+ .98
Horizontal circumference .	535.06	39.0	=	574.06	572.15	- 1.91
Min. frontal diameter ...	98.48	7.6	=	104.08	109.22	+ 5.14
Bizygomatic diameter ...	135.64	7.6	=	143.24	140.80	- 2.44
Bigonial diameter	102.67	7.6	=	110.27	109.26	- 1.01
Nasion-menton height ...	117.78	6.4	=	124.18	127.10	+ 2.92
Upper face	72.03	1.0	=	73.03	72.50	- .53
Nose height	51.36	2.0	=	53.36	56.30	+ 2.94
Nose breadth	24.23	11.0	=	35.23	56.02	+ .79
Length breadth				78.24	78.84	+ .60
Length height				62.85	63.89	+ 1.04
Fronto-parietal index ...				67.42	71.05	+ 3.63
Zygo-frontal index				72.66	77.78	+ 5.12
Zygo-gonial index				76.98	77.56	+ .58
Fronto-gonial index				94.38	99.80	+ 5.42
Facial index				86.69	90.20	+ 3.51
Upper facial index				50.98	51.62	+ .64
Nasal index				66.02	64.38	+ 1.64

TABLE XXI-1. COMPARATIVE DISTRIBUTION OF TYPES IN COUNTIES FURNISHING AND RECEIVING TRANSPLANTEES

	West Donegal	No. Ferm., E. Donegal, Tyrone, Londonderry	Antrim, Down	Mayo	West Galway	Ave.	Diff.
Pure and Pred.				Ave.			
Nordic	2.8	9.0	8.5	6.8 4.0	8.8	6.4	- .4
Keltic	24.8	29.4	28.1	27.4 19.7	26.8	23.2	-4.2
East Baltic	.9	1.7	.7	1.1 1.4	.7	1.05	- .05
Dinaric	21.1	15.1	13.8	16.7 22.5	13.0	17.8	1.1
Nord. Med.	33.5	25.0	32.9	30.4 29.8	29.6	29.7	- .7
Nord. Alp.	17.0	19.6	15.2	17.3 22.3	20.8	21.5	4.2

TABLE XXI-2. COMPARATIVE DISTRIBUTION OF TYPES IN COUNTIES FURNISHING AND RECEIVING TRANSPLANTEES

	Kerry	Tipperary, Kilkenny	Longford, Westmeath	Offaly, Leix, Kildare	Ave.	Clare	Diff.
Pure and Predominantly							
Nordic	5.6	6.1	12.7	6.6	7.75	4.7	-3.05
Keltic	15.2	25.9	24.8	30.3	24.05	21.0	-3.05
East Baltic	2.5	1.2	1.1	.8	1.4	1.0	- .4
Dinaric	25.9	24.2	14.9	14.6	19.9	27.4	7.5
Nordic Mediterranean .	25.7	28.4	32.3	30.7	29.3	24.7	-4.6
Nordic Alpine	25.1	13.6	13.3	16.3	17.0	20.8	3.8

TABLE XXI-3. COMPARATIVE DISTRIBUTION OF TYPES IN COUNTIES FURNISHING AND RECEIVING TRANSPLANTEES

	Wicklow, Carlow	Cork	Waterford, Wexford	Limerick	Offaly, Leix, Kildare	Meath, Louth, Dublin	Ave.	East Galway, Roscommon	Diff.
Pure and Predominantly .									
Nordic	6.5	7.1	9.6	7.3	6.6	7.3	7.4	8.1	.7
Keltic	31.7	16.5	22.3	17.6	30.3	33.8	26.3	26.8	.5
East Baltic . . .	1.0	1.8	.8	.9	.4	.4	.9	.6	- .3
Dinaric	13.6	21.8	18.3	23.0	14.6	12.4	17.3	16.3	-1.0
Nordic Mediterranean ..	26.5	24.7	25.0	28.5	30.7	32.5	28.6	30.6	2.0
Nordic Alpine .	15.0	23.0	23.7	22.7	16.3	12.8	18.9	17.5	-2.4

TABLE XXI-4. HAIR COLOR OF PERSONS CERTIFIED FOR TRANSPLANTATION (1653-54) WITH COMPARABLE DATA ON PRESENT MALE POPULATION

	Black or Dark	Brown	Red	Flaxen Yellow	White	Gray	Total
Waterford (1653) Males							
Number	38	42	1	10	10	9	110
Percent	34.55	38.18	0.9	9.09	9.09	8.18	
Waterford-Wexford (present) Males							
Percent	50.00	28.9	1.5	14.6		4.8	
Waterford (1653) Females							
Number	3	4	0	4	3	0	14
Percent	21.43	28.57	0	28.57	23.08	0	
Limerick (1653) Males							
Number	20	19	3	11	0	4	57
Percent	35.09	33.33	5.36	19.30	0	7.02	
Limerick (present) Males							
Percent	43.4	40.4	3.5	10.0		2.6	
Limerick (1653) Females							
Number	9	7	4	9	1	5	35
Percent	25.71	20.0	11.43	25.71	2.86	14.29	
East Galway Roscommon (present) Males							
Percent	33.6	46.2	5.4	11.5		3.3	

TABLE XXII-1. ADULT MEN --- WALES Rearrangement of Data of Fleure and James*

	Cephalic Index			
	Under 80		80 and over	
Pigmentation	Number	% of Total Series	Number	% of Total Series
Hair light, eye dark (darker than 10)..	44	2.38	21	1.13
Hair red	97	5.24	35	1.89
Hair fair or light brown, eye light ...	283	15.28	96	5.18
Hair dark, eye light (lighter than 10) .	412	22.25	121	6.53
Hair dark (but not black), eye dark (10 or darker)	427	23.06	124	6.70
Hair black, eye dark	142	7.67	50	2.70
Totals	1405	75.88	447	24.13

*Fleure and James, 1916, Table 2, p. 52.

TABLE XXII-2. ADULT WOMEN --- WALES Rearrangement of Data of Fleure and James*

	Cephalic Index			
	Under 80		80 and over	
Pigmentation	Number	% of Total Series	Number	% of Total Series
Hair light, eye dark (darker than 10)	6	1.74	3	.87
Hair red	11	3.20	7	2.03
Hair fair or light brown, eye light ...	41	11.92	31	9.01
Hair dark, eye light (lighter than 10) .	53	15.41	39	11.34
Hair dark (but not black), eye dark (10 or darker).........	70	20.35	60	17.44
Hair black, eye dark	12	3.49	11	3.20
Totals	193	56.11	151	43.89

*Fleure and James, 1916, Table 3, p. 53.

TABLE XXII-3. ADULT MEN --- ISLE OF MAN Rearrangement of Data of Davies and Fleure*

	Cephalic Index			
	Under 80		80 and over	
	Number	Per Cent	Number	Per Cent
Dark (dark brown and medium brown hair, pigmented iris)	261	21.72	178	14.83
Intermediate (dark brown hair, unpigmented iris)	106	8.83	70	5.83
Light (fair or lt. brown hair, unpigmented iris) plus light hair, pigmented iris	305	25.42	236	19.67
Red (red hair, iris pigmented or unpigmented)	26	2.17	18	1.50
Total	698	58.14	502	41.83

*Davies and Fleure, 1936, pp. 129-89; Table II, p. 136

WEST COAST IRISH FEMALES

TABLE XXV-1. MARITAL STATE BY COUNTY SUBGROUPS

	Single No.	%	Married No.	%	Widow No.	%	Total No.
Donegal	146	66.6	56	25.5	17	7.7	219
Leitrim	52	76.4	10	14.7	6	8.8	68
Sligo..	56	65.8	25	29.4	4	4.7	85
Mayo .	253	70.4	78	21.7	28	7.7	359
Galway	229	67.1	91	26.6	21	6.1	341
Clare..	376	75.5	112	22.4	10	2.0	498
Kerry .	176	58.3	111	38.8	8	9.7	286
Total..	1288	69.1	483	25.9	94	5.04	1865

TABLE XXV-2. NUMBER OF SIBLINGS BY COUNTY SUBGROUPS

	One No.	%	Two No.	%	Three No.	%	Four No.	%	Five No.	%	Six No.	%	Seven No.	%
Donegal	7	3.1	14	6.3	20	9.1	19	8.6	25	11.4	23	10.5	17	7.7
Leitrim	2	2.9	11	16.1	9	13.2	12	17.6	7	10.2	5	7.3	3	4.4
Sligo .	3	3.5	5	5.8	8	9.4	10	11.7	8	9.4	15	17.6	8	9.4
Mayo..	16	4.4	21	5.8	23	6.4	42	11.6	53	14.7	34	9.4	47	13.0
Galway	11	3.2	18	5.2	26	7.6	27	7.9	41	12.0	40	11.7	35	10.2
Clare .	21	4.2	29	5.8	47	9.4	62	12.4	54	10.8	71	14.2	45	9.0
Kerry .	14	4.8	19	6.6	18	6.2	27	9.4	37	12.9	35	12.2	29	10.1
Totals	74	4.0	117	6.3	151	8.1	199	10.7	225	12.1	223	12.0	184	9.9

NUMBER OF SIBLINGS BY COUNTY SUBGROUPS (Cont.)

	Eight No.	%	Nine No.	%	Ten No.	%	Eleven No.	%	Twelve No.	%	None No.	%	Total No.
Donegal.	28	12.7	20	9.1	15	6.8	13	5.9	9	4.1	9	4.1	219
Leitrim.	7	10.2	2	2.9	1	1.4	1	1.4	3	4.4	5	7.3	68
Sligo...	9	10.5	4	4.7	6	7.0	5	5.8	2	2.3	2	2.3	85
Mayo ..	35	9.7	33	9.1	19	5.2	17	4.7	14	3.8	5	1.3	359
Galway .	43	12.6	32	9.3	25	7.3	16	4.6	23	6.7	4	1.1	341
Clare ..	50	10.0	32	6.4	21	4.2	9	1.8	46	9.2	11	2.2	498
Kerry ..	27	9.4	30	10.4	17	5.9	6	2.0	19	6.6	8	2.7	286
Total ..	199	10.7	153	8.2	104	5.6	67	3.6	116	6.3	44	2.4	1856

TABLE XXV-3. NUMBER OF CHILDREN BY COUNTY SUBGROUPS

	One No.	%	Two No.	%	Three No.	%	Four No.	%	Five No.	%	Six No.	%	Seven No.	%
Donegal .	6	2.7	4	1.8	11	5.0	5	2.2	11	5.0	9	4.1	3	1.3
Leitrim .	2	2.9	4	5.8	1	1.4	1	1.4	2	2.9	1	1.4		
Sligo	2	2.3	5	5.8	2	2.3	1	1.1	4	4.7	2	2.3		
Mayo ..	6	1.6	9	2.5	7	1.9	6	1.6	14	3.8	11	3.0	8	2.2
Galway ..	13	3.8	12	3.5	12	3.5	4	1.1	11	3.2	9	2.6	11	3.2
Clare ...	19	3.8	20	4.0	12	2.4	6	1.2	12	2.4	6	1.2	6	1.2
Kerry ...	6	2.0	9	3.1	12	4.1	9	3.1	11	3.8	5	1.7	12	4.1
Total....	54	3.0	63	3.6	57	3.2	32	1.8	65	3.7	43	2.4	40	2.3

NUMBER OF CHILDREN BY COUNTY SUBGROUPS (Cont.)

	Eight No.	%	Nine No.	%	Ten No.	%	Eleven No.	%	Twelve No.	%	None No.	%	Total
Donegal.	3	1.3	3	1.3	5	2.2			4	1.8	155	70.7	219
Leitrim.	1	1.4	2	2.9	1	1.4					53	77.9	68
Sligo...	1	1.1							3	3.5	65	76.4	85
Mayo ..	8	2.2	9	2.5	6	1.6	4	1.1	5	1.3	266	74.0	359
Galway ..	9	2.6	2	.5	9	2.6	5	1.4	7	2.0	237	69.5	341
Clare ..	5	1.0	6	1.2	5	1.0	4	.8	4	.8	393	78.9	498
Kerry ..	8	2.7	5	1.7	8	2.7	5	1.7	6	2.0	190	66.4	286
Total ..	35	2.0	27	1.5	34	1.9	18	2.3	29	1.6	1359	76.7	1771

TABLE XXV-4. EDUCATION BY COUNTY SUBGROUPS

	Illiterate		Read and write		National school		Secondary school		University		Total
	No.	%	No.	%	No.	%	No.	%	No.	%	
Donegal.........	6	2.7			198	90.4	12	5.4	3	1.3	219
Leitrim..........	1	1.4			48	70.5	18	26.4	1	1.4	68
Sligo					69	81.1	9	10.5	7	8.2	85
Mayo	5	1.3	6	1.6	257	71.5	79	22.0	11	3.0	358
Galway	7	2.0	6	1.7	201	58.9	115	33.7	12	3.5	341
Clare	2	.4	6	1.2	284	57.0	201	40.3	5	1.0	498
Kerry	2	.6	2	.6	226	79.0	56	19.5			286
Females Total	23	1.2	20	1.1	1283	69.2	490	26.4	39	2.1	1855
Males Total	294	3.3	104	1.2	7260	81.7	1026	11.6	198	2.2	8882

TABLE XXV-5. LANGUAGE BY COUNTY SUBGROUPS

	No Irish		Native speaker		Irish only		School Irish		Total
	No.	%	No.	%	No.	%	No.	%	No.
Donegal	38	17.3	103	47.0			78	35.6	219
Leitrim	37	54.4					31	45.5	68
Sligo	49	57.6	2	2.3			34	40.0	85
Mayo	115	32.0	90	25.0			154	42.8	359
Galway	126	36.9	144	42.2	3	.8	68	19.9	341
Clare	142	28.5	25	5.0			331	66.4	498
Kerry	83	29.0	115	40.2			88	30.7	286
Females Total.....	590	31.9	479	25.9	3	.8	783	42.1	1856
Males Totals....	4881	54.8	1230	13.8	85	1.0	2704	30.4	8900

TABLE XXV-6. RELIGION BY COUNTY SUBGROUPS

	Catholic		Church of Ireland		Presbyterian		Total
	No.	%	No.	%	No.	%	
Donegal....	214	97.7			5	2.2	219
Leitrim ...	61	89.7	4	5.8	3	4.4	68
Sligo......	85	100.0					85
Mayo	358	99.7			1	.2	359
Galway	340	99.7	1	.2			341
Clare	495	99.3	1	.2	2	.4	498
Kerry	283	98.9	3				286
Total......	1836	83.4	9	.5	11	.1	1856

TABLE XXV-7. OCCUPATION BY COUNTY SUBGROUPS

	Household servant		At home		Factory worker		Shop assistant		Dressmaker		Clerk	
	No.	%	No.	%	No.	%	No.	%	No.	%	No.	%
Donegal	28	12.7	1	.4	47	21.4	6	2.7	1	.4		
Leitrim	4	5.8	12	17.6			4	5.8			6	8.8
Sligo	2	2.3	17	20.0			5	5.8	1	1.1		
Mayo......	41	11.4	18	5.0	62	17.2	10	2.7	5	1.3	7	1.9
Galway	41	12.0	15	4.3	68	19.9	13	3.8	3	.8	6	1.7
Clare	50	10.0	9	1.8	21	4.2	17	3.4	1	.2	13	2.6
Kerry	58	20.2	7	2.4			2	.6	1	.3	4	1.3
Total	224	12.1	79	4.3	198	10.7	57	3.1	12	.7	36	1.1

	Business		Housekeeper		Nurse		Schoolgirl		Teacher		Medical Profession		Total
	No.	%	No.	%	No.	%	No.	%	No.	%	No.	%	
Donegal....	12	5.4	112	51.1	1	.4	3	1.3	6	2.7	2	.9	219
Leitrim			19	27.9	13	19.1	7	10.2	1	1.4	2	2.9	68
Sligo......			39	45.8	12	14.1			2	2.3	7	8.2	85
Mayo......	5	1.3	143	39.8	27	7.5	30	8.3	1	.2	10	2.7	359
Galway	9	2.6	133	39.0	21	6.1	18	5.2	2	.5	12	3.5	341
Clare	24	4.8	204	40.9	33	6.6	102	20.4	22	4.4	2	.4	498
Kerry	1	.3	176	61.5	19	6.6	7	2.4	9	3.1	2	.6	286
Total	51	2.8	826	44.7	126	6.8	167	9.5	43	2.3	37	2.0	1846

TABLE XXVI-1. AGE BY COUNTY SUBGROUPS

County	No.	Range	Mean		S. D.
Donegal	210	15-69	32.45 +	.71	15.20
Leitrim	66	15-64	29.20 ∓	.99	11.95
Sligo	82	15-69	31.10 ∓	.97	13.00
Mayo	346	15-69	31.30 ∓	.56	15.50
Galway	332	15-69	32.65 ∓	.56	15.10
Clare	490	15-69	28.50 ∓	.41	13.60
Kerry	274	15-69	34.95 ∓	.62	15.30
Bordering Counties ..	70	15-69	28.95 ∓	1.13	14.00
West Coast	1800	15-69	31.40 +	.24	14.80
Males - Total	8909	15-94	35.70 +	.11	15.40

TABLE XXVI-2. WEIGHT BY COUNTY SUBGROUPS

County	No.	Range	Mean	S. D.
Donegal.........	210	81-270	135.20+1.16	24.90
Leitrim.........	66	101-270	136.70∓2.18	26.30
Sligo..........	83	91-250	133.00∓1.58	21.40
Mayo	346	81-230	135.60∓ .75	20.60
Galway	332	81-260	134.00∓ .87	23.60
Clare	489	81-230	130.60∓ .63	20.70
Kerry	258	81-230	139.50∓1.01	24.10
Bordering Counties ..	70	91-200	132.40∓1.68	20.90
West Coast	1784	81-270	134.40+ .37	22.90
Males - Total :....	8906	91-290	157.30+ .16	22.50

TABLE XXVI-3. STATURE BY COUNTY SUBGROUPS

County	No.	Range	Mean		S.D.
Donegal.........	210	137-178	158.43 +	.27	5.82
Leitrim..........	66	149-184	160.32 ∓	.48	5.73
Sligo	83	140-181	157.35 ∓	.48	6.54
Mayo	346	134-184	157.14 ∓	.24	6.72
Galway	332	140-175	158.79 ∓	.21	5.79
Clare	490	131-187	159.01 ∓	.19	6.12
Kerry	274	137-187	159.27 ∓	.24	5.91
Bordering Counties ..	70	137-175	158.52 ∓	.52	6.39
West Coast	1801	131-187	158.55 +	.10	6.18
Males - Total	8902	146-202	171.90 ∓	.05	6.84

TABLE XXVI-4. SPAN BY COUNTY SUBGROUPS

County	No.	Range	Mean		S. D.
Donegal........	206	145-183	163.01 +	.29	6.09
Leitrim.........	65	142-201	164.78 ∓	.66	7.92
Sligo	82	145-183	162.05 ∓	.57	7.71
Mayo	342	136-186	161.96 ∓	.27	7.50
Galway	331	142-186	163.13 ∓	.25	6.66
Clare	481	133-192	163.43 ∓	.22	7.20
Kerry	270	136-189	164.24 ∓	.30	7.35
Bordering Counties .	70	136-180	163.43 ∓	.64	7.98
West Coast	1777	133-201	163.16 +	.12	7.17
Males - Total	8675	146-211	181.14 ∓	.06	7.92

TABLE XXVI-5. RELATIVE SPAN BY COUNTY SUBGROUPS

County	No.	Range	Mean		S.D.
Donegal........	206	96-115	102.74 +	.13	2.82
Leitrim.........	65	96-111	102.68 ∓	.23	2.74
Sligo..........	82	96-109	103.02 ∓	.21	2.80
Mayo	342	92-111	102.90 ∓	.11	2.94
Galway	331	96-111	102.72 ∓	.10	2.66
Clare	481	88-119	102.72 ∓	.10	3.16
Kerry	270	88-119	102.98 ∓	.13	3.24
Bordering Counties .	70	96-109	102.98 ∓	.22	2.76
West Coast	1777	88-119	102.80 +	.05	2.98
Males - Totals....	8671	94-115	105.32 ∓	.02	2.52

TABLE XXVI-6 BIACROMIAL DIAMETER BY COUNTY SUBGROUPS

County	No.	Range	Mean		S.D.
Donegal	210	28 - 42	36.14 +	.10	2.13
Leitrim	66	31 - 42	36.05 ∓	.17	2.07
Sligo	83	31 - 42	36.05 ∓	.14	1.89
Mayo	346	31 - 45	36.35 ∓	.07	1.92
Galway	332	31 - 42	36.11 ∓	.12	3.36
Clare	489	25 - 42	35.78 ∓	.06	2.13
Kerry	274	31 - 48	37.25 ∓	.08	2.01
Bordering Counties	70	31 - 42	36.29 ∓	.17	2.07
West Coast	1800	25 - 48	36.59 +	.04	2.28
Males - Total	8880	28 - 48	38.57 ∓	.01	2.07

TABLE XXVI-7. RELATIVE SHOULDER BREADTH BY COUNTY SUBGROUPS

County	No.	Range	Mean		S.D.
Donegal	210	18-27	22.86 +	.06	1.28
Leitrim	66	20-25	22.50 ∓	.09	1.10
Sligo	83	18-29	22.90 ∓	.10	1.34
Mayo	346	20-27	22.94 ∓	.04	1.20
Galway	332	18-27	22.70 ∓	.04	1.18
Clare	489	16-27	22.56 ∓	.04	1.24
Kerry	274	20-29	23.38 ∓	.05	1.22
Bordering Counties	70	20-25	22.62 ∓	.08	1.02
West Coast	1800	16-29	22.84 +	.02	1.24
Males - Total	8875	18-27	22.44 ∓	.01	1.12

TABLE XXVI-8. SITTING HEIGHT BY COUNTY SUBGROUPS

County	No.	Range	Mean		S.D.
Donegal	210	64-95	83.18 +	.20	4.24
Leitrim	66	64-95	85.02 ∓	.34	4.04
Sligo	83	72-95	83.78 ∓	.27	3.64
Mayo	346	60-95	81.10 ∓	.23	6.36
Galway	332	64-91	83.46 ∓	.15	4.16
Clare	490	64-95	84.34 ∓	.12	3.88
Kerry	274	68-95	84.14 ∓	.15	3.80
Bordering Counties	70	60-90	82.70 ∓	.49	6.08
West Coast	1801	60-95	83.38 +	.07	4.68
Males - Total	8884	75-107	91.48 ∓	.02	3.60

TABLE XXVI-9. RELATIVE SITTING HEIGHT BY COUNTY SUBGROUPS

County	No.	Range	Mean		S.D.
Donegal	210	40-61	52.78 +	.10	2.24
Leitrim	66	40-57	53.04 ∓	.18	2.16
Sligo	83	50-57	53.32 ∓	.12	1.62
Mayo	346	48-57	52.66 ∓	.06	1.66
Galway	332	48-59	52.76 ∓	.07	1.76
Clare	490	38-63	52.96 ∓	.07	2.18
Kerry	274	46-59	53.02 ∓	.08	1.84
Bordering Counties	70	40-57	52.56 ∓	.18	2.20
West Coast	1801	38-63	52.88 +	.03	1.92
Males - Total	8881	46-59	53.22 ∓	.01	1.48

TABLE XXVI-10. HEAD LENGTH BY COUNTY SUBGROUPS

County	No.	Range	Mean		S.D.
Donegal	210	161-205	187.26 +	.29	6.18
Leitrim	66	173-214	187.14 ∓	.60	7.23
Sligo	83	167-202	186.69 ∓	.46	6.18
Mayo	346	161-205	187.62 ∓	.22	6.06
Galway	332	167-205	188.25 ∓	.22	6.06
Clare	489	167-202	185.97 ∓	.19	6.09
Kerry	274	167-208	187.59 ∓	.25	6.12
Bordering Counties	70	161-205	187.71 ∓	.53	6.57
West Coast	1800	161-214	187.17 +	.10	6.21
Males - Total	8900	170-223	195.63 ∓	.05	6.51

TABLE XXVI-11. HEAD BREADTH BY COUNTY SUBGROUPS

County	No.	Range	Mean	S.D.
Donegal	210	135-161	148.42 ± .23	4.92
Leitrim	66	135-161	148.78 ± .47	5.70
Sligo	83	135-155	146.95 ± .28	3.78
Mayo..........	344	132-164	148.63 ± .19	5.10
Galway	330	132-164	146.74 ± .20	5.22
Clare	489	132-167	148.78 ± .15	4.98
Kerry	274	135-164	149.74 ± .18	4.53
Bordering Counties	70	135-164	149.08 ± .44	5.49
West Coast	1796	132-167	148.51 ± .08	5.01
Males - Total....	8895	126-185	154.12 ± .04	5.73

TABLE XXVI-12. CEPHALIC INDEX BY COUNTY SUBGROUPS

County	No.	Range	Mean	S.D.
Donegal	210	68-88	79.23 ± .15	3.18
Leitrim	66	71-88	79.44 ± .26	3.09
Sligo..........	83	71-85	78.69 ± .20	2.70
Mayo..........	344	68-91	79.38 ± .12	3.30
Galway	332	65-94	78.45 ± .12	3.12
Clare	488	71-91	80.13 ± .10	3.33
Kerry	274	71-91	79.86 ± .12	2.91
Bordering Counties	70	71-91	79.62 ± .27	3.30
West Coast	1797	65-94	79.44 ± .05	3.24
Males - Total ...	8892	65-94	78.84 ± .02	3.30

TABLE XXVI-13. CEPHALIC INDEX BY COUNTY SUBGROUPS

	(65-76) Dolichocephalic		(77-82) Mesocephalic		(83-94) Brachycephalic		
	No.	%	No.	%	No.	%	Total
Donegal	37	17.6	139	66.2	34	16.2	210
Leitrim	11	16.7	45	68.2	10	15.1	66
Sligo	16	19.3	61	73.5	6	7.2	83
Mayo: Achile Island...	57	16.6	237	68.9	50	14.5	344
Galway: Aran Islands..	87	26.2	220	66.3	25	7.5	332
Clare.............	67	13.7	305	62.5	116	23.8	488
Kerry.............	31	11.3	195	71.2	48	17.5	274
Total	306	17.0	1202	66.9	289	16.1	1797

TABLE XXVI-14. HEAD HEIGHT BY COUNTY SUBGROUPS

County	No.	Range	Mean	S.D.
Donegal	210	99-138	122.62 ± .33	7.04
Leitrim	66	103-138	122.06 ± .60	7.20
Sligo	83	107-138	121.02 ± .52	7.08
Mayo	345	95-142	119.50 ± .27	7.36
Galway..........	332	99-138	118.26 ± .29	7.72
Clare...........	490	99-138	119.10 ± .20	6.64
Kerry...........	274	99-140	119.10 ± .32	7.80
Bordering Counties...	70	95-138	118.86 ± .70	8.68
West Coast	1800	95-142	119.74 ± .12	7.36
Males - Total ...:..	8898	102-149	124.98 ± .04	6.04

TABLE XXVI-15. LENGTH-HEIGHT INDEX BY COUNTY SUBGROUPS

County	No.	Range	Mean	S.D.
Donegal	210	52-75	65.54 ± .18	3.96
Leitrim	66	55-75	65.15 ± .32	3.90
Sligo	83	55-75	64.64 ± .29	3.93
Mayo	345	49-78	63.80 ± .15	4.17
Galway..........	332	52-75	62.90 ± .15	4.08
Clare...........	489	55-78	64.13 ± .11	3.75
Kerry...........	274	52-78	64.04 ± .18	4.32
Bordering Counties...	70	55-75	63.32 ± .33	4.14
West Coast	1799	49-78	64.04 ± .07	4.08
Males - Total	8891	52-78	63.89 ± .02	3.33

TABLE XXVI-16. BREADTH-HEIGHT INDEX BY COUNTY SUBGROUPS

County	No.	Range	Mean	S.D.
Donegal	210	67-96	83.03 + .23	4.95
Leitrim	66	70-96	82.31 ∓ .42	5.07
Sligo	83	70-96	82.28 ∓ .36	4.86
Mayo	343	64-96	80.36 ∓ .19	5.19
Galway	331	67-99	80.33 ∓ .19	5.16
Clare	489	70-93	80.12 ∓ .14	4.59
Kerry	274	67-96	80.27 ∓ .21	5.13
Bordering Counties	70	67-93	79.79 ∓ .42	5.16
West Coast	1796	64-99	80.75 + .08	5.07
Males - Total	8887	67-102	81.05 ∓ .03	4.26

TABLE XXVI-17. MINIMUM FRONTAL DIAMETER BY COUNTY SUBGROUPS

County	No.	Range	Mean	S.D.
Donegal	210	93-128	104.90 + .20	4.40
Leitrim	66	89-116	104.82 ∓ .42	5.00
Sligo	83	93-116	104.54 ∓ .30	4.08
Mayo	346	85-120	104.26 ∓ .17	4.60
Galway	332	89-116	103.70 ∓ .16	4.40
Clare	490	89-124	104.66 ∓ .14	4.56
Kerry	274	93-120	104.46 ∓ .18	4.44
Bordering Counties	70	93-116	104.90 ∓ .36	4.52
West Coast	1801	85-128	104.42 + .06	4.52
Males - Total	8898	89-128	109.22 ∓ .03	4.84

TABLE XXVI-18. FRONTO-PARIETAL INDEX BY COUNTY SUBGROUPS

County	No.	Range	Mean	S.D.
Donegal	210	60-86	70.84 + .15	3.12
Leitrim	66	63-80	70.45 ∓ .25	2.97
Sligo	83	63-80	71.35 ∓ .20	2.76
Mayo	344	63-83	70.12 ∓ .11	3.00
Galway	332	57-86	70.30 ∓ .12	3.15
Clare	489	60-80	70.30 ∓ .09	2.97
Kerry	274	60-83	70.06 ∓ .12	3.00
Bordering Counties	70	63-77	70.39 ∓ .23	2.91
West Coast	1798	57-86	70.36 + .05	3.03
Males - Total	8886	60-86	71.05 ∓ .02	3.09

TABLE XXVI-19. BIZYGOMATIC DIAMETER BY COUNTY SUBGROUPS

County	No.	Range	Mean	S.D.
Donegal	210	95-149	132.45 + .27	5.75
Leitrim	66	100-150	131.90 ∓ .54	6.50
Sligo	83	115-144	131.10 ∓ .31	4.25
Mayo	346	110-149	133.10 ∓ .18	4.85
Galway	332	115-159	132.10 ∓ .20	5.40
Clare	490	115-149	132.35 ∓ .15	5.00
Kerry	274	110-149	133.90 ∓ .22	5.45
Bordering Counties	70	110-149	132.00 ∓ .49	6.05
West Coast	1801	95-159	132.60 + .08	5.30
Males - Total	8891	110-169	140.80 ∓ .04	5.95

TABLE XXVI-20. CEPHALO-FACIAL INDEX BY COUNTY
SUBGROUPS

County	No.	Range	Mean	S.D.
Donegal	210	79-99	89.54 + .16	3.36
Leitrim	66	82-99	89.24 ∓ .23	2.73
Sligo	83	82-96	89.48 ∓ .20	2.73
Mayo	344	82-99	89.63 ∓ .11	3.06
Galway	331	79-105	89.69 ∓ .11	3.03
Clare	489	79-99	88.91 ∓ .09	2.88
Kerry	274	79-105	89.63 ∓ .13	3.12
Bordering Counties. . .	70	79-96	88.82 ∓ .23	2.85
West Coast	1797	79-105	89.52 + .05	3.06
Males - Total	8880	76-108	91.40 ∓ .02	3.30

TABLE XXVI-21. ZYGO-FRONTAL INDEX BY COUNTY
SUBGROUPS

County	No.	Range	Mean	S.D.
Donegal	210	64-99	78.94 + .17	3.68
Leitrim	66	68-87	79.02 ∓ .28	3.32
Sligo	83	72-87	79.66 ∓ .21	2.88
Mayo	346	68-91	78.34 ∓ .12	3.32
Galway	332	64-91	78.42 ∓ .12	3.36
Clare	490	68-95	79.18 ∓ .10	3.16
Kerry	274	64-87	77.94 ∓ .13	3.28
Bordering Counties. . .	70	72-87	79.22 ∓ .22	2.68
West Coast	1801	64-99	78.70 + .05	3.36
Males - Total	8882	64-95	77.78 ∓ .02	3.32

TABLE XXVI-22. BIGONIAL DIAMETER BY COUNTY
SUBGROUPS

County	No.	Range	Mean	S.D.
Donegal	210	86-121	101.70 + .23	4.84
Leitrim	66	86-117	101.50 ∓ .45	5.40
Sligo	83	90-113	100.30 ∓ .30	4.04
Mayo	346	90-129	102.30 ∓ .17	4.80
Galway	332	82-121	101.74 ∓ .17	4.72
Clare	490	86-117	101.06 ∓ .14	4.64
Kerry	274	86-121	102.06 ∓ .21	5.16
Bordering Counties. . .	70	90-117	102.14 ∓ .40	4.92
West Coast	1801	82-129	101.62 + .08	4.84
Males - Total	8897	86-133	109.26 ∓ .04	5.64

TABLE XXVI-23. FRONTO-GONIAL INDEX BY COUNTY
SUBGROUPS

County	No.	Range	Mean	S.D.
Donegal	210	80-114	96.55 + .23	4.90
Leitrim	66	85-109	96.70 ∓ .42	5.00
Sligo	83	85-114	96.05 ∓ .37	5.00
Mayo	346	80-114	97.80 ∓ .21	5.70
Galway	332	80-124	98.20 ∓ .21	5.60
Clare	490	80-114	96.50 ∓ .15	4.85
Kerry	274	75-119	98.05 ∓ .23	5.75
Bordering Counties. . .	70	85-109	97.15 ∓ .41	5.05
West Coast	1801	75-124	97.30 + .09	5.40
Males - Total	8888	80-124	99.90 ∓ .04	5.50

TABLE XXVI-24. ZYGO-GONIAL INDEX BY COUNTY SUBGROUPS

County	No.	Range	Mean	S.D.
Donegal	210	66-86	76.57 + .15	3.15
Leitrim	66	69-83	76.45 ∓ .23	2.82
Sligo	83	69-86	76.30 ∓ .23	3.15
Mayo	346	69-95	76.78 ∓ .12	3.21
Galway	332	63-95	77.05 ∓ .13	3.48
Clare	490	69-95	76.33 ∓ .10	3.21
Kerry	274	66-92	76.33 ∓ .15	3.69
Bordering Counties	70	69-86	77.02 ∓ .25	3.12
West Coast	1801	63-95	76.57 + .05	3.33
Males - Total	8880	63-92	77.56 ∓ .02	3.48

TABLE XXVI-25. TOTAL FACE HEIGHT BY COUNTY SUBGROUPS

County	No.	Range	Mean	S.D.
Donegal	210	100-134	116.60 + .30	6.35
Leitrim	66	95-139	115.85 ∓ .57	6.85
Sligo	83	100-129	116.90 ∓ .45	6.10
Mayo	346	100-134	116.05 ∓ .22	5.95
Galway	332	95-139	115.85 ∓ .24	6.60
Clare	490	90-144	114.05 ∓ .19	6.30
Kerry	274	95-134	115.00 ∓ .24	5.90
Bordering Counties	70	100-129	113.95 ∓ .48	6.00
West Coast	1801	90-144	115.40 + .10	6.35
Males - Total	8897	95-154	127.10 ∓ .05	6.95

TABLE XXVI-26. FACIAL INDEX BY COUNTY SUBGROUPS

County	No.	Range	Mean	S.D.
Donegal	210	75-104	87.80 + .24	5.05
Leitrim	66	75-99	87.55 ∓ .38	4.55
Sligo	83	75-104	89.05 ∓ .36	4.85
Mayo	346	75-104	87.00 ∓ .17	4.80
Galway	332	70-104	87.75 ∓ .20	5.45
Clare	490	70-109	86.10 ∓ .16	5.15
Kerry	274	70-104	85.85 ∓ .20	5.00
Bordering Counties	70	70-99	86.00 ∓ .41	5.05
West Coast	1801	70-189	86.95 + .08	5.10
Males - Total	8879	70-114	90.20 ∓ .04	5.50

TABLE XXVI-27. UPPER FACE HEIGHT BY COUNTY SUBGROUPS

County	No.	Range	Mean	S.D.
Donegal	210	55-79	68.40 + .20	4.20
Leitrim	66	50-89	67.75 ∓ .40	4.80
Sligo	83	55-79	67.50 ∓ .34	4.65
Mayo	346	55-84	67.50 ∓ .16	4.45
Galway	332	55-84	68.00 ∓ .18	4.75
Clare	490	50-84	66.15 ∓ .14	4.50
Kerry	274	55-79	67.70 ∓ .17	4.25
Bordering Counties	70	55-79	66.70 ∓ .36	4.45
West Coast	1801	50-89	67.35 + .07	4.60
Males - Total	8894	50-89	72.80 ∓ .03	4.50

TABLE XXVI-28. UPPER FACIAL INDEX BY COUNTY SUBGROUPS

County	No.	Range	Mean	S.D.
Donegal	210	43-60	51.20 + .15	3.21
Leitrim	66	40-60	50.87 ∓ .27	3.27
Sligo	83	43-60	51.47 ∓ .24	3.27
Mayo	346	40-63	50.69 ∓ .13	3.51
Galway	332	40-63	51.29 ∓ .15	3.93
Clare	490	37-63	50.01 ∓ .11	3.48
Kerry	274	37-69	50.18 ∓ .15	3.57
Bordering Counties	70	40-60	50.39 ∓ .27	3.36
West Coast	1801	37-69	50.63 + .06	3.60
Males - Total	8876	37-69	51.62 ∓ .02	3.45

TABLE XXVI-29. NOSE HEIGHT BY COUNTY SUBGROUPS

County	No.	Range	Mean	S.D.
Donegal	210	40-67	51.06 + .19	4.00
Leitrim	66	40-63	50.82 ∓ .34	4.12
Sligo	83	44-67	54.50 ∓ .33	4.40
Mayo	346	40-63	51.38 ∓ .15	4.24
Galway	332	40-67	51.86 ∓ .16	4.24
Clare	490	36-63	50.82 ∓ .12	3.92
Kerry	274	40-67	51.14 ∓ .16	3.88
Bordering Counties	70	44-59	51.06 ∓ .29	3.60
West Coast	1801	36-67	51.38 + .07	4.16
Males - Total	8898	40-71	56.30 ∓ .03	4.08

TABLE XXVI-30. NOSE BREADTH BY COUNTY SUBGROUPS

County	No.	Range	Mean	S.D.
Donegal	210	25-39	32.15 + .12	2.55
Leitrim	66	25-42	32.33 ∓ .22	2.67
Sligo	83	25-39	32.03 ∓ .21	2.88
Mayo	346	25-45	32.51 ∓ .09	2.61
Galway	332	25-42	32.12 ∓ .10	2.67
Clare	490	25-42	32.09 ∓ .08	2.55
Kerry	274	25-42	32.66 ∓ .11	2.76
Bordering Counties	70	25-42	32.33 ∓ .23	2.88
West Coast	1801	25-45	32.24 + .04	2.64
Males - Total	8904	25-57	36.02 ∓ .02	3.09

TABLE XXVI-31. NASAL INDEX BY COUNTY SUBGROUPS

County	No.	Range	Mean	S.D.
Donegal	210	48-83	63.42 + .28	6.08
Leitrim	66	48-83	62.34 ∓ .48	5.76
Sligo	83	48-87	63.78 ∓ .53	7.16
Mayo	346	48-87	63.54 ∓ .25	7.00
Galway	332	44-87	61.76 ∓ .24	6.48
Clare	490	44-91	63.54 ∓ .20	6.64
Kerry	274	44-87	64.46 ∓ .28	6.92
Bordering Counties	70	52-79	63.22 ∓ .45	5.56
West Coast	1801	44-91	63.42 + .11	6.68
Males - Total	8896	44-99	64.38 ∓ .05	6.48

TABLE XXVI-32. FEMALES vs. MALES: MEASUREMENTS

	Difference	Female as % of Male	S. D.
Age	- 4.30	87.95	+ .6
Weight	-22.90	85.40	+ .4
Stature	-13.35 cm.	92.2	- .66 cm.
Span	-17.98 "	90.1	- .75 "
Biacromial diameter	- 1.98 "	94.9	+ .21 "
Sitting height	- 8.10 "	91.1	+1.08 "
Average	10.35 cm.	92.07	.65 cm.
Head length	- 8.46 mm.	95.7	- .30 mm.
Head breadth	- 5.61 "	96.4	- .60 "
Head height	- 5.24 "	95.8	+1.32 "
Bizygomatic diameter	- 8.20 "	94.2	- .65 "
Total face height	-11.70 "	90.8	- .60 "
Upper face height	- 5.45 "	92.5	+ .10 "
Nose height	- 4.92 "	91.3	+ .08 "
Nose breadth	- 3.78 "	89.5	- .45 "
Minimum frontal diameter	- 4.80 "	95.6	- .32 "
Bigonial diameter	- 7.64 "	93.0	- .80 "
Average	6.58 mm.	93.5	.52 mm.

TABLE XXVI-33. FEMALES vs. MALES: INDICES

	Difference (index units)	Female as % of Male	S. D. (index units)
Relative span...........	-2.52	97.6	+ .46
Relative shoulder breadth .	+ .40	101.8	+ .12
Relative sitting height	- .34	99.4	+ .44
Average	1.09	99.6	.34
Cephalic.............	+ .60	100.8	- .06
Length height..........	+ .15	99.8	+ .75
Breadth height.........	- .30	99.6	+ .84
Cephalo facial	-1.98	97.8	- .21
Facial	-3.25	96.4	- .40
Upper facial	- .99	98.1	+ .15
Nasal	- .96	98.5	+ .20
Fronto-parietal	- .69	99.0	- .06
Zygo-frontal	+ .92	101.2	+ .04
Zygo-gonial...........	- .99	98.7	- .15
Fronto-gonial	-2.60	97.4	- .10
Average	1.22	98.8	.27

TABLE XXVI-34. DISTRIBUTION OF AGE GROUPS BY COUNTY SUBGROUPS

County	15-19 No.	%	20-24 No.	%	25-29 No.	%	30-34 No.	%	35-39 No.	%	40-44 No.	%	45-49 No.	%
Donegal ...	47	22.4	54	25.7	17	8.1	13	6.2	10	4.8	16	7.6	16	7.6
Leitrim ...	14	21.2	17	25.7	11	16.6	6	9.1	5	7.6	6	9.1	1	1.5
Sligo	16	19.5	17	20.7	13	15.8	9	11.0	7	8.5	7	8.5	5	6.1
Mayo	81	23.4	99	28.6	40	11.5	14	4.0	20	5.8	19	5.5	15	4.3
Galway....	51	15.4	104	31.3	30	9.0	27	8.1	25	7.5	25	7.5	13	3.9
Clare.....	168	34.3	101	20.6	57	11.6	40	8.2	31	6.3	20	4.1	20	4.1
Kerry.....	48	17.5	50	18.2	33	12.0	24	8.7	16	5.8	20	7.3	20	7.3
Total .	425	23.6	442	24.5	201	11.2	133	7.4	114	6.3	113	6.3	90	5.0

TABLE XXVI-34. DISTRIBUTION OF AGE GROUPS BY COUNTY SUBGROUPS (Cont.)

County	50-54 No.	%	55-59 No.	%	60-65 No.	%	65-69 No.	%	Total
Donegal ...	10	4.8	13	6.2	8	3.8	6	2.8	210
Leitrim ...	2	3.0	2	3.0	2	3.0	-	-	66
Sligo	2	2.4	2	2.4	2	2.4	2	2.4	82
Mayo	10	2.9	13	3.7	21	6.1	14	4.0	346
Galway....	15	4.5	12	3.6	9	2.7	21	6.3	332
Clare.....	12	2.4	15	3.1	18	3.8	8	1.6	490
Kerry.....	24	8.7	18	6.6	11	4.0	10	3.6	274
Total .	75	4.2	75	4.2	71	3.9	61	3.4	1800

TABLE XXVII-1. SKIN COLOR, INNER ARM, BY COUNTY SUBGROUPS

	Pale		Pink		Brunet		Swarthy		Light brown		Light yellow brown		Total
	No.	%	No.	%	No.	%	No.	%	No.	%	No.	%	
Donegal	6	2.7	200	91.3	12	5.4							218
Leitrim	3	4.4	62	91.1	3	4.4							68
Sligo	2	2.3	77	90.5	6	7.0							85
Mayo	14	3.8	325	90.5	18	5.0	1	.2					358
Galway........	15	4.3	294	86.2	26	1.1	4	1.1					339
Clare.........	22	4.4	423	84.9	50	10.0	1	.2	1	.2	1	.2	498
Kerry	8	2.7	256	89.5	19	6.6							283
Females Total ...	70	3.8	1637	88:5	134	7.2	6	.3	1	.1	1	.1	1849
Males Total.....	26	.3	8160	91.6	694	7.8	28	.3	-	-	-	-	8908

TABLE XXVII-2. VASCULARITY BY COUNTY SUBGROUPS

	Submedium		Medium		Pronounced		Total
	No.	%	No.	%	No.	%	
Donegal	10	4.5	181	82.6	28	12.7	219
Leitrim	2	2.9	62	91.1	4	5.8	68
Sligo	6	7.0	70	82.3	9	10.5	85
Mayo	19	5.2	266	74.0	74	20.6	359
Galway........	26	7.6	247	72.4	68	19.9	341
Clare.........	43	8.6	362	72.6	93	18.6	498
Kerry.........	14	4.8	222	77.6	50	17.4	286
Females Total ...	120	6.5	1410	75.6	326	17.6	1856
Males Total.....	63	.7	6686	75.1	2158	24.2	8907

TABLE XXVII-3. FRECKLES BY COUNTY SUBGROUPS

	Absent		Submedium		Medium		Pronounced		Massed		Total
	No.	%	No.	%	No.	%	No.	%	No.	%	
Donegal	120	54.7	75	34.2	22	10.0	1	.4	1	.4	219
Leitrim	50	73.5	15	22.0	3	4.4					68
Sligo	50	58.8	21	24.7	13	15.2	1	1.1			85
Mayo	198	55.1	112	31.1	45	12.5	4	1.1			359
Galway........	198	58.0	99	29.0	42	12.3	2	.5			341
Clare.........	237	47.5	144	28.9	102	20.4	14	2.8			497
Kerry.........	124	43.3	131	45.8	28	9.7	3	1.0			286
Females Total ...	977	52.0	597	31.8	255	13.6	25	1.3	1	.4	1880
Males Total.....	5371	60.3	2300	25.8	973	10.9	260	2.9	-	-	8904

TABLE XXVII-4. MOLES BY COUNTY SUBGROUPS

	Absent		Few		Many		Total
	No.	%	No.	%	No.	%	
Donegal	201	91.7	17	7.7	1	.4	219
Leitrim	61	89.7	6	8.8			67
Sligo	75	88.2	10	11.7			85
Mayo	310	86.3	47	13.0			357
Galway........	301	88.2	38	11.1	2	.5	341
Clare.........	456	91.5	36	7.2	1	.2	493
Kerry.........	258	90.2	28	9.7			286
Females Total ...	1662	89.9	182	9.8	4	.2	1848
Males Total.....	8359	93.9	495	5.6	47	.5	8901

TABLE XXVII-5. HAIR FORM BY COUNTY SUBGROUPS

	Straight		Low waves		Deep waves		Curly		Frizzly		Woolly		Total
	No.	%	No.	%	No.	%	No.	%	No.	%	No.	%	
Donegal	95	43.3	97	44.2	17	7.7	10	4.5					219
Leitrim	34	50.0	24	35.2	4	5.8	4	5.8			1	1.4	67
Sligo	43	50.5	37	43.5	2	2.3	3	3.5					85
Mayo	182	50.6	135	37.6	34	9.4	7	1.9	1	.2			359
Galway........	156	45.7	141	41.3	39	11.4	4	1.1	1	.2			341
Clare.........	206	41.3	224	44.9	54	10.8	3	.6					497
Kerry.........	139	48.6	112	39.1	27	9.4	7	2.4	1	.3			286
Females Total ...	855	46.1	770	41.5	177	9.5	38	2.0	3	.7	1	.1	1854
Males	2555	28.7	4437	49.8	1606	18.0	292	3.3	15	.2*			8905

*(Frizzly and Woolly)

TABLE XXVII-6. HAIR TEXTURE BY COUNTY SUBGROUPS

	Coarse No.	%	Medium No.	%	Fine No.	%	Total
Donegal	9	4.1	157	71.6	53	24.2	219
Leitrim	4	5.8	52	76.4	12	17.6	68
Sligo	5	5.8	68	80.0	12	14.1	85
Mayo	7	1.9	253	70.4	99	27.5	359
Galway	15	4.3	245	71.8	81	23.7	341
Clare	20	4.0	305	61.2	172	34.5	497
Kerry	6	2.0	198	69.2	82	28.6	286
Females Total ...	66	3.6	1287	69.4	511	27.5	1855
Males Total.....	415	4.6	8242	92.5	249	2.8	8906

TABLE XXVII-7. HAIR QUANTITY, HEAD, BY COUNTY SUBGROUPS

	Submedium No.	%	Medium No.	%	Pronounced No.	%	Total
Donegal	1	.4	201	91.7	17	7.7	219
Leitrim	2	2.9	59	86.7	7	10.2	68
Sligo	2	2.3	78	91.7	5	5.8	85
Mayo	6	1.6	312	86.9	41	11.4	359
Galway	6	1.7	295	86.5	40	11.7	341
Clare	9	1.8	409	82.1	79	15.8	497
Kerry	2	.6	251	87.7	33	11.5	286
Females Total ...	28	1.5	1555	83.8	222	12.0	1856
Males Total.....	208	2.3	8468	95.1	229	2.6	8905

TABLE XXVII-8. HAIR QUANTITY, BODY, BY COUNTY SUBGROUPS

	No.	%	Submedium No.	%	Medium No.	%	Pronounced No.	%	Total
Donegal			201	91.7	18	8.2			219
Leitrim			54	79.4	14	20.5			68
Sligo	1	1.1	80	94.1	4	4.7			85
Mayo	1	.2	345	96.1	13	3.6			359
Galway			333	97.6	8	2.3			341
Clare	5	1.0	487	97.7	5	1.0			497
Kerry	5	1.7	276	91.5	5	1.7			286
Females Total ...	12	.6	1776	95.7	67	3.6			1855
Males Total.....	33	.4	528	5.9	8112	91.1	234	2.6	8907

TABLE XXVII-9. GRAYNESS, HEAD, BY COUNTY SUBGROUPS

	Absent No.	%	Submedium No.	%	Medium No.	%	Pronounced No.	%	Total
Donegal	136	62.1	33	15.0	29	13.2	19	8.6	217
Leitrim	48	70.5	10	14.7	5	7.3	5	7.3	68
Sligo	56	65.8	15	17.6	6	7.0	8	9.4	85
Mayo	232	64.6	47	13.0	39	10.8	31	8.6	349
Galway	220	64.5	52	15.2	36	10.5	25	7.3	333
Clare	357	71.6	50	10.0	53	10.6	25	5.0	485
Kerry	159	55.5	59	20.6	38	13.2	27	9.4	283
Females Total ...	1208	66.4	266	14.6	206	11.3	115	6.3	1820
Males Total.....	4813	54.0	1934	21.7	1200	13.5	959	10.8	8906

TABLE XXVII-10. HAIR COLOR, HEAD, BY COUNTY SUBGROUPS

	Black No.	%	Dark brown No.	%	Brown No.	%	Red-brown No.	%	Golden-brown No.	%	Ash-brown No.	%
Donegal	9	4.1	128	58.4	42	19.1	18	8.2	3	1.3	2	.9
Leitrim	7	10.2	40	58.8	12	17.6	3	4.4	2	2.9	-	-
Sligo	1	1.1	56	65.8	18	21.1	6	7.0	-	-	1	1.1
Mayo	12	3.3	190	52.9	77	21.4	27	7.5	20	5.5	2	.5
Galway	12	3.5	107	48.9	77	22.5	24	7.0	28	8.2	6	1.7
Clare	19	3.8	225	45.1	124	24.8	44	8.8	32	6.4	9	1.8
Kerry	16	5.5	152	53.1	56	19.5	15	5.2	21	7.3	5	1.7
Females Total ...	76	4.1	958	51.6	406	21.9	137	7.4	106	5.7	25	1.3
Males Total.....	246	2.8	3536	39.8	3082	34.7	469	5.3	793	8.9	42	.5

TABLE XXVII-10. HAIR COLOR,,HEAD, BY COUNTY SUBGROUPS (Continued)

	Golden No.	%	Ash No.	%	Red No.	%	White No.	%	Total
Donegal	5	2.2	-	-	5	¹2.2	7	3.1	219
Leitrim	-	-	-	-	1	1.4	3	4.4	68
Sligo	-	-	-	-	1	1.1	2	2.3	85
Mayo	1	.2	1	.2	15	4.1	14	3.8	359
Galway	2	.5	13	3.8	12	3.5	-	-	341
Clare	7	1.4	1	.2	25	5.0	11	2.2	497
Kerry	2	.6	-	-	8	2.7	11	3.8	286
Females Total ...	17	.9	15	.8	67	3.6	48	2.6	1855
Males Total	81	.9	12	.1	370	4.2	257	2.9	8889

TABLE XXVII-11. EYE COLOR BY COUNTY SUBGROUPS

	Dark brown No.	%	Dark-light brown No.	%	Light brown No.	%	Gray-brown No.	%	Green-brown No.	%
Donegal	7	3.1	7	3.1	1	.4	63	28.7	9	4.1
Leitrim	2	2.9	3	4.4	2	2.9	23	33.8	1	1.4
Sligo	2	2.3	2	2.3	2	2.3	35	41.1	1	1.1
Mayo	13	3.6	6	1.6	1	.2	114	31.7	23	6.4
Galway	16	4.6	4	1.1	4	1.1	88	25.8	26	7.6
Clare	9	1.8	10	2.0	1	.2	122	24.4	78	15.6
Kerry	7	2.4	7	2.4	2	.6	61	21.3	25	8.7
Females Total ...	56	3.0	39	2.1	13	.7	506	27.3	163	8.8
Males Total	41	.5*					441	5.0	299	3.4

*dark brown, dark-light brown and light brown.

TABLE XXVII-11. EYE COLOR BY COUNTY SUBGROUPS (Continued)

	Blue-brown No.	%	Gray No.	%	Gray-blue No.	%	Blue No.	%	Unmatched No.	%	Total
Donegal	49	22.3	3	1.3	47	21.4	33	15.0			219
Leitrim	15	22.0	-	-	10	14.7	12	17.6			68
Sligo	16	18.8	1	1.1	11	12.9	15	17.6			85
Mayo	52	14.4	16	4.4	77	21.4	57	15.8			359
Galway	93	27.2	4	1.1	58	17.0	48	14.0			341
Clare	140	28.1	4	.8	106	21.2	28	5.6			498
Kerry	77	26.9	4	1.3	42	14.6	60	20.9	1	.3	286
Females Total ...	442	23.9	32	1.7	351	18.9	253	13.6	1	.05	1856
Males Total	3913	43.9	397	4.4*			3774	42.4	44	.5	8909

*gray and gray-blue.

TABLE XXVII-12. PIGMENT, MIXED EYES, BY COUNTY SUBGROUPS

	Very pro. dark No.	%	Pronouncedly dark No.	%	Even No.	%	Pronouncedly light No.	%	Very pro. light No.	%	Total
Donegal	-	-	12	5.4	12	5.4	40	18.2	154	70.3	218
Leitrim	-	-	6	8.8	5	7.3	14	20.5	43	63.2	68
Sligo	1	1.1	5	5.8	2	2.3	19	22.3	58	68.2	85
Mayo	5	1.3	17	4.7	17	4.7	104	28.9	215	59.8	358
Galway	10	2.9	13	3.8	11	3.2	87	25.5	220	64.5	341
Clare	7	1.4	18	3.6	28	5.6	220	44.1	224	44.9	497
Kerry	2	.6	12	4.1	14	4.8	75	26.2	182	63.6	285
Females Total ...	25	1.3	83	4.5	89	4.8	559	30.2	1096	59.2	1852
Males Total	159	3.2	361	7.2	620	12.4	895	17.9	2962	59.3	4997

TABLE XXVII-13. IRIS BY COUNTY SUBGROUPS

	Clear		Rayed		Zoned		Spotted		Diffuse		Scalloped		Total
	No.	%	No.	%	No.	%	No.	%	No.	%	No.	%	
Donegal	16	7.3	78	35.6	29	13.2	22	10.0	11	5.0	63	28.7	219
Leitrim	5	7.3	19	27.9	11	16.1	12	17.6	4	5.8	17	25.0	68
Sligo	4	4.7	26	30.5	15	17.6	10	11.7	3	3.5	27	31.7	85
Mayo	37	10.3	110	30.6	67	18.6	27	7.5	23	6.4	95	26.4	359
Galway	47	13.7	116	34.0	68	19.9	30	8.7	19	5.5	61	17.8	341
Clare	35	7.0	158	31.7	78	15.6	54	10.8	91	18.2	82	16.4	498
Kerry	20	6.9	143	50.0	36	12.5	13	4.5	35	12.2	38	13.2	285
Females Total ...	164	8.8	650	35.0	304	16.4	168	9.1	186	10.0	383	20.6	1855
Males Total	1975	22.3	1950	22.0	149	1.7	248	2.8	2885	32.6	1655	18.7	8862

TABLE XXVII-14. EYEFOLDS, EXTERNAL, BY COUNTY SUBGROUPS

	Absent		Submedium		Medium		Pronounced		Total
	No.	%	No.	%	No.	%	No.	%	
Donegal	209	95.4	5	2.2	5	2.2	-	-	219
Leitrim	67	98.5	1	1.4	-	-	-	-	68
Sligo	83	97.6	2	2.3	-	-	-	-	85
Mayo	340	94.7	11	3.0	8	2.2	-	-	359
Galway	325	95.3	5	1.4	9	2.6	2	.5	341
Clare	478	95.9	10	2.0	2	2.0	-	-	498
Kerry	272	95.1	10	3.4	4	1.3	-	-	286
Females Total ...	1774	95.6	44	2.4	28	1.5	2	.2	1856
Males Total.	7722	86.7	576	6.5	504	5.6	106	1.2	8908

TABLE XXVII-15. EYEFOLDS, MEDIAN, BY COUNTY SUBGROUPS

	Absent		Submedium		Medium		Pronounced		Total
	No.	%	No.	%	No.	%	No.	%	
Donegal	190	86.7	16	7.3	11	5.0	2	.9	219
Leitrim	64	94.1	3	4.4	1	1.4	-	-	68
Sligo	71	83.5	11	12.9	3	3.5	-	-	85
Mayo	312	86.9	33	9.1	14	3.8	14	3.8	359
Galway	293	85.9	20	5.8	21	6.1	7	2.0	341
Clare	439	88.1	32	6.4	24	4.8	3	.6	498
Kerry	244	85.3	23	8.0	17	5.9	2	.6	286
Females Total ...	1613	86.9	138	7.4	91	4.9	14	.8	1856
Males Total	8644	97.0	95	1.1	118	1.3	50	.6	8907

TABLE XXVII-16. EYEFOLDS, INTERNAL, BY COUNTY SUBGROUPS

	Absent		Submedium		Medium		Pronounced		Total
	No.	%	No.	%	No.	%	No.	%	
Donegal	216	98.6	3	1.3	-	-	-	-	219
Leitrim	67	98.5	1	1.4	-	-	-	-	68
Sligo	85	100.0	-	-	-	-	-	-	85
Mayo	355	98.8	3	.8	-	-	-	-	358
Galway	335	98.2	3	.8	3	.8	-	-	341
Clare	491	98.5	6	1.2	1	.2	-	-	498
Kerry	285	99.6	1	.3	-	-	-	-	286
Females Total ...	1834	98.9	17	.9	4	.2	-	-	1855
Males Total	8819	99.0	75	.8	11	.1*			8905

*Medium and Pronounced

TABLE XXVII-17. EYE OBLIQUITY BY COUNTY SUBGROUPS

	Absent		Submedium		Medium		Pronounced		Down		Total
	No.	%	No.	%	No.	%	No.	%	No.	%	
Donegal	31	14.1	122	55.7	63	28.7	2	.9	1	.4	219
Leitrim	11	16.1	44	64.7	13	19.1	-	-	-	-	68
Sligo	10	11.7	56	65.8	17	20.0	-	-	2	2.3	85
Mayo	38	10.5	252	70.1	59	16.4	1	.2	9	2.5	359
Galway	40	11.7	189	55.4	97	28.4	2	.5	13	3.8	341
Clare	38	7.6	211	42.3	229	45.9	4	.8	16	3.2	498
Kerry	10	3.4	188	65.7	85	29.7	-	-	3	1.0	286
Females Total ...	178	9.6	1062	57.2	563	30.3	9	.5	41	2.2	1856
Males Total	5738	64.4	2173	24.4	421	4.7	57	.6	520	5.8	8909

TABLE XXVII-18. EYE OPENING HEIGHT BY COUNTY SUBGROUPS

	Submedium No.	%	Medium No.	%	Pronounced No.	%	Total
Donegal	4	1.8	210	95.8	5	2.2	219
Leitrim	-	-	64	94.1	4	5.8	68
Sligo	1	1.1	81	95.2	3	3.5	85
Mayo	14	3.8	338	94.1	7	1.9	359
Galway	11	3.2	325	95.3	5	1.4	341
Clare	7	1.4	476	95.5	15	3.0	498
Kerry	8	2.7	271	94.7	7	2.4	286
Females Total . . .	45	2.4	1765	95.1	46	2.5	1856
Males Total.	533	6.0	8103	91.0	265	3.0	8901

TABLE XXVII-19. EYEBROW THICKNESS BY COUNTY SUBGROUPS

	Submedium No.	%	Medium No.	%	Pronounced No.	%	Very pronounced No.	%	Total
Donegal	1	.4	139	63.4	79	36.0	-	-	219
Leitrim	1	1.4	54	79.4	13	19.1	-	-	68
Sligo	1	1.1	60	70.5	24	28.2	-	-	85
Mayo	6	1.6	190	52.9	153	42.6	10	2.7	359
Galway	4	1.1	146	42.8	178	52.1	12	3.5	340
Clare	9	1.8	297	59.6	178	35.7	14	2.8	498
Kerry	3	1.0	148	51.7	135	47.2	-	-	286
Females Total . . .	25	1.3	1034	55.7	760	41.0	36	1.9	1855
Males Total.	287	3.2	8296	93.1	325	3.6*			8908

*(Pronounced and Very pronounced)

TABLE XXVII-20. EYEBROW CONCURRENCY BY COUNTY SUBGROUPS

	Absent No.	%	Submedium No.	%	Medium No.	%	Pronounced No.	%	Total
Donegal	48	21.9	163	74.4	8	3.6			219
Leitrim	24	35.2	41	60.7	3	4.4			68
Sligo	20	23.5	60	70.5	4	4.7	1	1.1	85
Mayo	79	22.0	243	67.6	33	9.1	3	.8	358
Galway	39	11.4	253	74.1	48	14.0	1	.2	341
Clare	41	8.2	368	73.8	76	15.2	12	2.4	497
Kerry	32	11.1	235	82.1	18	6.2	1	.3	286
Females Total . . .	283	15.3	1363	73.5	190	10.2	18	1.0	1854
Males Total.	156	1.8	2069	23.2	5767	64.7	916	10.3	8908

TABLE XXVII-21. BROW RIDGES BY COUNTY SUBGROUPS

	Absent No.	%	Submedium No.	%	Medium No.	%	Pronounced No.	%	Very pro. No.	%	Total
Donegal	36	16.4	89	40.6	86	39.2	8	3.6			219
Leitrim	12	17.6	43	63.2	12	17.6	1	1.4			68
Sligo	14	16.4	38	44.7	31	36.4	2	2.3			85
Mayo	81	22.5	181	50.4	90	25.0	7	1.9			359
Galway	95	27.8	147	43.1	88	25.8	11	3.2			341
Clare	215	43.1	169	33.9	105	21.0	9	1.8			498
Kerry	51	17.8	155	54.1	74	25.8	6	2.0			286
Females Total . . .	504	28.6	822	44.3	486	26.2	44	2.4			1856
Males Total.	195	2.2	1725	19.4	5135	57.6	1818	20.4	34	.4	8907

TABLE XXVII-22. FOREHEAD HEIGHT BY COUNTY SUBGROUPS

	Submedium No.	%	Medium No.	%	Pronounced No.	%	Total No.
Donegal	9	4.1	186	84.9	24	10.9	219
Leitrim	5	7.3	52	76.4	11	16.1	68
Sligo	1	1.1	75	88.2	9	10.5	85
Mayo . . . :	22	6.1	309	86.0	28	7.7	359
Galway	35	10.2	286	83.8	19	5.5	340
Clare	31	6.2	404	81.1	62	12.4	497
Kerry	15	5.2	242	84.6	29	10.1	313
Females-Total	118	6.4	1554	83.8	182	9.8	1854
Males-Total . .	333	3.7	3786	42.5	4783	53.7	8902

TABLE XXVII-23. FOREHEAD SLOPE BY COUNTY SUBGROUPS

	Forward No.	Forward %	Absent No.	Absent %	Submedium No.	Submedium %	Medium No.	Medium %	Pronounced No.	Pronounced %	Very pro. No.	Very pro. %	Total
Donegal	4	1.8	82	37.4	74	33.7	53	24.2	6	2.7			219
Leitrim	1	1.4	23	33.8	26	38.2	17	25.0	1	1.4			68
Sligo........	1	1.1	23	27.0	36	42.3	22	25.8	3	3.5			85
Mayo	9	2.5	98	27.2	153	42.6	98	27.2	1	.2			359
Galway	4	1.1	97	28.4	141	41.3	92	26.9	7	2.0			341
Clare	11	2.2	191	38.3	163	32.7	122	24.4	11	2.2			498
Kerry	3	1.0	48	16.7	101	35.3	125	43.7	8	2.7	1	.3	286
Females-Total	33	1.7	562	30.3	694	37.4	529	28.5	37	2.0	1	.05	1856
Males-Total..	106	1.2	587	6.6	4048	45.4	3503	39.3	642	7.2	22	.2	8908

TABLE XXVII-24. NASION DEPRESSION BY COUNTY SUBGROUPS

	Absent No.	Absent %	Very small No.	Very small %	Submedium No.	Submedium %	Medium No.	Medium %	Pronounced No.	Pronounced %	Very pro. No.	Very pro. %	Total
Donegal	11	5.0	138	63.0	46	21.0	24	10.9	-	-			219
Leitrim	5	7.3	47	69.1	15	22.0	1	1.4	-	-			68
Sligo......	6	7.0	56	65.8	19	27.3	4	4.7	-	-			85
Mayo......	19	5.2	230	64.0	79	22.0	26	7.2	3	.8			357
Galway	31	9.0	221	64.8	49	14.3	39	11.4	1	.2			341
Clare	140	28.1	243	48.7	75	15.0	36	7.2	4	.8			498
Kerry	21	7.3	185	64.6	52	18.1	24	8.3	4	1.3			286
Females-Total	197	10.6	1120	60.4	335	18.1	154	8.3	12	.6			1854
Males-Total .	20	.2	133	1.5	1181	13.2	5413	60.8	2041	22.9	119	1.3	8907

TABLE XXVII-25. NASAL ROOT HEIGHT BY COUNTY SUBGROUPS

	Very small No.	Very small %	Submedium No.	Submedium %	Medium No.	Medium %	Pronounced No.	Pronounced %	Very pro. No.	Very pro. %	Total
Donegal.....	2	.4	27	12.3	157	71.6	34	15.5	-	-	219
Leitrim.....			4	5.8	46	67.6	18	26.4	-	-	68
Sligo.......	1	1.1	5	5.8	65	76.4	13	15.2	1	1.1	85
Mayo	3	.8	59	16.4	264	73.5	33	9.1	-	-	359
Galway	3	.8	53	15.5	237	69.5	47	13.7	1	.2	341
Clare	1	.2	93	18.6	335	67.2	67	13.4	2	.4	498
Kerry	1	.3	39	13.6	193	67.4	53	18.5	-	-	286
Females-Total	10	.5	280	13.7	1297	69.9	265	14.3	4	.2	1856
Males-Total	268	3.0*			6877	77.2	1685	18.9	74	.8	8904

*(Very small and Submedium)

TABLE XXVII-26. NASAL ROOT BREADTH BY COUNTY SUBGROUPS

	Very small No.	Very small %	Submedium No.	Submedium %	Medium No.	Medium %	Pronounced No.	Pronounced %	Very pro. No.	Very pro. %	Total
Donegal	1	.4	5	2.2	167	76.2	41	18.7	4	1.8	218
Leitrim			3	4.4	52	76.4	13	19.1	-	-	68
Sligo........			8	9.4	55	64.7	21	24.7	1	1.1	85
Mayo.......			9	2.5	263	73.2	85	23.6	2	.5	359
Galway			12	3.5	256	75.0	71	20.8	2	.5	341
Clare			14	2.8	366	73.4	114	22.8	4	.8	498
Kerry	1	.3	8	2.7	237	82.8	38	13.2	2	.6	286
Females-Total	2	.1	59	3.2	1396	75.3	383	20.6	15	.8	1855
Males-Total..	179	2.0*			6437	72.3	2212	24.8	75	.8	8903

*(Very small and Submedium)

TABLE XXVII-27. NASAL BRIDGE HEIGHT BY COUNTY SUBGROUPS

	Submedium No.	Submedium %	Medium No.	Medium %	Pronounced No.	Pronounced %	Very pro. Very small No.	Very pro. Very small %	Total
Donegal	33	15.0	170	77.6	16	7.3			219
Leitrim	1	1.4	53	77.9	14	20.5			68
Sligo......	10	11.7	66	77.6	9	10.5			85
Mayo........	51	14.2	281	78.2	27	7.5			359
Galway	40	11.7	256	75.0	44	12.9	1	.2	341
Clare	61	12.2	380	76.3	56	11.2	1	.2	498
Kerry	29	10.1	215	75.1	40	13.9	2	.6	286
Females-Total	225	12.1	1421	76.6	206	11.1	4	.2	1856
Males-Total	279	3.1*	6788	76.2	1720	19.3	115	1.3	8902

*(Very small and Submedium)

TABLE XXVII-28. NASAL BRIDGE BREADTH BY COUNTY SUBGROUPS

	Submedium		Medium		Pronounced		Very pro. Very small		Total
	No.	%	No.	%	No.	%	No.	%	
Donegal	7	3.1	186	84.9	25	11.4	1	.4	219
Leitrim	6	8.8	59	86.7	3	4.4	-	-	68
Sligo	5	5.8	72	84.7	8	9.4	-	-	85
Mayo	6	1.6	297	82.7	55	15.3	1	.2	359
Galway	11	3.2	281	82.4	47	13.7	1	.2	340
Clare......	11	2.2	410	82.3	77	15.4	-	-	498
Kerry......	11	3.8	246	86.0	28	9.7	1	.3	286
Females-Total	57	3.1	1552	83.1	243	13.1	4	.2	1855
Males-Total .	74	.8	6955	78.2	1831	20.6	39	.4	8899

TABLE XXVII-29. NASAL SEPTUM BY COUNTY SUBGROUPS

	Straight, concave		Convex		Total
	No.	%	No.	%	
Donegal	184	84.0	34	15.5	218
Leitrim	60	88.2	7	10.2	67
Sligo	70	82.3	15	17.6	85
Mayo.......	293	81.6	66	18.3	359
Galway	264	77.4	75	21.9	339
Clare.......	316	63.4	177	35.5	493
Kerry	241	84.2	43	15.0	284
Females-Total	1428	77.4	417	22.6	1845
Males-Total ..	3397	38.3	5469	61.7	8866

TABLE XXVII-30. NASAL TIP, THICKNESS, BY COUNTY SUBGROUPS

	Submedium		Medium		Pronounced		Very pro., Very small		Total
	No.	%	No.	%	No.	%	No.	%	
Donegal	7	3.1	172	78.5	39	17.8	1	.4	219
Leitrim	4	5.8	55	80.8	9	13.2	-	-	68
Sligo.......	2	2.3	71	83.5	11	12.9	1	1.1	85
Mayo	8	2.2	275	76.6	75	20.8	1	.2	359
Galway	15	4.3	285	83.5	41	12.0	-	-	341
Clare	29	5.8	384	77.1	85	17.0	-	-	498
Kerry	9	3.1	229	80.0	45	15.7	2	.6	285
Females-Total	74	4.0	1471	79.3	305	16.4	5	.3	1855
Males-Total .	151	1.7	6512	73.1	2203	24.7	37	.4	8903

TABLE XXVII-31. NASAL TIP, INCLINATION, BY COUNTY SUBGROUPS

	Up, medium		Up, submedium		Horizontal		Down, submedium		Down, medium		Total
	No.	%	No.	%	No.	%	No.	%	No.	%	
Donegal	19	8.6	175	79.9	13	5.9	11	5.0	-	-	218
Leitrim	4	5.8	56	82.3	7	10.2	1	1.4	-	-	68
Sligo	2	2.3	75	88.2	7	8.2	1	1.1	-	-	85
Mayo.......	16	4.4	304	84.6	32	8.9	6	1.6	1	.2	359
Galway	17	4.9	221	64.8	85	24.9	16	4.6	-	-	339
Clare	88	17.6	310	62.2	85	17.0	15	3.0	-	-	498
Kerry	8	2.7	240	83.9	27	9.4	10	3.4	-	-	285
Females-Total	154	8.3	1381	74.6	256	14.3	60	3.2	1	.05	1852
Males-Total ..	1012	11.4	7348	82.6	381	4.3	119	1.3	35	.4	8895

TABLE XXVII-32. NASAL WINGS BY COUNTY SUBGROUPS

	Compressed		Medium		Flaring		Total
	No.	%	No.	%	No.	%	No.
Donegal	6	2.7	212	96.8	1	.4	219
Leitrim	2	2.9	66	97.0	-	-	68
Sligo	4	4.7	80	94.1	1	1.1	85
Mayo.......	9	2.5	344	95.8	6	1.6	359
Galway	12	3.5	320	93.8	9	2.6	341
Clare	22	4.4	467	93.7	9	1.8	498
Kerry	15	5.2	269	94.0	2	.6	286
Females-Total	69	3.8	1758	95.0	28	1.5	1856
Males-Total ..	462	5.2	7876	88.5	557	6.3	8895

TABLE XXVII-33. NOSTRIL VISIBILITY, FRONTAL, BY COUNTY SUBGROUPS

	Absent No.	%	Submedium, medium No.	%	Pronounced No.	%	Total
Donegal	9	4.1	208	94.9	2	.9	219
Leitrim	1	1.4	67	98.5	-	-	68
Sligo	-	-	85	100.0	-	-	85
Mayo	13	3.6	346	96.3	-	-	359
Galway	17	4.9	323	94.7	1	.2	341
Clare.	8	1.6	480	96.3	10	2.0	498
Kerry	10	3.4	275	96.1	1	.3	286
Females-Total	58	3.1	1784	96.1	14	.7	1856
Males-Total . .	430	4.8	8395	94.4	70	.8	8895

TABLE XXVII-34. NASAL PROFILE BY COUNTY SUBGROUPS

	Concave No.	%	Concave, snub tip No.	%	Straight No.	%	Straight, snub tip No.	%	Convex No.	%	Wavy No.	%	Total
Donegal.	17	7.7			123	56.1			77	35.1	-	-	217
Leitrim	4	5.8			39	57.3			25	36.7	-	-	68
Sligo.	5	5.8			47	55.2			33	38.8	-	-	85
Mayo	27	7.5			196	54.5			136	37.8	-	-	359
Galway	23	6.4			183	53.6			135	39.5	1	.2	341
Clare	27	5.4			274	55.0			196	39.3	-	-	497
Kerry	21	7.3			139	48.6			126	44.0	-	-	286
Female-Total.	124	6.7	-	-	1001	54.0	-	-	728	39.3	1	.05	1853
Males-Total .	595	6.7	63	.7	3916	44.0	322	3.6	3564	40.0	-	-	8897

TABLE XXVII-35. LIPS, INTEGUMENTAL THICKNESS, BY COUNTY SUBGROUPS

	Submedium No.	%	Medium No.	%	Pronounced No.	%	Total
Donegal.	12	5.4	195	89.0	12	5.4	219
Leitrim	4	5.8	61	89.7	3	4.4	68
Sligo	5	5.8	75	88.2	5	5.8	85
Mayo	14	3.8	330	91.9	15	4.1	359
Galway	18	5.2	307	90.0	16	4.6	341
Clare	36	7.2	438	87.9	23	4.6	497
Kerry	9	3.1	270	94.4	7	2.4	286
Females-Total	98	5.3	1676	90.4	81	4.4	1855
Males-Total	102	1.1	8440	94.7	367	4.1	8909

TABLE XXVII-36. UPPER LIP, MEMBRANOUS THICKNESS, BY COUNTY SUBGROUPS

	Very small No.	%	Submedium No.	%	Medium No.	%	Pronounced No.	%	Very pro. No.	%	Total
Donegal.	-	-	30	13.6	164	74.8	24	10.9	1	.4	219
Leitrim.	-	-	7	10.2	54	79.4	7	10.2	-	-	68
Sligo.	-	-	11	12.9	67	78.8	7	8.2	-	-	85
Mayo.	5	1.3	35	9.7	286	79.6	32	9.1	1	.2	359
Galway	2	.5	41	12.0	271	79.4	27	7.9	-	-	341
Clare	6	1.2	80	16.0	385	77.3	26	5.2	-	-	497
Kerry	-	-	52	18.1	215	75.1	17	5.9	2	.6	286
Females-Total .	13	.7	256	13.8	1442	77.7	140	7.5	4	.2	1855
Males-Total . . .	106	1.2	2067	23.2	6494	72.9	239	2.7	-	-	8906

TABLE XXVII-37. LIPS, EVERSION, BY COUNTY SUBGROUPS

	Submedium No.	%	Medium No.	%	Pronounced No.	%	Total
Donegal.	29	13.2	185	84.4	5	2.2	219
Leitrim	8	11.7	59	86.8	1	1.4	68
Sligo.	14	16.4	70	82.3	1	1.1	85
Mayo	38	10.5	313	87.1	8	2.2	359
Galway	35	10.2	303	88.8	3	.8	341
Clare	64	12.8	420	84.3	13	2.6	497
Kerry	51	17.8	233	81.4	2	.6	286
Females-Total	239	12.9	1583	85.3	33	1.8	1855
Males-Total. .	1968	22.1	6591	74.0	348	3.9	8907

TABLE XXVII-38. LIP SEAM BY COUNTY SUBGROUPS

	Absent No.	%	Submedium No.	%	Medium No.	%	Pronounced No.	%	Total
Donegal	200	91.3	11	5.0	8	3.6	-	-	219
Leitrim	60	88.2	7	10.2	1	1.4	-	-	68
Sligo	67	78.8	12	14.1	5	5.8	1	1.1	85
Mayo	296	82.4	42	11.6	21	5.8	-	-	359
Galway	298	87.3	25	7.3	17	4.9	-	-	340
Clare	361	72.4	89	19.8	48	9.6	-	-	498
Kerry	249	87.0	28	9.7	9	3.1	-	-	286
Females-Total	1531	82.5	214	11.5	109	5.9	1	.05	1855
Males-Total	8712	97.9	172	1.9	18	.2	-	-	8902

TABLE XXVII-39. ALVEOLAR PROGNATHISM BY COUNTY SUBGROUPS

	Absent No.	%	Submedium No.	%	Medium No.	%	Pronounced No.	%	Total
Donegal	214	97.7	2	.9	2	.9	-	-	218
Leitrim	25	95.5	1	1.4	1	1.4	1	1.4	68
Sligo	84	98.8	1	1.1	-	-	-	-	85
Mayo	345	96.1	7	1.9	4	1.1	2	.5	358
Galway	331	97.0	7	2.0	1	.2	-	-	339
Clare	483	96.9	9	1.8	6	1.2	-	-	498
Kerry	281	98.2	3	1.0	-	-	-	-	284
Females-Total	1803	97.4	30	1.6	14	.8	3	.2	1851
Males-Total	8699	97.7	121	1.4	85	1.0*			8905

*(Medium and Pronounced)

TABLE XXVII-40. MID-FACIAL PROGNATHISM BY COUNTY SUBGROUPS

	Absent No.	%	Submedium No.	%	Medium No.	%	Pronounced No.	%	Total
Donegal	196	89.4	20	9.1	2	.9	-	-	218
Leitrim	56	82.3	11	16.1	1	1.4	-	-	68
Sligo	72	84.7	13	15.2	-	-	-	-	85
Mayo	309	86.0	46	12.8	2	.5	-	-	357
Galway	281	82.4	53	15.5	6	1.7	-	-	340
Clare	397	79.7	76	15.2	24	4.8	1	.2	498
Kerry	267	93.3	18	6.2	1	.3	-	-	286
Females-Total	1578	85.2	237	12.8	36	1.9	1	.05	1852
Males-Total	8191	92.0	586	6.4	130	1.5	16	.2	8903

TABLE XXVII-41. CHIN PROMINENCE BY COUNTY SUBGROUPS

	Submedium No.	%	Medium No.	%	Pronounced No.	%	Total
Donegal	8	3.6	199	90.8	12	5.4	219
Leitrim	5	7.3	60	88.2	3	4.4	68
Sligo	4	4.7	74	87.0	7	8.2	85
Mayo	24	6.6	311	86.6	24	6.6	359
Galway	26	7.6	287	84.1	28	8.2	341
Clare	54	10.8	390	78.3	54	10.8	498
Kerry	11	3.8	249	87.0	26	9.0	286
Females-Total	132	6.6	1570	84.6	154	8.3	1856
Males-Total	974	10.9	7106	79.8	825	9.3	8905

TABLE XXVII-42. CHIN TYPE BY COUNTY SUBGROUPS

	Median No.	%	Bilateral No.	%	Total No.
Donegal	217	99.0	1	.4	218
Leitrim	68	100.0	-	-	68
Sligo	85	100.0	-	-	85
Mayo	350	97.4	9	2.5	359
Galway	334	97.9	6	1.7	~340
Clare	479	96.1	19	3.8	498
Kerry	277	96.8	9	3.1	286
Females-Total	1810	97.6	44	2.4	1854
Males-Total	305	3.4	8597	96.6	8902

TABLE XXVII-43. BITE BY COUNTY SUBGROUPS

	Under No.	Under %	Edge-to-edge No.	Edge-to-edge %	Submedium over No.	Submedium over %	Pronounced over No.	Pronounced over %	Total
Donegal	3	1.9	1	.6	140	89.7	12	7.7	156
Leitrim	-	-	-	-	49	92.5	4	7.5	53
Sligo	-	-	-	-	58	95.1	3	4.9	61
Mayo.	-	-	1	.5	240	92.3	19	7.3	260
Galway	2	.9	2	.9	219	93.6	11	4.7	234
Clare	1	.3	4	1.1	332	93.0	20	5.6	357
Kerry	2	1.1	5	2.7	171	92.9	6	3.3	184
Females-Total	8	.6	13	1.0	1209	92.6	75	5.7	1305
Males-Total . .	42	.6	28	.4	6595	96.0	207	3.0	6872

TABLE XXVII-44. TEETH, WEAR, BY COUNTY SUBGROUPS

	Absent, submedium No.	Absent, submedium %	Medium No.	Medium %	Pron., very pronounced No.	Pron., very pronounced %	Total
Donegal	136	79.1	29	16.9	7	4.1	172
Leitrim	47	78.3	12	20.0	1	1.7	60
Sligo	51	69.9	18	24.7	4	5.5	73
Mayo	214	68.8	59	19.0	38	12.2	311
Galway	180	68.0	42	15.8	43	16.2	265
Clare	240	55.9	127	22.6	62	14.5	429
Kerry	106	50.2	65	30.8	40	19.0	211
Females-Total	974	64.0	352	23.1	195	12.8	1521
Males-Total . .	5169	75.8	1335	19.6	316	4.6	6820

TABLE XXVII-45. TEETH, LOSS, BY COUNTY SUBGROUPS

	None No.	None %	Very small (1-4) No.	Very small (1-4) %	Submedium (5-8) No.	Submedium (5-8) %	Medium (9-16) No.	Medium (9-16) %	Pronounced (17-) No.	Pronounced (17-) %	Total
Donegal	16	7.3	87	39.7	29	13.2	15	6.8	72	32.8	219
Leitrim	8	11.7	29	42.6	12	17.6	-	-	19	27.9	68
Sligo	4	4.7	37	43.5	7	8.2	6	7.0	31	36.4	85
Mayo	82	22.8	100	27.8	41	11.4	23	6.4	113	31.4	359
Galway	72	21.1	89	26.0	34	9.9	25	7.3	121	35.4	341
Clare	62	12.4	172	34.5	61	12.2	56	11.2	147	29.5	498
Kerry	14	4.8	78	27.3	34	11.8	19	6.6	141	49.3	286
Females-Total	258	13.9	592	31.9	218	11.7	144	7.8	644	34.7	1856
Males-Total . .	710	8.0	3536	39.7	1871	21.0	627	7.0	2159	24.2	8903

TABLE XXVII-46. TEETH, CARIES, BY COUNTY SUBGROUPS

	Absent No.	Absent %	Very small No.	Very small %	Submedium No.	Submedium %	Medium No.	Medium %	Pronounced No.	Pronounced %	Total
Donegal	30	19.1	70	44.6	50	34.0	7	4.4	-	-	157
Leitrim	4	7.4	24	44.4	20	37.0	6	11.1	-	-	54
Sligo	5	8.2	34	55.7	19	31.1	3	4.9	-	-	61
Mayo	101	38.1	109	41.1	44	16.6	10	3.8	1	.4	265
Galway	65	26.3	92	37.2	63	25.5	23	9.3	4	1.6	247
Clare	31	7.0	156	35.4	106	24.0	71	16.1	76	17.3	440
Kerry	26	13.9	67	35.8	63	33.7	21	11.2	10	5.3	187
Females-Total	262	18.5	552	39.1	365	25.8	141	10.0	100	7.1	1411
Males-Total . .	58	.8	610	8.9	3778	55.1	1640	23.9	771	11.2	6857

TABLE XXVII-47. FACE SHORTENING BY COUNTY SUBGROUPS

	Absent No.	Absent %	Submedium No.	Submedium %	Medium No.	Medium %	Pronounced No.	Pronounced %	Total
Donegal	142	64.8	10	4.5	48	21.9	19	8.6	219
Leitrim	49	72.0	13	19.1	5	7.3	1	1.4	68
Sligo	55	64.7	8	9.4	14	16.4	8	9.4	85
Mayo	235	65.4	43	11.9	57	15.8	24	6.6	359
Galway	217	63.6	31	9.0	61	17.8	31	9.0	340
Clare	319	64.0	66	13.2	77	15.4	36	7.2	498
Kerry	142	49.6	9	3.1	78	27.3	56	19.5	285
Females-Total	1159	62.5	180	9.7	340	18.3	175	9.4	1854
Males-Total . .	6499	73.3	719	8.1	1159	13.0	495	5.6	8871

TABLE XXVII-48. TEETH, CROWDING, BY COUNTY SUBGROUPS

	Absent No.	%	Medium No.	%	Pronounced No.	%	Total
Donegal	155	84.6	27	14.7	1	.5	183
Leitrim	55	87.3	8	12.7	-	-	63
Sligo	62	86.1	10	13.9	-	-	72
Mayo	267	91.1	26	8.8	-	-	293
Galway	224	88.2	29	11.4	1	.4	254
Clare	325	78.7	80	19.4	8	1.9	413
Kerry	204	93.1	14	6.4	1	.5	219
Females-Total	1292	86.3	194	12.9	11	.7	1497
Males-Total ..	2922	42.6	3542	51.6	395	5.8	6859

TABLE XXVII-49. MALARS, FRONTAL PROJECTION, BY COUNTY SUBGROUPS

	Absent, submedium No.	%	Medium No.	%	Pronounced No.	%	Total
Donegal	5	2.2	137	62.5	77	35.1	219
Leitrim	6	8.8	47	69.1	15	22.0	68
Sligo	5	5.8	43	50.5	37	43.5	85
Mayo	18	5.0	194	54.0	147	40.9	359
Galway	13	3.8	207	60.7	121	35.4	341
Clare	21	4.2	326	65.4	151	30.3	498
Kerry	13	4.5	168	58.7	105	36.7	286
Females-Total	81	4.4	1122	60.4	653	35.2	1856
Males-Total ..	47	.5	7387	82.9	1473	16.5	8907

TABLE XXVII-50. MALARS, LATERAL PROJECTION, BY COUNTY SUBGROUPS

	Absent No.	%	Submedium No.	%	Medium No.	%	Pronounced No.	%	Very pro. No.	%	Total
Donegal	-	-	15	6.8	118	53.8	84	38.3	2	.9	219
Leitrim	-	-	11	16.1	38	55.8	19	27.9	-	-	68
Sligo	-	-	11	12.9	39	45.8	35	41.1	-	-	85
Mayo	-	-	22	6.1	146	40.6	176	49.0	12	3.3	356
Galway	-	-	15	4.3	182	53.3	143	41.9	1	.2	341
Clare	2	.4	19	3.8	311	62.4	162	32.5	3	.6	497
Kerry	-	-	11	3.8	135	47.2	134	46.8	6	2.0	286
Females-Total	2	.1	104	5.6	969	52.3	753	40.6	24	1.3	1852
Males-Total ..	35	.4*			5778	64.9	2918	32.8	173	1.9	8904

*(Absent and Submedium)

TABLE XXVII-51. GONIAL ANGLES BY COUNTY SUBGROUPS

	Submedium No.	%	Medium No.	%	Pronounced No.	%	Very pro. No.	%	Total
Donegal	6	2.7	198	90.4	15	6.8	-	-	219
Leitrim	2	2.9	64	94.1	2	2.9	-	-	68
Sligo	1	1.1	80	94.1	4	4.7	-	-	85
Mayo	5	1.3	318	88.5	35	9.7	-	-	358
Galway	3	.8	294	86.2	43	12.6	-	-	340
Clare	4	.8	428	85.9	65	13.0	-	-	497
Kerry	4	1.3	265	92.6	17	5.9	-	-	286
Females-Total	25	1.3	1647	88.9	181	9.7	-	-	1853
Males-Total ..	247	2.8	5742	64.5	2773	31.1	145	1.6	8907

TABLE XXVII-52. EAR HELIX BY COUNTY SUBGROUPS

	Very small No.	%	Submedium No.	%	Medium No.	%	Pronounced No.	%	Total
Donegal	9	4.1	78	35.6	124	56.6	8	3.6	219
Leitrim	2	2.9	27	39.7	33	48.5	6	8.8	68
Sligo	1	1.1	33	38.8	39	45.8	11	12.9	84
Mayo	15	4.1	109	30.3	196	54.5	39	10.8	359
Galway	19	5.5	104	30.4	178	52.1	39	11.4	340
Clare	18	3.6	137	27.5	276	55.4	66	13.2	497
Kerry	8	2.7	99	34.6	147	51.3	31	10.8	285
Females-Total	72	3.9	587	31.7	993	53.6	200	10.8	1852
Males-Total ..	49	.6	1987	22.3	6507	73.0	366	4.1	8909

TABLE XXVII-53. EAR ANTIHELIX BY COUNTY SUBGROUPS

	Absent No.	%	Submedium No.	%	Medium No.	%	Pronounced No.	%	Total
Donegal	4	1.8	41	18.7	170	77.6	4	1.8	219
Leitrim	1	1.4	14	20.5	51	75.0	2	2.9	68
Sligo	-	-	17	20.0	63	74.1	5	5.8	85
Mayo	7	1.9	74	20.6	266	74.0	12	3.3	359
Galway	4	1.1	95	27.8	234	68.6	7	2.0	340
Clare	5	1.0	95	19.0	367	73.6	31	6.2	498
Kerry	5	1.7	62	21.6	192	67.1	25	8.7	284
Females-Total	26	1.4	398	21.5	1343	72.5	86	4.6	1853
Males-Total	16	.2	416	4.7	7336	82.4	1137	12.8	8905

TABLE XXVII-54. DARWIN'S POINT BY COUNTY SUBGROUPS

	Absent No.	%	Submedium No.	%	Medium No.	%	Pronounced No.	%	Total
Donegal	210	95.8	9	4.1	-	-	-	-	219
Leitrim	65	95.5	3	4.4	-	-	-	-	68
Sligo	81	95.2	1	1.1	-	-	-	-	85
Mayo	349	97.2	9	2.5	1	.2	-	-	359
Galway	332	97.3	8	2.3	1	.2	-	-	341
Clare	462	92.7	26	5.2	9	1.8	1	.2	498
Kerry	276	96.5	9	3.1	1	.3	-	-	286
Females-Total	1775	95.6	67	3.6	13	.7	1	.05	1856
Males-Total	6611	74.3	2021	22.7	247	2.8	18	.2	8897

TABLE XXVII-55. EAR LOBE BY COUNTY SUBGROUPS

	Soldered No.	%	Attached No.	%	Free No.	%	Total
Donegal	9	4.1	99	45.2	111	50.6	219
Leitrim	2	2.9	37	54.4	29	42.6	68
Sligo	1	1.1	37	43.5	47	55.2	85
Mayo	15	4.1	180	50.1	164	45.6	359
Galway	15	4.3	187	54.8	138	40.4	340
Clare	32	6.4	340	68.2	126	25.3	498
Kerry	17	5.9	125	43.7	144	50.3	286
Females-Total	91	4.9	1005	54.2	759	40.9	1855
Males-Total	127	1.4	3599	40.4	5181	58.2	8907

TABLE XXVII-56. EAR LOBE SIZE BY COUNTY SUBGROUPS

	Absent No.	%	Submedium No.	%	Medium No.	%	Pronounced No.	%	Total
Donegal	4	1.8	48	21.9	167	76.2	-	-	219
Leitrim	1	1.4	19	27.9	46	67.6	2	2.9	68
Sligo	1	1.1	21	24.7	62	72.9	1	1.1	85
Mayo	11	3.0	109	30.3	232	64.6	7	1.9	359
Galway	15	4.3	88	25.8	231	67.7	7	2.0	341
Clare	30	6.0	155	31.1	287	57.6	26	5.2	498
Kerry	3	1.0	65	22.7	212	74.1	6	2.0	286
Females-Total	65	3.5	505	27.2	1237	66.6	49	2.6	1856
Males-Total	42	.5*			4834	54.3	4031	45.2	8907

*(Absent and Submedium)

TABLE XXVII-57. EAR PROTRUSION BY COUNTY SUBGROUPS

	Submedium No.	%	Medium No.	%	Pronounced No.	%	Total
Donegal	11	5.0	185	84.4	22	10.0	218
Leitrim	5	7.3	57	83.8	6	8.8	68
Sligo	5	5.8	73	85.8	7	8.2	85
Mayo	20	5.5	309	86.0	29	8.0	358
Galway	20	5.8	281	82.4	40	11.7	341
Clare	19	3.8	440	88.3	39	9.6	498
Kerry	20	6.9	235	82.1	31	10.8	286
Females-Total	100	5.4	1580	85.2	174	9.4	1854
Males-Total	60	.7	6896	77.4	1948	21.9	8904

TABLE XXVII-58.   TEMPORAL FULLNESS BY COUNTY SUBGROUPS

	Submedium		Medium		Pronounced		Total
	No.	%	No.	%	No.	%	
Donegal	14	6.3	183	83.5	22	10.0	219
Leitrim	5	7.3	60	88.2	3	4.4	68
Sligo	5	5.8	75	88.2	5	5.8	85
Mayo	16	4.4	319	88.8	24	6.6	359
Galway	42	12.3	288	84.4	11	3.2	341
Clare	75	15.0	383	76.9	40	8.0	498
Kerry	13	4.5	262	91.6	11	3.8	286
Females-Total	170	9.2	1570	84.6	116	6.3	1856
Males-Total . .	1406	15.8	5431	61.0	2070	23.2	8907

TABLE XXVII-59.   OCCIPITAL PROTRUSION BY COUNTY SUBGROUPS

	Absent		Submedium		Medium		Pronounced		Total
	No.	%	No.	%	No.	%	No.	%	
Donegal	1	.4	14	6.3	182	83.1	22	10.0	219
Leitrim	-	-	5	7.3	60	88.2	3	4.4	68
Sligo	-	-	7	8.2	73	85.8	5	5.8	85
Mayo	3	.8	44	12.7	286	79.6	25	6.9	358
Galway	-	-	19	5.5	292	85.6	30	8.7	341
Clare	4	.8	76	15.2	405	81.3	13	2.6	498 ·
Kerry	-	-	19	6.6	247	86.3	20	6.9	286
Females-Total	8	.4	184	9.9	1545	83.2	118	6.4	1856
Males-Total . .	713	8.0*			6622	74.4	1571	17.6	8906

*Absent and Submedium

TABLE XXVII-60.   LAMBDOID FLATTENING BY COUNTY SUBGROUPS

	Absent		Submedium		Medium		Pronounced		Disharmonic		Total
	No.	%	No.	%	No.	%	No.	%	No.	%	
Donegal	212	96.8	2	.9	4	1.8	1	.4	-	-	219
Leitrim	64	94.1	3	4.4	1	1.4	-	-	-	-	68
Sligo	80	94.1	4	4.7	1	1.1	-	-	-	-	85
Mayo	318	88.5	21	5.8	19	5.2	1	.2	-	-	359
Galway	281	82.4	30	8.7	27	7.9	3	.8	-	-	341
Clare	365	73.2	72	14.4	56	11.2	5	1.0	-	-	498
Kerry	258	90.2	13	4.5	14	4.8	1	.3	-	-	286
Females-Total	1578	85.0	145	7.8	122	6.6	11	.6	-	-	1856
Males-Total . .	1701	19.1	912	10.2	3972	44.6	2312	26.0	-	-	8897

TABLE XXVII-61.   OCCIPITAL FLATTENING BY COUNTY SUBGROUPS

	Absent		Medium		Pronounced		Total
	No.	%	No.	%	No.	%	
Donegal	199	90.8	20	9.1	-	-	219
Leitrim	62	91.1	6	8.8	-	-	68
Sligo	74	87.0	11	12.9	-	-	85
Mayo	308	86.0	48	13.4	2	.5	358
Galway	298	87.6	41	12.0	1	.2	340
Clare	399	80.1	98	19.6	1	.2	498
Kerry	263	91.9	22	7.6	1	.3	286
Females-Total	1603	86.4	246	13.3	5	.3	1855
Males-Total . .	7246	81.4	1253	14.1	406	4.6	8905

TABLE XXVII-62.   FACIAL ASYMMETRY BY COUNTY SUBGROUPS

	Absent		Left		Right		Total
	No.	%	No.	%	No.	%	
Donegal	215	98.1	2	.9	1	.4	218
Leitrim	61	89.7	5	7.3	2	2.9	68
Sligo	81	95.2	3	3.5	1	.1	85
Mayo	341	94.9	14	3.8	4	1.1	359
Galway	329	96.4	8	2.3	4	1.1	341
Clare	413	82.9	51	10.2	33	6.6	497
Kerry	278	97.2	8	2.7	-	-	286
Females-Total	1718	92.7	91	4.9	45	2.4	1854
Males-Total . .	6582	74.0	697	7.8	1612	18.1	8891

TABLE XXVIII-1. RACIAL TYPE BY COUNTY SUBGROUPS

	Pure Nordic No.	%	Predom. Nordic No.	%	Keltic No.	%	East Baltic No.	%	Dinaric No.	%
Donegal	1	.4	17	8.0	40	18.8	2	.9	44	20.7
Leitrim	-	-	-	-	11	16.9	-	-	23	35.3
Sligo	-	-	6	7.2	14	16.8	-	-	17	20.4
Mayo	-	-	28	8.1	66	19.1	5	1.4	90	26.0
Galway	1	.3	39	11.8	51	15.5	1	.3	79	24.0
Clare	2	.4	40	8.2	44	9.0	12	2.4	158	32.5
Kerry	1	.3	17	6.2	48	17.9	3	1.0	65	23.8
Females-Total	5	.3	147	8.2	274	15.3	23	1.3	476	26.6
Males-Total	..	.6		6.8		25.3		1.1		18.6

TABLE XXVIII-1. RACIAL TYPE BY COUNTY SUBGROUPS (Continued)

	Nordic Med. No.	%	Pure Med. No.	%	Nordic Alpine No.	%	Pure Alpine No.	%	Total
Donegal	62	29.2	7	3.3	35	16.5	4	1.8	212
Leitrim	19	29.2	5	7.6	7	10.7	-	-	65
Sligo	28	33.7	4	4.8	12	14.4	2	2.4	83
Mayo	73	21.1	11	3.1	71	20.5	1	.2	345
Galway	110	33.4	15	4.5	33	10.0	-	-	329
Clare	112	23.0	7	1.4	108	22.2	2	.4	485
Kerry	60	21.9	6	2.1	69	25.2	4	1.4	273
Females-Total	464	25.9	55	3.1	335	18.7	13	.7	1792
Males-Total	..	28.9		.3		18.4		0.0	9521

SOCIOLOGICAL OBSERVATIONS

TABLE XXIX-1. MARITAL STATE BY AGE GROUPS

	Single No.	%	Married No.	%	Widow No.	%	Total
15-19	425	100.0					425
20-34	672	86.6	103	13.27	1	.1	776
35-54	132	33.6	237	60.4	23	5.8	392
55 plus	41	19.8	119	57.4	47	22.7	207
Total	1270	70.6	459	25.5	71	3.9	1800

TABLE XXIX-2. NO. OF SIBLINGS BY AGE GROUPS

	One No.	%	Two No.	%	Three No.	%	Four No.	%	Five No.	%
15-19	17	4.0	31	7.3	39	9.2	53	12.5	58	13.6
20-34	31	3.9	57	7.3	74	9.5	75	9.6	109	14.0
35-54	13	3.3	18	4.5	24	6.1	40	10.2	37	9.4
55 plus	12	5.7	6	2.8	8	3.8	25	12.0	15	7.2
Total	73	4.1	112	6.2	145	8.1	193	10.7	219	12.2

TABLE XXIX-2. NO. OF SIBLINGS BY AGE GROUPS (Continued)

	Six No.	%	Seven No.	%	Eight No.	%	Nine No.	%	Ten No.	%
15-19	67	15.7	37	8.8	44	10.3	32	7.5	13	3.1
20-34	85	10.9	67	8.6	69	8.8	60	7.7	50	6.4
35-54	46	11.7	45	11.4	47	11.9	41	10.4	21	5.3
55 plus	22	10.6	29	14.0	33	15.9	17	8.2	15	7.2
Total	220	12.2	178	9.9	193	10.7	150	8.3	99	5.5

TABLE XXIX-2. NO. OF SIBLINGS BY AGE GROUPS (Continued)

	Eleven		Twelve and more		None		Total
	No.	%	No.	%	No.	%	
15-19	9	2.1	16	3.7	9	2.1	425
20-34	36	4.6	43	5.5	18	2.3	776
35-54	17	4.3	36	9.1	7	1.7	392
55 plus....	3	1.4	18	8.6	3	1.4	207
Total	65	3.6	113	6.3	37	2.1	1797

TABLE XXIX-3. NO. OF CHILDREN BY AGE GROUPS

	One		Two		Three		Four		Five	
	No.	%	No.	%	No.	%	No.	%	No.	%
15-19	-		-		-		-		-	
20-34	28	26.9	22	21.1	12	11.5	7	6.7	9	8.6
35-54	17	6.5	24	9.2	26	10.0	16	6.1	35	13.4
55 plus....	6	3.6	13	7.8	16	9.6	8	4.8	17	10.2
Total	51	9.6	59	11.1	54	10.2	31	5.8	61	11.5

TABLE XXIX-3. NO. OF CHILDREN BY AGE GROUPS (Continued)

	Six		Seven		Eight		Nine		Ten	
	No.	%	No.	%	No.	%	No.	%	No.	%
15-19	-	.-	-		-		-		-	-
20-34	6	5.7	3	2.8	-		-		-	-
35-54	20	7.6	18	6.9	18	6.9	11	4.2	11	4.2
55 plus....	11	6.6	16	9.6	10	6.0	12	7.2	19	11.4
Total	37	7.0	37	7.0	28	5.3	23	4.3	30	5.6

TABLE XXIX-3. NO. OF CHILDREN BY AGE GROUPS (Continued)

	Eleven		Twelve and more		None		Total
	No.	%	No.	%	No.	%	
15-19	-	-	-	-	-	-	-
20-34	-	-	-	-	17	16.3	104
35-54	6	2.3	13	5.0	45	17.3	260
55 plus....	10	6.0	14	8.4	14	8.4	166
Total	16	3.0	27	5.1	76	14.3	530

TABLE XXIX-4. EDUCATION BY AGE GROUPS

	Illiterate		Read and write		National school		Secondary school		University		Total
	No.	%	No.	%	No.	%	No.	%	No.	%	
15-19			2	.47	246	57.9	170	40.0	7	1.6	425
20-34	2	.2	8	1.0	526	57.8	212	27.3	27	3.5	775
35-54	7	1.7	4	1.0	290	73.9	87	22.1	4	1.0	392
55 plus....	7	3.3	3	1.4	175	84.5	21	10.1	1	.4	207
Females Total	16	.9	17	.9	1237	68.8	490	27.2	39	2.7	1799
Males Total	307	3.1	111	1.1	8089	81.5	1192	12.0	222	2.2	9921

TABLE XXIX-5. LANGUAGE BY AGE GROUPS

	No Irish		Native speaker		Irish only		School Irish		Total
	No.	%	No.	%	No.	%	No.	%	
15-19	30	7.1	63	14.8	2	.5	330	77.6	425
20-34	277	35.7	138	17.8	1	.1	360	46.3	776
35-54	193	49.2	123	31.3			76	19.3	392
55 plus	74	35.7	116	56.0			17	8.2	207
Females Total ..	574	31.9	440	24.4	3	.7	783	43.5	1800
Males Total....	5774	58.0	1248	12.5	89	.9	2844	28.6	9955

TABLE XXX-1. WEIGHT BY AGE GROUPS

	No.	Range	Mean	S.D.
15–19	422	91–190	127.70±.52	15.80
20–34	765	81–270	130.40±.45	18.30
35–54	389	81–260	143.67±.97	28.40
55 on ...	207	81–270	145.20±1.38	29.40

TABLE XXX-2. STATURE BY AGE GROUPS

	No.	Range	Mean	S.D.
15–19	425	140–193	159.15±.20	5.94
20–34	776	131–184	158.85±.15	6.18
35–54	392	137–193	158.46±.22	6.27
55 on	207	134–169	156.36±.29	6.15

TABLE XXX-3. SPAN BY AGE GROUPS

	No.	Range	Mean	S.D.
15–19	423	136–186	163.34±.22	6.75
20–34	767	136–186	163.67±.18	7.14
35–54	386	139–201	163.00±.25	7.29
55 on	200	133–189	161.21±.36	7.53

TABLE XXX-4. RELATIVE SPAN BY AGE GROUPS

	No.	Range	Mean	S.D.
15–19	423	88–111	102.56±.09	2.80
20–34	767	92–119	102.98±.07	3.00
35–54	386	88–119	102.81±.11	3.12
55 on	200	88–109	102.69±.15	3.06

TABLE XXX-5. BIACROMIAL DIAMETER BY AGE GROUPS

	No.	Range	Mean	S.D.
15–19	425	25–42	35.72±.07	2.19
20–34	776	25–42	36.11±.05	1.86
35–54	391	31–45	36.86±.07	2.04
55 on	207	31–48	36.57±.11	2.25

TABLE XXX-6. RELATIVE SHOULDER BREADTH BY AGE GROUPS

	No.	Range	Mean	S.D.
15–19	425	16–27	22.44±.04	1.24
20–34	776	16–29	22.74±.03	1.18
35–54	391	20–27	23.17±.04	1.24
55 on	207	20–29	23.35±.06	1.30

TABLE XXX-7. SITTING HEIGHT BY AGE GROUPS

	No.	Range	Mean	S.D.
15–19	425	64–95	83.06±.11	3.51
20–34	776	60–95	83.62±.11	4.52
35–54	392	64–95	83.36±.16	4.76
55 on	207	60–95	80.98±.42	5.16

TABLE XXX-8. RELATIVE SITTING HEIGHT BY AGE GROUPS

	No.	Range	Mean	S.D.
15–19	425	40–59	52.74±.07	2.06
20–34	776	38–63	52.90±.05	1.94
35–54	392	40–59	53.05±.07	1.92
55 on	207	46–57	52.66±.08	1.72

TABLE XXX-9. HEAD LENGTH BY AGE GROUPS

	No.	Range	Mean	S.D.
15–19	425	161–202	186.51±.19	5.82
20–34	775	164–208	186.48±.15	6.12
35–54	392	161–214	188.38±.22	6.42
55 on	207	167–205	188.88±.29	6.15

TABLE XXX-10. HEAD BREADTH BY AGE GROUPS

	No.	Range	Mean	S.D.
15–19	425	132–167	148.42±.16	5.01
20–34	773	132–164	148.63±.18	7.23
35–54	391	132–164	148.62±.17	4.98
55 on	206	132–161	147.85±.24	5.16

TABLE XXX-11. CEPHALIC INDEX BY AGE GROUPS

	No.	Range	Mean	S.D.
15–19	425	68–91	79.74±.10	3.09
20–34	773	65–91	79.77±.08	3.27
35–54	391	68–88	78.87±.10	3.00
55 on	207	71–94	78.57±.16	3.42

TABLE XXX-12. HEAD HEIGHT BY AGE GROUPS

	No.	Range	Mean	S.D.
15–19	424	95–137	119.70±.22	6.84
20–34	776	99–142	119.58±.18	7.52
35–54	392	99–142	120.08±.26	7.56
55 on	207	99–142	120.33±.36	7.80

TABLE XXX-13. LENGTH-HEIGHT INDEX BY AGE GROUPS

	No.	Range	Mean	S.D.
15–19	424	49–75	64.13±.13	3.87
20–34	775	52–78	64.16±.10	4.11
35–54	392	52–78	63.12±.16	4.53
55 on	207	55–78	63.77±.20	4.17

TABLE XXX-14. BREADTH-HEIGHT INDEX BY AGE GROUPS

	No.	Range	Mean	S.D.
15–19	424	64–96	80.54±.16	4.98
20–34	773	64–96	80.57±.12	5.10
35–54	391	67–99	80.94±.17	4.89
55 on	207	67–96	81.45±.26	5.40

TABLE XXX-15. MINIMUM FRONTAL DIAMETER BY AGE GROUPS

	No.	Range	Mean	S.D.
15-19....	425	93-120	104.86+ .14	4.32
20-34....	776	89-128	104.50∓ .11	4.52
35-54....	392	89-120	104.14∓ .15	4.40
55 on	207	85-120	103.68∓ .23	4.92

TABLE XXX-16. FRONTO-PARIETAL INDEX BY AGE GROUPS

	No.	Range	Mean	S.D.
15-19....	425	60-80	70.48+ .10	3.00
20-34....	774	60-86	69.61∓ .07	3.03
35-54....	391	60-80	70.23∓ .21	2.91
55 on	207	57-80	70.10∓ .16	3.33

TABLE XXX-17. BIZYGOMATIC DIAMETER BY AGE GROUPS

	No.	Range	Mean	S.D.
15-19....	425	95-149	131.20+ .17	5.20
20-34....	776	95-159	132.20∓ .13	5.30
35-54....	392	120-154	133.06∓ .18	5.05
55 on	207	100-149	133.81∓ .28	5.90

TABLE XXX-18. CEPHALO-FACIAL INDEX BY AGE GROUPS

	No.	Range	Mean	S.D.
15-19....	425	79-99	89.09+ .09	2.88
20-34....				
35-54....	391	79-99	89.69+ .10	2.94
55 on	207	79-99	90.57∓ .16	3.36

TABLE XXX-19. ZYGO-FRONTAL INDEX BY AGE GROUPS

	No.	Range	Mean	S.D.
15-19....	425	72-91	79.06+ .10	3.00
20-34....	776	64-99	78.98∓ .08	3.36
35-54....	392	68-71	78.30∓ .22	3.48
55 on	207	64-91	77.46∓ .16	3.36

TABLE XXX-20. BIGONIAL DIAMETER BY AGE GROUPS

	No.	Range	Mean	S.D.
15-19....	425	86-121	101.14+ .13	4.08
20-34....	776	86-129	100.90∓ .12	5.04
35-54....	392	86-121	102.26∓ .16	4.76
55 on	207	82-121	102.24∓ .24	5.16

TABLE XXX-21. FRONTO-GONIAL INDEX BY AGE GROUPS

	No.	Range	Mean	S.D.
15-19....	425	80-119	96.40+ .17	5.10
20-34....	776	75-119	96.95∓ .13	5.35
35-54....	392	85-114	98.11∓ .19	5.45
55 on	207	85-119	98.83∓ .25	5.30

TABLE XXX-22. ZYGO-GONIAL INDEX BY AGE GROUPS

	No.	Range	Mean	S.D.
15-19....	425	69-95	76.33+ .11	3.36
20-34....	776	63-95	76.57∓ .08	3.39
35-54....	392	66-92	76.87∓ .11	3.24
55 on	207	66-86	76.49∓ .15	3.21

TABLE XXX-23. TOTAL FACE HEIGHT BY AGE GROUPS

	No.	Range	Mean	S.D.
15-19....	425	95-134	114.85+ .19	5.70
20-34....	776	95-139	116.20∓ .19	6.20
35-54....	392	95-144	115.24∓ .23	6.70
55 on	207	90-134	114.00∓ .33	7.00

TABLE XXX-24. FACIAL INDEX BY AGE GROUPS

	No.	Range	Mean	S.D.
15-19....	425	70-104	86.80+ .16	4.90
20-34....	776	70-104	87.80∓ .12	4.90
35-54....	392	70-109	86.53∓ .18	5.20
55 on	207	70-104	84.90∓ .26	5.65

TABLE XXX-25. UPPER FACE HEIGHT BY AGE GROUPS

	No.	Range	Mean	S.D.
15-19....	425	55-79	66.40+ .13	4.20
20-34....	776	55-84	67.40∓ .11	4.35
35-54....	392	55-89	68.04∓ .16	4.75
55 on	207	50-84	67.87∓ .24	5.25

TABLE XXX-26. UPPER FACIAL INDEX BY AGE GROUPS

	No.	Range	Mean	S.D.
15-19....	425	37-63	50.06+ .11	3.39
20-34....	776	40-69	50.87∓ .08	3.36
35-54....	392	37-63	50.85∓ .13	3.72
55 on	207	40-63	50.47∓ .20	4.35

TABLE XXX-27. NOSE HEIGHT BY AGE GROUPS

	No.	Range	Mean	S.D.
15-19....	425	40-67	50.50+ .13	4.00
20-34....	776	40-67	51.10∓ .10	4.04
35-54....	392	40-67	51.78∓ .14	4.24
55 on	207	36-67	51.64∓ .19	4.04

TABLE XXX-28. NOSE BREADTH BY AGE GROUPS

	No.	Range	Mean	S.D.
15-19....	425	25-42	31.97+ .08	2.43
20-34....	776	25-39	31.76∓ .09	2.31
35-54....	392	25-42	32.56∓ .09	2.82
55 on	207	25-45	34.06∓ .14	2.97

TABLE XXX-29. NASAL INDEX BY AGE GROUPS

	No.	Range	Mean	S. D.
15-19..	425	48-87	63.46+ .21	6.44
20-34..	776	44-87	62.66∓ .16	6.32
35-54..	392	44-87	63.24∓ .24	6.88
55 on..	207	48-91	66.29∓ .30	6.32

MORPHOLOGICAL OBSERVATIONS

TABLE XXXI-1. SKIN COLOR, INNER ARM, BY AGE GROUPS

	Pale No.	%	Pink No.	%	Brunet No.	%	Swarthy No.	%	Total
Donegal	18	4.2	397	93.4	10	2.3	-	-	425
20-34	28	3.6	695	89.5	52	6.7	1	.1	776
35-54	12	3.0	337	85.9	40	10.2	3	.7	392
55 +	8	3.8	168	81.1	26	12.5	2	.9	204
Females-Total	66	3.7	1597	88.9	128	7.1	6	.3	1797
Males-Total	30	.3	9135	91.7	768	7.7	32	.3	9965

TABLE XXXI-2. VASCULARITY BY AGE GROUPS

	Absent No.	%	Submedium No.	%	Medium No.	%	Pronounced No.	%	Total
15-19	-	-	25	5.9	286	67.3	114	26.8	425
20-34	-	-	40	5.1	582	75.0	154	19.8	776
35-54	-	-	22	8.6	327	83.4	43	10.9	392
55 +	-	-	22	10.6	167	80.6	18	8.6	207
Females-Total	-	-	109	6.0	1362	75.7	329	18.3	1800
Males-Total	70	.7*			7450	74.8	2442	24.5	9962

*(Absent and Submedium)

TABLE XXXI-3. FRECKLES BY AGE GROUPS

	Absent No.	%	Submedium No.	%	Medium No.	%	Pronounced No.	%	Total
15-19	152	35.7	153	36.0	104	24.5	16	3.7	425
20-34	352	45.4	297	38.3	119	15.3	7	.9	775
35-54	279	71.1	89	22.7	22	5.6	2	.5	392
55 +	154	74.3	47	22.7	6	2.8	-	-	207
Females-Total	937	52.1	586	32.5	251	14.0	25	1.1	1799
Males-Total	6005	60.3	2631	26.4	1048	10.5	274	2.8	9958

TABLE XXXI-4. MOLES BY AGE GROUPS

	Absent No.	%	Few No.	%	Many No.	%	Total
15-19	379	89.2	43	10.1	-	-	422
20-34	706	91.5	64	8.3	2	.3	772
35-54	357	91.0	33	8.4	1	.2	391
55 +	176	88.4	29	14.0	1	.4	206
Females-Total	1618	90.3	169	9.4	4	.2	1791
Males-Total	9362	94.0	545	5.5	51	.5	9958

TABLE XXXI-5.   HAIR FORM BY AGE GROUPS

	Straight No.	%	Low waves No.	%	Deep waves No.	%	Curly No.	%	Woolly No.	%	Total
15-19	188	44.2	178	41.9	47	11.1	12	2.8	1	.1	425
20-34	333	43.0	310	39.9	105	13.5	24	3.1	2	.5	390
35-54	203	52.0	160	41.0	20	5.0	5	1.2			207
55 + ...	99	47.8	98	47.3	6	2.8	4	1.9	–	–	
Females-Total	823	45.8	746	41.5	178	9.9	45	2.5	3	.2	1798
Males-Total .	2993	30.0	4886	49.0	1742	17.5	325	3.3	16	.2	9962

TABLE XXXI-6.   HAIR TEXTURE BY AGE GROUPS

	Coarse No.	%	Medium No.	%	Fine No.	%	Total
15-19	9	2.1	275	64.0	141	33.2	425
20-34	27	3.5	522	67.3	227	29.3	776
35-54	16	4.0	295	75.4	80	20.4	391
55 + ...	13	6.2	146	70.5	48	23.1	207
Females-Total	65	3.6	1238	68.8	496	27.6	1799
Males-Total .	456	4.6	9220	92.6	282	2.8	9958

TABLE XXXI-7.   HAIR QUANTITY, HEAD, BY AGE GROUPS

	Submedium No.	%	Medium No.	%	Pronounced No.	%	Total
15-19	2	.5	364	85.6	59	14.0	425
20-34	7	.9	672	86.6	97	12.5	776
35-54	7	1.7	336	85.9	48	12.2	391
55 + ...	7	3.3	186	87.9	18	8.6	207
Females-Total	23	1.3	1554	86.4	222	12.3	1799
Males-Total .	225	2.2	9474	95.1	262	2.6	9961

TABLE XXXI-8.   HAIR QUANTITY, BODY, BY AGE GROUPS

	Absent No.	%	Submedium No.	%	Medium No.	%	Pronounced No.	%	Total
15-19	2	.5	410	96.5	13	3.1			425
20-34	6	.8	747	96.3	23	3.0			776
35-54	1	.2	364	93.0	26	6.6			391
55 + ...	2	.9	200	96.6	5	2.4			207
Females-Total	11	.6	1721	95.6	67	3.7			1799
Males-Total	37	.4	599	6.0	9064	91.0	263	2.6	9963

TABLE XXXI-9.   GRAYNESS, HEAD, BY AGE GROUPS

	Absent No.	%	Submedium No.	%	Medium No.	%	Pronounced No.	%	Total
15-19	422	99.3	3	.7	-	-	-	-	425
20-34	703	90.6	59	7.6	12	1.5	2	.3	776
35-54	113	28.8	146	37.2	96	24.4	37	9.4	392
55 + ...	10	4.8	53	25.7	81	39.3	62	30.0	206
Females-Total	1248	69.4	261	14.5	189	10.5	101	5.6	1799
Males-Total .	5370	53.9	2186	22.0	1333	13.4	1069	10.7	9958

TABLE XXXI-10.   HAIR COLOR BY AGE GROUPS

	Black No.	%	Dark brown No.	%	Brown No.	%	Red-brown No.	%	Golden brown No.	%	Ash-brown No.	%
15-19	10	2.3	176	41.1	135	31.7	29	6.8	43	10.1	-	-
20-34	32	4.1	412	53.1	178	22.9	61	7.8	47	6.0	7	.9
35-54	29	7.4	223	57.0	64	16.3	31	7.9	9	2.3	14	3.5
55 + ...	5	2.4	117	56.5	28	13.5	15	7.2	5	2.4	4	1.9
Females-Total	76	4.2	928	51.6	405	22.5	136	7.6	104	5.8	25	1.4
Males-Total .	267	2.7	3912	39.3	3500	35.2	502	5.0	903	9.1	45	.4

TABLE XXXI-10. HAIR COLOR BY AGE GROUPS (Continued)

	Golden		Ash		Red		White		Total
	No.	%	No.	%	No.	%	No.	%	
15-19	6	1.4	1	.2	25	5.9	-	-	425
20-34	9	1.2	-	-	29	3.7	1	.3	776
35-54	3	.7	1	.2	6	1.5	11	2.8	391
55 + ...	-	-	-	-	7	3.3	26	12.5	207
Females-Total	18	1.0	2	.1	67	3.8	38	2.1	1799
Males-Total .	93	.9	19	.2	414	4.2	289	2.9	9944

TABLE XXXI-11. EYE COLOR BY AGE GROUPS

	Black		Dark brown		Dark-light brown		Light brown		Gray-brown		Green-brown	
	No.	%	No.	%	No.	%	No.	%	No.	%	No.	%
15-19......	-	-	9	2.1	2	.5	2	.4	99	23.3	41	9.6
20-34	-	-	25	3.2	14	1.8	7	.9	206	26.6	82	10.6
35-54	-	-	16	4.0	5	1.2	2	.5	124	31.6	27	6.8
55 + ...	-	-	5	2.4	5	2.4	1	.4	62	29.9	13	6.2
Females-Total			55	4.1	34	1.9	12	.7	491	27.3	163	9.1
Males-Total .			51	.5*					515	5.2	4319	43.3

*(Dark brown, Dark-light brown, Light brown)

EYE COLOR BY AGE GROUPS (continued)

	Blue-brown		Gray		Gray-blue		Blue		Unmatched		Total
	No.	%	No.	%	No.	%	No.	%	No.	%	
15-19	108	25.4	10	2.3	89	20.9	56	13.2	1	.2	425
20-34	177	22.8	13	1.6	142	18.3	106	13.6	3	.4	775
35-54	94	23.9	4	1.0	70	17.8	49	12.5	1	.2	392
55 + ...	52	25.1	4	1.9	40	19.3	25	12.0	-	-	207
Females-Total	431	24.0	31	1.7	323	18.0	236	13.1	4	.2	1799
Males-Total .	4319	43.3	469	4.7*			4192	42.1	54	.5	9965

*(Gray and Gray-blue)

TABLE XXXI-12. PIGMENT, MIXED EYES, BY AGE GROUPS

	Very pro. dark		Pronouncedly dark		Even		Pronouncedly light		Very pro. light		Total
	No.	%	No.	%	No.	%	No.	%	No.	%	
15-19	-	-	4	1.6	18	7.2	122	49.2	104	41.9	248
20-34	-	-	2	.4	36	7.7	189	40.6	238	51.2	465
35-54	-	-	1	.4	8	3.2	58	23.6	178	72.6	245
55 + ...	-	-	1	.7	9	7.0	57	44.8	60	47.2	127
Females-Total			8	.7	71	6.5	426	39.3	580	53.5	1085
Males-Total .	430	7.7	187	3.3	716	12.8	1002	17.9	3257	58.2	5592

TABLE XXXI-13. IRIS BY AGE GROUPS

	Clear		Rayed		Zoned		Spotted and clear		Diffuse		Scalloped		Diffuse and spotted	
	No.	%	No.	%	No.	%	No.	%	No.	%	No.	%	No.	%
15-19......	49	11.5	144	33.8	62	14.6	1	.2	32	7.5	92	21.6	4	.9
20-34......	73	9.4	265	34.1	133	17.1	2	.2	72	9.3	149	19.2	3	.4
35-54......	22	5.6	153	39.0	60	15.3	1	.2	25	6.3	75	19.1	7	1.7
55 + ...	14	6.7	68	32.8	32	15.4	2	.9	12	5.7	52	25.1	3	1.4
Females Total .	158	8.8	630	35.0	287	16.0	6	.3	141	7.8	368	20.5	17	.9
Males Total...	2142	21.6	2138	21.6	163	1.6	265	2.7	3265	33.0	1933	19.5	-	-

TABLE XXXI-13. IRIS BY AGE GROUPS (Continued)

	Diffuse and zoned		Spotted and scalloped		Diffuse and rayed		Diffuse and scalloped		Spotted and rayed		Spotted and zoned		Total
15-19	3	.7	4	.9	1	.2	19	4.4	11	2.6	3	.7	425
20-34	3	.4	11	1.4	3	.4	16	.4	32	4.1	13	1.6	775
35-54	1	.2	8	2.0	1	.2	7	1.2	22	5.6	10	2.5	392
55+	-	-	9	4.3	-	-	-	-	8	3.8	7	3.3	207
Females Total	7	.4	32	1.8	5	.3	42	2.3	73	4.1	33	1.8	1799
Males Total													9906

TABLE XXXI-14. EYEFOLDS, EXTERNAL, BY AGE GROUPS

	Absent		Submedium		Medium		Pronounced		Total
	No.	%	No.	%	No.	%	No.	%	
15-19	424	99.7	1	.2	-	-	-	-	425
20-34	762	98.2	12	1.5	2	.2	-	-	776
35-54	361	92.0	15	3.8	16	4.0	-	-	392
55 +	184	88.8	11	5.3	12	5.7	-	-	207
Females Total	1731	96.2	39	2.7	30	1.7	-	-	1800
Males Total	8599	86.3	676	6.8	572	5.7	118	1.2	9965

TABLE XXXI-15. EYEFOLDS, MEDIAN, BY AGE GROUPS

	Absent		Submedium		Medium		Pronounced		Total
	No.	%	No.	%	No.	%	No.	%	
15-19	371	87.3	39	9.2	15	3.5	-	-	425
20-34	684	88.1	50	6.4	39	5.0	3	.4	776
35-54	337	85.9	30	7.6	23	5.8	2	.5	392
55 +	175	84.5	14	6.7	13	6.2	5	2.4	207
Females Total	1567	87.1	133	7.4	90	5.0	10	.6	1800
Males Total	9667	97.0	109	1.1	131	1.3	55	.6	9962

TABLE XXXI-16. EYEFOLDS, INTERNAL, BY AGE GROUPS

	Absent		Submedium		Medium		Pronounced		Total
	No.	%	No.	%	No.	%	No.	%	
15-19	421	99.0	4	.9	-	-	--	-	425
20-34	771	99.3	5	.6	-	-	-	-	776
35-54	384	97.9	6	1.5	2	.5	-	-	392
55 +	202	97.5	3	1.4	2	.9	-	-	207
Females Total	1778	98.8	18	1.0	4	.2	-	-	1800
Males Total	9864	99.0	87	.9	11	.1*			9962

*Medium and Pronounced

TABLE XXXI-17. EYE OBLIQUITY BY AGE GROUPS

	Absent		Submedium		Medium		Pronounced		Down		Total
	No.	%	No.	%	No.	%	No.	%	No.	%	
15-19	29	6.8	215	50.6	174	40.9	3	.7	4	.9	425
20-34	69	8.9	458	59.0	226	29.1	3	.4	20	2.6	776
35-54	42	10.7	230	58.6	105	26.7	3	.7	12	3.0	392
55 +	31	14.9	123	59.4	47	22.7	-	-	6	2.8	207
Females Total	171	9.5	1026	57.0	552	30.7	9	.5	42	2.3	1800
Males Total	6253	62.7	2580	25.9	487	4.9	62	.6	583	5.8	9965

TABLE XXXI-18. EYE OPENING HEIGHT BY AGE GROUPS

	Submedium		Medium		Pronounced		Total
	No.	%	No.	%	No.	%	
15-19	5	1.2	406	95.5	14	3.3	425
20-34	8	1.0	744	95.9	24	3.1	776
35-54	7	1.7	379	96.6	6	1.5	392
35 +	19	9.1	186	89.8	2	.9	207
Females Total	39	2.2	1715	95.3	46	2.6	1800
Males Total	620	6.2	9034	90.8	296	3.0	9950

TABLE XXXI-19. EYEBROW THICKNESS BY AGE GROUPS

	Submedium No.	%	Medium No.	%	Pronounced No.	%	Very pro. No.	%	Total
15-19	7	1.6	238	56.0	173	40.7	1	1.6	425
20-34	5	.6	398	51.3	354	45.7	18	2.3	775
35-54	6	1.5	239	60.9	140	35.7	7	1.7	392
55 +	5	2.4	125	60.3	73	35.2	4	1.9	207
Females Total	23	1.3	1000	55.6	740	41.4	36	2.0	1799
Males Total	347	3.5	9268	93.0	349	3.5*			9964

*(Pronounced and Very pronounced)

TABLE XXXI-20. EYEBROW CONCURRENCY BY AGE GROUPS

	Absent No.	%	Submedium No.	%	Medium No.	%	Pronounced No.	%	Total
15-19	57	13.4	311	73.4	50	11.8	6	1.4	424
20-34	87	11.2	579	74.7	101	13.0	8	1.0	775
35-54	69	17.6	292	74.4	29	7.3	2	.5	392
55 +	50	24.1	144	69.5	11	5.3	2	.9	207
Females Total	263	14.6	1726	73.7	191	10.6	18	1.0	1798
Males Total	186	1.9	2327	23.4	6449	64.7	1003	10.1	9965

TABLE XXXI-21. BROW RIDGES BY AGE GROUPS

	Absent No.	%	Submedium No.	%	Medium No.	%	Pronounced No.	%	Very pro. No.	%	Total
15-19	191	45.0	172	40.5	60	14.1	2	.5			425
20-34	222	28.6	375	48.3	169	21.8	10	1.3			776
35-54	73	18.6	174	44.3	136	34.6	9	2.2			392
55 +	16	7.7	79	38.1	95	45.8	17	8.2			207
Females Total	502	27.9	800	44.4	460	25.6	38	2.1			1800
Males Total	237	2.4	1970	19.8	5631	56.5	2086	20.9	39	.4	9963

TABLE XXXI-22. FOREHEAD HEIGHT BY AGE GROUPS

	Submedium No.	%	Medium No.	%	Pronounced No.	%	Total
15-19	24	5.6	362	85.2	39	9.2	425
20-34	55	7.1	657	85.0	63	8.1	775
35-54	24	6.1	323	82.3	44	11.2	391
55 +	13	6.2	162	78.2	32	15.4	207
Females Total	116	6.5	1504	83.6	178	9.9	1798
Males Total	361	3.6	4146	41.6	5452	64.7	9959

TABLE XXXI-23. FOREHEAD SLOPE BY AGE GROUPS

	Forward No.	%	Absent No.	%	Submedium No.	%	Medium No.	%	Pronounced No.	%	Very pro. No.	%	Total
15-19	11	2.6	182	42.8	162	38.1	68	16.0	1	.2	1	.2	425
20-34	15	1.9	267	34.4	306	39.4	175	22.5	13	1.6	-	-	776
35-54	7	1.7	77	19.6	134	34.1	163	41.5	11	2.8	-	-	392
55 +	-	-	31	14.9	74	35.7	92	44.4	10	4.8	-	-	207
Females-Total	33	1.8	557	30.9	676	37.6	498	27.7	35	1.9	1	.05	1800
Males-Total	119	1.2	653	6.6	4551	45.7	3862	38.8	747	7.5	31	.3	9963

TABLE XXXI-24. NASION DEPRESSION BY AGE GROUPS

	Absent No.	%	Very small No.	%	Submedium No.	%	Medium No.	%	Pronounced No.	%	Very pro. No.	%	Total
15-19	71	16.7	272	64.0	53	12.5	25	5.6	4	.9	-	.-	425
20-34	119	15.3	485	62.6	122	15.7	46	5.9	3	.4	-	-	775
35-54	35	8.9	229	58.4	84	21.4	41	10.4	2	.5	-	-	391
55 +	6	2.8	113	54.5	53	25.6	32	15.4	3	1.4	-	-	207
Females-Total	231	12.8	1099	61.1	312	17.3	144	8.0	12	.7	-	-	1798
Males-Total	25	.2	148	1.5	1290	13.0	5982	60.1	2381	23.9	133	1.3	9959

TABLE XXXI-25. NASAL ROOT HEIGHT BY AGE GROUPS

	Very small No.	Very small %	Submedium No.	Submedium %	Medium No.	Medium %	Pronounced No.	Pronounced %	Very pro. No.	Very pro. %	Total
15-19	1	.2	73	17.2	294	69.2	57	13.4	-	-	425
20-34	3	.4	101	13.0	541	69.7	128	16.5	3	.4	776
35-54	2	.5	54	13.7	286	72.9	50	12.7	-	-	392
55 + ...	4	1.9	43	20.7	132	63.7	27	13.0	1	.4	207
Females-Total	10	.6	271	15.1	1253	69.6	262	14.6	4	.2	1800
Males-Total .	298	3.0*			7698	77.3	1885	18.9	80	.8	9961

*(Very small and Submedium)

TABLE XXXI-26. NASAL ROOT BREADTH BY AGE GROUPS

	Very small No.	Very small %	Submedium No.	Submedium %	Medium No.	Medium %	Pronounced No.	Pronounced %	Very pro. No.	Very pro. %	Total
15-19	-	-	9	2.1	303	71.3	109	25.6	4	.9	425
20-34	1	.1	28	3.6	580	74.7	160	20.6	7	.9	776
35-54	-	-	16	4.0	319	81.3	55	14.0	2	.5	392
55 + ...	1	.4	5	2.4	148	71.8	49	23.7	3	1.4	206
Females-Total	2	.1	58	3.2	1350	75.0	373	20.7	16	.9	1799
Males-Total .	194	1.9*			7192	72.2	2487	25.0	86	.9	9959

*(Very small and Submedium)

TABLE XXXI-27. NASAL BRIDGE HEIGHT BY AGE GROUPS

	Submedium No.	Submedium %	Medium No.	Medium %	Pronounced No.	Pronounced %	Very pro., Very small No.	Very pro., Very small %	Total
15-19	61	14.3	329	77.4	35	8.2	-	-	425
20-34	78	10.0	591	76.2	104	13.4	3	.4	776
35-54	44	11.2	305	77.8	43	10.9	-	-	392
55 + ...	33	15.9	150	72.4	23	11.1	1	.4	207
Females-Total	216	12.0	1375	76.4	205	11.4	4	.2	1800
Males-Total .	310	3.1*	7559	75.9	1957	19.6	132	1.3**	9958

*(Submedium and Very small)
**(Very pronounced)

TABLE XXXI-28. NASAL BRIDGE BREADTH BY AGE GROUPS

	Submedium No.	Submedium %	Medium No.	Medium %	Pronounced No.	Pronounced %	Very pro., Very small No.	Very pro., Very small %	Total
15-19	10	2.3	357	84.0	57	13.4	1	.2	425
20-34	34	4.4	646	83.2	96	12.4	1	-	776
35-54	11	2.8	336	85.7	44	11.2	1	.2	392
55 + ...	1	.4	167	81.0	36	17.4	2	.9	206
Females-Total	56	3.1	1506	83.7	233	13.0	4	.2	1799
Males-Total .	84	.8	7704	77.4	2123	21.3	44	.4	9955

TABLE XXXI-29. NASAL SEPTUM BY AGE GROUPS

	Straight, concave No.	Straight, concave %	Convex No.	Convex %	Total
15-19	322	76.3	100	23.7	422
20-34	601	77.8	171	22.2	772
35-54	298	76.4	92	23.5	390
55 + ...	159	77.5	46	22.4	205
Females-Total	1380	77.1	409	22.9	1789
Males-Total .	3871	39.0	6048	61.0	9919

TABLE XXXI-30. NASAL TIP, THICKNESS, BY AGE GROUPS

	Submedium		Medium		Pronounced		Very pro., Very small		Total
	No.	%	No.	%	No.	%	No.	%	
15-19	11	2.6	322	75.7	89	20.9	3	.7	425
20-34	31	3.9	637	82.1	107	13.8	1	.3	776
35-54	21	5.3	324	82.8	46	11.7	-	-	391
55+	8	3.8	146	70.5	52	25.1	1	.4	207
Females-Total	71	3.9	1429	80.2	294	16.3	5	.3	1799
Males-Total .	169	1.7	7241	72.7	2512	25.2	37	.4	9959

TABLE XXXI-31. NASAL TIP, INCLINATION, BY AGE GROUPS

	Up, medium		Up, submedium		Horizontal		Down, submedium		Down, medium		Total
	No.	%	No.	%	No.	%	No.	%	No.	%	
15-19	55	12.9	323	76.0	39	9.2	8	1.9	-	-	425
20-34	75	9.7	573	74.1	112	14.5	13	1.6	-	-	773
35-54	18	3.0	306	78.0	58	14.8	9	2.3	-	-	391
55+	5	2.4	143	69.0	35	16.9	23	11.1	1	.4	207
Females-Total	153	8.5	1345	74.9	244	13.6	53	3.0	1	.05	1796
Males-Total .	1104	11.1	8229	82.7	447	4.5	131	1.3	39	.4	9950

TABLE XXXI-32. NASAL WINGS BY AGE GROUPS

	Compressed		Medium		Flaring		Total
	No.	%	No.	%	No.	%	
15-19	15	3.5	406	95.5	4	.9	425
20-34	30	3.8	739	95.3	6	.7	775
35-54	18	4.5	368	93.8	6	1.5	392
55+	7	3.3	189	91.3	11	5.3	207
Females-Total	70	3.9	1702	94.6	27	1.5	1799
Males-Total .	501	5.0	8842	88.9	606	6.1	9949

TABLE XXXI-33. NOSTRIL VISIBILITY, FRONTAL BY AGE GROUPS

	Absent		Submedium, medium		Pronounced		Total
	No.	%	No.	%	No.	%	
15-19	10	2.3	407	95.7	8	1.9	425
20-34	18	2.3	754	97.2	4	.5	776
35-54	12	3.0	378	96.4	2	.5	392
55+	16	7.7	191	92.2	-	-	207
Females-Total	56	3.1	1730	96.1	14	.8	1800
Males-Total .	507	5.1	9369	94.2	75	.8	9951

TABLE XXXI-34. NASAL PROFILE BY AGE GROUPS

	Concave		Straight		Convex		Concave snub nose		Convex snub nose		Total
	No.	%	No.	%	No.	%	No.	%	No.	%	
15-19	34	8.0	248	58.3	143	33.6	-	-	-	-	425
20-34	55	7.1	394	50.8	326	42.0	-	-	-	-	775
35-54	21	5.3	204	52.0	167	42.6	-	-	-	-	392
55+	14	6.8	120	58.5	71	34.6	-	-	-	-	205
Females-Total	124	6.9	966	53.8	707	39.3	-	-	-	-	1797
Males-Total .	659	6.6	4384	44.0	4007	40.2	69	.7	489	4.9	9954

TABLE XXXI-35. LIPS, INTEGUMENTAL THICKNESS, BY AGE GROUPS

	Submedium		Medium		Pronounced		Total
	No.	%	No.	%	No.	%	
15-19	4	.9	397	93.4	24	5.6	425
20-34	22	2.8	711	97.8	42	5.4	775
35-54	33	8.4	350	89.2	9	2.2	392
55+	32	15.4	170	82.1	5	2.4	207
Females-Total	91	5.1	1628	90.5	80	4.4	1799
Males-Total .	126	1.3	9418	94.5	422	4.2	9966

TABLE XXXI-36.   UPPER LIP, MEMBRANOUS THICKNESS, BY AGE GROUPS

	Very small No.	%	Submedium No.	%	Medium No.	%	Pronounced No.	%	Very pro. No.	%	Total
15-19	-	-	15	3.5	360	84.7	49	11.5	1	.2	425
20-34	2	.2	45	5.8	661	85.3	65	8.4	2	.2	775
35-54	2	.5	87	22.1	285	72.7	17	4.3	1	.2	392
55 + ...	6	2.8	80	38.6	113	54.5	8	3.8	-	-	207
Females-Total	10	.6	227	12.6	1419	78.9	139	7.7	4	.2	1799
Males-Total .	114	1.1	2355	23.6	7181	72.1	313	3.1	-	-	9963

TABLE XXXI-37.   LOWER LIP, MEMBRANOUS THICKNESS, BY AGE GROUPS

	Submedium No.	%	Medium No.	%	Pronounced No.	%	Very pro. No.	%	Very sm. No.	%	Total
15-19	14	3.3	361	85.0	49	11.5	1	.2			425
20-34	36	4.6	664	85.6	71	9.1	2	.2	2	.2	775
35-54	75	19.1	294	75.0	19	4.8	2	.5	2	.5	392
55 + ...	78	37.6	112	54.1	11	5.3	-	-	6	2.8	207
Females-Total	203	11.3	1431	79.5	150	8.3	5	.3	10	.5	1799

TABLE XXXI-38.   LIPS, EVERSION, BY AGE GROUPS

	Submedium No.	%	Medium No.	%	Pronounced No.	%	Very pro. No.	%	Total
15-19	13	3.1	402	95.0	9	2.1	-	-	424
20-34	48	6.2	713	91.8	15	1.9	-	-	776
35-54	76	19.3	309	78.8	7	1.7	-	-	392
55 + ...	82	39.6	125	60.3	-	-	-	-	207
Females-Total	219	12.2	1549	86.1	31	1.7	-	-	1799
Males-Total .	2245	22.5	7290	73.2	429	4.3	-	-	9964

TABLE XXXI-39.   MID-FACIAL PROGNATHISM BY AGE GROUPS

	Absent No.	%	Submedium No.	%	Medium No.	%	Pronounced No.	%	Total
15-19	356	83.7	59	13.9	10	3.7	-	-	425
20-34	633	82.0	118	15.3	20	2.6	1	.1	772
35-54	342	87.2	47	11.9	3	.7	-	-	392
55 + ...	193	93.2	12	5.7	2	.9	-	-	207
Females-Total	1524	84.9	236	13.1	35	1.9	1	.05	1786
Males-Total .	9155	91.9	649	6.5	137	1.4	16	.2	9957

TABLE XXXI-40.   CHIN PROMINENCE BY AGE GROUPS

	Submedium No.	%	Medium No.	%	Pronounced No.	%	Total
15-19	43	10.1	359	84.5	23	5.4	425
20-34	58	7.5	672	86.6	46	5.9	776
35-54	22	5.6	319	81.3	51	13.0	392
55 + ...	5	2.4	170	82.1	32	15.4	207
Females-Total	128	7.1	1520	84.4	152	8.4	1800
Males-Total .	1086	10.9	7937	79.7	938	9.4	9961

TABLE XXXI-41.   BITE BY AGE GROUPS

	Under No.	%	Edge-to-edge No.	%	Submedium over No.	%	Pronounced over No.	%	Total
15-19	1	.2	2	.5	405	96.2	13	3.1	421
20-34	4	.6	10	1.5	598	92.1	37	5.7	649
35-54	2	1.2	1	.6	143	87.1	18	10.9	164
55 + ...	1	1.8	-	-	53	88.3	6	10.0	60
Females-Total	8	.6	13	1.0	1201	92.8	74	5.7	1294
Males-Total .	48	.6	34	.4	7339	96.1	218	2.8	7639

TABLE XXXI-42.   TEETH, WEAR, BY AGE GROUPS

	Absent, submedium		Medium		Pronounced, very, pro.		Total
	No.	%	No.	%	No.	%	
15-19	390	92.0	34	8.0	-	-	424
20-34	513	70.4	182	25.0	34	4.6	729
35-54	66	26.9	97	39.5	82	33.4	245
55 + ...	8	7.8	35	34.3	59	57.8	102
Females - Total	977	65.1	348	23.2	175	11.7	1500
Males - Total .	5795	76.4	1451	19.1	340	4.5	7586

TABLE XXXI-43.   TEETH, LOSS, BY AGE GROUPS

	None		Very small (1-4)		Submedium (5-8)		Medium (9-16)		Pronounced (17-)		Total
	No.	%	No.	%	No.	%	No.	%	No.	%	
15-19	140	32.9	242	57.0	35	8.2	4	.9	4	.9	425
20-34	114	14.7	321	41.3	130	16.7	72	9.3	139	17.9	776
35-54	4	1.0	27	6.8	45	11.4	50	12.7	266	67.8	392
55 + ...	2	.9	3	1.4	7	3.3	16	7.7	179	86.4	207
Females - Total	260	14.4	593	32.9	217	12.1	142	7.9	588	32.7	1800
Males - Total .	785	7.9	3947	39.6	2073	20.8	694	7.0	2461	24.7	9960

TABLE XXXI-44.   TEETH, CARIES, BY AGE GROUPS

	Absent		Very small		Submedium		Medium		Pronounced		Total
	No.	%	No.	%	No.	%	No.	%	No.	%	
15-19	104	24.6	183	43.3	106	25.1	26	6.1	4	.9	423
20-34	133	19.0	257	36.7	195	27.8	83	11.8	32	4.6	700
35-54	20	10.0	83	41.7	44	22.1	25	12.5	27	13.5	199
55 + ...	5	6.7	26	35.1	15	20.2	5	6.7	23	31.0	74
Females - Total	262	18.8	549	39.3	360	25.9	139	10.0	86	6.6	1396
Males - Total .	75	1.0	682	9.0	4241	55.7	1793	23.5	827	10.8	7618

TABLE XXXI-45.   MALARS, FRONTAL PROJECTION, BY AGE GROUPS

	Absent, submedium		Medium		Pronounced		Total
	No.	%	No.	%	No.	%	
15-19	16	3.7	276	64.9	133	31.2	425
20-34	39	5.0	475	61.2	262	33.7	776
35-54	20	5.1	217	55.3	155	39.5	392
55 + ...	5	2.4	113	54.5	89	42.9	207
Females - Total	80	4.4	1081	60.1	639	35.5	1800
Males - Total .	48	.5	8335	83.6	1580	15.8	9963

TABLE XXXI-46.   MALARS, LATERAL PROJECTION, BY AGE GROUPS

	Absent		Submedium		Medium		Pronounced		Very pro.		Total
	No.	%	No.	%	No.	%	No.	%	No.	%	
15-19	1	.2	35	8.2	232	54.6	153	36.0	4	.9	425
20-34	1	.1	37	4.7	407	52.5	317	40.9	13	1.7	775
35-54	-	-	21	5.3	198	50.5	172	43.8	1	.2	392
55 + ...	-	-	5	2.4	105	50.7	91	43.9	6	2.8	207
Females - Total	2	.1	98	5.5	942	52.4	733	40.8	24	1.3	1799
Males - Total .	37	.4	-	-	6534	65.6	3213	32.2	177	1.8	9961

TABLE XXXI-47.   GONIAL ANGLES BY AGE GROUPS

	Submedium		Medium		Pronounced		Very pro.		Total
	No.	%	No.	%	No.	%	No.	%	
15-19	6	1.4	350	82.3	69	16.2	-	-	425
20-34	10	1.3	676	87.3	88	11.4	-	-	774
35-54	7	1.7	366	93.6	18	4.6	-	-	391
55 + ...	1	.4	199	96.1	7	3.3	-	-	207
Females - Total	24	1.3	1591	88.5	182	9.6	-	-	1797
Males - Total .	283	2.8	6424	64.5	3096	31.1	160	1.6	9963

TABLE XXXI-48. EAR HELIX BY AGE GROUPS

	Very small No.	%	Submedium No.	%	Medium No.	%	Pronounced No.	%	Total
15-19	9	2.1	144	33.9	229	54.0	42	9.9	424
20-34	33	4.2	253	32.6	409	52.8	79	10.2	774
35-54	20	5.1	122	31.2	213	54.4	36	9.2	391
55 + ...	8	3.8	57	27.5	109	52.6	33	15.9	207
Females-Total	72	4.0	576	32.1	960	53.5	190	10.6	1796
Males-Total .	64	.4	2230	22.4	7242	72.7	430	4.3	9966

TABLE XXXI-49. EAR ANTIHELIX BY AGE GROUPS

	Absent No.	%	Submedium No.	%	Medium No.	%	Pronounced No.	%	Total
15-19	4	.9	91	21.4	314	73.8	16	3.7	425
20-34	11	1.4	167	21.5	561	72.4	36	4.6	775
35-54	3	.7	90	23.0	283	72.5	14	3.5	390
55 + ...	6	2.8	42	20.2	141	68.1	18	8.6	207
Females-Total	24	1.3	390	21.7	1299	72.3	84	4.7	1797
Males-Total .	17	.2	447	4.5	8214	82.5	1283	12.9	9961

TABLE XXXI-50. DARWIN'S POINT BY AGE GROUPS

	Absent No.	%	Submedium No.	%	Medium No.	%	Pronounced No.	%	Total
15-19	400	94.1	19	4.4	5	1.2	1	.2	425
20-34	736	94.8	36	4.6	4	.5	-	-	776
35-54	380	96.9	8	2.0	4	1.0	-	-	392
55 + ...	204	98.5	3	1.4	-	-	-	-	207
Females-Total	1720	95.6	66	3.7	13	.7	1	.05	1800
Males-Total .	7372	74.1	2289	23.0	274	2.8	19	.2	9954

TABLE XXXI-51. EAR LOBE ATTACHMENT BY AGE GROUPS

	Soldered No.	%	Attached No.	%	Free No.	%	Total
15-19	17	4.0	261	61.4	147	34.6	425
20-34	45	5.8	463	59.6	268	34.5	776
35-54	18	4.5	192	48.9	182	46.4	392
55 + ...	8	3.8	81	39.3	117	56.7	206
Females-Total	88	4.9	997	55.4	714	39.7	1799
Males-Total .	143	1.4	4122	41.4	5699	57.2	9964

TABLE XXXI-52. EAR LOBE SIZE BY AGE GROUPS

	Absent No.	%	Submedium No.	%	Medium No.	%	Pronounced No.	%	Total
15-19	14	3.3	122	28.7	282	66.3	7	1.6	
20-34	39	5.0	240	30.9	485	62.5	12	1.5	776
35-54	9	2.2	104	26.5	267	68.1	12	3.0	392
55 + ...	3	1.4	33	15.9	161	77.7	10	4.8	207
Females-Total	65	3.6	499	27.7	1195	66.4	41	2.3	1800
Males-Total .	46	.5*			5368	53.9	4549	45.6	9963

*(Absent and Submedium)

TABLE XXXI-53. EAR PROTRUSION BY AGE GROUPS

	Submedium No.	%	Medium No.	%	Pronounced No.	%	Total
15-19	16	3.7	367	86.5	41	9.6	424
20-34	37	4.7	651	84.1	86	11.1	774
35-54	22	5.6	338	86.2	32	8.1	392
55 + ...	18	8.6	178	85.9	11	5.3	207
Females-Total	93	5.2	1943	85.9	170	9.5	1797
Males-Total .	79	.8	7672	77.0	2210	22.2	9962

TABLE XXXI-54.   TEMPORAL FULLNESS BY AGE GROUPS

	Submedium No.	Submedium %	Medium No.	Medium %	Pronounced No.	Pronounced %	Total
15-19	19	4.4	339	79.7	67	15.7	425
20-34	60	7.7	683	88.0	33	4.2	776
35-54	49	12.5	334	85.2	9	2.2	392
55 + ...	28	13.5	174	84.0	5	2.4	207
Females-Total	156	8.7	1530	85.0	114	6.3	1800
Males-Total .	1558	15.6	6175	62.0	2231	22.4	9964

TABLE XXXI-55.   OCCIPITAL PROTRUSION BY AGE GROUPS

	Absent No.	Absent %	Submedium No.	Submedium %	Medium No.	Medium %	Pronounced No.	Pronounced %	Total
15-19	2	.4	54	12.7	351	82.6	18	4.2	425
20-34	2	.2	98	12.6	637	82.0	39	5.0	776
35-54	2	.5	26	6.6	333	85.1	30	7.6	391
55 + ...	2	.9	7	3.3	178	85.9	20	9.6	207
Females-Total	8	.4	185	10.3	1499	83.3	107	5.9	1799
Males-Total .	735	7.4*			7459	74.9	1769	17.8	9963

*(Absent and Submedium)

TABLE XXXI-56. LAMBDOID FLATTENING BY AGE GROUPS

	Absent No.	Absent %	Submedium No.	Submedium %	Medium No.	Medium %	Pronounced No.	Pronounced %	Total
15-19	354	83.3	45	10.6	24	5.6	2	.4	425
20-34	664	85.5	51	6.5	55	.7	-	-	776
35-54	329	83.9	28	7.1	33	8.4	2	.5	392
55 + ...	183	88.4	15	7.2	9	4.3	-	-	207
Females-Total	1530	85.0	139	7.7	121	6.7	10	.6	1800
Males-Total .	2280	22.9	991	10.0	4251	42.7	2430	24.5	9952

TABLE XXXI-57.   OCCIPITAL FLATTENING BY AGE GROUPS

	Absent No.	Absent %	Medium No.	Medium %	Pronounced No.	Pronounced %	Total
15-19	335	79.0	88	20.7	1	.2	424
20-34	651	83.8	122	15.7	3	.3	776
35-54	362	92.5	28	7.1	1	.2	391
55 + ...	196	94.6	11	5.3	-	-	207
Females-Total	1544	85.9	249	13.8	5	.3	1798
Males-Total .	7915	79.4	1545	15.5	501	5.0	9961

TABLE XXXI-58.   FACIAL ASYMMETRY BY AGE GROUPS

	Absent No.	Absent %	Left No.	Left %	Right No.	Right %	Total
15-19	386	90.8	23	5.4	16	3.7	425
20-34	715	92.1	42	5.4	19	2.4	776
35-54	369	94.6	13	3.3	8	2.0	390
55 + ...	197	95.1	9	4.3	1	.4	207
Females-Total	1667	92.7	87	4.8	44	2.4	1798
Males-Total .	7388	74.3	775	7.8	1784	17.9	9947

MORPHOLOGICAL (SUBRACIAL) TYPES

BY BIRTHPLACE

No. 4483

No. 4471

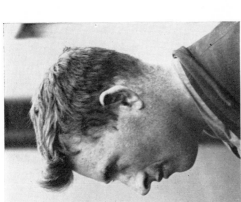

WEST DONEGAL

Figure 39.

No. 4487

No. 4486

FIGURE 39

No. 4487 Birthplace, West Donegal. Age, 22. Weight, 156 lbs. Stature, 170.4 cm. Cephalic index, 78. Nasal index, 60. Hair color, brown. Eye color, blue. Type: Keltic.

No. 4483 Birthplace, West Donegal. Age, 54. Weight, 132 lbs. Stature, 165.3 cm. Cephalic index, 75. Nasal index, 70. Hair color, dark brown. Eye color, blue. Type: Keltic.

No. 4486 Birthplace, West Donegal. Age, 17. Weight, 126 lbs. Stature, 162.9 cm. Cephalic index, 84. Nasal index, 56. Hair color, dark brown. Eye color, blue-brown. Type: Dinaric.

No. 4471 Birthplace, West Donegal. Age, 35. Weight, 156 lbs. Stature, 165.7 cm. Cephalic index, 77. Nasal index, 58. Hair color, brown. Eye color, blue-brown. Type: Nordic Mediterranean.

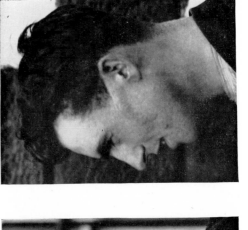

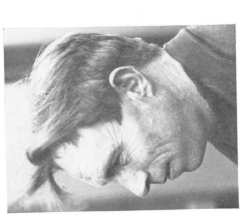

No. 4666

No. 3769

WEST DONEGAL

MAYO

Figure 40.

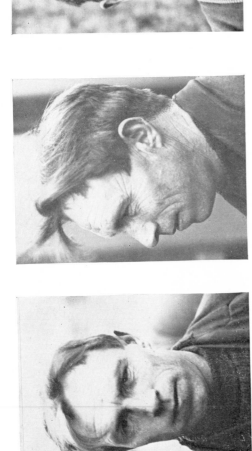

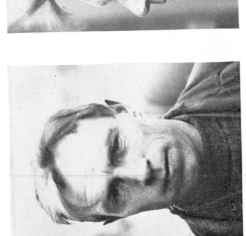

No. 4470

No. 3763

FIGURE 40

No. 4470 Birthplace, West Donegal. Age, 28. Weight, 144 lbs. Stature, 165.0 cm. Cephalic index, 79. Nasal index, 72. Hair color, brown. Eye color, blue-brown. Type: Nordic Mediterranean.

No. 4666 Birthplace, West Donegal. Age, 23. Weight, 162 lbs. Stature, 176.1 cm. Cephalic index, 81. Nasal index, 73. Hair color, brown. Eye color, blue-brown. Type: Nordic Alpine.

No. 3763 Birthplace, Mayo. Age, 22. Weight, 175 lbs. Stature, 183.2 cm. Cephalic index, 73. Nasal index, 62. Hair color, dark brown. Eye color, blue. Type: Keltic.

No. 3769 Birthplace, Mayo. Age, 19. Weight, 158 lbs. Stature, 172.9 cm. Cephalic index, 89. Nasal index, 61. Hair color, brown. Eye color, blue. Type: Dinaric.

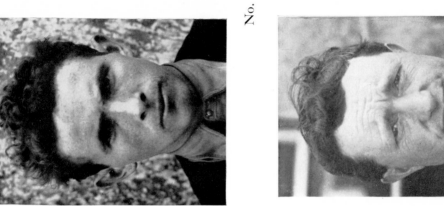

No. 3890

No. 3897

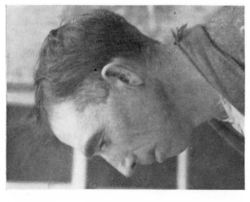

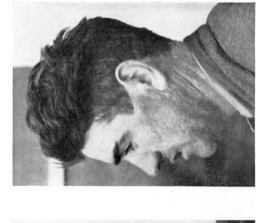

No. 3898

No. 3881

MAYO

FIGURE 41.

FIGURE 41

No. 3898 Birthplace, Mayo. Age, 43. Weight, 156 lbs. Stature, 176.0 cm. Cephalic index, 80. Nasal index, 58. Hair color, black. Eye color, blue-brown. Type: Dinaric.

No. 3890 Birthplace, Mayo. Age, 20. Weight, 162 lbs. Stature, 171.0 cm. Cephalic index, 85. Nasal index, 66. Hair color, dark brown. Eye color, blue-brown. Type: Nordic Alpine.

No. 3881 Birthplace, Mayo. Age, 28. Weight, 156 lbs. Stature, 172.8 cm. Cephalic index, 79. Nasal index, 61. Hair color, black. Eye color, blue-brown. Type: Nordic Mediterranean.

No. 3897 Birthplace, Mayo. Age, 40. Weight, 196 lbs. Stature, 171.1 cm. Cephalic index, 80. Nasal index, 70. Hair color, black. Eye color, gray-brown. Type: Nordic Alpine.

No. 1157

No. 1589

No. 1202

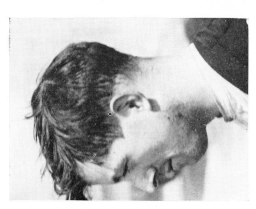

No. 1735

LEITRIM

FIGURE 42.

FIGURE 42

No. 1202 Birthplace, Leitrim. Age, 30. Weight, 160 lbs. Stature, 170.0 cm. Cephalic index, 78. Nasal index, 69. Hair color, red. Eye color, blue. Type: Keltic.

No. 1157 Birthplace, Leitrim. Age, 50. Weight, 175 lbs. Stature, 178.5 cm. Cephalic index, 82. Nasal index, 55. Hair color, dark brown. Eye color, blue-brown. Type: Dinaric.

No. 1735 Birthplace, Leitrim. Age, 24. Weight, 148 lbs. Stature, 168.1 cm. Cephalic index, 77. Nasal index, 65. Hair color, dark brown. Eye color, blue-brown. Type: Nordic Mediterranean.

No. 1589 Birthplace, Leitrim. Age, 28. Weight, 145 lbs. Stature, 171.5 cm. Cephalic index, 78. Nasal index, 71. Hair color, dark brown. Eye color, blue-brown. Type: Nordic Mediterranean.

No. 4432

LEITRIM

No. 1159

WEST GALWAY

FIGURE 43.

No. 3964

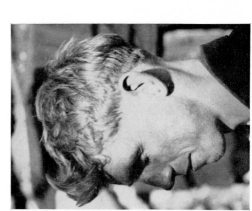

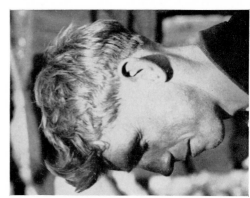

No. 3962

FIGURE 43

No. 1159   Birthplace, Leitrim. Age, 60. Weight, 196 lbs. Stature, 176.7 cm. Cephalic index, 81. Nasal index, 67. Hair color, dark brown. Eye color, blue. Type: Nordic Alpine.

No. 4432   Birthplace, Leitrim. Age, 27. Weight, 130 lbs. Stature, 167.6 cm. Cephalic index, 84. Nasal index, 68. Hair color, brown. Eye color, blue-brown. Type: Nordic Alpine.

No. 3962   Birthplace, West Galway. Age, 20. Weight, 144 lbs. Stature, 173.7 cm. Cephalic index, 75. Nasal index, 71. Hair color, golden-brown. Eye color, blue. Type: Predominantly Nordic.

No. 3964   Birthplace, West Galway. Age, 51. Weight, 177 lbs. Stature, 165.0 cm. Cephalic index, 77. Nasal index, 66. Hair color, dark brown. Eye color, gray-blue. Type: Keltic.

No. 3974

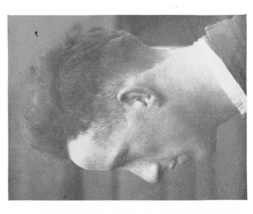

No. 3965

No. 3971

No. 3966

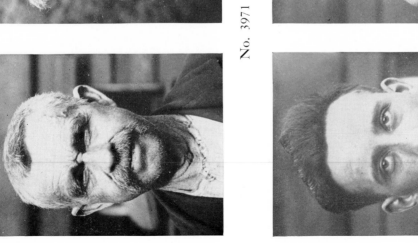

WEST GALWAY

FIGURE 44.

Figure 44

No. 3971 Birthplace, West Galway. Age, 69. Weight, 156 lbs. Stature, 176.3 cm. Cephalic index, 78. Nasal index, 75. Hair color, dark brown. Eye color, blue. Type: Keltic.

No. 3974 Birthplace, West Galway. Age, 37. Weight, 150 lbs. Stature, 170.8 cm. Cephalic index, 85. Nasal index, 55. Hair color, brown. Eye color, blue-brown. Type: Dinaric.

No. 3966 Birthplace, West Galway. Age, 21. Weight, 162 lbs. Stature, 177.8 cm. Cephalic index, 80. Nasal index, 58. Hair color, dark brown. Eye color, blue-brown. Type: Dinaric.

No. 3965 Birthplace, West Galway. Age, 18. Weight, 160 lbs. Stature, 177.5 cm. Cephalic index, 79. Nasal index, 62. Hair color, brown. Eye color, blue-brown. Type: Nordic Mediterranean.

No. 3982

No. 610

WEST GALWAY

ARAN ISLANDS

FIGURE 45.

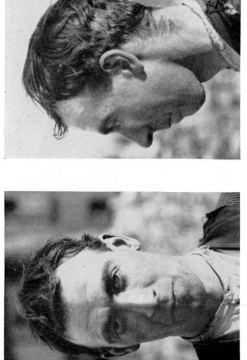

No. 3996

No. 587

FIGURE 45

No. 3996 Birthplace, West Galway. Age, 25. Weight, 148 lbs. Stature, 171.4 cm. Cephalic index, 78. Nasal index, 71. Hair color, brown. Eye color, blue-brown. Type: Nordic Mediterranean.

No. 3982 Birthplace, West Galway. Age, 20. Weight, 154 lbs. Stature, 170.5 cm. Cephalic index, 80. Nasal index, 63. Hair color, brown. Eye color, blue. Type: Nordic Alpine.

No. 587 Birthplace, Aran Islands. Age, 46. Weight, 148 lbs. Stature, 176.8 cm. Cephalic index, 75. Nasal index, 60. Hair color, brown. Eye color, blue. Type: Keltic.

No. 610 Birthplace, Aran Islands. Age, 48. Weight, 177 lbs. Stature, 174.0 cm. Cephalic index, 78. Nasal index, 68. Hair color, brown. Eye color, blue. Type: Keltic.

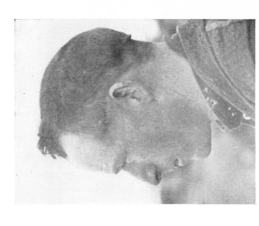

No. 631

No. 620

No. 621

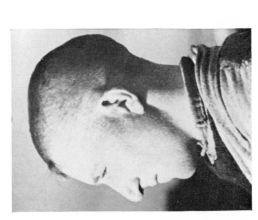

No. 629

ARAN ISLANDS

Figure 46.

FIGURE 46

No. 621   Birthplace, Aran Islands. Age, 29. Weight, 182 lbs. Stature, 188.0 cm. Cephalic index, 71. Nasal index, 68. Hair color, brown. Eye color, blue. Type: Keltic.

No. 631   Birthplace, Aran Islands. Age, 20. Weight, 162 lbs. Stature, 180.2 cm. Cephalic index, 85. Nasal index, 57. Hair color, red-brown. Eye color, blue-brown. Type: Dinaric.

No. 629   Birthplace, Aran Islands. Age, 19. Weight, 164 lbs. Stature, 181.3 cm. Cephalic index, 77. Nasal index, 59. Hair color, red. Eye color, blue-brown. Type: Nordic Mediterranean.

No. 620   Birthplace, Aran Islands. Age, 34. Weight, 173 lbs. Stature, 175.5 cm. Cephalic index, 76. Nasal index, 66. Hair color, red-brown. Eye color, blue-brown. Type: Nordic Mediterranean.

No. 591

No. 3024

ARAN ISLANDS

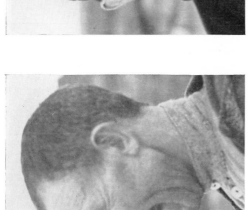

CLARE

Figure 47.

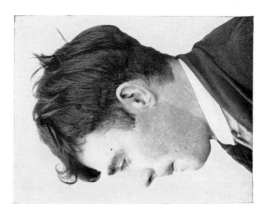

No. 593

No. 3284

FIGURE 47

No. 593   Birthplace, Aran Islands. Age, 57. Weight, 132 lbs. Stature, 165.4 cm. Cephalic index, 76. Nasal index, 61. Hair color, dark brown. Eye color, blue-brown. Type: Nordic Mediterranean.

No. 591   Birthplace, Aran Islands. Age, 36. Weight, 154 lbs. Stature, 168.0 cm. Cephalic index, 82. Nasal index, 64. Hair color, dark brown. Eye color, blue-brown. Type: Nordic Alpine.

No. 3284   Birthplace, Clare. Age, 24. Weight, 150 lbs. Stature, 166.5 cm. Cephalic index, 79. Nasal index, 68. Hair color, dark brown. Eye color, blue. Type: Keltic.

No. 3024   Birthplace, Clare. Age, 43. Weight, 140 lbs. Stature, 170.2 cm. Cephalic index, 82. Nasal index, 52. Hair color, dark brown. Eye color, blue-brown. Type: Dinaric.

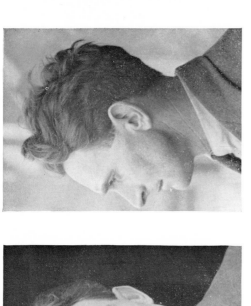

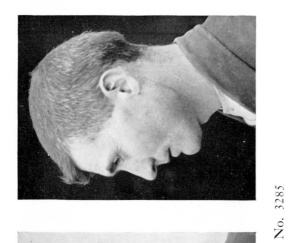

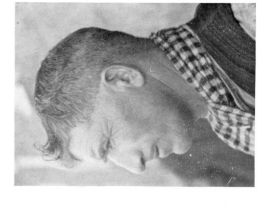

No. 3033

No. 3008

No. 3285

No. 2638

CLARE

FIGURE 48.

FIGURE 48

No. 3285 Birthplace, Clare. Age, 35. Weight, 144 lbs. Stature, 171.0 cm. Cephalic index, 84. Nasal index, 57. Hair color, dark brown. Eye color, blue-brown. Type: Dinaric.

No. 3033 Birthplace, Clare. Age, 36. Weight, 157 lbs. Stature, 172.5 cm. Cephalic index, 79. Nasal index, 57. Hair color, black. Eye color, blue-brown. Type: Nordic Mediterranean.

No. 2638 Birthplace, Clare. Age, 42. Weight, 163 lbs. Stature, 162.9 cm. Cephalic index, 79. Nasal index, 66. Hair color, red-brown. Eye color, gray-brown. Type: Nordic Mediterranean.

No. 3008 Birthplace, Clare. Age, 40. Weight, 158 lbs. Stature, 171.8 cm. Cephalic index, 79. Nasal index, 66. Hair color, brown. Eye color, blue-brown. Type: Nordic Mediterranean.

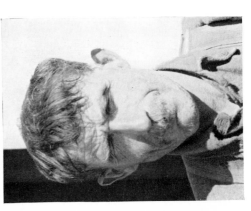

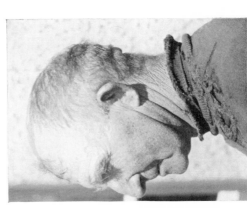

No. 3004

No. 5665

CLARE

KERRY

FIGURE 49.

No. 3026

No. 5650

FIGURE 49

No. 3026 Birthplace, Clare. Age, 26. Weight, 137 lbs. Stature, 165.5 cm. Cephalic index, 80. Nasal index, 65. Hair color, dark brown. Eye color, blue-brown. Type: Nordic Alpine.

No. 3004 Birthplace, Clare. Age, 25. Weight, 134 lbs. Stature, 165.5 cm. Cephalic index, 83. Nasal index, 63. Hair color, dark brown. Eye color, blue. Type: Nordic Alpine.

No. 5650 Birthplace, Kerry. Age, 65. Weight, 188 lbs. Stature, 169.2 cm. Cephalic index, 78. Nasal index, 58. Hair color, brown. Eye color, blue. Type: Keltic.

No. 5665 Birthplace, Kerry. Age, 48. Weight, 146 lbs. Stature, 165.5 cm. Cephalic index, 81. Nasal index, 55. Hair color, brown. Eye color, blue-brown. Type: Dinaric.

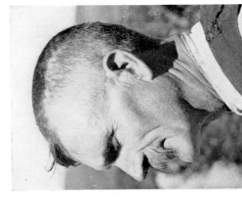

No. 5765

No. 5410

No. 5761

No. 5766

KERRY

FIGURE 50.

FIGURE 50

No. 5410 Birthplace, Kerry. Age, 19. Weight, 138 lbs. Stature, 169.2 cm. Cephalic index, 80. Nasal index, 57. Hair color, dark brown. Eye color, blue-brown. Type: Dinaric.

No. 5765 Birthplace, Kerry. Age, 17. Weight, 135 lbs. Stature, 167.0 cm. Cephalic index, 75. Nasal index, 56. Hair color, brown. Eye color, blue-brown. Type: Nordic Mediterranean.

No. 5766 Birthplace, Kerry. Age, 25. Weight, 168 lbs. Stature, 178.7 cm. Cephalic index, 82. Nasal index, 70. Hair color, dark brown. Eye color, blue-brown. Type: Nordic Alpine.

No. 5761 Birthplace, Kerry. Age, 60. Weight, 170 lbs. Stature, 174.8 cm. Cephalic index, 80. Nasal index, 69. Hair color, dark brown. Eye color, blue-brown. Type: Nordic Alpine.

No. 5764

No. 5538

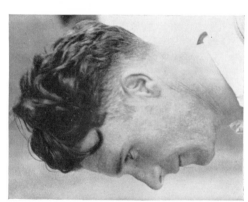

KERRY

CORK

FIGURE 51.

No. 5662

No. 5963

FIGURE 51

No. 5662   Birthplace, Kerry. Age, 22. Weight, 163 lbs. Stature, 172.3 cm. Cephalic index, 85. Nasal index, 67. Hair color, golden brown. Eye color, blue. Type: Nordic Alpine.

No. 5764   Birthplace, Kerry. Age, 50. Weight, 170 lbs. Stature, 177.7 cm. Cephalic index, 81. Nasal index, 67. Hair color, brown. Eye color, blue. Type: Nordic Alpine.

No. 5963   Birthplace, Cork. Age, 32. Weight, 137 lbs. Stature, 167.2 cm. Cephalic index, 79. Nasal index, 64. Hair color, dark brown. Eye color, blue. Type: Keltic.

No. 5538   Birthplace, Cork. Age, 71. Weight, 184 lbs. Stature, 172.7 cm. Cephalic index, 83. Nasal index, 64. Hair color, red. Eye color, blue. Type: East Baltic.

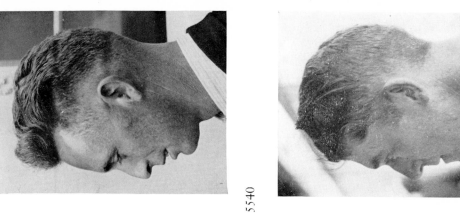

No. 5540

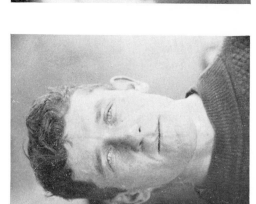

No. 5967

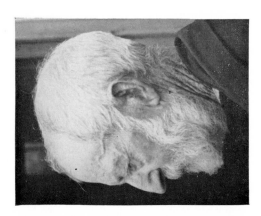

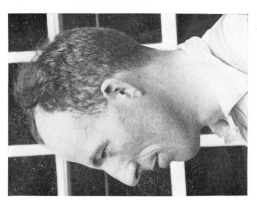

CORK

FIGURE 52.

No. 5542

No. 5987

FIGURE 52

No. 5542 Birthplace, Cork. Age, 73. Weight, 147 lbs. Stature, 160.0 cm. Cephalic index, 81. Nasal index, 58. Hair color, dark brown. Eye color, blue. Type: Dinaric.

No. 5540 Birthplace, Cork. Age, 30. Weight, 173 lbs. Stature, 179.5 cm. Cephalic index, 82. Nasal index, 61. Hair color, brown. Eye color, blue-brown. Type: Dinaric.

No. 5987 Birthplace, Cork. Age, 30. Weight, 148 lbs. Stature, 174.2 cm. Cephalic index, 79. Nasal index, 58. Hair color, dark brown. Eye color, blue-brown. Type: Nordic Mediterranean.

No. 5967 Birthplace, Cork. Age, 25. Weight, 157 lbs. Stature, 180.0 cm. Cephalic index, 87. Nasal index, 66. Hair color, dark brown. Eye color, blue-brown. Type: Nordic Alpine.

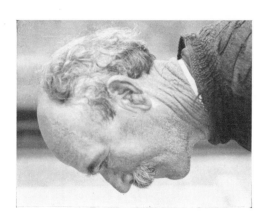

No. 5545

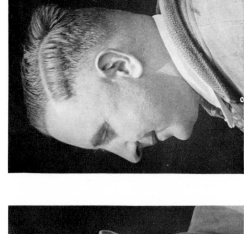

No. 4890

CORK

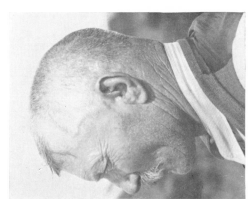

No. 5959

No. 4922

LIMERICK

FIGURE 53.

FIGURE 53

No. 5959 Birthplace, Cork. Age, 67. Weight, 135 lbs. Stature, 162.3 cm.
Cephalic index, 81. Nasal index, 70. Hair color, dark brown. Eye
color, blue-brown. Type: Nordic Alpine.

No. 5545 Birthplace, Cork. Age, 29. Weight, 169 lbs. Stature, 168.7 cm.
Cephalic index, 82. Nasal index, 70. Hair color, dark brown. Eye
color, blue. Type: Nordic Alpine.

No. 4922 Birthplace, Limerick. Age, 54. Weight, 227 lbs. Stature, 176.5 cm.
Cephalic index, 77. Nasal index, 71. Hair color, dark brown. Eye
color, blue. Type: Keltic.

No. 4890. Birthplace, Limerick. Age, 36. Weight, 212 lbs. Stature, 173.4 cm.
Cephalic index, 80. Nasal index, 54. Hair color, brown. Eye color,
blue-brown. Type: Dinaric.

No. 4900

No. 4913

No. 4918

No. 4919

LIMERICK

FIGURE 54.

FIGURE 54

No. 4913   Birthplace, Limerick. Age, 53. Weight, 173 lbs. Stature, 180.5 cm. Cephalic index, 71. Nasal index, 62. Hair color, brown. Eye color, blue-brown. Type: Nordic Mediterranean.

No. 4900   Birthplace, Limerick. Age, 18. Weight, 156 lbs. Stature, 165.5 cm. Cephalic index, 73. Nasal index, 60. Hair color, black. Eye color, blue-brown. Type: Nordic Mediterranean.

No. 4919   Birthplace, Limerick. Age, 44. Weight, 150 lbs. Stature, 161.4 cm. Cephalic index, 82. Nasal index, 70. Hair color, dark brown. Eye color, gray-brown. Type: Nordic Alpine.

No. 4918   Birthplace, Limerick. Age, 48. Weight, 132 lbs. Stature, 158.4 cm. Cephalic index, 82. Nasal index, 67. Hair color, dark brown. Eye color, gray-brown. Type: Nordic Alpine.

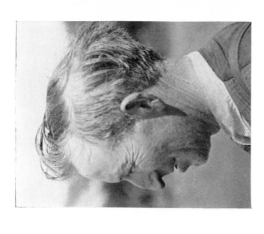

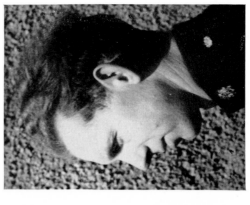

No. 4915

No. 1588

LIMERICK

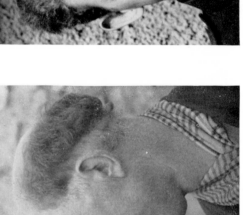

No. 4901

ROSCOMMON

FIGURE 55.

No. 9261

FIGURE 55

No. 4901   Birthplace, Limerick. Age, 35. Weight, 147 lbs. Stature, 171.3 cm. Cephalic index, 79. Nasal index, 68. Hair color, dark brown. Eye color, blue. Type: Keltic.

No. 4915   Birthplace, Limerick. Age, 52. Weight, 134 lbs. Stature, 167.8 cm. Cephalic index, 81. Nasal index, 62. Hair color, golden brown. Eye color, blue. Type: Dinaric.

No. 9261   Birthplace, Roscommon. Age, 40. Weight, 170 lbs. Stature, 180.5 cm. Cephalic index, 78. Nasal index, 52. Hair color, golden brown. Eye color, gray-blue. Type: Predominantly Nordic.

No. 1588   Birthplace, Roscommon. Age, 27. Weight, 177 lbs. Stature, 187.7 cm. Cephalic index, 79. Nasal index, 52. Hair color, golden brown. Eye color, blue. Type: Predominantly Nordic.

No. 1199

No. 6995

ROSCOMMON

Figure 56.

No. 1148

No. 1160

FIGURE 56

No. 1148   Birthplace, Roscommon. Age, 24. Weight, 150 lbs. Stature, 167.0 cm. Cephalic index, 84. Nasal index, 62. Hair color, red. Eye color, blue-brown. Type: Dinaric.

No. 1199   Birthplace, Roscommon. Age, 21. Weight, 172 lbs. Stature, 175.0 cm. Cephalic index, 82. Nasal index, 53. Hair color, brown. Eye color, blue-brown. Type: Dinaric.

No. 1160   Birthplace, Roscommon. Age, 45. Weight, 176 lbs. Stature, 171.4 cm. Cephalic index, 81. Nasal index, 71. Hair color, red-brown. Eye color, blue. Type: Nordic Alpine.

No. 6995   Birthplace, Roscommon. Age, 29. Weight, 200 lbs. Stature, 181.2 cm. Cephalic index, 80. Nasal index, 67. Hair color, dark brown. Eye color, blue. Type: Nordic Alpine.

No. 827

No. 821

LONGFORD

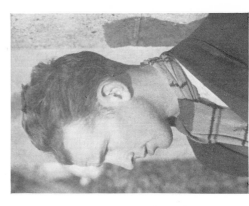

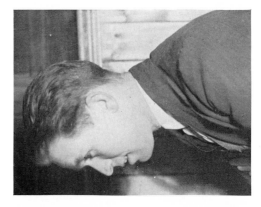

No. 144

No. 106

WESTMEATH

Figure 57.

Figure 57

No. 821   Birthplace, Longford. Age, 22. Weight, 157 lbs. Stature, 169.2 cm. Cephalic index, 79. Nasal index, 62. Hair color, dark brown. Eye color, blue-brown. Type: Nordic Mediterranean.

No. 827   Birthplace, Longford. Age, 48. Weight, 159 lbs. Stature, 165.2 cm. Cephalic index, 76. Nasal index, 62. Hair color, dark brown. Eye color, blue-brown. Type: Nordic Mediterranean.

No. 106   Birthplace, Westmeath. Age, 30. Weight, 146 lbs. Stature, 171.5 cm. Cephalic index, 77. Nasal index, 66.67. Hair color, golden brown. Eye color, blue-brown. Type: Predominantly Nordic.

No. 144   Birthplace, Westmeath. Age, 22. Weight, 149 lbs. Stature, 171.0 cm. Cephalic index, 78. Nasal index, 65. Hair color, golden brown. Eye color, blue. Type: Predominantly Nordic.

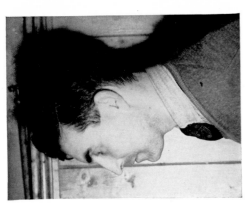

No. 378

No. 7969
LEIX

WESTMEATH

FIGURE 58.

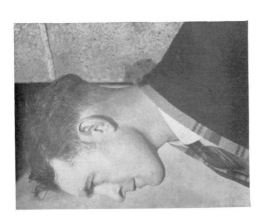

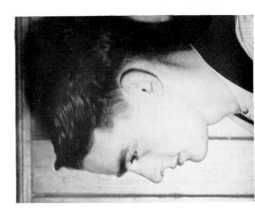

No. 43

No. 385
OFFALY

FIGURE 58

No. 43   Birthplace, Westmeath. Age, 22. Weight, 171 lbs. Stature, 183.3 cm. Cephalic index, 74. Nasal index, 84. Hair color, brown. Eye color, gray-blue. Type: Keltic.

No. 378   Birthplace, Westmeath. Age, 29. Weight, 156 lbs. Stature, 173.0 cm. Cephalic index, 84. Nasal index, 59. Hair color, dark brown. Eye color, gray-brown. Type: Dinaric.

No. 385   Birthplace, Offaly. Age, 19. Weight, 140 lbs. Stature, 173.8 cm. Cephalic index, 78. Nasal index, 54. Hair color, brown. Eye color, blue-brown. Type: Nordic Mediterranean.

No. 7969   Birthplace, Leix. Age, 27. Weight, 146 lbs. Stature, 170.0 cm. Cephalic index, 76. Nasal index, 63. Hair color, brown. Eye color, blue. Type: Keltic.

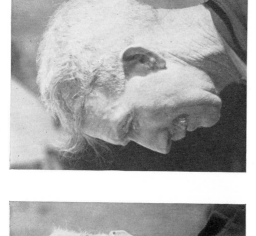

No. 7978

No. 7638

KILDARE

LEIX

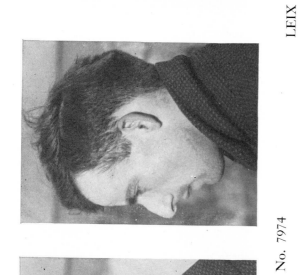

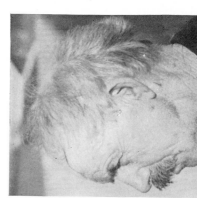

No. 7974

No. 7975

LEIX

FIGURE 59.

Figure 59

No. 7974   Birthplace, Leix. Age, 26. Weight, 143 lbs. Stature, 162.0 cm. Cephalic index, 82. Nasal index, 60. Hair color, dark brown. Eye color, blue-brown. Type: Dinaric.

No. 7978   Birthplace, Leix. Age, 54. Weight, 147 lbs. Stature, 168.6 cm. Cephalic index, 76. Nasal index, 58. Hair color, red-brown. Eye color, green-brown. Type: Nordic Mediterranean.

No. 7975   Birthplace, Leix. Age, 60. Weight, 132 lbs. Stature, 163.4 cm. Cephalic index, 79. Nasal index, 69. Hair color, brown. Eye color, gray-blue. Type: Nordic Mediterranean.

No. 7638   Birthplace, Kildare. Age, 64. Weight, 132 lbs. Stature, 166.1 cm. Cephalic index, 76. Nasal index, 61. Hair color, dark brown. Eye color, blue. Type: Keltic.

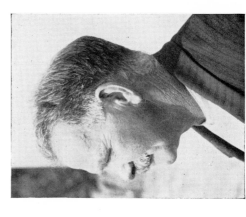

No. 7644

No. 6141

KILDARE

TIPPERARY

FIGURE 60.

No. 7633

No. 6304

FIGURE 60

No. 7633 Birthplace, Kildare. Age, 24. Weight, 149 lbs. Stature, 177.5 cm. Cephalic index, 77. Nasal index, 57. Hair color, dark brown. Eye color, gray-blue. Type: Keltic.

No. 7644 Birthplace, Kildare. Age, 41. Weight, 150 lbs. Stature, 173.5 cm. Cephalic index, 77. Nasal index, —. Hair color, black. Eye color, blue-brown. Type: Nordic Mediterranean.

No. 6304 Birthplace, Tipperary. Age, 45. Weight, 223 lbs. Stature, 182.8 cm. Cephalic index, 76. Nasal index, 53. Hair color, golden brown. Eye color, gray-blue. Type: Predominantly Nordic.

No. 6141 Birthplace, Tipperary. Age, 54. Weight, 170 lbs. Stature, 160.7 cm. Cephalic index, 74. Nasal index, 77. Hair color, brown. Eye color, blue. Type: Keltic.

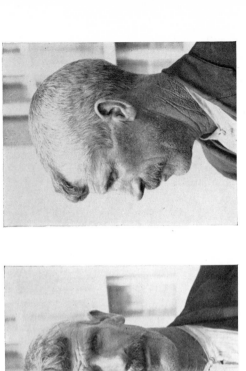
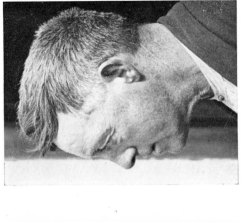
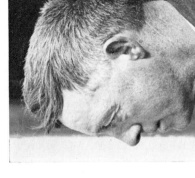

No. 6142

No. 6309

No. 6321

No. 6493

TIPPERARY

FIGURE 61.

FIGURE 61

No. 6321 Birthplace, Tipperary. Age, 42. Weight, 175 lbs. Stature, 182.0 cm. Cephalic index, 74. Nasal index, 67. Hair color, brown. Eye color, blue-brown. Type: Nordic Mediterranean.

No. 6142 Birthplace, Tipperary. Age, 50. Weight, 171 lbs. Stature, 174.7 cm. Cephalic index, 72. Nasal index, 65. Hair color, black. Eye color, blue-brown. Type: Nordic Mediterranean.

No. 6493 Birthplace, Tipperary. Age, 27. Weight, 134 lbs. Stature, 165.7 cm. Cephalic index, 81. Nasal index, 65. Hair color, golden brown. Eye color, blue-brown. Type: Nordic Alpine.

No. 6309 Birthplace, Tipperary. Age, 60. Weight, 202 lbs. Stature, 170.3 cm. Cephalic index, 82. Nasal index, 67. Hair color, red-brown. Eye color, blue-brown. Type: Nordic Alpine.

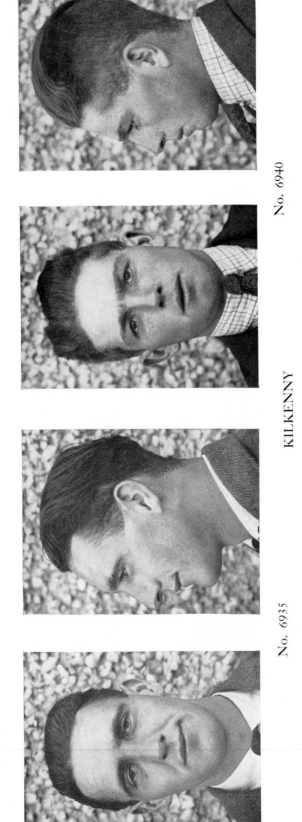

No. 6940

KILKENNY

No. 6935

No. 6657

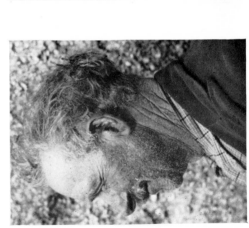

WATERFORD

FIGURE 62.

No. 6572

FIGURE 62

No. 6935   Birthplace, Kilkenny. Age, 21. Weight, 180 lbs. Stature, 181.8 cm.
Cephalic index, 78. Nasal index, 60. Hair color, red-brown. Eye
color, gray-blue. Type: Keltic.

No. 6940   Birthplace, Kilkenny. Age, 20. Weight, 136 lbs. Stature, 171.0 cm.
Cephalic index, 84. Nasal index, 60. Hair color, golden brown. Eye
color, blue-brown. Type: Dinaric.

No. 6572   Birthplace, Waterford. Age, 60. Weight, 173 lbs. Stature, 176.0 cm.
Cephalic index, 77. Nasal index, 61. Hair color, brown. Eye color,
gray-blue. Type: Keltic.

No. 6657   Birthplace, Waterford. Age, 16. Weight, 148 lbs. Stature, 171.8 cm.
Cephalic index, 80. Nasal index, 60. Hair color, red. Eye color, blue.
Type: Dinaric.

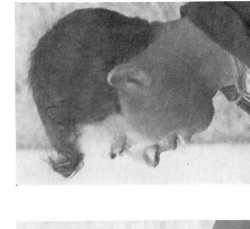

No. 6738

No. 7067

WEXFORD

WATERFORD

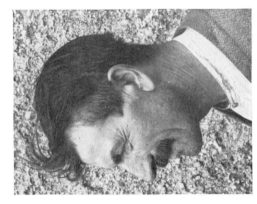

No. 6744

No. 6571

WATERFORD

FIGURE 63.

FIGURE 63

No. 6744 Birthplace, Waterford. Age, 39. Weight, 204 lbs. Stature, 168.6 cm. Cephalic index, 76. Nasal index, 66. Hair color, dark brown. Eye color, gray-brown. Type: Nordic Mediterranean.

No. 6738 Birthplace, Waterford. Age, 23. Weight, 142 lbs. Stature, 172.3 cm. Cephalic index, 78. Nasal index, 58. Hair color, dark brown. Eye color, blue-brown. Type: Nordic Mediterranean.

No. 6571 Birthplace, Waterford. Age, 50. Weight, 154 lbs. Stature, 171.3 cm. Cephalic index, 81. Nasal index, 64. Hair color, red-brown. Eye color, gray-brown. Type: Nordic Alpine.

No. 7067 Birthplace, Wexford. Age, 36. Weight, 160 lbs. Stature, 168.5 cm. Cephalic index, 78. Nasal index, 53. Hair color, dark brown. Eye color, blue. Type: Keltic.

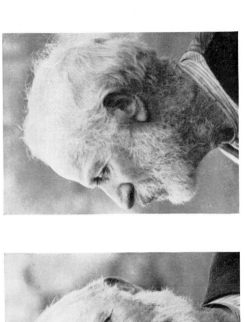

No. 7102

No. 6901

WEXFORD

CARLOW

Figure 64.

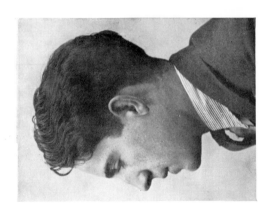

No. 7037

No. 6525

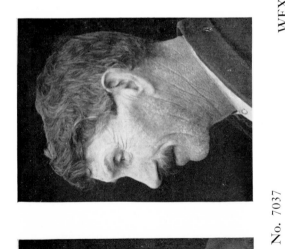

FIGURE 64

No. 7037 Birthplace, Wexford. Age, 56. Weight, 168 lbs. Stature, 173.0 cm. Cephalic index, 78. Nasal index, 67. Hair color, dark brown. Eye color, blue. Type: Keltic.

No. 7102 Birthplace, Wexford. Age, 71. Weight, 155 lbs. Stature, 171.3 cm. Cephalic index, 85. Nasal index, 63. Hair color, white. Eye color, blue-brown. Type: Nordic Alpine.

No. 6525 Birthplace, Carlow. Age, 19. Weight, 144 lbs. Stature, 172.0 cm. Cephalic index, 78. Nasal index, 57. Hair color, dark brown. Eye color, blue. Type: Keltic.

No. 6901 Birthplace, Carlow. Age, 20. Weight, 145 lbs. Stature, 168.8 cm. Cephalic index, 76. Nasal index, 62. Hair color, brown. Eye color, blue-brown. Type: Nordic Mediterranean.

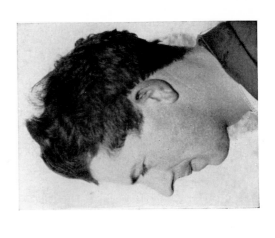

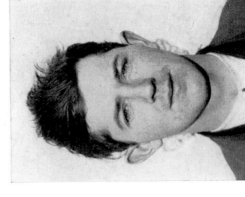

No. 8396 MEATH

No. 8276

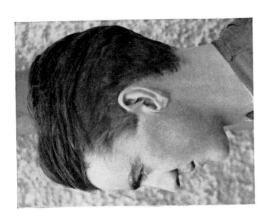

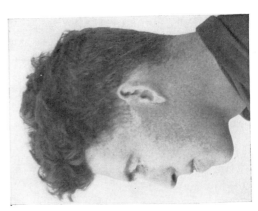

No. 6897 CARLOW

No. 8407

MEATH

FIGURE 65.

FIGURE 65

No. 6897 Birthplace, Carlow. Age, 21. Weight, 148 lbs. Stature, 182.5 cm. Cephalic index, 78. Nasal index, 74. Hair color, dark brown. Eye color, blue-brown. Type: Nordic Mediterranean.

No. 8396 Birthplace, Meath. Age, 40. Weight, 147 lbs. Stature, 165.2 cm. Cephalic index, 76. Nasal index, 76. Hair color, golden brown. Eye color, blue. Type: Predominantly Nordic.

No. 8407 Birthplace, Meath. Age, 22. Weight, 168 lbs. Stature, 179.0 cm. Cephalic index, 76. Nasal index, 61. Hair color, dark brown. Eye color, blue. Type: Keltic.

No. 8276 Birthplace, Meath. Age, 25. Weight, 149 lbs. Stature, 170.2 cm. Cephalic index, 78. Nasal index, 65. Hair color, brown. Eye color, blue. Type: Keltic.

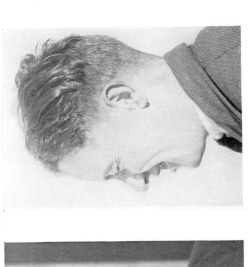

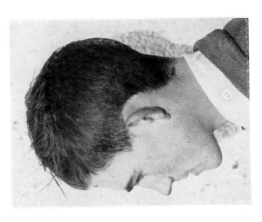

MEATH

Figure 66.

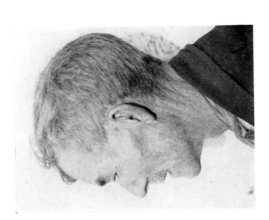

FIGURE 66

No. 8280 Birthplace, Meath. Age, 55. Weight, 124 lbs. Stature, 164.8 cm. Cephalic index, 79. Nasal index, 73. Hair color, dark brown. Eye color, blue. Type: Keltic.

No. 8398 Birthplace, Meath. Age, 21. Weight, 145 lbs. Stature, 162.5 cm. Cephalic index, 80. Nasal index, 61. Hair color, dark brown. Eye color, blue-brown. Type: Dinaric.

No. 8275 Birthplace, Meath. Age, 19. Weight, 127 lbs. Stature, 167.5 cm. Cephalic index, 76. Nasal index, 65. Hair color, red. Eye color, blue-brown. Type: Nordic Mediterranean.

No. 8281 Birthplace, Meath. Age, 19. Weight, 120 lbs. Stature, 163.8 cm. Cephalic index, 78. Nasal index, 73. Hair color, dark brown. Eye color, green-brown. Type: Nordic Mediterranean.

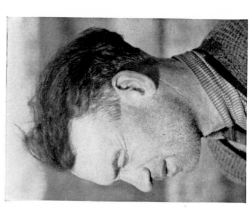

No. 8710

EAST CAVAN

No. 8711

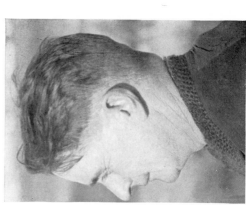

EAST CAVAN

FIGURE 67.

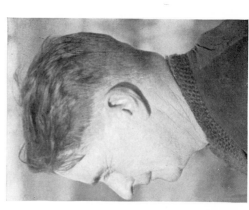

No. 8706

No. 8402

MEATH

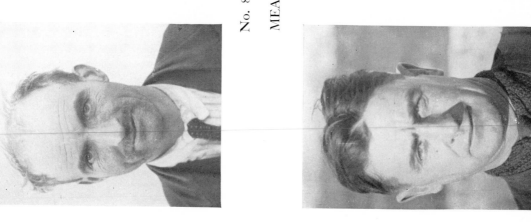

FIGURE 67

No. 8402 Birthplace, Meath. Age, 35. Weight, 135 lbs. Stature, 162.0 cm. Cephalic index, 76. Nasal index, 61. Hair color, dark brown. Eye color, blue. Type: Keltic.

No. 8710 Birthplace, East Cavan. Age, 26. Weight, 156 lbs. Stature, 167.1 cm. Cephalic index, 79. Nasal index, 59. Hair color, brown. Eye color, blue. Type: Keltic.

No. 8706 Birthplace, East Cavan. Age, 38. Weight, 150 lbs. Stature, 163.5 cm. Cephalic index, 78. Nasal index, 70. Hair color, dark brown. Eye color, blue. Type: Keltic.

No. 8711 Birthplace, East Cavan. Age, 29. Weight, 147 lbs. Stature, 165.5 cm. Cephalic index, 73. Nasal index, 74. Hair color, dark brown. Eye color, blue-brown. Type: Nordic Mediterranean.

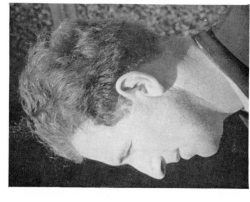
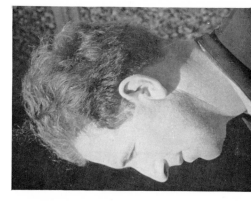

No. 6996
MONAGHAN

No. 10006
ANTRIM

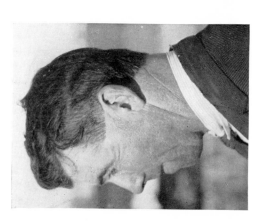

No. 8714
EAST CAVAN

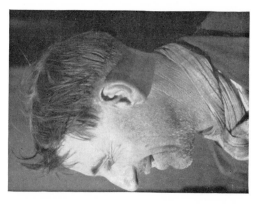

No. 9077
ARMAGH

FIGURE 68.

FIGURE 68

No. 8714 Birthplace, East Cavan. Age, 35. Weight, 174 lbs. Stature, 178.8 cm. Cephalic index, 80. Nasal index, 64. Hair color, dark brown. Eye color, blue-brown. Type: Nordic Alpine.

No. 6996 Birthplace, Monaghan. Age, 21. Weight, 160 lbs. Stature, 177.5 cm. Cephalic index, 75. Nasal index, 62. Hair color, dark brown. Eye color, gray-blue. Type: Keltic.

No. 9077 Birthplace, Armagh. Age, 45. Weight, 144 lbs. Stature, 164.5 cm. Cephalic index, 77. Nasal index, 66. Hair color, dark brown. Eye color, blue-brown. Type: Nordic Mediterranean.

No. 10006 Birthplace, Antrim. Age, 30. Weight, 192 lbs. Stature, 180.0 cm. Cephalic index, 78. Nasal index, 62. Hair color, golden brown. Eye color, blue. Type: Predominantly Nordic.

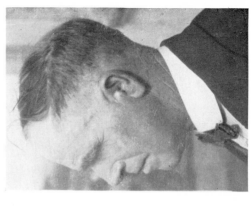

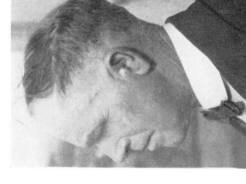

No. 10004

No. 9719

No. 9321

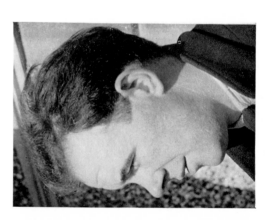

No. 10002

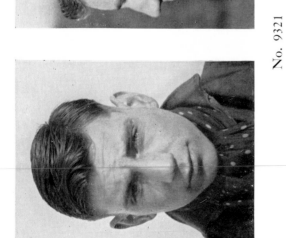

ANTRIM

FIGURE 69.

FIGURE 69

No. 9321 Birthplace, Antrim. Age, 18. Weight, 128 lbs. Stature, 163.7 cm. Cephalic index, 71. Nasal index, 67. Hair color, brown. Eye color, blue. Type: Keltic.

No. 10004 Birthplace, Antrim. Age, 52. Weight, 194 lbs. Stature, 188.9 cm. Cephalic index, 81. Nasal index, 53. Hair color, dark brown. Eye color, blue. Type: Dinaric.

No. 10002 Birthplace, Antrim. Age, 25. Weight, 161 lbs. Stature, 176.0 cm. Cephalic index, 80. Nasal index, 74. Hair color, dark brown. Eye color, blue. Type: Nordic Alpine.

No. 9719 Birthplace, Down. Age, 55. Weight, 164 lbs. Stature, 166.3 cm. Cephalic index, 76. Nasal index, 73. Hair color, brown. Eye color, blue. Type: Keltic.

No. 9264

NORTH FERMANAGH

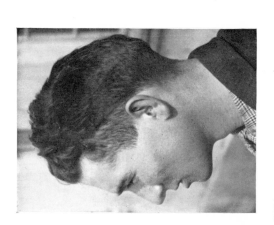

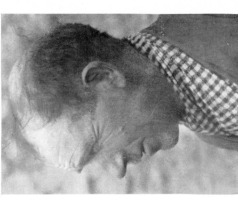

No. 9269

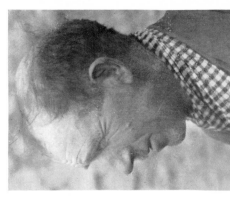

NORTH FERMANAGH

No. 9721

ANTRIM

No. 9275

FIGURE 70

No. 9721 Birthplace, Down. Age, 17. Weight, 134 lbs. Stature, 166.1 cm. Cephalic index, 76. Nasal index, 70. Hair color, dark brown. Eye color, green-brown. Type: Nordic Mediterranean.

No. 9264 Birthplace, N. Fermanagh. Age, 26. Weight, 150 lbs. Stature, 175.0 cm. Cephalic index, 84. Nasal index, 59. Hair color, brown. Eye color, blue-brown. Type: Dinaric.

No. 9275 Birthplace, N. Fermanagh. Age, 45. Weight, 190 lbs. Stature, 182.8 cm. Cephalic index, 76. Nasal index, 69. Hair color, dark brown. Eye color, unmatched. Type: Nordic Mediterranean.

No. 9269 Birthplace, N. Fermanagh. Age, 50. Weight, 166 lbs. Stature, 172.7 cm. Cephalic index, 81. Nasal index, 68. Hair color, dark brown. Eye color, blue-brown. Type: Nordic Alpine.

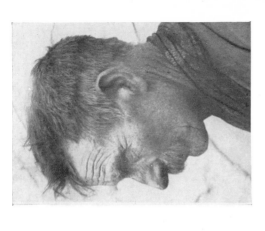

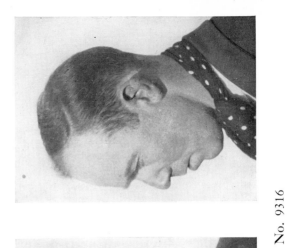

No. 9405

No. 9316

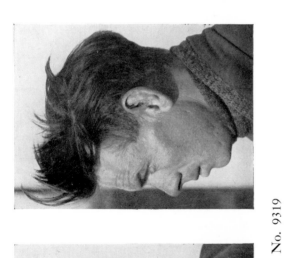

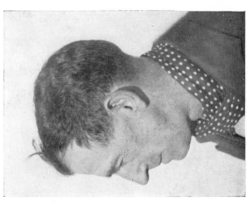

No. 9319

No. 9314

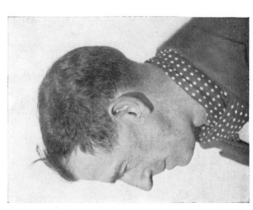

TYRONE

Figure 71.

FIGURE 71

No. 9319 Birthplace, Tyrone. Age, 26. Weight, 152 lbs. Stature, 168.0 cm. Cephalic index, 74. Nasal index, 71. Hair color, brown. Eye color, blue. Type: Keltic.

No. 9405 Birthplace, Tyrone. Age, 59. Weight, 142 lbs. Stature, 164.3 cm. Cephalic index, 78. Nasal index, 62. Hair color, brown. Eye color, blue. Type: Keltic.

No. 9314 Birthplace, Tyrone. Age, 45. Weight, 115 lbs. Stature, 156.0 cm. Cephalic index, 77. Nasal index, 52. Hair color, dark brown. Eye color, blue. Type: Keltic.

No. 9316 Birthplace, Tyrone. Age, 30. Weight, 162 lbs. Stature, 172.8 cm. Cephalic index, 80. Nasal index, 61. Hair color, red. Eye color, blue-brown. Type: Dinaric.

MORPHOLOGICAL (SUBRACIAL) TYPES

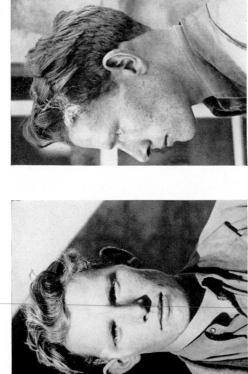

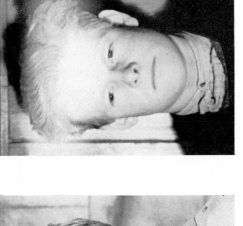

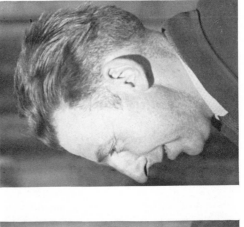

No. 389

No. 5968

PURE NORDIC

PREDOMINANTLY NORDIC

FIGURE 72.

No. 6417

No. 2904

FIGURE 72

No. 6417 Birthplace, Tipperary. Age, 18. Weight, 165 lbs. Stature, 173.2 cm. Cephalic index, 76. Nasal index, 65. Hair color, golden. Eye color, gray-blue. Type: Pure Nordic.

No. 389 Birthplace, Offaly. Age, 21. Weight, 144 lbs. Stature, 165.2 cm. Cephalic index, 75. Nasal index, 72. Hair color, golden. Eye color, blue. Type: Pure Nordic.

No. 2904 Birthplace, East Galway. Age, 32. Weight, 174 lbs. Stature, 170.1 cm. Cephalic index, 78. Nasal index, 57. Hair color, golden brown. Eye color, blue. Type: Predominantly Nordic.

No. 5968 Birthplace, Cork. Age, 17. Weight, 142 lbs. Stature, 171.3 cm. Cephalic index, 78. Nasal index, 66. Hair color, golden brown. Eye color, blue. Type: Predominantly Nordic.

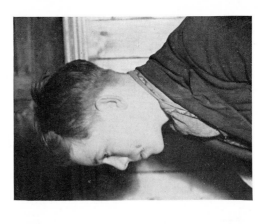

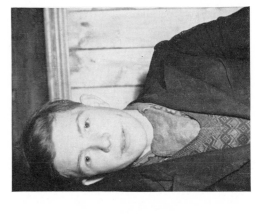

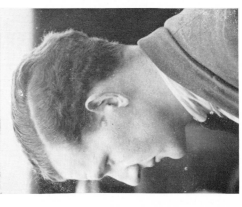

No. 7655

No. 29

No. 5408

No. 1196

PREDOMINANTLY NORDIC

FIGURE 73.

FIGURE 73

No. 5408   Birthplace, Kerry. Age, 45. Weight, 186 lbs. Stature, 171.9 cm. Cephalic index, 78. Nasal index, 66. Hair color, golden brown. Eye color, blue. Type: Predominantly Nordic.

No. 7655   Birthplace, Kildare. Age, 58. Weight, 126 lbs. Stature, 168.7 cm. Cephalic index, 76. Nasal index, 61. Hair color, golden brown. Eye color, blue. Type: Predominantly Nordic.

No. 1196   Birthplace, Leitrim. Age, 20. Weight, 162 lbs. Stature, 181.5 cm. Cephalic index, 78. Nasal index, 72. Hair color, red. Eye color, green-brown. Type: Predominantly Nordic.

No. 29   Birthplace, Westmeath. Age, 18. Weight, 133 lbs. Stature, 166.4 cm. Cephalic index, 72. Nasal index, 73. Hair color, golden brown. Eye color, green-brown. Type: Predominantly Nordic.

No. 6520

No. 7635

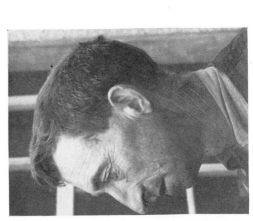

No. 6938

No. 5402

KELTIC

Figure 74.

FIGURE 74

No. 6938 Birthplace, Kilkenny. Age, 35. Weight, 161 lbs. Stature, 180.5 cm. Cephalic index, 74. Nasal index, 52. Hair color, dark brown. Eye color, blue. Type: Keltic.

No. 6520 Birthplace, Kilkenny. Age, 39. Weight, 178 lbs. Stature, 181.7 cm. Cephalic index, 77. Nasal index, 62. Hair color, dark brown. Eye color, blue. Type: Keltic.

No. 5402 Birthplace, Kerry. Age, 42. Weight, 154 lbs. Stature, 172.8 cm. Cephalic index, 74. Nasal index, 55. Hair color, brown. Eye color, blue. Type: Keltic.

No. 7635 Birthplace, Kildare. Age, 34. Weight, 149 lbs. Stature, 167.5 cm. Cephalic index, 65. Nasal index, 65. Hair color, brown. Eye color, blue. Type: Keltic.

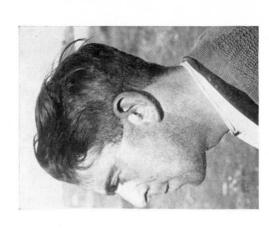

No. 5756

No. 6747

No. 10008

No. 8274

KELTIC

FIGURE 75.

FIGURE 75

No. 10008 Birthplace, Antrim. Age, 27. Weight, 173 lbs. Stature, 175.2 cm. Cephalic index, 76. Nasal index, 54. Hair color, dark brown. Eye color, blue. Type: Keltic.

No. 5756 Birthplace, Kerry. Age, 28. Weight, 148 lbs. Stature, 171.6 cm. Cephalic index, 79. Nasal index, 60. Hair color, black. Eye color, blue. Type: Keltic.

No. 8274 Birthplace, Meath. Age, 23. Weight, 155 lbs. Stature, 172.5 cm. Cephalic index, 78. Nasal index, 67. Hair color, dark brown. Eye color, blue. Type: Keltic.

No. 6747 Birthplace, Waterford. Age, 27. Weight, 158 lbs. Stature, 174.5 cm. Cephalic index, 77. Nasal index, 62. Hair color, brown. Eye color, blue. Type: Keltic.

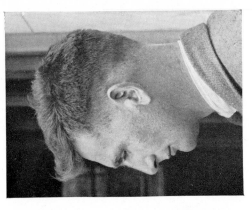

No. 5541

No. 988

KELTIC

EAST BALTIC

FIGURE 76.

No. 3877

No. 5760

FIGURE 76

No. 3877   Birthplace, Mayo. Age, 39. Weight, 162 lbs. Stature, 178.1 cm. Cephalic index, 76. Nasal index, 61. Hair color, brown. Eye color, blue. Type: Keltic.

No. 5541   Birthplace, Cork. Age, 26. Weight, 172 lbs. Stature, 168.6 cm. Cephalic index, 78. Nasal index, 59. Hair color, brown. Eye color, blue. Type: Keltic.

No. 5760   Birthplace, Kerry. Age, 23. Weight, 138 lbs. Stature, 172.5 cm. Cephalic index, 85. Nasal index, 66. Hair color, red. Eye color, blue-brown. Type: East Baltic.

No. 988   Birthplace, Longford. Age, 65. Weight, 181 lbs. Stature, 173.3 cm. Cephalic index, 82. Nasal index, 85. Hair color, white. Eye color, blue. Type: East Baltic.

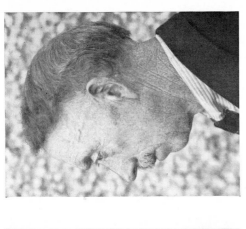

No. 6943

No. 5409

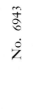

EAST BALTIC

DINARIC

Figure 77.

No. 1738

No. 7103

FIGURE 77

No. 1738   Birthplace, Leitrim. Age, 23. Weight, 112 lbs. Stature, 156.7 cm. Cephalic index, 81. Nasal index, 66. Hair color, red. Eye color, blue-brown. Type: East Baltic.

No. 6943   Birthplace, Kilkenny. Age, 55. Weight, 164 lbs. Stature, 174.3 cm. Cephalic index, 80. Nasal index, 66. Hair color, red. Eye color, blue-brown. Type: East Baltic.

No. 7103   Birthplace, Wexford. Age, 30. Weight, 135 lbs. Stature, 173.2 cm. Cephalic index, 82. Nasal index, 54. Hair color, ash brown. Eye color, blue. Type: Dinaric.

No. 5409   Birthplace, Kerry. Age, 23. Weight, 168 lbs. Stature, 181.5 cm. Cephalic index, 80. Nasal index, 62. Hair color, dark brown. Eye color, blue-brown. Type: Dinaric.

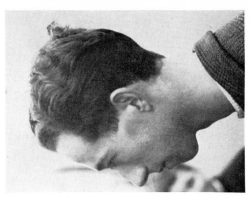

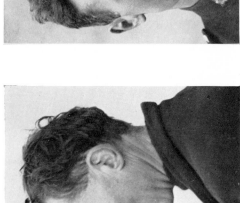

DINARIC

FIGURE 78.

FIGURE 78

No. 505   Birthplace, Aran Islands. Age, 40. Weight, 156 lbs. Stature, 184.7 cm. Cephalic index, 80. Nasal index, 57. Hair color, brown. Eye color, gray-blue. Type: Dinaric.

No. 6521   Birthplace, Roscommon. Age, 28. Weight, 169 lbs. Stature, 185.5 cm. Cephalic index, 82. Nasal index, 57. Hair color, brown. Eye color, blue. Type: Dinaric.

No. 3134   Birthplace, Clare. Age, 57. Weight, 180 lbs. Stature, 176.9 cm. Cephalic index, 81. Nasal index, 59. Hair color, brown. Eye color, blue. Type: Dinaric.

No. 4485   Birthplace, Donegal. Age, 19. Weight, 119 lbs. Stature, 163.1 cm. Cephalic index, 82. Nasal index, 56. Hair color, dark brown. Eye color, blue-brown. Type: Dinaric.

DINARIC

FIGURE 79.

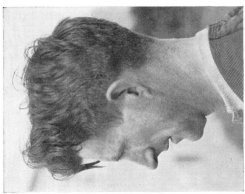 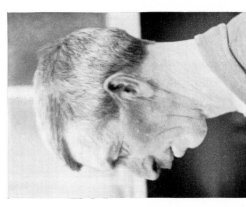

No. 4911

No. 3306

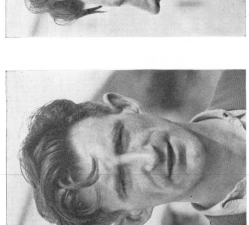 

FIGURE 79

No. 4911   Birthplace, Limerick. Age, 24. Weight, 156 lbs. Stature, 177.2 cm. Cephalic index, 88. Nasal index, 61. Hair color, dark brown. Eye color, blue-brown. Type: Dinaric.

No. 2900   Birthplace, Dublin. Age, 22. Weight, 151 lbs. Stature, 172.2 cm. Cephalic index, 80. Nasal index, 54. Hair color, red-brown. Eye color, blue. Type: Dinaric.

No. 3306   Birthplace, Clare. Age, 42. Weight, 190 lbs. Stature, 195.3 cm. Cephalic index, 81. Nasal index, 55. Hair color, brown. Eye color, blue. Type: Dinaric.

No. 3889   Birthplace, Mayo. Age, 55. Weight, 162 lbs. Stature, 166.5 cm. Cephalic index, 86. Nasal index, 62. Hair color, dark brown. Eye color, blue-brown. Type: Dinaric.

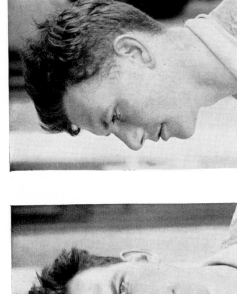

No. 5965

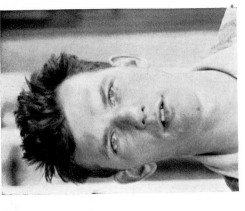

No. 6494

DINARIC

No. 5349

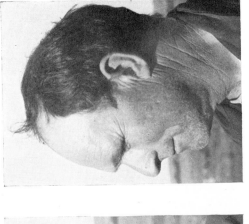

No. 6746

NORDIC MEDITERRANEAN

FIGURE 80.

FIGURE 80

No. 6494   Birthplace, Tipperary. Age, 23. Weight, 134 lbs. Stature, 165.7 cm. Cephalic index, 81. Nasal index, 57. Hair color, dark brown. Eye color, blue-brown. Type: Dinaric.

No. 5965   Birthplace, Cork. Age, 27. Weight, 140 lbs. Stature, 168.3 cm. Cephalic index, 80. Nasal index, 62. Hair color, brown. Eye color, blue-brown. Type: Dinaric.

No. 6746   Birthplace, Waterford. Age, 52. Weight, 212 lbs. Stature, 178.1 cm. Cephalic index, 79. Nasal index, 66. Hair color, dark brown. Eye color, gray-brown. Type: Nordic Mediterranean.

No. 5349   Birthplace, Kerry. Age, 60. Weight, 194 lbs. Stature, 173.8 cm. Cephalic index, 72. Nasal index, 65. Hair color, brown. Eye color, blue-brown. Type: Nordic Mediterranean.

No. 4663

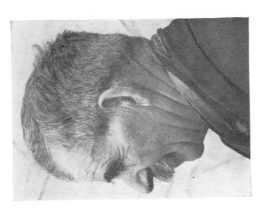

No. 9406

No. 8272

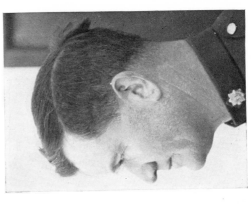

No. 8409

NORDIC MEDITERRANEAN

FIGURE 81.

FIGURE 81

No. 9406 Birthplace, Tyrone. Age, 68. Weight, 170 lbs. Stature, 172.5 cm. Cephalic index, 77. Nasal index, 77. Hair color, black. Eye color, gray-brown. Type: Nordic Mediterranean.

No. 4663 Birthplace, Donegal. Age, 19. Weight, 143 lbs. Stature, 173.2 cm. Cephalic index, 79. Nasal index, 69. Hair color, dark brown. Eye color, green-brown. Type: Nordic Mediterranean.

No. 8409 Birthplace, Monaghan. Age, 40. Weight, 184 lbs. Stature, 177.2 cm. Cephalic index, 78. Nasal index, 79. Hair color, dark brown. Eye color, blue-brown. Type: Nordic Mediterranean.

No. 8272 Birthplace, Westmeath. Age, 60. Weight, 202 lbs. Stature, 173.0 cm. Cephalic index, 79. Nasal index, 81. Hair color, brown. Eye color, blue-brown. Type: Nordic Mediterranean.

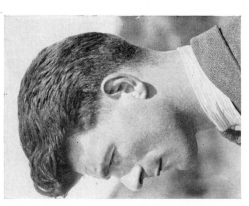

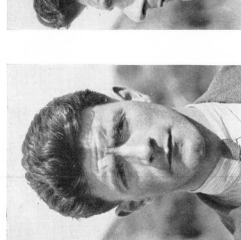

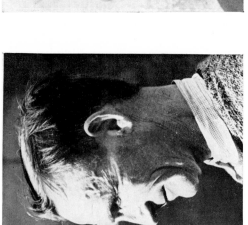

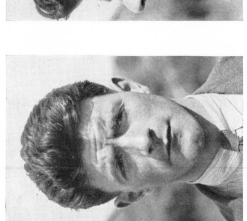

No. 3172

No. 4914

NORDIC MEDITERRANEAN

No. 1151

No. 6415

PURE MEDITERRANEAN

Figure 82.

FIGURE 82

No. 4914   Birthplace, Limerick. Age, 24. Weight, 175 lbs. Stature, 179.5 cm. Cephalic index, 79. Nasal index, 70. Hair color, red-brown. Eye color, blue-brown. Type: Nordic Mediterranean.

No. 3172   Birthplace, Clare. Age, 45. Weight, 170 lbs. Stature, 170.8 cm. Cephalic index, 79. Nasal index, 59. Hair color, dark brown. Eye color, blue-brown. Type: Nordic Mediterranean.

No. 6415   Birthplace, Tipperary. Age, 48. Weight, 128 lbs. Stature, 168.3 cm. Cephalic index, 75. Nasal index, 68. Hair color, brown. Eye color, dark brown. Type: Pure Mediterranean.

No. 1151   Birthplace, Leitrim. Age, 54. Weight, 146 lbs. Stature, 167.1 cm. Cephalic index, 79. Nasal index, 70. Hair color, dark brown. Eye color, dark-light brown. Type: Pure Mediterranean.

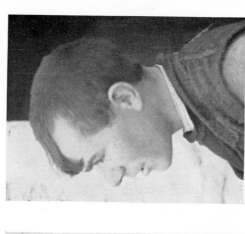

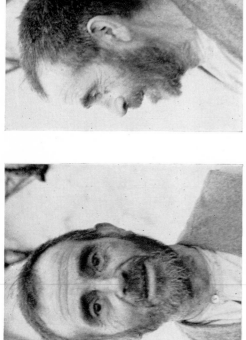

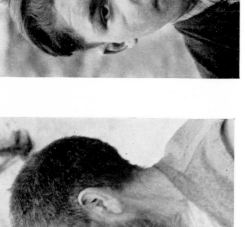

No. 9308

No. 612

PURE MEDITERRANEAN

NORDIC ALPINE

FIGURE 83.

No. 2175

No. 382

FIGURE 83

No. 2175   Birthplace, West Galway. Age, 67. Weight, 126 lbs. Stature, 163.2 cm. Cephalic index, 75. Nasal index, 67. Hair color, dark brown. Eye color, dark brown. Type: Pure Mediterranean.

No. 9308   Birthplace, Tyrone. Age, 18. Weight, 144 lbs. Stature, 165.0 cm. Cephalic index, 79. Nasal index, 63. Hair color, dark brown. Eye color, dark brown. Type: Pure Mediterranean.

No. 382   Birthplace, Antrim. Age, 19, Weight, 119 lbs. Stature, 162.4 cm. Cephalic index, 87. Nasal index, 64. Hair color, dark brown. Eye color, green-brown. Type: Nordic Alpine.

No. 612   Birthplace, Aran Islands. Age, 16. Weight, 130 lbs. Stature, 160.5 cm. Cephalic index, 87. Nasal index, 72. Hair color, brown. Eye color, blue. Type: Nordic Alpine.

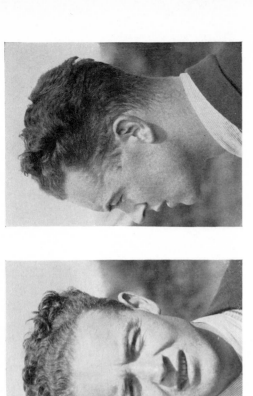

No. 6495

No. 4923

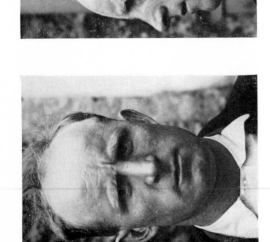

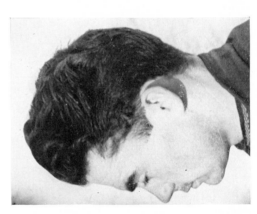

No. 7071

No. 455

NORDIC ALPINE

FIGURE 84.

FIGURE 84

No. 6495   Birthplace, Tipperary. Age, 29. Weight, 188 lbs. Stature, 180.8 cm. Cephalic index, 84. Nasal index, 63. Hair color, golden brown. Eye color, blue. Type: Nordic Alpine.

No. 4923   Birthplace, Wexford. Age, 27. Weight, 189 lbs. Stature, 176.9 cm. Cephalic index, 82. Nasal index, 65. Hair color, golden brown. Eye color, blue. Type: Nordic Alpine.

No. 455   Birthplace, Westmeath. Age, 22. Weight, 123 lbs. Stature, 160.7 cm. Cephalic index, 80. Nasal index, 68. Hair color, dark brown. Eye color, blue-brown. Type: Nordic Alpine.

No. 7071   Birthplace, Longford. Age, 36. Weight, 213 lbs. Stature, 179.6 cm. Cephalic index, 80. Nasal index, 65. Hair color, brown. Eye color, gray-brown. Type: Nordic Alpine.

No. 1155

No. 3896

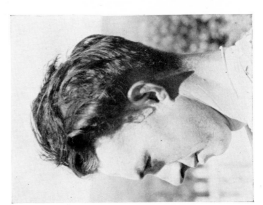

No. 4431

No. 5763

NORDIC ALPINE

Figure 85.

FIGURE 85

No. 4431   Birthplace, Leitrim. Age, 81. Weight, 141 lbs. Stature, 157.0 cm. Cephalic index, 82. Nasal index, 66. Hair color, red-brown. Eye color, blue. Type: Nordic Alpine.

No. 1155   Birthplace, Leitrim. Age, 62. Weight, 199 lbs. Stature, 170.9 cm. Cephalic index, 80. Nasal index, 68. Hair color, brown. Eye color, blue-brown. Type: Nordic Alpine.

No. 5763   Birthplace, Kerry. Age, 19. Weight, 171 lbs. Stature, 180.6 cm. Cephalic index, 84. Nasal index, 66. Hair color, dark brown. Eye color, gray-brown. Type: Nordic Alpine.

No. 3896   Birthplace, Mayo. Age, 60. Weight, 197 lbs. Stature, 172.5 cm. Cephalic index, 82. Nasal index, 63. Hair color, dark brown. Eye color, blue. Type: Nordic Alpine.